Seismic Inversion

Investigations in Geophysics Series No. 20

Gerard T. Schuster

Ian Jones, managing editor
Yonghe Sun, volume editor

SOCIETY OF EXPLORATION
— GEOPHYSICISTS —

ISBN 978-0-931830-46-4 (Series)
ISBN 978-1-56080-341-6 (Volume)

Library of Congress Control Number: 2017938778

Copyright 2017
Society of Exploration Geophysicists
8801 S. Yale Ave., Ste. 500
Tulsa, OK U.S.A. 74137-3575

Published 2017
Reprinted 2018
Printed in the United States of America

Contents

Part IV: Reflection Migration

About the Author

Gerard Schuster is currently a professor of geophysics at King Abdullah University Science and Technology (KAUST) and an adjunct professor at University of Utah and University of Wyoming. He was the founder and director of the Utah Tomography and Modeling/Migration consortium from 1987 to 2009 and is now the co-director and founder of the Center for Fluid Modeling and Seismic Imaging at KAUST. Schuster helped pioneer seismic interferometry and its practical applications in applied geophysics through his active research program and through his extensive publications. He also has extensive experience in developing innovative migration and inversion methods for both exploration and earthquake seismology.

Schuster has an MS (1982) and a PhD (1984) from Columbia University and was a postdoctoral researcher there from 1984–1985. From 1985 to 2009, he was a professor of geophysics at University of Utah. He left Utah to start his current position as professor of geophysics at KAUST in 2009. He received a number of teaching and research awards while at University of Utah. He was editor of GEOPHYSICS 2004–2005 and was awarded SEG's Virgil Kauffman Gold Medal in 2010 for his work in seismic interferometry. He was the SEG Distinguished Lecturer in 2013.

Preface

This book describes the theory and practice of inverting seismic data for the subsurface rock properties of the earth. The primary application is for inverting reflection and/or transmission data from engineering or exploration surveys, but the methods described also can be used for earthquake studies. I have written this book with the hope that it will be largely comprehensible to scientists and advanced students in engineering, earth sciences, and physics. It is desirable that the reader has some familiarity with certain aspects of numerical computation, such as finite-difference solutions to partial differential equations, numerical linear algebra, and the basic physics of wave propagation (e.g., Snell's law and ray tracing). For those not familiar with the terminology and methods of seismic exploration, a brief introduction is provided in the Appendix of Chapter 1. Computational labs are provided for most of the chapters, and some field data labs are given as well.

MATLAB and Fortran labs at the end of some chapters are used to deepen the reader's understanding of the concepts and their implementation. Such exercises are introduced early and geophysical applications are presented in every chapter. For the non-geophysicist, geophysical concepts are introduced with intuitive arguments, and their description by rigorous theory is deferred to later chapters.

The lab exercises in the Computational Toolkit can be found at http://csim.kaust.edu.sa/web/SeismicInversion and http://utam.gg.utah.edu/SeismicInversion/; the exercises can be accessed using the login Paulina and the password Brozina.

Acknowledgments

The author wishes to thank the long-term support provided by the sponsors of the Utah Tomography and Modeling/Migration consortium. Their continued financial support through both lean and bountiful years was necessary in bringing this book to fruition. Strong support was also provided by King Abdullah University of Science and Technology who financially supported me while writing the last ten chapters. I am very much indebted to the book editors Yonghe Sun and Ian Jones, as well as Chaiwoot Boonyasiriwat and Yunsong Huang for carefully editing every chapter in this book. Yonghe Sun's suggestions for improving the book were invaluable. I also thank Susan Stamm at SEG for her diligent efforts in getting this book to press.

I also thank the following reviewers who provided very valuable edits: Abduhlrahman Alshuhail, Abdullah AlTheyab, Pawan Bharawadj, Chaiwoot Boonyasiriwat, Derrick Cerwinsky, Yuqing Chen, Wei Dai, Li Deng, Craig Douglas, Gaurav Dutta, Zongcai Feng, Shihang Feng, Bowen Guo, Sherif Hanafy, Libo Huang, Kai Lu, Veronika Pelletier, Mrinal Sinha, Ahmad Tarhini, Xin Wang, Han Yu, Ge Zhan, Zhendong Zhang, and Sanzong Zhang. The last two chapters on image-domain inversion are modified versions of Sanzong Zhang's dissertation, and the description of the viscoacoustic gradient in Chapter 15 is a modified version of an appendix in Gaurav Dutta's dissertation. The derivation of the VTI adjoint equations are from Mrinal Sinha and Bowen Guo. I also thank Yue Wang and Ken Bube for their derivation of the adjoint of the viscoelastic wave equation in Chapter 22. Bowen Guo also helped generalize the gradient equation for inverting trim statics with the wave equation. Zongcai Feng scrupulously checked the accuracy of the equations in Chapters 20 through 23.

Finally, many thanks go to the following people who generously donated their results or computer codes to this book: Abdullah AlTheyab, Chaiwoot Boonyasiriwat, Wei Dai, Gaurav Dutta, Yunsong Huang, Xin Wang, Han Yu, and Ge Zhan. Their diligent efforts have resulted in the many interesting labs and results discussed in this book.

Notation Convention

- $\mathbb{R}^N$ denotes the N-dimensional real vector space.
- $\mathbb{C}^N$ denotes the N-dimensional complex vector space.
- A column vector will be denoted by boldface lower-case letters. For example, $\mathbf{x} = [x_1, x_2, ..., x_N]^T$ represents the $N \times 1$ vector where x_i is the ith element of $\mathbf{x}$.
- A matrix will be denoted by boldface upper-case letters. For example, $\mathbf{A} \in \mathbb{R}^{M \times N}$ represents an $M \times N$ real matrix whose ij^{th} element is denoted by A_{ij}.
- An order-of-magnitude estimate of a variable whose precise value is unknown is an estimate rounded to the nearest power of ten.
- A scalar will be denoted by lower-case letters.
- Subscripts are usually used to denote the element index of a vector or matrix.
- Superscripts with parentheses are used to denote an iterate of a vector or matrix. For example, $\mathbf{x}^{(k)}$ denotes the kth iterate of an iterative scheme.
- $\mathbf{x} \cdot \mathbf{y} = \mathbf{x}^T \mathbf{y} = <\mathbf{x}, \mathbf{y}> = \sum_{i=1}^{N} x_i^* y_i$ represents a dot product or an inner product between finite-dimensional vectors $\mathbf{x}$ and $\mathbf{y}$.
- MATLAB syntax is sometimes used to represent vectors or matrices. For example, $[a\ b; c\ d]$ denotes the matrix

$$\begin{bmatrix} a & b \\ c & d \end{bmatrix}.$$

- $||\mathbf{x}||_1$ denotes the 1-norm of the $N \times 1$ vector $\mathbf{x}$ which is equal to

$$||\mathbf{x}||_1 = \sum_{i=1}^{N} |x_i|.$$

- $|\mathbf{x}| = ||\mathbf{x}||_2$ denotes the 2-norm or Euclidean norm of the $N \times 1$ vector $\mathbf{x}$ which is equal to

$$||\mathbf{x}||_2 = \sqrt{\sum_{i=1}^{N} x_i^2}.$$

If the subscript is missing then the 2-norm is indicated, l_2 for a discrete vector and L_2 for a well-behaved function of a continuous variable.

- The length of a vector $\mathbf{x}$ will often be denoted as $|\mathbf{x}|$ rather than $||\mathbf{x}||_2$.
- $||\mathbf{x}||_p$ denotes the p-norm or Euclidean norm of the $N \times 1$ vector $\mathbf{x}$ which is equal to

$$||\mathbf{x}||_p = \left(\sum_{i=1}^{N} x_i^p \right)^{\frac{1}{p}}.$$

- $\hat{\mathbf{x}} = \frac{\mathbf{x}}{|\mathbf{x}|}$ denotes the unit vector.
- $\mathbf{A}^*$ denotes the complex conjugate of the matrix $\mathbf{A}$.
- $\mathbf{A}^T$ denotes the transpose of matrix $\mathbf{A}$. We will often insist it also means the transpose and complex conjugated matrix $\mathbf{A}$.
- $\mathbf{A}^\dagger$ denotes the conjugated and transposed matrix $\mathbf{A}$.
- $\star$ denotes temporal convolution. For example, assuming $f(t)$ and $g(t)$ are real continuous functions of the scalar variable t and are square integrable then

$$f(t) \star g(t) = \int_{-\infty}^{\infty} f(t-\tau)g(\tau)d\tau = \int_{-\infty}^{\infty} f(\tau)g(t-\tau)d\tau. \tag{1}$$

- $\otimes$ denotes temporal correlation. For example, assuming $f(t)$ and $g(t)$ are real continuous functions of the scalar variable t and are square integrable then

$$f(t) \otimes g(t) = f(-t) \star g(t) = \int_{-\infty}^{\infty} f(\tau)g(t+\tau)d\tau. \tag{2}$$

- $\mathcal{F}[f(t)] = F(\omega)$ denotes the Fourier transform of $f(t)$ and $\mathcal{F}^{-1}[F(\omega)]$ is the inverse Fourier transform of $F(\omega)$. For example,

$$F(\omega) = \mathcal{F}[f(t)] = \int_{-\infty}^{\infty} f(t)e^{-i\omega t}dt,$$

$$f(t) = \mathcal{F}^{-1}[F(\omega)] = \frac{1}{2\pi} \int_{-\infty}^{\infty} F(\omega)e^{i\omega t}d\omega,$$

$$\frac{d^n f(t)}{dt^n} = \frac{1}{2\pi} \int_{-\infty}^{\infty} (i\omega)^n F(\omega)e^{i\omega t}d\omega,$$

$$f(-t) = \mathcal{F}^{-1}[F(\omega)^*],$$

$$\mathcal{F}[f(t) \star g(t)] = F(\omega)G(\omega),$$

$$\mathcal{F}[f(t) \otimes g(t)] = \mathcal{F}[f(-t) \star g(t)] = F(\omega)^* G(\omega),$$

$$f(t) \star g(t) = \frac{1}{2\pi} \int_{-\infty}^{\infty} F(\omega) G(\omega) e^{i\omega t} d\omega,$$

$$f(t) \otimes g(t) = \frac{1}{2\pi} \int_{-\infty}^{\infty} F(\omega)^* G(\omega) e^{i\omega t} d\omega,$$

$$f(t) \otimes g(t)|_{t=0} = \int_{-\infty}^{\infty} f(\tau) g(\tau) d\tau$$

$$= \frac{1}{2\pi} \int_{-\infty}^{\infty} F(\omega)^* G(\omega) d\omega,$$

$$f(t) \otimes f(t)|_{t=0} = \int_{-\infty}^{\infty} f(\tau)^2 d\tau = \frac{1}{2\pi} \int_{-\infty}^{\infty} |F(\omega)|^2 d\omega.$$

$$(3)$$

- The Dirac delta function $\delta(t)$ is a generalized function (Zemanian, 1965) that is zero everywhere on the real line, except at $t = 0$. The Dirac delta function has a broadband spectrum with the constant amplitude 1:

$$\delta(t - t') = \frac{1}{2\pi} \int_{-\infty}^{\infty} e^{i\omega(t-t')} d\omega. \tag{4}$$

For a smooth function $f(\tau)$, the delta function has the sifting property:

$$f(t) = \int_{-\infty}^{\infty} f(\tau) \delta(\tau - t) d\tau. \tag{5}$$

Abbreviations

ABC	absorbing boundary condition		KM	Kirchhoff migration
ADCIG	angle-domain common image gather		LSM	least squares migration
CAG	common angle gather		LSRTM	least squares reverse time migration
CFL	Courant-Friedrichs-Lewy		MD	migration deconvolution
CG	conjugate gradient		MVA	migration velocity analysis
CIG	common image gather		NLCG	nonlinear conjugate gradient
CMG	common midpoint gather		NMO	normal moveout
COG	common offset gather		PDE	partial differential equation
CSG	common shot gather		PML	perfectly matched layer
DFP	Davidon-Fletcher-Powell		PSTM	prestack time migration
DM	diffraction-stack migration		QN	quasi-Newton
DOD	domain of dependence		RTM	reverse time migration
DSO	differential semblance optimization		SD	steepest descent
EWT	early arrival wave equation tomography		SE	spectral element
FD	finite difference		SLS	standard linear solid
FE	finite element		SPD	symmetric positive definite
FWI	full waveform inversion		SSP	surface seismic profile
GCV	generalized cross validation		SV	singular vector
GDM	generalized diffraction-stack migration		VSP	vertical seismic profile
GDSO	generalized differential semblance optimization		WT	wave equation traveltime tomography
GIDI	generalized image domain inversion		WTW	wave equation traveltime and waveform tomography
GOM	Gulf of Mexico		ZO	zero offset
IDI	image domain inversion			

Part I

Iterative Optimization Methods

Chapter 1: Introduction to Seismic Inversion

Seismic inversion, or tomography,[1] is the procedure for reconstructing earth properties from seismic data (Aki et al., 1977; Aki and Richards, 1980; Bishop et al., 1985; Nolet, 1987, and Tarantola, 1987). The tomogram is presented graphically as a two- or three-dimensional (2D or 3D) grid of pixels, in which each pixel contains the model parameter of interest, such as the velocity value or its reciprocal value known as slowness. An example is shown in Figure 1.1, which is a vertical slice of a 3D tomogram inverted from first-arrival traveltimes picked from seismic data. These arrivals are assumed to propagate mostly along the dashed raypaths (see Figure 1.2a) from the source at **s** to the geophone **g**, and they are recorded as a seismic trace.[2] An actual set of traces recorded for one shot is shown in Figure 1.2b, and Figure 1.3 depicts several rays associated with different types of events. Appendix 1A provides an overview of exploration seismology.

Tomograms such as the one in Figure 1.1 are used to determine the geometry and lithology of geologic layers in the earth, which involves a low-velocity colluvial wedge and an earthquake-induced fault scarp in this case.[3] The low-velocity zone denoted by the dark-blue color in Figure 1.1b represents a colluvial wedge, a geological scar from the last earthquake. The soft soil sediments here reveal a velocity contrast of over 100%.

For deeper portions of the earth, consolidation and cementation of sediments into rocks often show much smaller P-wave velocity contrasts. For example, at oil exploration depths of 5 to 10 km, the velocity contrasts of sandstones and shales typically are no more than 10% to 20%, and the sediment-salt interfaces can have more than 100% velocity contrast. At large depths of hundreds of kilometers, the typical P-wave velocity variations are no more than about 5% in the mantle. Here, large globs of material with a few percent lower velocity than the surrounding mantle are attributed to hotter (i.e., weaker) rock and delineate plumes of molten material. Higher velocities are thought to correspond to colder, denser, and stiffer rock, and so they delineate downgoing slabs of tectonic plates (Stein and Wyession, 2003).

Applications of seismic inversion include subsurface characterization for engineering geology, such as road, tunnel, reservoir, or building construction; oil and mineral exploration; and scientific characterization of volcanoes, tectonic plates, and the earth in general. The inversion of sound-wave measurements also is used for nondestructive testing of materials, military sonar ranging, and medical imaging.

1.1 Notation

Operators and matrices are indicated by bold uppercase letters, vectors by bold lowercase letters, and scalars by lowercase letters. Earth models typically are discretized into vector space elements in $\mathbb{R}^N$. Components of the matrix **L** and vector **m** are defined as L_{ij} and m_i; typically, the model vector is expressed as **m**, the data vector is **d**, and the forward-modeling matrix (or operator) is denoted as **L**. For iterative solutions, the index associated with the kth iterate solution is placed as a superscript enclosed by parentheses; e.g., $\mathbf{x}^{(k)}$ is the solution vector at the kth iterate.

The $N \times 1$ column vector denoted by **x**, and its inner product with the $N \times 1$ vector **y** is defined by

$$\mathbf{x}^\dagger \mathbf{y} = (\mathbf{x}, \mathbf{y}) = \sum x_i^* y_i, \qquad (1.1)$$

in which the † symbol in $\mathbf{x}^\dagger$ indicates the complex conjugation and transpose of the vector **x**. The transpose operation is indicated by the superscript T so the Hermitian adjoint

---

[1]The word tomography is derived from the Greek *tomē* ("cut") or *tomos* ("part" or "section") and *graphein* ("to write").

[2]The geophone typically measures the particle-velocity motion as the wiggly seismic trace denoted by $d(\mathbf{g}, t|\mathbf{s},0)$, in which t denotes the listening time at **g** for a source at **s** excited at time zero. The amplitude of the seismic trace is proportional to the magnitude of the particle velocity at the geophone. Darkened (lightened) wiggles denote downward (upward) movement of the ground motion, and time is increasing upward along each trace.

[3]A colluvial wedge is the rubble (with slower propagation velocity) that accumulates at the base of the downthrown fault scarp within about 50 years of an earthquake rupture. The surrounding sediments are more consolidated, so they are stiffer and have faster P-wave velocity. A P wave (primary or pressure wave) is an example of a seismic wave through the earth, frequently produced by an earthquake or a controlled source and recorded by seismographs. In an isotropic medium, an S wave (secondary or shear wave) propagates with particle motion perpendicular to the direction of wave propagation, and the P wave has particle motion parallel to the direction of propagation.

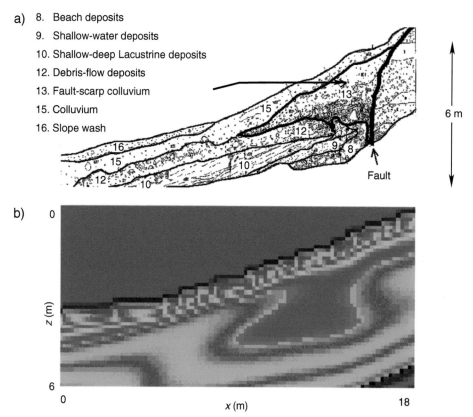

a)
8. Beach deposits
9. Shallow-water deposits
10. Shallow-deep Lacustrine deposits
12. Debris-flow deposits
13. Fault-scarp colluvium
15. Colluvium
16. Slope wash

6 m

Fault

Figure 1.1. Comparison of (a) the geologic cross section (Olig et al., 1996) showing a colluvial wedge (dark line), and (b) the corresponding portion of the velocity tomogram obtained by inverting first-arrival traveltimes over the Oquirrh fault, Utah (Morey and Schuster, 1999, Figure 11). In (b), the irregular black line is the topographic surface at the field site, and the dark-blue and light-green colors correspond to velocities of about 300 m/s and 550 m/s, respectively.

of a matrix with scalar elements is the conjugate transpose of **L**:

$$\mathbf{L}^{\dagger} = (\mathbf{L}^{*})^{T}, \qquad (1.2)$$

in which the $*$ symbol indicates the complex conjugation of the elements of **L**. Morse and Feshbach (1953) distinguish an adjoint operator from a Hermitian adjoint operator. However, we will abide by the mathematical definition that the Hermitian adjoint of a matrix is its conjugated transpose. We also will use the $*$ symbol to indicate complex conjugation of a complex number or function. A self-adjoint matrix has the property $\mathbf{L} = \mathbf{L}^{\dagger}$, in which a symmetric real matrix is an example.

1.2 Inverse problem

The discrete inverse problem for geophysics can be defined generally as inverting for the model vector **m** from the recorded data vector **d**, where **d** is related to **m** by

$$\mathbf{d} = \mathbf{Lm}. \qquad (1.3)$$

Here, **L** represents a nonlinear forward-modeling operator that depends implicitly on **m** and predicts the data **d**

from the model **m**. If the original forward-modeling operator is nonlinear, then it usually is linearized about some background model. According to Hadamard (1902), well-posed mathematical models, such as the linearized version of equation 1.3, of physical systems should have the following characteristics:

1. A solution exists. For many geophysical data sets, a solution does not exist because the data are too noisy and lead to an inconsistent and overdetermined set of equations. For example, the equations $x = 3$ and $x = 4$ represent an overdetermined and inconsistent system of equations. The remedy is to seek the solution that minimizes, e.g., a weighted sum of squared data residuals[4] and an additive penalty functional.[5]

---

[4]A data residual is the difference between a measured data value, e.g., a traveltime for the first arrival at a specified recording station, and the predicted data. The predicted data might be generated by, for example, ray tracing in the predicted velocity model.

[5]The penalty function becomes large when the inverted model strays from some preferred characteristic of the assumed model. For example, smooth velocity models with small spatial velocity gradients might be preferred, so the squared magnitude of the velocity gradient is used as a penalty function.

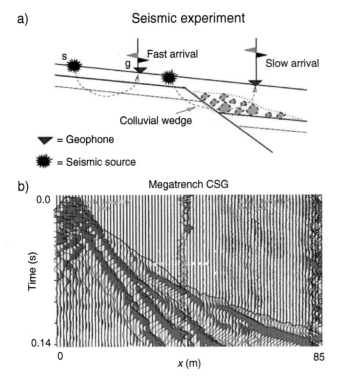

a)

Seismic experiment

Fast arrival

Slow arrival

Colluvial wedge

▼ = Geophone

✸ = Seismic source

b)

Megatrench CSG

Time (s)

0.0

0.14

0   x (m)   85

Figure 1.2. (a) Depiction of dashed raypaths that originate from seismic sources (stars) and terminate at geophones (triangles). (b) Shot gather of traces with picked first-arrival traveltimes (black line) recorded by a seismic experiment over the Megatrench colluvial wedge (Buddensiek et al., 2008). The red amplitudes correspond to the downward particle-velocity motion of the ground surface.

2. The solution is unique. In a typical geophysical experiment, the sources and receivers are located only over a small portion of the body of interest. This often leads to a nonempty null space for **L**, and consequently zero eigenvalues for $\mathbf{L}^T\mathbf{L}$. Geophysicists use regularization to mitigate this problem.

3. The solution should depend continuously on the data, otherwise the solution is unstable. For example, an unstable solution is one in which small changes in the noise level of the data lead to discontinuous changes in the model.[6] In this case, a regularization method is used to steer the solution to one with preferred characteristics.

The typical approach to geophysical inversion is to recast the problem so that we seek the optimal model which minimizes a weighted combination of data misfit and model penalty functions (Fletcher, 1980; Meyer et al., 2004), also known as objective functions. Typically, the objective function is a nonlinear function of the model parameters. The solution procedure falls under the class of nonlinear

optimization methods, which now is illustrated with the example of traveltime tomography.

The goal of traveltime tomography is to estimate the subsurface velocity distribution of the earth by inverting the picked traveltimes of specific events. Six steps are used to implement traveltime tomography, and are representative of the steps used to implement most geophysical inverse algorithms (see Figure 1.3).

1. **Discretization of the model m.** The slowness model of the earth is discretized into a grid of unknown slownesses, as illustrated in Figure 1.4. Each gridpoint of the cell is associated with an unknown slowness value. For convenience, we will assume a fine grid spacing so the slowness s_j is assumed to be constant in the jth cell, to give an $N \times 1$ model vector **m** of N unknown slownesses.

2. **Discretization of the data d.** For first-arrival traveltime tomography, the traveltime of the first arrival in each trace is picked and denoted as t_i for the ith ray. For M traces, the traveltime measurements form the $M \times 1$ data vector **d**.

3. **Discrete modeling operator L.** The inverse problem is solved by assuming a starting model and a modeling operator **L** to generate the predicted data. For traveltime tomography, a high-frequency approximation is assumed[7] so that the total traveltime along the ith ray is the sum of the individual traveltimes d_i in each cell:

$$\sum_j l_{ij} m_j = d_i \quad \text{or} \quad \mathbf{Lm} = \mathbf{d}, \tag{1.4}$$

in which l_{ij} is the raypath segment length of the ith ray in the jth cell, and m_j is the constant slowness s_j in the jth cell. Here, **L** is an $M \times N$ matrix.

4. **Linearization.** Equation 1.4 is a nonlinear equation because the raypath segment length l_{ij} depends on the velocity model. This is not surprising because, according to Snell's law, large gradients in the velocity distribution will lead to large changes in the raypaths. Therefore, **L** implicitly depends on **m**, and so inverting the above system of equations will not yield an acceptable answer unless our starting slowness model is close to the true model! The remedy is to start with a model $\mathbf{m}^{(0)} = \mathbf{m}_o$ close to the actual model and linearize the relationship between the data and model. Then, the data can be inverted for a more accurate model $\mathbf{m}^{(1)}$. Using $\mathbf{m}^{(1)}$ as a new starting model, this procedure usually can be repeated until convergence.

---

[6]This is a symptom of an ill-conditioned matrix **L**, in which many of the eigenvalues are nearly zero so that many different models nearly fit the same data.

[7]Bleistein (1984) infers that the high-frequency approximation is appropriate if the maximum wavelength $\lambda^{\max}$ of the wavefield is less than 1/3 the minimum wavelength of velocity variations. The value of $\lambda^{\max}$ can be estimated by dividing the maximum model velocity by the minimum frequency of the source wavelet.

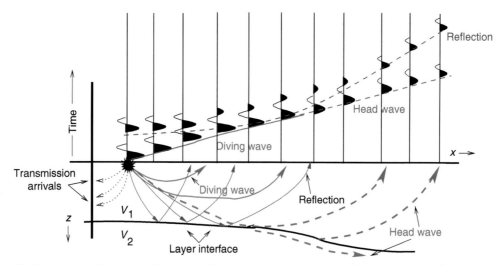

Figure 1.3. Rays for four types of events: refraction, reflection, transmission, and diving waves. Refraction waves, also known as head waves, will exist if velocities V_1 just above and V_2 below the interface satisfy the condition $V_2 > V_1$, and the source either can be a controlled source or an earthquake. Here, it is assumed that the velocity increases with depth in the first layer.

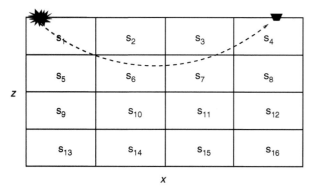

Figure 1.4. Diagram of the ith ray in a discretized earth model, where the jth cell has a constant slowness $m_j = s_j$. The segment length of the ith ray in the jth cell is given by l_{ij}.

Defining the jth model parameter as m_j, the linearization step starts by expanding the ith data measurement d_i to first order in a Taylor series about a first-guess model $\mathbf{m}_o$ close to the true model:

$$d_i(\mathbf{m}) \approx d_i(\mathbf{m}_o) + \sum_j \left[\frac{\partial d_i(\mathbf{m})}{\partial m_j} \right]\Bigg|_{\mathbf{m}_o} \delta m_j, \quad (1.5)$$

in which $\mathbf{m} = \mathbf{m}_o + \delta\mathbf{m}$. Rearranging terms gives the linearized equation

$$\delta d_i(\mathbf{m}) = \sum_j \left[\frac{\partial d_i(\mathbf{m})}{\partial m_j} \right]\Bigg|_{\mathbf{m}_o} \delta m_j, \quad (1.6)$$

or in matrix-vector notation,

$$\delta\mathbf{d}(\mathbf{m}) = \mathbf{L}\delta\mathbf{m}. \quad (1.7)$$

Here, the data residual $\delta d_i = [d_i(\mathbf{m}) - d_i(\mathbf{m}_o)]$ is the ith component of the difference between the observed data vector $\mathbf{d}_i(\mathbf{m})$ and the predicted data vector $\mathbf{d}_i(\mathbf{m}_o)$. The model perturbation $\delta\mathbf{m} = \mathbf{m} - \mathbf{m}_o$ is the difference between the actual model $\mathbf{m}$ and the guessed model $\mathbf{m}_o$. The matrix $\mathbf{L}$ is the Jacobian matrix and its elements $l_{ij} = \partial d_i(\mathbf{m}_o)/\partial m_j$, also known as a Fréchet derivative, determine the sensitivity of the ith data to the model perturbations in the jth cell.

For traveltime tomography and a small cell size, the Fréchet derivative $\partial d_i(\mathbf{m}_o)/\partial m_j$ can be shown (see Chapter 5) to be the raypath segment length l_{ij} in the jth cell for the ith ray, i.e., equation 1.6 becomes

$$\delta t_i = \sum_j l_{ij} \delta s_j, \quad (1.8)$$

where a raypath is illustrated in Figure 1.4. Chapters 5 and 19 present the derivations for the equations of traveltime and waveform tomography, respectively.

5. **Regularized solution.** The recorded data contain noise and this leads to an inconsistent[8] set of overdetermined equations. Also, the solution can be unstable where many models might nearly satisfy the same data.

To partially remedy these problems, we seek the model that best minimizes the objective function ϵ, which is the sum of a penalty term and the p-norm of the data residual taken to the pth power:

$$\epsilon = \frac{1}{p} \| \overbrace{\mathbf{L}\delta\mathbf{m} - \delta\mathbf{d}}^{\text{residual vector}} \|_p^p + \eta^2 g(\mathbf{m}), \quad (1.9)$$

---

[8]Inconsistency also can arise because the assumed modeling operator does not model all of the important physics associated with the data.

in which η^2 is a small positive scalar and $g(\mathbf{m})$ is a penalty function that becomes smaller as the estimated model approaches an a priori estimate of the actual model. Here, p is a positive integer and the residual vector $\mathbf{L}\delta\mathbf{m} - \delta\mathbf{d}$ is the difference between the predicted and observed data. For $p = 2$, the squared length of the residual vector is the misfit function.

The penalty term is sometimes expressed as $g(\mathbf{m}) = \frac{1}{p}||\mathbf{m} - \mathbf{m}'||_p^p$ for some a priori model $\mathbf{m}'$. Often, $p \to 2$ and the objective function is chosen to be the sum of the squared data residuals and a constrained model penalty term $||\mathbf{L}\delta\mathbf{m} - \delta\mathbf{d}||^2 + \eta^2||\delta\mathbf{m}||^2$. In this case, the regularized damped least-squares solution is

$$\delta\mathbf{m} = [\mathbf{L}^T\mathbf{L} + \eta^2\mathbf{I}]^{-1}\mathbf{L}^T\delta\mathbf{d}, \qquad (1.10)$$

in which $\mathbf{I}$ is the identity matrix, and the transpose operation indicates complex conjugation if the elements are complex numbers. For complex numbers, we will use the adjoint symbol $\dagger$ to replace the transpose notation. This type of regularized solution procedure is sometimes known as the Levenberg-Marquardt method (Gill et al., 1981). Chapters 3 to 5 discuss regularization methods for other penalty terms, such as derivative-like terms that reward smoother models or entropy-like terms that reward sparse models.

6. **Iterative regularized solution.** The data are related nonlinearly to the model, so the solution of equation 1.10 is found by an iterative updating scheme

$$\mathbf{m}^{(k+1)} = \mathbf{m}^{(k)} - \alpha[\mathbf{L}^T\mathbf{L} + \eta^2\mathbf{I}]^{-1}\mathbf{L}^T\delta\mathbf{d}^{(k)}, \quad (1.11)$$

in which α is the step length and $\mathbf{m}^{(k)}$ ($\delta\mathbf{d}^{(k)}$) denotes the kth iterate model (data residual). The rays associated with the matrix $\mathbf{L}$ are computed in the kth velocity model and a sequence of models is generated until the data residual falls below some acceptable level. The matrix $[\mathbf{L}^T\mathbf{L}]$ typically is too expensive to compute, store, and invert, so often it is approximated by its diagonal components $[\mathbf{L}^T\mathbf{L}]_{ij} \approx [\mathbf{L}^T\mathbf{L}]_{ii}\delta_{ij}$ to give the preconditioned steepest descent solution

$$m_i^{(k+1)} = m_i^{(k)} - \frac{\alpha[\mathbf{L}^T\delta\mathbf{d}^{(k)}]_i}{[\mathbf{L}^T\mathbf{L}]_{ii} + \eta^2}, \qquad (1.12)$$

with regularization and the step-length parameter α. Chapters 2 to 4 present some gradient-optimization schemes, and later chapters show their application to seismic problems.

The main problem with nonlinear seismic inversion is that the objective function often is plagued by many local minima. Thus, the iterative solution often gets stuck in a local minimum and never reaches the global minimum, or

actual model. To mitigate this problem, the data set can be simplified by skeletonizing it (Luo and Schuster, 1991a; 1991b) and inverting only its essential features, i.e., solving for longer wavelength features, at the early iterations. At the later iterations, higher-order details are admitted into the data and model.

Some skeletonization methods include multiscale inversion (Bunks et al., 1995), in which the traces are low-pass filtered to get a somewhat linearized objective function, and higher frequencies are admitted gradually with increasing iteration number. Another data reduction method is to invert initially the early arrivals, near-offset traces, and/or phases of select arrivals. At later iterations, wider offset traces, longer listening times, and more complex physics are admitted into the inversion (see Chapter 20). Avoiding local minima still is an active area of research.

1.3 Types of seismic inversion

There are several types of seismic data that are inverted: traveltimes (Chapters 5 and 20), phase information (Chapters 20 and 21), waveform information (Chapters 15, 19, 20, 21, 22, and 23), and migration images (Chapters 18, 24, 25, and 26), as represented in Figure 1.5. Under the high-frequency approximation, the phase-inversion method of traveltime tomography inverts picked traveltimes for the smoothly varying component of the earth's velocity distribution. It is computationally efficient and convergence is often robust, but it assumes a high-frequency approximation and is able to reconstruct only the low to intermediate wavenumbers of the model. As a partial remedy, wave-equation phase and waveform inversion methods sometimes can achieve higher resolution but at the expense of much larger computational cost and reduced robustness. Convergence to the correct solution often is spoiled if the modeling operator $\mathbf{L}$ does not take into account the significant physics of waveform propagation. To mitigate this problem, the data set can be skeletonized so that only the essential and accurately modeled parts are inverted initially (Chapter 20).

Sometimes, the data are transformed to a domain where the events are more focused and do not overlap one another excessively. One such method is migration velocity analysis (see Chapters 18, 24, 25, and 26), which inverts the estimated migration image for the velocity distributions.

In the not-too-distant future, computers will be powerful enough to accommodate full 3D anelastic and anisotropic effects in wave propagation, so the incomplete physics problem will be mitigated significantly. However, this will exacerbate the problem of nonuniqueness because of the many unknowns that need to be determined from the limited coverage of data.

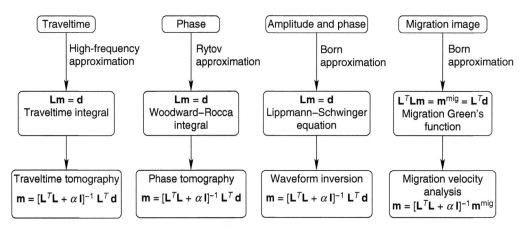

Figure 1.5. Organization chart for inverting four types of seismic data by a nonlinear least-squares method: amplitude, phase, and traveltime. The Fourier transform of the data trace $d(t)$ is denoted as $D(\omega) = |D(\omega)|e^{i\phi(\omega)}$, where $|D(\omega)|$ is the amplitude spectrum and $\phi(\omega)$ is the phase spectrum. If the trace only contains one impulsive event that arrives at the traveltime τ, then $\phi(\omega) = \omega\tau$. The traces can be migrated by $\mathbf{L}^T\mathbf{d}$ to give the migration image $\mathbf{m}^{\text{mig}}$. Here, the adjoint of the operator $\mathbf{L}$ is denoted by $\mathbf{L}^T$.

1.4 Inverse crimes

Wirgin (2008, 3) defines the expression *inverse crime* from Colton and Kress (1998, 304) as denoting the act of using the same modeling operator to generate, as well as to invert, synthetic data. To avoid the inverse crime of trivial inversion, Colton and Kress (1998) write: "It is crucial that the synthetic data be computed by a forward solver which has no connection to the inverse solver." As egregious examples, some geophysical inverse felonies include the following:

- Perfect modeling. Exclusively modeling and inverting clean data with wideband frequencies, where the forward and adjoint operations are computed from the same finite-difference algorithm and the starting model is close to the actual model. An especially egregious crime is to use Born modeling to simulate the recorded data, and then use Born modeling again for forward and adjoint modeling of the predicted data.
- False flag. Declaration of a successful inverse algorithm without being accompanied by rigorous tests on noisy bandlimited synthetics,[9] realistic models, and representative field data. Field-data validation should include well-log comparisons, flattening of reflections in the common-image or common-angle gathers, and wiggle-by-wiggle comparisons of synthetic traces with recorded traces.
- Finest gridding. Discretizing the model at too fine of a grid so that there are more unknowns than independent equations. In this case, many models can fit the same data.

- Too close to be true. The starting model is a smoothed version of the true model so many of the local minima problems are bypassed unrealistically.

In defense of some of the alleged crimes, the development of a new inverse algorithm often starts with an elegant theory, and it is followed by a long series of messy tests that are restricted initially to synthetic data and simple models. Each test can delineate the capabilities and limitations of the method, and possibly lead to further improvements and practical field-data applications. In fact, one might commit an inverse crime if these self-consistency tests are not performed. This is how computational geophysics should proceed, as long as the published papers remind us of these limitations.

Some tips for avoiding severe inverse crimes are the following:

- Solution sensitivity to model discretization. Discretize the model so that there are many more independent equations than unknowns. Sensitivity tests can be conducted to assign smaller cell sizes to well-resolved parts of the model and larger cell sizes to the poorly resolved parts. Sometimes, covariance matrices (Chapter 6), checkerboard tests (Lévêque et al., 1993), or analytical formulas for resolution (Chapters 12 and 14) can be used for a priori assignments of cell size. If feasible, the input data to the checkerboard tests should be numerical solutions to the elastic or viscoelastic wave equations in order to realistically simulate battlefield conditions.
- Solution sensitivity to starting model. Tests should assess the solution sensitivity to different starting models.
- Realistic modeling. Model the data with realistic physics seen in the field data, such as bandlimited sources and viscoelasticity.

---

[9]Ideally, the synthetics should be computed using an elastic modeling code with realistic model parameters such as attenuation and anisotropy. However, this type of realism often is not needed for inverse tests with limited aims.

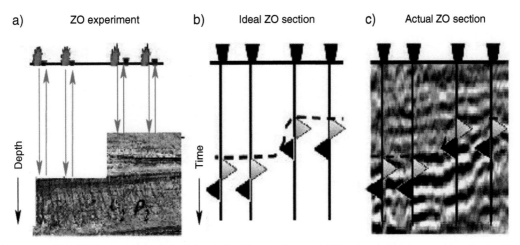

Figure 1.6. (a) Zero-offset (ZO) experiment, and (b–c) the ideal and actual ZO seismic sections, respectively. Each trace is recorded by a geophone coincident with the source position; and the light- and dark-colored amplitudes correspond to the particle velocity of the ground in the upward and downward directions, respectively. An implicit assumption here is that the specular reflection point is directly beneath the geophone, which is incorrect for earth models with dipping structures or lateral velocity variations.

- Blind tests. To validate a mature inverse algorithm, apply it to blind data independently generated by someone else who will not provide details of the elastic model or modeling algorithm.
- Data from physical modeling. The recorded data are from physical seismic experiments at the lab scale or in the field, where the actual model is known. These are the input data to test the inverse algorithm.
- Field data tests. Apply the inverse algorithm to different field-data sets that have well-log information. As mentioned above, field-data validation should include well-log comparisons, flattening of reflections in the common image gathers, and wiggle-by-wiggle comparisons of synthetic traces with recorded traces.
- Clear delineation of both the benefits and limitations of the inverse algorithm. Show results not only for successful inversion of modeled data, but also show where it fails.

Successful numerical tests are empirical results that validate your method for a limited number of data sets. They never can prove your method works for all cases, which are theoretically infinite in number and variety. Conclusions should be consistent with this fact and the assertion by Karl Popper that a theory in the empirical sciences can never be proven, but it can be falsified.

1.5 Summary

The general inverse problem is defined as finding the model $\mathbf{m}$ that best explains the recorded data $\mathbf{L}(\mathbf{m}) = \mathbf{d}$. For seismic inversion, the recorded data also can be considered as the migration image computed from the recorded data.

Waveform inversion is characterized by a high computational cost and poor robustness, but with the possible reward of a highly resolved model. In contrast, phase inversion typically provides intermediate resolution with relatively better convergence properties. For most practical seismic problems, the predicted data are inconsistent with the noisy recorded data, many models almost fit the data equally well, and $\mathbf{L}(\mathbf{m}) = \mathbf{d}$ is a nonlinear set of equations. The partial solution is an iterative nonlinear optimization that uses regularization so the model is guided to the one we consider most reasonable. Also, some type of data skeletonization or multiscale optimization is essential for overcoming the local minima problem. The remaining part of this book addresses all of the above issues for inversion of seismic data and migration images.

Appendix 1A:
Basics of exploration seismology

The principal goal of exploration seismology is to map out oil and gas reservoirs and aquifers by imaging the earth's seismic reflectivity and velocity distributions. Exploration geophysicists perform seismic experiments ideally equivalent to that shown in Figure 1.6, where the source excites seismic waves, and the resulting primary reflections are recorded by a geophone located at the source position. For this ideal zero-offset (ZO) experiment, we assume only primary reflections[10] in the records and that waves travel only in the vertical direction.

---

[10] A primary reflection is a wave that propagates downward, reflects off of a reflector, and propagates back up to the surface, without any reverberations between layers.

a)   Road cut   b)   Seismic section

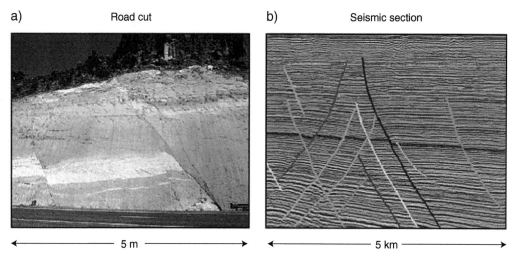

←————— 5 m —————→   ←————— 5 km —————→

Figure 1.7. Geologic faults revealed by (a) road cut and (b) marine seismic section. The length scales above are estimated approximately.

a)   Vibroseis truck   b)   Geophones and cables

Figure 1.8. (a) Vibroseis truck and (b) geophones attached to cables at a desert base camp. Inset is a particle-velocity geophone that is about 10 cm long.

After recording at one location, the source and receiver are moved laterally by approximately 1/2 source wavelength and the experiment is repeated at different ground positions. All recorded traces are lined up next to one another and the resulting section is defined as the zero-offset (ZO) or poststack seismic section, as shown in Figure 1.6. This section resembles the actual geology, where one side of the signal is colored black to help enhance visual identification of the interface. Note that the depth d of the first reflector can be calculated by multiplying the two-way up-and-down reflection time t by half the P-wave velocity v of the first layer, i.e., $d = tv/2$.

Seismic images of the subsurface are used to assess the geology of the earth. For example, Figure 1.7 shows both optical and seismic pictures of faults. These images provide an understanding of the fault's characteristics and so aid geologists in deciphering the tectonic forces that shaped the earth. Faults also can serve as impermeable traps for oil and gas deposits, waiting to be found by the explorationist with the most capable seismic camera and digital processing algorithms.

Seismic sources

A land seismic source consists of a mechanical device or explosive located at **s** that thumps the earth (see Figure 1.8a) at time $t = 0$, and a geophone (see Figure 1.8b) at **g** records the time history of the earth's vertical particle velocity, denoted as a seismic trace $d(\mathbf{g}, t | \mathbf{s}, 0)$. A marine source is usually an array of air guns. Larger amplitudes on the Figure 1.6 traces correspond to faster particle velocity, and the upgoing and downgoing motion is

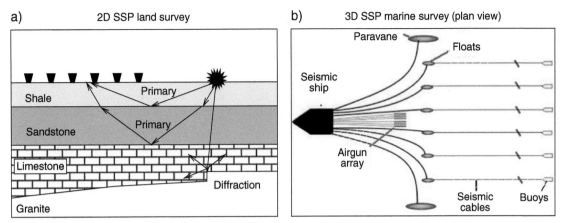

Figure 1.9. (a) Two-dimensional (2D) land and (b) 3D marine (courtesy of www.blendspace.com) survey geometries to record surface seismic profiles (SSPs). The hydrophone streamer for a marine survey can be as long as 12 km with a hydrophone spacing of 15 to 30 m. The typical 3D survey might consist of several source boats and often more than a dozen parallel hydrophone streamers, with a separation distance of up to 100 m. A survey where the sources and receivers are along the free surface is known as a surface seismic profile (SSP) survey.

denoted here by the blackened and unblackened lobes, respectively. The lobe amplitude is proportional approximately to the reflectivity strength $m(\mathbf{x})$ of the corresponding reflector at $\mathbf{x} = (x, y, z)$. Assuming a constant density and a layered medium, the pressure reflectivity model $m(\mathbf{x})$ is approximated sometimes for a normally incident wave as

$$m(\mathbf{x}) \approx \frac{v(z + dz) - v(z)}{v(z + dz) + v(z)}, \qquad (1.13)$$

in which $v(z)$ is the P-wave propagation velocity at depth z in a layered medium and dz is a small increment in depth.

Nonzero-offset seismic experiment

In practice, a ZO experiment cannot generate the ideal seismic section because the source also generates strong coherent noise and near-source scattering energy. In addition, the waves are propagating in all directions and contain distracting noise such as multiples, surface waves, scattered arrivals, out-of-plane reflections, and converted waves. To account for these complexities, geophysicists perform nonzero offset experiments in which the vibrations are recorded by many receivers as shown in Figure 1.9b. As before, each experiment consists of a shot at a different location, except that hundreds of active receivers are spread out over a long line for a 2D survey and a large area for a 3D survey. Figure 1.10 depicts a collage of pictures associated with a 3D marine survey.

Reflection amplitudes

Reflection waveform arrival times also are influenced by velocity, but their amplitudes are controlled strongly

by density ρ and velocity v changes across an interface. The product $I = \rho v$ is known as impedance, and the normalized difference $(I_2 - I_1)/(I_1 + I_2)$ across an interface is the acoustic reflection coefficient at zero-incidence angle, where I_1 and I_2 are the impedances above and below the interface. The bottom illustration in Figure 1.2 depicts a shot gather of traces collected over the Wasatch fault, Utah, where refractions, diffractions, surface waves, and reflections are present in these data.

Seismic processing

For surveys over a mostly layered medium, data processing consists of the following steps:

1. Filtering of noise and near-surface statics corrections.
2. Reassembly of common-shot-gather (CSG) traces in Figure 1.11a into the common-midpoint gather (CMG) shown in Figure 1.11b.
3. The traces in the CMG are time shifted to align the common-midpoint reflections with the ZO reflection event in Figure 1.11c. The time shift that aligns the nonzero-offset reflections with the ZO reflection is known as the normal-moveout operation (NMO).
4. Stack[11] the traces in the time-shifted CMG to form a single trace at the common-midpoint position in Figure 1.11d. This stacked trace approximates a ZO trace at that position.

---

[11]Summing, or stacking, N traces together gives a stacked trace, where the signal-to-noise ratio can be enhanced by $\sqrt{N}$. This assumes that the coherent signals are aligned with one another from trace to trace and the zero-mean additive noise is white.

Marine seismic survey

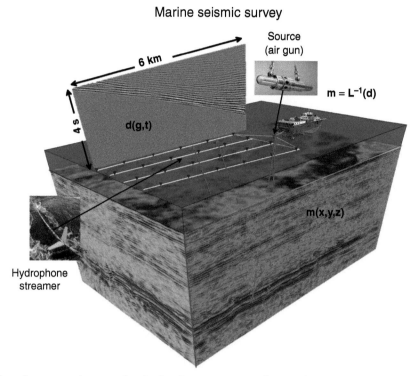

Figure 1.10. Picture of marine survey boat towing hydrophone streamers (insets along right and lower left). A common-shot gather recorded along one streamer is depicted in the upper left inset with time increasing upward. A 3D reflectivity image computed from Gulf of Mexico data is depicted along the faces of the cube. The goal of seismic imaging is to invert the earth model **m** from the data **d**. Courtesy of Sherif Hanafy.

5. Repeat steps 3 and 4 for all midpoint gathers to give the seismic section shown in Figure 1.7b. If the subsurface reflectivity is extremely complex then steps 2 to 5 are skipped, and instead the algorithm known as prestack migration (see Chapters 10, 11, 13, and 15) is used. However, an accurate migration image requires an accurate migration velocity model, so first we should use traveltime tomography (Chapter 5), full waveform inversion (Chapters 19 to 23), and/or migration velocity analysis (Chapters 24 to 26) to estimate the migration velocity model.

In almost all processing of exploration data, the above stacking process is skipped and instead the data are migrated to form the reflectivity section.

Reflection imaging

Figure 1.2b depicts a shot gather of traces collected over the Wasatch fault, Utah, where refractions, diffractions, surface waves, and reflections are present in these data. Relocating the primary reflection arrivals in the recorded

traces to their reflection-points model yields an approximation to the reflectivity distribution, otherwise known as the migration image. As noted in Figure 1.6, the specular reflection point can emanate from a location laterally offset from the geophone location. An example of a typical migration section is shown in Figure 1.7.

Key difficulty with migration images

A key problem in obtaining an accurate migration image is the estimation of a sufficiently accurate velocity model for migration. The migration velocity model is used to map the reflection events to their correct locations of origin, i.e. the reflecting interface. Large errors in this velocity model will lead to inaccurate, defocused, and sometimes unusable migration images. As an example, Figures 15.2 and 15.3 (Chapter 15) show different migration images obtained with different velocity errors, where velocity errors typically should be less than 5% to obtain an accurate rendering of the reflectivity model. This book largely concentrates on inverting seismic data for a more accurate velocity model and reflectivity distribution of the earth.

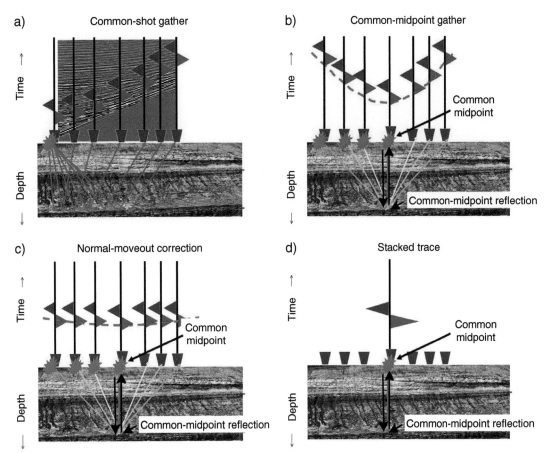

Figure 1.11. Simple processing steps for seismic data recorded over a layered medium, where the layers are mostly horizontal. (a) Common-shot gather, in which a single source is recorded by all of the geophones to form a CSG of traces. (b) The traces from many CSGs can be reassembled to form a common-midpoint gather (CMG), in which a trace associated with each source-receiver pair has the same midpoint position on the surface. The common subsurface reflection point is known as the common reflection point; if the interface is dipping, then rays associated with traces in the same CMG do not share a common reflection point. (c) Traces after time shifting the CMG traces to align with the zero-offset trace. (d) The stacked trace is formed by adding the NMO corrected traces. In this case, the fold is seven and the signal-to-noise ratio (S/N) is enhanced by a factor of $\sqrt{7}$ if there is only additive white noise in the traces. This stacked trace approximates a zero-offset (ZO) trace, in which the source and geophone are coincident with one another.

Chapter 2: Introduction to Gradient Optimization

The *unconstrained* optimization problem (Fletcher, 1987) for the real-valued functional $f(\mathbf{x})$ is defined as finding the optimal model vector $\mathbf{x}^*$ that satisfies the following condition[1]:

$$f(\mathbf{x}^*) \leq f(\mathbf{x}) \text{ for all } \mathbf{x}. \qquad (2.1)$$

This is known as a *constrained* optimization problem if the solution $\mathbf{x}$ also is subject to the N constraint equations

$$c_i(\mathbf{x}) \geq 0 \ i \in (1, 2, 3 \ldots N). \qquad (2.2)$$

This book will be confined mainly to the unconstrained optimization problem, in which a geophysical example of $f(\mathbf{x})$ is the data misfit function in equation 1.9 for traveltime tomography.

Sometimes a model penalty function $g(\mathbf{x})$ is added to the data objective function

$$\epsilon = f(\mathbf{x}) + \lambda g(\mathbf{x}), \qquad (2.3)$$

in which $\lambda > 0$ is the scalar parameter that governs the tradeoff between reducing the penalty function at the expense of an increased value of the data objective function. As an example, it is reasonable to enforce agreement between the inverted velocity model $\mathbf{x}$ and the sonic-log velocity $\mathbf{x}^{\text{well}}$ measured at a well so $g(\mathbf{x}) = \|\mathbf{x} - \mathbf{x}^{\text{well}}\|^2$ for values of the velocity model at the well location. Large values of λ yield an inverted model that mostly agrees with the well log, despite the possibility of a large disagreement between the predicted and observed data at the well location.

Two classes of optimization methods

There are two classes (Gill et al., 1981) of optimization methods: global optimization and gradient optimization.

In global optimization (Horst and Pardalos, 1995; Horst et al., 2000; Pardalos and Romeijn, 2002; Forst and Hoffman, 2010), a search is carried out globally over all of model space to find $\mathbf{x}^*$ at the global minimum of ϵ (see Figure 2.1) in equation 2.3 and avoids getting stuck in a local minimum. This optimization is performed in a variety of ways, such as a search by a Monte Carlo method (Fu and Hu, 1997), linear and nonlinear programming (Horst and Pardalos, 1995), simulated annealing, a genetic algorithm (Sen and Stoffa, 1995), or hybrid algorithms (Sen and Stoffa, 1992). If the problem size is small enough or the computer is fast enough, global optimization methods can be quite effective in seismic inversion (Sen and Stoffa, 1991; 1992; 1995). Unfortunately, global search methods often require impractically large amounts of CPU time to solve large seismic problems in three dimensions. Hence, the default optimization algorithm in 3D exploration and earthquake seismology typically is a gradient-based method.

The other class of optimization methods is gradient optimization that iteratively searches for models downhill[2] along the objective function, and usually stops at the first minimum encountered. The advantage compared to nonlinear global optimization is that it takes many fewer iterations to converge and there is no need for expensive computation or to store large matrices with algorithms such as the conjugate-gradient or steepest-descent methods. However, the disadvantage is that gradient optimization often gets stuck in a local minimum. For example, if the starting model is at the far left of the Figure 2.1 plot, then a gradient optimization method will get stuck in the first minimum encountered, labeled as *local minimum*. Starting the gradient search at the far right of the curve, on the other hand, will lead to the desired convergence to the global minimum, the first minimum encountered to the left of this starting point. Unfortunately, choosing a starting model that bypasses local minima and leads directly into the global minimum is impractical for most geophysical inversion problems. A partial remedy to this problem is

---

[1]More generally, optimization can be defined as finding the extremum (maximum or minimum) of $f(\mathbf{x})$, but historically, geophysicists are almost always seeking a model that minimizes $f(\mathbf{x})$. A functional is a scalar-valued function in which the input argument can be, e.g., a vector in $\mathbb{R}^N$ or another function. A linear functional is a linear map from a vector space to its field of scalars.

[2]A downhill direction in Figure 2.1 leads to a smaller value of $f(\mathbf{x})$.

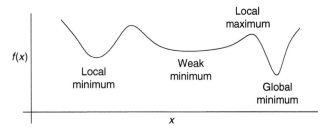

Figure 2.1. Function $f(x)$ with different stationary points: local minimum, weak minimum surrounded by flat topography, strong global minimum, local maximum, and a strong global minimum.

the multiscale-gradient method (Bunks et al., 1995; Nemeth et al., 1997; Ravaut et al., 2004; Krebs et al., 2009), which can bypass local minima to converge to a model near or at the global minimum.

Multiscale strategy

The multiscale strategy applies a low-pass filter to the data to make it simpler, which leads to an objective function with a smoother topography. A gradient search then is used until there is little reduction in the smoothed objective function (see Figure 19.1). Higher frequencies (or more complex data) are added back into the filtered data and a new gradient search is started. This procedure is iterated until all of the important components in the data are added back into the data. Variations of a multiscale strategy include skeletonizing the data (Luo and Schuster, 1991a; 1991b) and restricting the data with limited offset and time windows at the early iterations. Results with multiscale waveform inversion (Bunks et al., 1995; Ravaut et al., 2004; Krebs et al., 2009) suggest that multiscale gradient optimization is an essential tool for inverting seismic data.

2.1 Mathematical definitions

The gradient of a function $f(\mathbf{x})$ is defined[3] as

$$\nabla f(\mathbf{x}) := \begin{bmatrix} \dfrac{\partial f}{\partial x_1} \\ \cdot \\ \cdot \\ \cdot \\ \dfrac{\partial f}{\partial x_N} \end{bmatrix}, \qquad (2.4)$$

[3]In the following sections, it will be assumed (unless otherwise stated) that the function $f(\mathbf{x})$ is infinitely differentiable with respect to model parameters and is characterized by a unique global minimum.

in which $\mathbf{x} \in \mathbb{R}^N$ and the $N \times N$ Hessian matrix $\mathbf{H}$ is defined as $\nabla\nabla^T f(\mathbf{x})$ with components

$$H_{ij} := [\nabla\nabla^T f(\mathbf{x})]_{ij} = \frac{\partial^2 f(\mathbf{x})}{\partial x_i \partial x_j}. \qquad (2.5)$$

The matrix $\mathbf{H}$ is symmetric because $\frac{\partial^2 f(\mathbf{x})}{\partial x_i \partial x_j} = \frac{\partial^2 f(\mathbf{x})}{\partial x_j \partial x_i}$. It will be shown in the next section that the Hessian matrix contains information about the curvature or type of bumps associated with $f(\mathbf{x})$, and the negative gradient $-\mathbf{g} = -\nabla f(\mathbf{x})$ points in the steepest downhill direction of $f(\mathbf{x})$ at $\mathbf{x}$.

Following Kelley (1999), the Euclidean norm for the $N \times 1$ vector $\mathbf{x}$ is defined as

$$\|\mathbf{x}\|_2 := \sqrt{\sum_{i=1}^{N} x_i^2}, \qquad (2.6)$$

and the matrix norm induced by the Euclidean norm is

$$\|\mathbf{L}\|_2 := \max_{\mathbf{x} \neq 0} \frac{\|\mathbf{L}\mathbf{x}\|_2}{\|\mathbf{x}\|_2}. \qquad (2.7)$$

To avoid displaying too many vertical bars, the notation $|\mathbf{x}|$ sometimes will be used to denote the norm of the vector $\mathbf{x}$.

We will assume a twice continuously differentiable $f(\mathbf{x})$ in a neighborhood of points so that $f(\mathbf{x}_o + \Delta\mathbf{x})$ can be expanded about the starting point $\mathbf{x}_o$, to give

$$f(\mathbf{x}_o + \Delta\mathbf{x}) = f(\mathbf{x}_o) + \mathbf{g}^T \Delta\mathbf{x} + \frac{1}{2}\Delta\mathbf{x}^T \nabla\nabla^T f(\mathbf{x}_o)\Delta\mathbf{x}$$
$$+ o(\|\Delta\mathbf{x}\|^3), \qquad (2.8)$$

in which $\nabla\nabla^T f(\mathbf{x})|_{\mathbf{x}=\mathbf{x}_o}$ is symbolized by $\nabla\nabla^T f(\mathbf{x}_o)$. Truncating after the third term gives the *quadratic-model* approximation

$$f(\mathbf{x}_o + \Delta\mathbf{x}) \approx f(\mathbf{x}_o) + \mathbf{g}^T \Delta\mathbf{x} + \frac{1}{2}\Delta\mathbf{x}^T \nabla\nabla^T f(\mathbf{x}_o)\Delta\mathbf{x},$$

$$= f(\mathbf{x}_o) + \mathbf{g}^T \Delta\mathbf{x} + \frac{1}{2}\Delta\mathbf{x}^T \mathbf{H}\Delta\mathbf{x}, \qquad (2.9)$$

to the original objective function about $\mathbf{x}_o$.

For a local or global minimum point $\mathbf{x}^*$ to exist, the 1D curve in Figure 2.1 must satisfy the following two conditions (Kelley, 1999): $\partial f(\mathbf{x}^*)/\partial x = 0$ and $\partial^2 f(\mathbf{x}^*)/\partial x^2 > 0$. Similar optimality conditions exist for a multidimensional function, i.e.,

$$\nabla f(\mathbf{x}^*) = 0 \quad \text{and} \quad \Delta\mathbf{x}^T \nabla\nabla^T f(\mathbf{x}^*)\Delta\mathbf{x} > 0, \qquad (2.10)$$

in which the last condition defines the symmetric positive-definite (SPD) property of the Hessian matrix. The first condition is necessary for optimality, and sufficiency is achieved when the second condition is included.

Many geophysical problems use the concatenation $\mathbf{L}^T\mathbf{L}$ of the back-propagation $\mathbf{L}^T$ and forward-modeling $\mathbf{L}$ operations to approximate the Hessian matrix $\mathbf{H}$. If $\mathbf{L}$ is real, then for some real eigenvector $\mathbf{x}_i$, $[\mathbf{L}^T\mathbf{L}]\mathbf{x}_i = \lambda_i\mathbf{x}_i$ where λ_i is the eigenvalue for $\mathbf{x}_i$. Multiplying this equation by $\mathbf{x}_i^T$ gives

$$\mathbf{x}_i^T[\mathbf{L}^T\mathbf{L}]\mathbf{x}_i = \lambda_i\mathbf{x}_i^T\mathbf{x}_i \geq 0, \qquad (2.11)$$

in which the inequality follows by definition of the norm $\|\mathbf{L}\mathbf{x}_i\| \geq 0$. Because $\mathbf{x}_i^T\mathbf{x}_i > 0$ for $\mathbf{x}$ not at the origin, then equation 2.11 implies $\lambda_i \geq 0$ so that, in the space-time domain, the Hessian for least-squares migration or full-waveform inversion is, at worst, a positive semidefinite matrix in which $\lambda_i \geq 0$.

2.2 Gradient optimization, Taylor series, and Newton's method

Equation 2.9 can be expressed as

$$f(\mathbf{x}_o + \Delta\mathbf{x}) \approx f(\mathbf{x}_o) + \sum_{i=1}^{N}\frac{\partial f(\mathbf{x}_o)}{\partial x_i}\Delta x_i$$
$$+ \frac{1}{2}\sum_{i=1}^{N}\sum_{j=1}^{N}\frac{\partial^2 f(\mathbf{x}_o)}{\partial x_i \partial x_j}\Delta x_i\Delta x_j, \qquad (2.12)$$

so that for a sufficiently small value of $\Delta\mathbf{x}$, the truncated Taylor series is a good approximation to the actual function at $\mathbf{x}_o + \Delta\mathbf{x}$. For $N = 2$, equation 2.12 plots out as an ellipse with the minimum at $\mathbf{x}^*$. If the cross terms in the Hessian are zero (i.e., $\partial^2 f(\mathbf{x})/\partial x_i \partial x_j = 0$ for $i \neq j$), then the major and minor axes of the ellipse are parallel to the x_1 and x_2 axes, otherwise they are rotated as shown in Figure 2.2.

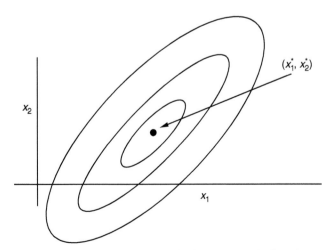

Figure 2.2. Contours associated with a quadratic function $f(\mathbf{x})$ define an ellipse that in general is rotated and shifted from the origin.

Defining $\Delta\mathbf{x} = \mathbf{x} - \mathbf{x}_o$ and $\partial\Delta x_i/\partial x_k = \delta_{ik}$, and taking the kth component of the gradient in equation 2.12 gives

$$\frac{\partial f(\mathbf{x})}{\partial x_k} = \frac{\partial f(\mathbf{x}_o + \Delta\mathbf{x})}{\partial x_k}$$
$$\approx \frac{\partial f(\mathbf{x}_o)}{\partial x_k} + \frac{1}{2}\sum_{i=1}^{N}\sum_{j=1}^{N}\frac{\partial^2 f(\mathbf{x}_o)}{\partial x_i \partial x_j}\Delta x_j\delta_{ki}$$
$$+ \frac{1}{2}\sum_{i=1}^{N}\sum_{j=1}^{N}\frac{\partial^2 f(\mathbf{x}_o)}{\partial x_i \partial x_j}\Delta x_i\delta_{kj},$$
$$= \frac{\partial f(\mathbf{x}_o)}{\partial x_k} + \sum_{j=1}^{N}\frac{\partial^2 f(\mathbf{x}_o)}{\partial x_k \partial x_j}\Delta x_j. \qquad (2.13)$$

If $\mathbf{x}$ is evaluated at the minimum point of $f(\mathbf{x})$, then $\frac{\partial f(\mathbf{x})}{\partial x_k} = 0$ and equation 2.13 reduces to the linear system of equations

$$g_k = -\sum_{j=1}^{N}\frac{\partial^2 f(\mathbf{x}_o)}{\partial x_k \partial x_j}\Delta x_j \quad \text{or} \quad \mathbf{g} = -\mathbf{H}\Delta\mathbf{x}, \qquad (2.14)$$

in which $g_k = \partial f(\mathbf{x})/\partial x_k|_{\mathbf{x}=\mathbf{x}_o}$ and $\Delta\mathbf{x}$ is the unknown vector.

Solving for $\Delta\mathbf{x}$ in equation 2.14 gives

$$\Delta\mathbf{x} = -\mathbf{H}^{-1}\mathbf{g}. \qquad (2.15)$$

Therefore, given a trial model $\mathbf{x}_o$, a gradient optimization method solves equation 2.14 for $\Delta\mathbf{x}$ so that $\mathbf{x}^* = \mathbf{x}_o + \Delta\mathbf{x}$ minimizes the objective function $f(\mathbf{x})$.

If the system of equations is linear, the associated elements of the Hessian are independent of $\mathbf{x}$ so that the quadratic function plots as an ellipse in Figure 2.2. In this case, a direct solver such as an LU decomposition method can be used to solve for $\mathbf{x}^*$. This procedure is known as a linear Newton method (Gill et al., 1981). If a direct solver is too expensive, then the iterative equation

$$x_i^{(k+1)} = x_i^{(k)} - \sum_{j}\beta_{ij}^{(k)}g_j^{(k)}, \qquad (2.16)$$

is used to update the kth iterate solution $x_i^{(k)}$ by a weighted sum of the gradient components $\beta_{ij}^{(k)}g_j^{(k)}$, in which β_{ij} is the weight. For example, the steepest-descent method defines $\beta_{ij}^{(k)} = \delta_{ij}\alpha^{(k)}$, in which $\alpha^{(k)}$ is the step length at the kth iterate. Under suitable conditions the iterative gradient method converges to $\mathbf{x}^*$. Subtracting $\mathbf{x}_o$ from both sides of equation 2.16 gives the equivalent update equation

$$\Delta x_i^{(k+1)} = \Delta x_i^{(k)} - \sum_{j}\beta_{ij}^{(k)}g_j^{(k)}, \qquad (2.17)$$

in which the perturbed vector components Δx_i are updated rather than the actual solution components. Here, it is assumed that a starting model $\mathbf{x}^0$ is specified for $k = 0$.

If $f(\mathbf{x})$ has a polynomial dependency that is higher order than a quadratic, then its contours are nonelliptical as illustrated in Figure 2.3, the Hessian $\mathbf{H} = \mathbf{H}(\mathbf{x})$ depends on $\mathbf{x}$, and the iterative nonlinear Newton's method is used to update the solution:

$$\mathbf{x}^{(k+1)} = \mathbf{x}^{(k)} - \alpha[\mathbf{H}^{(k)}]^{-1}\mathbf{g}^{(k)}. \qquad (2.18)$$

Here, α is the scalar step length that is equal to one for a quadratic objective function and must be determined numerically at each iteration for nonquadratic functions. If $[\mathbf{H}^{(k)}]_{ij}^{-1}$ is approximated by $\delta_{ij}/H_{ii}^{(k)}$, then equation 2.18 is that of the preconditioned steepest-descent method. The goal of a preconditioned system of equations is to find a preconditioner $\mathbf{P}$ that reduces the condition number of the right $\mathbf{HP}$ or left $\mathbf{PH}$ preconditioned system matrix, where the preconditioner $\mathbf{P}$ approximates the inverse of $\mathbf{H}$.

Another approximation replaces $[\mathbf{H}^{(k)}]^{-1}\mathbf{g}^{(k)}$ with a vector that is conjugate to the previous update direction, and the resulting scheme is known as a conjugate-direction method of which the conjugate-gradient (CG) method is a special case. The main advantage of the CG or steepest-descent methods compared to the Newton method is that there is no need for expensive computation of the Hessian inverse or to store large matrices. However, convergence to the global minimum for any gradient-optimization method is not guaranteed for objective functions with many local minima.

2.3 Geometric interpretation of the gradient and Hessian

A geometric interpretation of the gradient and the Hessian can be illustrated with the Rosenbrock function

$$f(\mathbf{x}) = 100(x_2 - x_1^2)^2 + (1 - x_1)^2, \qquad (2.19)$$

a smooth but highly nonlinear function plotted in Figure 2.3. In this case, the gradient vector becomes

$$\nabla f(\mathbf{x}) = \mathbf{g} = \begin{bmatrix} \dfrac{\partial f}{\partial x_1} \\[2mm] \dfrac{\partial f}{\partial x_2} \end{bmatrix} = \begin{bmatrix} -400x_1(x_2 - x_1^2) - 2(1 - x_1) \\[2mm] 200(x_2 - x_1^2) \end{bmatrix}. $$
$$(2.20)$$

To assess the physical meaning of the gradient, we define the points on a line in multidimensional space by

$$\mathbf{x}(\alpha) = \mathbf{x}' + \alpha\hat{\mathbf{s}}, \qquad (2.21)$$

where $\hat{\mathbf{s}}$ is the unit vector parallel to a specified line and α is the scalar parameter that controls how far $\mathbf{x}$ is from the

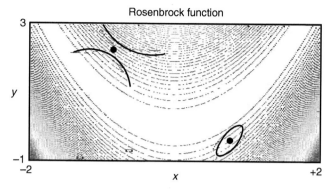

Figure 2.3. Contours of the Rosenbrock function along with icons (thick contours) indicating either a saddle-like or elongated-ellipse geometry of $\mathbf{x}^T\mathbf{H}\mathbf{x}$ at the points indicated by solid circles (courtesy of Yunsong Huang).

specified starting point $\mathbf{x}(\alpha = 0) = \mathbf{x}'$. A directional derivative along the line direction $\hat{\mathbf{s}}$ in equation 2.21 is defined as $df/d\alpha$:

$$\frac{df(\mathbf{x})}{d\alpha} = \sum_i \overbrace{\frac{df(\mathbf{x})}{dx_i}}^{\nabla f(\mathbf{x})} \overbrace{\frac{dx_i}{d\alpha}}^{\hat{\mathbf{s}}} = \hat{\mathbf{s}}^T \nabla f(\mathbf{x}), \qquad (2.22)$$

in which $\hat{\mathbf{s}}^T \nabla f(\mathbf{x})$ is the projection of the gradient along the line direction. If $\hat{\mathbf{s}}$ is parallel to the contour tangent, then $f(\mathbf{x})$ does not change in this direction so $\hat{\mathbf{s}}^T \nabla f(\mathbf{x}) = 0$. This means that the gradient $\mathbf{g} = \nabla f(\mathbf{x})$ is perpendicular to the contour tangent, or parallel to the direction of steepest descent. For a 1D function, this gradient also is known as the slope; if it is positive, then the uphill direction is to the right, otherwise it is to the left.

The second derivatives of $f(\mathbf{x})$ for the Rosenbrock function form the 2×2 Hessian matrix

$$\mathbf{H} = [\nabla\nabla^T]f(\mathbf{x}) = \begin{bmatrix} \dfrac{\partial^2 f}{\partial x_1^2} & \dfrac{\partial^2 f}{\partial x_1 \partial x_2} \\[3mm] \dfrac{\partial^2 f}{\partial x_1 \partial x_2} & \dfrac{\partial^2 f}{\partial x_2^2} \end{bmatrix}$$
$$= \begin{bmatrix} 1200x_1^2 - 400x_2 + 2 & -400x_1 \\[2mm] -400x_1 & 200 \end{bmatrix}. \qquad (2.23)$$

Unlike a quadratic function with elliptical contours and a constant Hessian matrix, equation 2.23 says that the curvature values in the Hessian matrix depend on $\mathbf{x}$ for $f(\mathbf{x})$ with polynomial order > 2.

Similar to defining $\hat{\mathbf{s}}^T \nabla f$ to be the slope of $f(\mathbf{x})$ along the line direction $\hat{\mathbf{s}}$, the second derivative or curvature of

$f(\mathbf{x})$ along the same line is given by

$$\frac{d^2f}{d\alpha^2} = \frac{d}{d\alpha}\frac{df}{d\alpha} = \frac{d}{d\alpha}[(\nabla f)^T\hat{\mathbf{s}}]$$

$$= \hat{\mathbf{s}}^T[\nabla(\nabla f)^T]\hat{\mathbf{s}} = \hat{\mathbf{s}}^T\overbrace{[\nabla\nabla^Tf(\mathbf{x})]}^{\text{Hessian}}\hat{\mathbf{s}}. \qquad (2.24)$$

Therefore, $\hat{\mathbf{s}}^T\mathbf{H}\hat{\mathbf{s}}$ gives the curvature of $f(\mathbf{x})$ along the direction specified by $\hat{\mathbf{s}}$.

2.4 Eigenvalues of the Hessian determine shape of contours

The sign and magnitude of the eigenvalue λ_i of $\mathbf{H}$ determine the shape of $f(\mathbf{x})$ along the ith coordinate direction. For a 2D geometry, this can be shown by setting $\mathbf{x} = \mathbf{x}^* + \alpha\mathbf{e}_1 + \beta\mathbf{e}_2$, in which $\mathbf{e}_i$ is the ith orthonormal eigenvector of the symmetric real matrix $\mathbf{H}$, $\mathbf{x}^*$ is the point where $f(\mathbf{x})$ is a minimum (i.e., $\mathbf{g}(\mathbf{x}^*) = 0$), and α and β are scalars. Expanding $f(\mathbf{x})$ about the minimum point $\mathbf{x}^*$, equation 2.9 becomes

$$f(\mathbf{x}^* + \alpha\mathbf{e}_1 + \beta\mathbf{e}_2) = f(\mathbf{x}^*) + [\alpha^2\mathbf{e}_1^T\mathbf{H}\mathbf{e}_1 + \beta^2\mathbf{e}_2^T\mathbf{H}\mathbf{e}_2]/2,$$

$$= f(\mathbf{x}^*) + [\lambda_1\alpha^2\mathbf{e}_1^T\mathbf{e}_1 + \lambda_2\beta^2\mathbf{e}_2^T\mathbf{e}_2]/2,$$

$$= f(\mathbf{x}^*) + [\lambda_1\alpha^2 + \lambda_2\beta^2]/2, \qquad (2.25)$$

in which the gradient term $\mathbf{g}^T\Delta\mathbf{x}$ is dropped because it is equal to zero at the minimum point $\mathbf{x}^*$. The eigenvalues are positive if $\mathbf{H}$ is a SPD matrix, so any move along an eigenvector direction from $\mathbf{x}^*$ will increase the value of the function. Hence, $f(\mathbf{x})$ describes a bowl-like surface around the minimum point $\mathbf{x}^*$ (see Figure 2.4a–c). Large positive eigenvalues suggest that small changes in position from the minimum point lead to large changes in $f(\mathbf{x})$ so the bowl has steeply curving sides; conversely, small positive eigenvalues suggest a bowl with gently curving sides.

If the Hessian is negative definite (i.e., $\mathbf{H}$ has only negative eigenvalues) then equation 2.25 says that any move from $\mathbf{x}^*$ along an eigenvector direction will decrease the function, i.e., $f(\mathbf{x})$ describes an inverted bowl about the maximal point $\mathbf{x}^*$. If the Hessian is indefinite (both positive and negative eigenvalues), then a move along one eigenvector direction will decrease the function value and a move along the other eigenvector direction will increase the function value. This latter surface describes the saddles depicted in Figures 2.3 and 2.4f.

2.5 MATLAB examples of Newton's method

Newton's methods are used to solve some specific 1D and 2D nonlinear functions. Mathworks MATLAB® codes

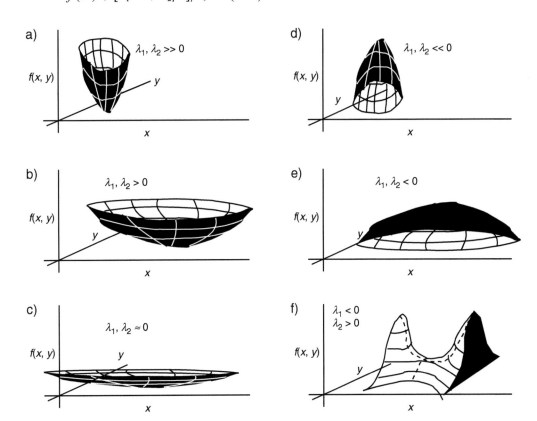

Figure 2.4. Plots of functions with different eigenvalues λ_1 and λ_2 for the 2×2 Hessian matrix. Panels (a–c) are associated $\lambda_1, \lambda_2 > 0$, and (d–f) correspond to examples in which at least one of the eigenvalues is negative.

are provided so the reader can explore finding optimal points for different nonlinear functions.

Example 2.5.1. 1D function

For a 1D equation, 2.14 becomes

$$\frac{\partial f(x_o)}{\partial x} = -\frac{\partial^2 f(x_o)}{\partial x^2}\Delta x, \qquad (2.26)$$

which can be solved for Δx to give

$$\Delta x = -\frac{\partial f(x_o)}{\partial x} \Big/ \frac{\partial^2 f(x_o)}{\partial x^2}. \qquad (2.27)$$

The Newton iteration formula (equation 2.18) for a 1D nonlinear function reduces to

$$x^{(k+1)} = x^{(k)} - \alpha\frac{\partial f(x^{(k)})}{\partial x} \Big/ \frac{\partial^2 f(x^{(k)})}{\partial x^2}. \qquad (2.28)$$

In general, the convergence rate of Newton's method depends on the topography, determined by the curvature and slope terms, of the function and how far the starting point is from the global minimum.

MATLAB script that implements Newton's method for the 1D nonquadratic function $f(x) = ax^4 + x^2 - 2x$ is given below:

```
%%%%%%%%%%%%%%%%%%%%%%%%%%%%%%%%%%%%%%%%%%%%%%%%%%%%
% 1D Newton method to find zeros of a quartic function
%
%%%%%%%%%%%%%%%%%%%%%%%%%%%%%%%%%%%%%%%%%%%%%%%%%%%%
clear all;
a = 7;
subplot(121);x=[-2:.1:2];
plot(x,a*x.^4 + x.^2 - 2*x);
%
x    = -1.5;% starting point
f(1) = (a*x.^4 + x.^2 - 2*x);      % Quartic Function
xx(1)=x;
for it = 2:10                      % Start iterations
  f1prime = a*4*x.^3 + 2*x - 2;
  f2prime = a*12*x.^2 + 2;
  x       = x-f1prime/f2prime;     % Newton formula
  xx(it)  = x;
  f(it)   = (a*x.^4 + x.^2 - 2*x);
  residual(it-1) = abs(f(it)-f(it-1));
end
```

The values of $f(x^{(k)})$ are plotted against $x^{(k)}$ in Figure 2.5.

Example 2.5.2. 2D function

The Rosenbrock function is plotted in Figure 2.3, and a MATLAB code for finding its minimum by Newton's method is below. Unlike a quadratic objective function, the curvature value depends on the location of (x_1, x_2).

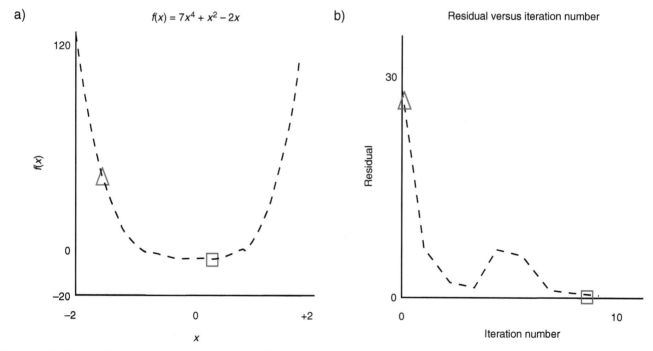

a) $f(x) = 7x^4 + x^2 - 2x$

b)   Residual versus iteration number

Figure 2.5. Plots of (a) quartic function and (b) residual versus iteration curve. The diamonds and squares represent the starting and ending models, respectively.

```
%%%%%%%%%%%%%%%%%%%%%%%%%%%%%%%%%%%%%
% Iterative Newton method for finding minimizer
% of Rosenbrock function
% f=100.*(x2-x1.^2).^2+(1-x1).^2
% Minimizer point=(1,1)
%%%%%%%%%%%%%%%%%%%%%%%%%%%%%%%%%%%%%%%
x1 =.6;
x2 =.4;
x  = [x1;x2];                            % Define starting point (x1,x2)
%
iter    = 10;
xx      = zeros(iter,2);
xx(1,1) = x1;
xx(1,2) = x2;
%
for it = 2:iter                          % Begin non-linear iterations
 g=[-400*x1*(x2-x1^2)-2*(1-x1); 200*(x2-x1^2)]; % 2x1 gradient vector
 H=[1200*x1^2-400*x2+2 -400*x1; -400*x1 200];   % 2x2 Hessian matrix
 x = x-inv(H)*g; % Non-linear Newton formula
 xx(it,:) = x;                           % Update iterative solution
 x1 = x(1);
 x2 = x(2);
end
xmx    = 2;                              % Define plotting parameters
xmin   = -1;
ymin0  = 0;
ymx    = 2;
x      = [xmin:.01:xmx];
y      = [ymin0:.01:ymx];
[X,Y] = meshgrid(xmin:.01:xmx,ymin0:.01:ymx );
f      = 100.*(Y-X.^2).^2+(1-X).^2;      % Rosenbrock Function
imagesc(x,y,f);
hold on;
contour(X,Y,f,80,'w');                   % Plot Rosenbrock function ith contours
hold off
hold on;
for i = 1:iter;
 plot(xx(i,1),xx(i,2),'w*');
end
plot(x1,x2,'*r');
plot(xx(1,1),xx(1,2),'*g');
hold off;
xlabel('X');
ylabel('Y');
title('f(X,Y)=100*(Y-X^2)^2+(1-X)^2 and Iterates (Red * = Final, Green * = Initial)')
```

2.6 Summary

The unconstrained optimization problem is defined as finding the model **x** that minimizes the objective function $f(\mathbf{x}) + \lambda g(\mathbf{x})$, in which $f(\mathbf{x})$ typically is related to the misfit between the predicted and observed data, and the penalty function $g(\mathbf{x})$ is based on the model. The penalty function can depend on the misfit between an a priori model and the estimated one, in which case it also is known as a model misfit function. The tradeoff between honoring the data misfit and penalty functions is determined by the value of the positive scalar λ, where this value generally is decreased as the iterations proceed.

Global search methods typically are too expensive for large 3D seismic problems, so geophysicists resort to gradient methods. The starting point for gradient methods is to approximate the objective function as a Taylor series truncated after the second-order terms. This truncated series is a sum of 1) an inner product between the $N \times 1$ gradient vector and the search direction **x**, and 2) the curvature term represented by a Hessian and its projection along the search-direction vector. The solution that minimizes this sum leads to the iterative Newton formula for nonlinear optimization.

A SPD Hessian matrix $\mathbf{H}(\mathbf{x})$ says that $f(\mathbf{x})$ describes a surface with a global minimum, and a surface with a global maximum is associated with a negative-definite Hessian matrix. An indefinite Hessian is characterized by a saddle-like surface for $f(\mathbf{x})$. Ill-conditioned Hessians describe surfaces with long narrow valleys, which will lead to slow convergence rates for gradient-optimization methods such as the steepest-descent method.

In general, gradient-optimization methods are not guaranteed to converge to the global minimum, but there is no need to compute the Hessian inverse or store large matrices with, for example, the conjugate-gradient or steepest-descent methods. These last two advantages compel most geophysicists to solve their large-scale problems by gradient-optimization solutions.

2.7 Exercises

1. Find the zeros of $f(x) = x^4 + x^2 - 3x$ using the 1D Newton method and the MATLAB script given in the previous section. Test the sensitivity of the convergence rate to different starting points.

2. Find the eigenvalues (use "eig" in MATLAB) and plot the contours associated with $\mathbf{x}^T\mathbf{H}\mathbf{x}$ for the following Hessian matrices:

$$\mathbf{H} = \begin{bmatrix} 5 & 3 \\ 3 & 2 \end{bmatrix}; \quad \mathbf{H} = \begin{bmatrix} 4 & 2 \\ 2 & 1 \end{bmatrix}; \quad \mathbf{H} = \begin{bmatrix} 3 & -1 \\ -1 & -8 \end{bmatrix}.$$
$$(2.29)$$

Which Hessian is positive definite, indefinite, or positive semidefinite[4]?

3. Plot the Rosenbrock function with the MATLAB® commands:

```
xl=-1.25;xr=1.05;dx=.05; yl=-.3;yr=1.2;dy=.05; facx=1;facy=1;
[xx,yy]=meshgrid([xl:dx:xr]*facx,[yl:dy:yr]*facy);
%[xx,yy]=meshgrid([-0.05:0.005:0.45],[-0.06:0.005:0.12]);
mis=100*(yy - xx.^2).^2 + (1-xx).^2; contour(xx,yy,mis,252)
```

Now plot the contours for $\partial f/\partial x_1$ and $\partial f/\partial x_2$. Is $f(\mathbf{x})$ a quadratic or nonquadratic function? Are the elements of the Hessian matrix, the components of the gradient, or the curvature along the x_1 direction functions of (x_1, x_2)? For an objective function that is strictly quadratic, are the elements of the Hessian and gradient a function of spatial position?

4. Assume $f(\mathbf{x}) = x_1^2 + x_2^2 - 2x_1x_2$. Plot the contours of $f(\mathbf{x})$. Is $f(\mathbf{x})$ a quadratic or nonquadratic function? Are the elements of the Hessian matrix, the components of the gradient, or the curvature along the x_1 direction functions of (x_1, x_2)? For the above quadratic function, how many minima are there in the objective function? Identify the local and global minimum points for $f(\mathbf{x})$.

5. Can there ever be more than one isolated minimum for a quadratic function? Prove your answer. Can there ever be more than one isolated minimum for a nonquadratic function?

6. Show that $\frac{dx_i}{d\alpha} = s_i$, where s_i is the ith component of the unit vector $\mathbf{s}$ in equation 2.21.

7. Find the slope of the Rosenbrock function $f(\mathbf{x})$ at $\mathbf{x} = (2, 3)$ along the line direction parallel to the vector $(1, 1)$. Find the slope of $f(\mathbf{x})$ at $(2, 3)$ that is parallel to the vector orthogonal to the vector $(1, 1)$. Show work using the 2×1 gradient vector.

8. Answer the same question as the previous one, except find the maximum and minimum curvatures of the Rosenbrock function instead of the slope. What is the curvature along the slope direction?

9. Prove that the gradient vector of $f(\mathbf{x})$ is perpendicular to the contour line tangent at $\mathbf{x}$ and points uphill. Hint: $f(\mathbf{x})$ does not change along a contour, so the directional derivative along the tangent $df(\mathbf{x})/dt \to 0$. This says that $df(\mathbf{x})/dt = d\mathbf{x}^T/dt \nabla f(\mathbf{x}) = 0$.

10. Show that a general quadratic function $f(\mathbf{x}) = (1/2)\mathbf{x}^T\mathbf{H}\mathbf{x} + \mathbf{g}^T\mathbf{x} + c$ where $\mathbf{H}$ is symmetric, also can be described as $f(\mathbf{x}) = (1/2)(\mathbf{x} - \mathbf{x}')^T\mathbf{H}(\mathbf{x} - \mathbf{x}') + c'$ in which $\mathbf{H}\mathbf{x}' = -\mathbf{g}$ and $c' = c - (1/2)\mathbf{x}'^T\mathbf{H}\mathbf{x}'$. What is the geometrical meaning of this transformation?

2.8 Computational labs

1. Find the global minimum of a 1D function using Newton's method in the Computational Toolkit under the topic "Newton's method."

2. Find the global minimum of the 2D Rosenbrock function using Newton's method in the Computational Toolkit under the topic "Newton's method." Answer all questions.

3. Visualize the geometries of $\mathbf{x}^T\mathbf{H}\mathbf{x}$ for the Rosenbrock function in the Computational Toolkit under the topic "Newton's method." Answer all questions.

4. Carry out one of the labs in the Computational Toolkit under the topics "Newton's method" and "Steepest descent."

---

[4]Positive-semidefinite matrices have both positive and zero eigenvalues; indefinite matrices have both positive and negative eigenvalues.

Chapter 3: Steepest-Descent Method

This chapter introduces the optimization method known as steepest descent (SD), in which the solution is found by searching iteratively along the negative gradient $-\mathbf{g}$ direction, the path of steepest descent. Relative to the Newton method for large problems, SD is inexpensive computationally because the Hessian inverse is not needed, but it can suffer from slow convergence with ill-conditioned Hessians because it does not take into account information about the curvature. Nevertheless, experience shows that iterative SD with preconditioning and regularization can be quite useful when combined with multiscale methods for solving large seismic inverse problems.

3.1 Steepest-descent method

In most 3D geophysical problems, the Hessian matrix $\mathbf{H}$ is too large to be stored and inverted by a direct method. For example, the velocity model associated with a 3D seismic survey might require $1000 \times 1000 \times 1000 = 10^9$ grid-points of unknown velocity values, so the Hessian matrix will require the storage and computation of 10^{18} matrix elements! An alternative approach, which avoids the expensive matrix inverse calculation but could suffer from slow convergence, is the steepest-descent method. Here, $\mathbf{H}^{-1}$ in equation 2.18 is approximated by an identity matrix[1] to give the steepest-descent formula

$$\mathbf{x}^{(k+1)} = \mathbf{x}^{(k)} - \alpha \mathbf{g}^{(k)}, \qquad (3.1)$$

in which α is a positive number denoted as the step length. The iterative formula for $\mathbf{x}^{(k+1)}$ searches downhill for a better solution along the negative gradient direction $-\mathbf{g}^{(k)}$. Given the starting point $\mathbf{x}^{(k)}$ and search direction $-\mathbf{g}^{(k)}$, the value of α is computed so that $f(\mathbf{x}^{(k)} + \alpha \mathbf{g}^{(k)})$ is minimized. Equivalently, the step length is computed so that the $\mathbf{x}^{(k+1)} - \mathbf{x}^{(k)}$ vector is just tangent to (or *kisses*) the contour at $\mathbf{x}^{(k+1)}$ (see Figure 3.1b). The iterations are stopped

when the length of the residual vector (i.e., the square root of the misfit functional) becomes less than some specified tolerance.

3.1.1 Convergence rate

Approximating the Hessian by an identity matrix is valid if the topography of the functional conforms approximately to the round bowl in Figure 3.1a. In this case, the condition number is $\lambda_{\max}/\lambda_{\min} \approx 1$ and a move along any direction from the bowl's bottom will increase the functional value by the same amount. In equation 2.25, this means that $\lambda_1 \approx \lambda_2$.

As the condition number becomes larger, the bullseye in Figure 3.1a becomes more elliptical as the diagonal terms of $\mathbf{H}$ deviate from one another. Thus, the steepest-descent approximation becomes less accurate and will lead to a slowdown in the convergence rate. In fact, for a quadratic functional with a symmetric positive-definite (SPD) Hessian, the convergence ratio κ is given (Gill et al., 1981, 103) by

$$\kappa = \lim_{k \to \infty} \frac{|f(\mathbf{x}^{(k+1)}) - f(\mathbf{x}^*)|^{1/2}}{|f(\mathbf{x}^{(k)}) - f(\mathbf{x}^*)|^{1/2}},$$

$$= \frac{|\lambda_{\max} - \lambda_{\min}|}{|\lambda_{\max} + \lambda_{\min}|},$$

$$= \frac{|\text{cond}(\mathbf{H}) - 1|}{|\text{cond}(\mathbf{H}) + 1|}, \qquad (3.2)$$

where $\mathbf{x}^*$ is the point of convergence and $\text{cond}(\mathbf{H}) = $ |largest eigenvalue|/|smallest eigenvalue| is the condition number of $\mathbf{H}$. Equation 3.2 suggests that large condition numbers lead to slow convergence. Quoting from Fletcher (1980, 22), "...the method usually terminates far from the solution owing to round-off effects. In practice, therefore, the method is usually inefficient and unreliable." However, this dire prediction is not experienced often with preconditioned steepest-descent methods with regularization applied to nonlinear traveltime tomography. Empirical evidence suggests that a regularized-preconditioned steepest-descent method (see equation 1.12) combined with a multiscale method (Nemeth et al., 1997) often can perform about as well as other methods for traveltime tomography. See Box 3.1.1 for definitions of different convergence rates.

---

[1] Approximating the Hessian by an identity matrix sometimes is justified if $\mathbf{H}$ is diagonally dominant. The identity matrix multiplied by the step length α has the proper units for the inverse Hessian. If the diagonal elements of the Hessian have radically different values, then a scaled diagonal matrix with elements $[\mathbf{H}^{-1}]_{ij} \approx \delta_{ij}/H_{ii}$ can be used for the preconditioned steepest-descent method.

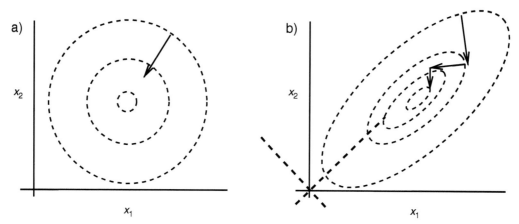

Figure 3.1. (a) Circular misfit contours characteristic of a well-conditioned Hessian matrix. Even a steepest-descent method will converge quickly for this type of functional. (b) Elliptical misfit contours characteristic of a poorly conditioned Hessian matrix. Dashed dark lines represent the rotated coordinate system that diagonalizes the Hessian. Successive search directions in the SD method are orthogonal to one another, as illustrated in (b).

Box 3.1.1 Convergence Rates for Series

Following Nocedal and Wright (1999), the sequence $\{\mathbf{x}^{(k)}\}$ in $\mathbb{R}^n$ is said to converge to $\mathbf{x}^*$ with Q-linear convergence if there is a positive constant $c \in (0, 1)$ such that

$$\frac{\|\mathbf{x}^{(k+1)} - \mathbf{x}^*\|}{\|\mathbf{x}^{(k)} - \mathbf{x}^*\|} \le c, \tag{3.3}$$

for all sufficiently large k. This means that the normalized distance to the solution after each iteration decreases by at least a constant factor. The prefix "Q" denotes quotient because this type of convergence is defined in terms of quotients of successive errors.

The convergence is Q-superlinear if

$$\lim_{k \to \infty} \frac{\|\mathbf{x}^{(k+1)} - \mathbf{x}^*\|}{\|\mathbf{x}^{(k)} - \mathbf{x}^*\|} = 0, \tag{3.4}$$

and an even more rapid convergence is Q-quadratic convergence if

$$\frac{\|\mathbf{x}^{(k+1)} - \mathbf{x}^*\|}{\|\mathbf{x}^{(k)} - \mathbf{x}^*\|^2} < |M|, \tag{3.5}$$

for a constant M. In general (Gill et al., 1981), a sequence has order of convergence r if

$$\frac{\|\mathbf{x}^{(k+1)} - \mathbf{x}^*\|}{\|\mathbf{x}^{(k)} - \mathbf{x}^*\|^r} < \infty. \tag{3.6}$$

Here, Q-quadratic convergence (e.g., Newton methods) is faster than Q-superlinear convergence (quasi-Newton methods), and the slowest is Q-linear (e.g., steepest descent). The convergence rate of the conjugate-gradient method is shown to be linear, and that Q-superlinear convergence is not achievable with an exact line search according to Nocedal and Wright (1999). Quasi-Newton methods converge Q-superlinerarly, whereas Newton's methods converge Q-quadratically; in contrast, steepest-descent methods only converge at a Q-linear rate, and if the problem is ill conditioned, the convergence constant c in equation 3.3 is close to 1. See page 132 in Nocedal and Wright (1999) for a short summary of convergence rates for the conjugate-gradient method.

As an example from Gill et al. (1981), consider $x^{(k)} = c^{2^k}$, $0 < c < 1$, and $x^* = 0$, so that $|x^{(k+1)} - 0|/|x^{(k)} - 0|^2 = 1$. Thus, the convergence rate is quadratic. Another sequence is $x^{(k)} = c^{2^{-k}}$, where $c > 0$. Each member of the sequence is the square root of the previous element and $x^* = 1$. It is easy to show that this sequence is Q-linear convergent.

Unfortunately, most multidimensional seismic inverse problems are immune to rigorous analysis for convergence, mainly because the misfit functions are highly nonlinear with respect to the model parameters. Gradient methods too often get stuck in local minima and rarely can reach the global minimum for real-data problems. Even worse, the important physics of wave propagation is not modeled fully by numerical solutions to the acoustic or elastic wave equations, so convergence to the "global minimum" might not give the correct model associated with the real earth.

3.2 Step-length calculation

There are two popular algorithms for computing the step length α in equation 3.1: an exact line search and a numerical line search to find α such that

$$\min_{\alpha>0} f(\mathbf{x}^{(k)} - \alpha \Delta \mathbf{x}), \qquad (3.7)$$

in which $-\Delta \mathbf{x}$ is a predefined search direction that is downhill from the current model. The exact line-search method uses an analytical formula for determining the value of α. In contrast, the numerical line-search method approximates $f(\mathbf{x})$ in the direction $-\Delta \mathbf{x}$ as a polynomial in α, and uses a formula for the value α^* that minimizes this functional (Nocedal and Wright, 1999). Certain conditions on the gradient and curvature are used sometimes to avoid stopping too early or too far from the local minimum (Nocedal and Wright, 1999; Gill et al., 1981; Bank and Mittleman, 1989).

A *restricted-step* search method only searches for the optimal model $\mathbf{x}^{(k)} + \alpha \Delta \mathbf{x}$ within a defined trust region (Nocedal and Wright, 1999) with radius r centered at $\mathbf{x}^{(k)}$ such that $\|\alpha \Delta \mathbf{x}\| < r$. This restriction is sometimes necessary because the gradient and curvature estimated from the nonlinear objective function at $\mathbf{x}$ might be appropriate only near $\mathbf{x}$, but not too far from it. For example, jumping off a ski lift in Park City, Utah, might show an easy green-diamond route a few paces from the steep black-diamond route. In this case, the novice skier should decide which way to go by examining slope values within a small exploratory trust region around the jump-off point, not near the bottom of either route.

Sometimes an ill-conditioned Hessian is stabilized by forming a new damped objective function $\tilde{f}(\mathbf{x}) = \mathbf{x}^T \mathbf{H} \mathbf{x} + \eta^2 \mathbf{x}^T \mathbf{x} + \mathbf{g}^T \mathbf{x}$ compared to the original one $f(\mathbf{x}) = \mathbf{x}^T \mathbf{H} \mathbf{x} + \mathbf{g}^T \mathbf{x}$. Here, η^2 is a positive scalar that controls the trust region size. Larger values of η^2 will lead to smaller steps (i.e., $\Delta \tilde{x}_i \approx \frac{g_i}{H_{ii} + \eta^2}$), so the reduction in the objective function $\Delta \tilde{f} = \tilde{f}(\mathbf{x} + \Delta \tilde{\mathbf{x}}) - \tilde{f}(\mathbf{x})$ will be less than $\Delta f = f(\mathbf{x} + \Delta \mathbf{x}) - f(\mathbf{x})$. If $\Delta \tilde{f}/\Delta f > 0.5$, then we aren't damping enough, so the value of η^2, the trust region radius, should be increased until $\Delta \tilde{f}/\Delta f$ is between 0.25 and 0.5. For large-scale 3D seismic imaging, a trial-and-error trust-region procedure often is too computationally expensive.

3.2.1 Exact line search

The derivation of the step length for the exact line search now is given. The 1D line-search problem is defined as finding the optimal value of the scalar α that minimizes $f(\mathbf{x} + \alpha \Delta \mathbf{x})$ for a fixed $\mathbf{x}$ and $\Delta \mathbf{x}$. In this case, equation 2.9 becomes

$$f(\mathbf{x} + \alpha \Delta \mathbf{x}) \approx f(\mathbf{x}) + \alpha \mathbf{g}^T \Delta \mathbf{x} + \frac{\alpha^2}{2} \Delta \mathbf{x}^T \mathbf{H} \Delta \mathbf{x}. \qquad (3.8)$$

Differentiating the above equation with respect to α, and setting the result equal to zero yields

$$\frac{\partial f(\mathbf{x} + \alpha \Delta \mathbf{x})}{\partial \alpha} = \mathbf{g}^T \Delta \mathbf{x} + \alpha \Delta \mathbf{x}^T \mathbf{H} \Delta \mathbf{x},$$

$$= 0. \qquad (3.9)$$

Solving for the optimal α^* gives

$$\alpha^* = \frac{-\mathbf{g}^T \Delta \mathbf{x}}{\Delta \mathbf{x}^T \mathbf{H} \Delta \mathbf{x}}, \qquad (3.10)$$

the exact step length. This method is called an exact line search because the step-length formula in equation 3.10 is exactly correct if $f(\mathbf{x})$ is a quadratic functional. For the steepest-descent method, $\Delta \mathbf{x} = -\mathbf{g}$ so that

$$\alpha^* = \frac{\mathbf{g}^T \mathbf{g}}{\mathbf{g}^T \mathbf{H} \mathbf{g}}. \qquad (3.11)$$

In practical seismic inverse problems such as nonlinear full-waveform inversion, experience suggests that the exact line search almost never works well, so a numerical line-search method is used instead.

3.2.2 Inexact Newton method and inexact line search

Approximating the inverse to the Hessian is known as an inexact Newton method (Gill et al., 1981). The inexact Newton method sometimes is called a truncated Newton method if a conjugate-gradient (CG) method (see Chapter 4) is used for a small number of iterations to approximate the solution. After a few iterations, the CG solution vector lies between the steepest-descent and Newton vectors, as illustrated in Figure 3.2. As an example, AlTheyab et al. (2013) propose a full-waveform-inversion (FWI) algorithm with both an outer loop and an inner loop. In the inner loop, a linear conjugate-gradient (CG) method is used to approximate the Hessian inverse. As discussed in Chapter 21, the computed velocity model obtained from this inner loop is used as the background velocity model in the outer nonlinear loop that uses nonlinear CG.

Stopping the line search so that it satisfies specified termination conditions is known as an inexact line-search method. For the Wolfe conditions (Nocedal and Wright, 1999), the inexact line-search brackets a series of trial step lengths that satisfy the Wolfe condition

$$\overbrace{f(\mathbf{x}^{(k)} + \alpha \Delta \mathbf{x}^{(k)})}^{\text{actual function}} \leq \overbrace{f(\mathbf{x}^{(k)}) + c_1 \alpha \Delta \mathbf{x}^{(k)T} \nabla f(\mathbf{x}^{(k)})}^{\text{linear prediction of function}}, \qquad (3.12)$$

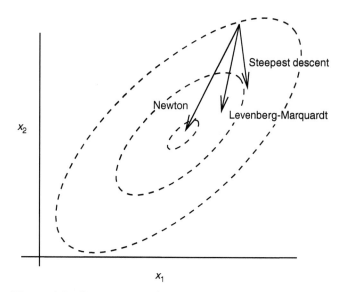

Figure 3.2. Contours associated with the $f(\mathbf{x})$ functional and the vectors associated with the Newton (see equation 2.18 and Appendix 3A), Levenberg-Marquardt, and steepest-descent directions. Here, the Levenberg-Marquardt procedure is classified as an inexact Newton method.

where $0 < c_1 < 1$. Here, the linear prediction of the function at $\mathbf{x}^{(k)} + c_1 \alpha \Delta \mathbf{x}^{(k)}$ should be larger than the actual value there; otherwise the step length has gone beyond the validity of this linear approximation. The initial choice of the step length is determined by the user, and if the above condition is satisfied, then a new gradient is computed and the search procedure is repeated. If the above condition is violated, then the original step length is halved and tested against the Wolfe condition.

The condition above is sometimes too easy to satisfy for very small step lengths, which then can lead to an inefficient search. To avoid excessively small steps, we also demand the satisfaction of the curvature condition for an acceptable step length:

$$\overbrace{\Delta \mathbf{x}^{(k)^T} \nabla f(\mathbf{x}^{(k)} + \alpha \Delta \mathbf{x}^{(k)})}^{\text{slope at new pt.}} \geq \overbrace{c_2 \Delta \mathbf{x}^{(k)^T} \nabla f(\mathbf{x}^{(k)})}^{\text{scaled slope at starting pt.}}, \quad (3.13)$$

in which $0 < c_1 < c_2 < 1$. This condition says that scaled slope along the search direction at $\mathbf{x}^{(k)}$ should be less than or equal to that at $\mathbf{x}^{(k)} + \alpha \Delta \mathbf{x}^{(k)}$. This will avoid the problem of too small of a step size, because the slope at $\mathbf{x}^{(k)} + \alpha \Delta \mathbf{x}^{(k)}$ is likely to be equal to that at the starting point $\mathbf{x}^{(k)}$.

3.2.3 Numerical line search

The local quadratic assumption breaks down when the misfit functional is highly nonlinear so that the exact line search can be inaccurate. An alternative is the numerical line-search method, which estimates the step length by

evaluating the objective function at several points along a downhill direction. For example, a quadratic line search begins by defining the search direction $\Delta \mathbf{x}$, computing several reasonable values of the step length, e.g., $\alpha_1 = 0.5$ and $\alpha_2 = 1$, and testing the functional values $f(\mathbf{x} + \alpha_1 \Delta \mathbf{x})$ and $f(\mathbf{x} + \alpha_2 \Delta \mathbf{x})$ to determine if they are less than $f(\mathbf{x})$, and if $f(\mathbf{x} + \alpha_1 \Delta \mathbf{x}) \leq f(\mathbf{x} + \alpha_2 \Delta \mathbf{x})$. Then, the following quadratic formula is used to determine the interpolated value of the functional:

$$f(\mathbf{x} + \alpha \Delta \mathbf{x}) = \frac{(\alpha - \alpha_1)(\alpha - \alpha_2)}{\alpha_1 \alpha_2} f(\mathbf{x})$$
$$+ \frac{\alpha(\alpha - \alpha_2)}{\alpha_1(\alpha_1 - \alpha_2)} f(\mathbf{x} + \alpha_1 \Delta \mathbf{x})$$
$$+ \frac{\alpha(\alpha - \alpha_1)}{\alpha_2(\alpha_2 - \alpha_1)} f(\mathbf{x} + \alpha_2 \Delta \mathbf{x}) \quad 0 \leq \alpha \leq \alpha_2.$$
$$(3.14)$$

The above function represents a quadratic polynomial in α that returns the values $f(\mathbf{x})$, $f(\mathbf{x} + \alpha_1 \Delta \mathbf{x})$, and $f(\mathbf{x} + \alpha_2 \Delta \mathbf{x})$ for $\alpha = 0$, α_1, and α_2, respectively. The scalar value of α that minimizes the above formula is found by differentiating $f(\alpha)$ with respect to α, setting the result to zero, and solving for α.

The above interpolation formula (equation 3.14) requires three functional evaluations of $f(\mathbf{x})$, so an alternative is to use the values of $f(\mathbf{x})$, $f(\mathbf{x} + \alpha_1 \Delta \mathbf{x})$, and the existing directional derivative of $f(\mathbf{x})'$ at $\mathbf{x}$ to get the quadratic interpolation formula

$$f(\mathbf{x} + \alpha \Delta \mathbf{x}) = \frac{\alpha^2}{\alpha_1^2} [f(\mathbf{x} + \alpha_1 \Delta \mathbf{x}) - \alpha_1 f(\mathbf{x})' - f(\mathbf{x})]$$
$$+ \alpha f(\mathbf{x})' + f(\mathbf{x}), \quad (3.15)$$

in which $f(\mathbf{x})' = \frac{df(\mathbf{x} + \alpha \Delta \mathbf{x})}{d\alpha}|_{\alpha=0}$ represents the derivative of $f(\mathbf{x})$ along the search direction. Note that $f(\mathbf{x} + \alpha \Delta \mathbf{x})$ evaluated at $\alpha = 0$ returns the value of $f(\mathbf{x})$, $df(\mathbf{x} + \alpha \Delta \mathbf{x})/d\alpha$ returns the value $f(\mathbf{x})'$ at $\alpha = 0$, and $f(\mathbf{x} + \alpha \Delta \mathbf{x})|_{\alpha=\alpha_1}$ yields $f(\mathbf{x} + \alpha_1 \Delta \mathbf{x})$.

3.2.4 2D plane minimization

Sometimes two different types of model parameters are inverted from the same data set. These types of parameters might have different units and sensitivities with respect to the data. For example, both the slowness distribution and static delays[2] might be the unknowns in the traveltime

---

[2] Static delays are traveltime shifts in the seismic record that are caused by, for example, local velocity variations, i.e., within a wavelength or two, underneath the receiver and/or source.

tomography problem, but the static delays might be less sensitive to model variations. This is somewhat equivalent to the static delay axis being along the long, narrow valley axis in Figure 3.1b, where the steepest-descent method suffers from slow convergence. Another example is when one of the component vectors represents the isotropic slowness model and the other one represents the anisotropic parameters.

To expedite convergence to the optimal model, we can use a two-dimensional search in a hyperplane spanned by the $N \times 1$ vectors $\Delta\mathbf{x}_1$ and $\Delta\mathbf{x}_2$ associated with the static delays and the slowness model, respectively. That is, the search direction $\Delta\mathbf{x}$ can be decomposed into

$$\Delta\mathbf{x} = \alpha_1 \Delta\mathbf{x}_1 + \alpha_2 \Delta\mathbf{x}_2, \qquad (3.16)$$

in which α_1 and α_2 are two unknown scalars and $\Delta\mathbf{x}_1$ and $\Delta\mathbf{x}_2$ are specified. For example, one of the component vectors might represent the slowness vector and the other represents the static delay at each recording station. Compare this to the standard line-search method, which only searches along a given 1D line in an N-dimensional space.

The problem now is to find the scalar values of α_1 and α_2 that minimize $f(\mathbf{x} + \alpha_1\Delta\mathbf{x}_1 + \alpha_2\Delta\mathbf{x}_2)$. Plugging equation 3.16 into equation 2.9 gives

$$f(\mathbf{x} + \alpha_1\Delta\mathbf{x}_1 + \alpha_2\Delta\mathbf{x}_2)$$
$$\approx f(\mathbf{x}) + (\alpha_1\Delta\mathbf{x}_1 + \alpha_2\Delta\mathbf{x}_2)^T\mathbf{g}$$
$$+ \frac{1}{2}(\alpha_1\Delta\mathbf{x}_1 + \alpha_2\Delta\mathbf{x}_2)^T\mathbf{H}(\alpha_1\Delta\mathbf{x}_1 + \alpha_2\Delta\mathbf{x}_2). \quad (3.17)$$

Differentiating the above with respect to α_1 and α_2, and setting the resulting two equations to zero, we get

$$\begin{bmatrix} \Delta\mathbf{x}_1^T\mathbf{H}\Delta\mathbf{x}_1 & \Delta\mathbf{x}_1^T\mathbf{H}\Delta\mathbf{x}_2 \\ \Delta\mathbf{x}_2^T\mathbf{H}\Delta\mathbf{x}_1 & \Delta\mathbf{x}_2^T\mathbf{H}\Delta\mathbf{x}_2 \end{bmatrix} \begin{bmatrix} \alpha_1 \\ \alpha_2 \end{bmatrix} + \begin{bmatrix} \Delta\mathbf{x}_1^T\mathbf{g} \\ \Delta\mathbf{x}_2^T\mathbf{g} \end{bmatrix} = \begin{bmatrix} 0 \\ 0 \end{bmatrix}.$$
$$(3.18)$$

The above 2×2 system of equations can be solved to find α_1 and α_2. This 2D plane search can speed up convergence greatly relative to 1D line searches when there are different types of model parameters with different units. This procedure can be extended to any number of different types of model parameters (Kennett et al., 1988; Oldenburg et al., 1993) or to different types of data in joint inversion.

It is interesting to view this multidimensional step-length procedure as similar to preconditioned steepest descent. Both procedures aim to reshape the elliptical contours of misfit functionals into rounded ones. If the misfit functional is elongated for certain model components (e.g., the deep reflectivity structure of a basin model might not

influence the surface seismic data too much compared to the shallow model), then it might make sense to assign deep model components to the vector $\Delta\mathbf{x}_2$ and the shallow ones to $\Delta\mathbf{x}_1$. Thus, the convergence to the elongated bullseye in Figure 3.1 can be accomplished in one step.

3.3 Steepest-descent method and linear systems of equations

An SPD matrix $\mathbf{L}$ that forms the $N \times N$ linear system of equations $\mathbf{Lx} = \mathbf{t}$ has a solution that also minimizes the quadratic functional

$$f(\mathbf{x}) = -\mathbf{t}^T\mathbf{x} + \frac{1}{2}\mathbf{x}^T\mathbf{Lx}. \qquad (3.19)$$

The gradient of $f(\mathbf{x})$ is $(\mathbf{Lx} - \mathbf{t})$ so the steepest-descent formula becomes

$$\mathbf{x}^{(k+1)} = \mathbf{x}^{(k)} - \alpha(\mathbf{Lx}^{(k)} - \mathbf{t}),$$
$$= \mathbf{x}^{(k)} - \alpha\mathbf{r}^{(k)}, \qquad (3.20)$$

in which the residual vector is $\mathbf{r}^{(k)} = \mathbf{Lx}^{(k)} - \mathbf{t}$.

An overdetermined $M \times N$ system of equations[3] $\mathbf{Lx} = \mathbf{t}$ (when $M > N$) also can be solved by a steepest-descent method by minimizing the misfit function

$$f(\mathbf{x}) = \frac{1}{2}(\mathbf{Lx} - \mathbf{t})^T(\mathbf{Lx} - \mathbf{t})$$
$$= \frac{1}{2}\mathbf{t}^T\mathbf{t} - \mathbf{t}^T\mathbf{Lx} + \frac{1}{2}\mathbf{x}^T\mathbf{L}^T\mathbf{Lx}. \qquad (3.21)$$

The gradient of $f(\mathbf{x})$ is obtained by differentiating the above equation with respect to the unknown components of $\mathbf{x}$ to give

$$\nabla f(\mathbf{x}) = \mathbf{L}^T\mathbf{Lx} - \mathbf{L}^T\mathbf{t}, \qquad (3.22)$$

so that the steepest-descent solution is

$$\mathbf{x}^{(k+1)} = \mathbf{x}^{(k)} - \alpha\mathbf{L}^T(\mathbf{Lx}^{(k)} - \mathbf{t}),$$
$$= \mathbf{x}^{(k)} - \alpha\mathbf{L}^T\mathbf{r}^{(k)}, \qquad (3.23)$$

and $\mathbf{r}^{(k)} = \mathbf{Lx}^{(k)} - \mathbf{t}$ is the residual at the kth iteration. Comparison of this formula with that in equation 3.20 for a square $\mathbf{L}$ shows that the residual now is modified by the transpose of the $\mathbf{L}$ matrix. If the eigenvalues of $\mathbf{L}$ are σ_i, then they become σ_i^2 for $\mathbf{L}^T\mathbf{L}$, so the normal equations are typically more ill-conditioned than the original square matrix $\mathbf{L}$. As will be shown in the chapters

---

[3]An inconsistent system of equations does not have an exact solution, but it has a solution that minimizes the sum of squared residuals.

on tomography and migration, this transpose matrix is equivalent to backprojection of traveltime residuals for traveltime tomography and migration of seismic traces for least-squares migration.

3.3.1 Regularized steepest descent

If the condition number of $\mathbf{H} = \mathbf{L}^T\mathbf{L}$ is large, then there can be many different models $\mathbf{x}$ that nearly can predict the same data, which violates the conditions for Hadamard's well-posed problem discussed in section 1.2. To remedy this problem, we can impose the constraint that the solution must be small, which is saying that it should lie near the origin. For a linear system of equations, this is equivalent to the constrained $(M + N) \times N$ system of equations

$$\begin{bmatrix} \mathbf{L} \\ \eta\mathbf{I} \end{bmatrix} \mathbf{x} = \begin{pmatrix} \mathbf{t} \\ \mathbf{0} \end{pmatrix}, \qquad (3.24)$$

in which $\mathbf{I}$ is an $N \times N$ identity matrix, $\mathbf{0}$ is the $N \times 1$-vector of zeros, and η is a positive scalar damping parameter; large values of η increase the importance of satisfying this constraint over satisfying $\mathbf{Lx} = \mathbf{t}$, and small ones diminish it.

The associated normal equations are obtained by multiplying the above system by $[\mathbf{L}^T \ \eta\mathbf{I}]$ to get

$$[\mathbf{L}^T\mathbf{L} + \eta^2\mathbf{I}]\mathbf{x} = \mathbf{L}^T\mathbf{t}. \qquad (3.25)$$

Similar to equation 3.22, the solution to these normal equations is the stationary vector that minimizes[4] the objective function ϵ

$$f(\mathbf{x}) = \overbrace{\frac{1}{2}(\mathbf{Lx} - \mathbf{t})^T(\mathbf{Lx} - \mathbf{t})}^{\text{data misfit}} + \overbrace{\frac{\eta^2}{2}\mathbf{x}^T\mathbf{x}}^{\text{penalty term}} . \qquad (3.26)$$

Note, the above equation suggests that regularization can be introduced into a general nonlinear optimization problem by adding a weighted penalty functional to the misfit function, as done to get equation 1.9. Indeed, this is how regularization almost always is implemented. As the iterations proceed, the value of η is decreased gradually to zero when the solution is close enough to $\mathbf{x} = 0$; this procedure is known as the Levenberg-Marquardt, damped least-squares, or zeroth-order Tikhonov (Aster et al., 2005) algorithm described in Appendix 3A. See Appendix 3B for selecting the value of η.

Therefore, the gradient of $f(\mathbf{x})$ is

$$\nabla f(\mathbf{x}) = \mathbf{L}^T(\mathbf{Lx} - \mathbf{t}) + \eta^2\mathbf{x}, \qquad (3.27)$$

---

[4]This assumes an SPD matrix $\mathbf{L}^T\mathbf{L}$.

so that the regularized steepest-descent formula is

$$\begin{aligned} \mathbf{x}^{(k+1)} &= \mathbf{x}^{(k)} - \alpha([\mathbf{L}^T\mathbf{L} + \eta^2\mathbf{I}]\mathbf{x}^{(k)} - \mathbf{L}^T\mathbf{t}), \\ &= \mathbf{x}^{(k)} - \alpha(\mathbf{L}^T\mathbf{r}^{(k)} + \eta^2\mathbf{x}^{(k)}). \end{aligned} \qquad (3.28)$$

In the context of traveltime tomography discussed in Chapter 1, the residual vector $\mathbf{r}^{(k)} = \mathbf{Lx}^{(k)} - \mathbf{t}$ is the difference between the observed traveltimes $\mathbf{t}$ and the predicted times $\mathbf{Lx}^{(k)}$.

3.3.2 MATLAB steepest-descent code

A MATLAB® code for solving a square system of equations by steepest descent is given below. The plot of error versus iteration number in Figure 3.3 is that for a steepest-descent solution with regularization and preconditioning.

```
%
% Steepest Descent to solve square Lx=t
% where gradient gk = L*xk-t;
% and iterate soln xk = xk - alpha*gk
%
clear all;
close all;
clc;
L = [400 1; 1 4];      % 2x2 matrix
t = [5 2]';
PL = [1/400 0; 0 1/4];
%PL=[1 0;0 1];          % No Preconditioning
%
L=PL*L;t=PL*t;%Precondition
L=L+.01*eye(2,2)*max(L(:));  %Regularization
[m,n]=size(L);nit=50;
xk=zeros(n,1);         % Starting point at origin
gk=(L*xk-t);           % Starting gradient
xt = [0.0113 0.4970]'; % True solution.
residual = zeros(nit,1);
%
for q=1:nit;
alpha = gk'*gk/(gk'*L*gk);% Exact Step length
residual(q) = sqrt(sum(abs(xk-xt).^2)); % RMS true residual
if (residual(q)<1e-6)
    break;
end
xk = xk - alpha*gk;    % Compute new iterate
gk=(L*xk-t)            % Find new gradient
end
plot(residual)
```

3.3.3 Preconditioned steepest descent

If $\mathbf{P}$ is an inexpensive approximation to the inverse Hessian $\mathbf{H}^{-1}$ matrix, then the left-preconditioned steepest-descent formula is

$$\mathbf{x}^{(k+1)} = \mathbf{x}^{(k)} - \alpha\mathbf{P}\mathbf{g}^{(k)}, \qquad (3.29)$$

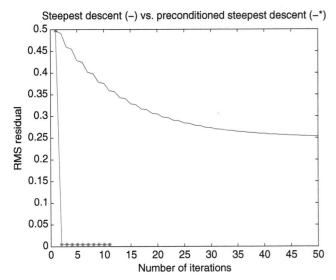

Figure 3.3. RMS residual versus iteration number for standard and preconditioned steepest-descent solutions to the 2×2 system of equations $\mathbf{Lx} = \mathbf{t}$, when $\mathbf{t} = [5 \ 2]^T$ and $\mathbf{L} = [400 \ 1; 1 \ 4]$. Preconditioned steepest descent (see MATLAB code) effectively converged in two steps because the misfit ellipses were reshaped into nearly concentric circles by the preconditioning matrix (courtesy of Umair bin Waheed).

in which the condition number of $\mathbf{PH}$ should be less than $\mathbf{H}$. For seismic imaging, an inexpensive preconditioner often is taken to be a scaled diagonal matrix, in which the elements of $\mathbf{P}_{ii}$ are the reciprocals of $\mathbf{H}_{ii}$. If $\mathbf{H}_{ii}$ is nearly zero, then a regularized preconditioner is used where $\mathbf{P}_{ii} = 1/(\mathbf{H}_{ii} + \eta^2)$. Here, η is the damping parameter. The value of preconditioning is that it reshapes the elliptical contours of $f(\mathbf{x})$ into round contours, so we can quickly iterate to the minimum of $f(\mathbf{x})$.

3.4 Summary

An overview of various unconstrained steepest-descent methods is given for solving nonlinear and linear equations. The general formula for preconditioned and regularized steepest descent is equation 3.29. It reduces to the standard steepest-descent formula if $\eta^2 = 0$ and if the diagonal components of the Hessian are all equal to the value 1. Faster convergence typically is achieved if preconditioned steepest descent is used, especially if the Hessian is ill-conditioned. Ill-conditioning also suggests a nonuniqueness problem, which can be addressed by adding a regularization term to the misfit function. Thus, the regularized solution is guided to the region in the model space that we think is most reasonable, and preconditioning gets us there faster.

3.5 Exercises

1. Find the global minimum of the Rosenbrock function by a steepest-descent method and by a Newton method, with and without preconditioning and/or regularization. Plot residual curves. Create a table that summarizes the results (number of iterations for convergence) for the different combinations of preconditioning and regularization. One table will be for a starting point close to the global minimum, and the other will be for a starting point far from the global minimum. The penalty function for regularization is $\|(1, 1) - \mathbf{x}\|^2$. Comment on results with a fixed value of η^2 compared to one where η^2 goes to zero with increasing iteration number.

2. Show that the minimizer of equation 3.19 exactly solves $\mathbf{Lx} = \mathbf{t}$.

3. Show that the series defined by $x^{(k)} = c^{2^{-k}}$ is Q-linear convergent, where $0 < c < 1$.

4. Solve a 4×2 system of equations by steepest descent, in which $\mathbf{L} = [1 \ 4; 0 \ 2; 3 \ 0; 6 \ 2]$ and $\mathbf{t} = [5 \ 2 \ 3 \ 8]$.

5. For a linear system of equations, an inexact line search should be no better than an exact line search with a steepest-descent solution. Test the validity of this statement with a numerical example.

6. For a nonlinear system of equations, an inexact line search might be better than an exact line search with a steepest-descent solution. Explain why this statement is true.

7. Test the validity of the statement in the previous exercise using the Rosenbrock function.

8. Find the exact formula for α that minimizes equation 3.14.

9. Solve a 4×2 system of equations by steepest descent, in which $\mathbf{L} = [1 \ 4 \ 100; 0 \ 2 \ 90; 3 \ 0 \ 200; 6 \ 2 \ 100]$ and $\mathbf{t} = [105 \ 92 \ 203 \ 108]$, and the step length is computed by the 2D plane-minimization method. In this case, the 3×1 vector of unknowns $\mathbf{x}$ is decomposed into two component vectors; one of them is $[x_1 \ x_2 \ 0]$ and the other one is $[0 \ 0 \ x_3]$. See Figure 3.4.

10. Solve the previous problem by a preconditioned steepest-descent method, when the preconditioner is the diagonal matrix with the diagonal elements equal to the reciprocal of the diagonal elements of $[\mathbf{L}^T\mathbf{L}]$. Compare the convergence rate for each method by plotting $\|\mathbf{x}^{(k+1)} - \mathbf{x}^*\|$ vs $\|\mathbf{x}^{(k)} - \mathbf{x}^*\|$. Classify the Q-convergence rate of each method according to your plots.

11. Explicitly derive equation 3.27.

12. Derive the exact step length for the regularized steepest-descent formula.

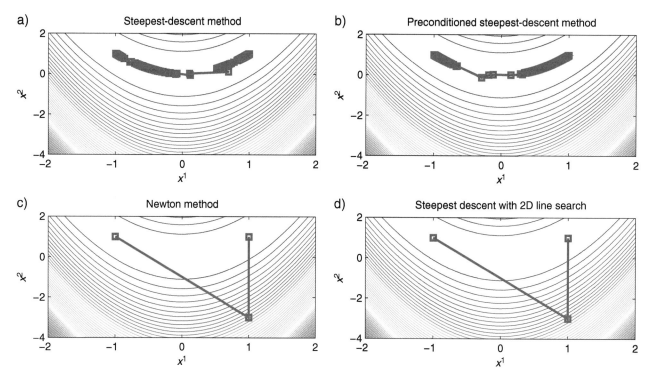

Figure 3.4. Comparison of iterative solutions associated with the SD (5652 iterations), preconditioned SD (362 iterations), Newton (two iterations), and SD with subspace line-search (two iterations) methods for finding the minimizer of the Rosenbrock function; the same starting point $(-1,1)$ and stopping criterion $(f(x) < 1.0e - 7)$ were used for these tests. Note that SD with a 2D line search behaves exactly the same as the Newton method in this example. Figure courtesy of Wei Dai.

13. Show that a negative value for the damping parameter can lead to a damped Hessian with zero eigenvalues. Assume an undamped Hessian that is symmetric positive definite.

14. Show that the gradient minimization of the L_1 norm misfit function $\epsilon = \sum_i |[\mathbf{L}\mathbf{x}]_i - t_i|$ leads to the reweighted least-squares method.

15. An $N \times N$ symmetric matrix[5] $\mathbf{H}$ is positive definite if $\mathbf{x}^T \mathbf{H} \mathbf{x} > 0$ for all real nonzero vectors $\mathbf{x}$. Show that this condition implies that the eigenvalues of $\mathbf{H}$ are positive real.

16. Show that, for a real symmetric matrix $\mathbf{H}$, the eigenvectors of $\mathbf{H}$ are orthogonal. Hint: let $\mathbf{y}$ and $\mathbf{x}$ be eigenvectors of $\mathbf{H}$ with unique eigenvalues λ_y and λ_x. Then $\mathbf{y}^T \mathbf{H} \mathbf{x} = \lambda_x \mathbf{y}^T \mathbf{x}$ and $\mathbf{x}^T \mathbf{H} \mathbf{y} = \lambda_y \mathbf{x}^T \mathbf{y}$, so that $\mathbf{y}^T \mathbf{H} \mathbf{x} - \mathbf{x}^T \mathbf{H} \mathbf{y} = (\lambda_x - \lambda_y)\mathbf{x}^T \mathbf{y}$ and $\mathbf{H}$ is symmetric.

3.6 Computational labs

1. Find the global minimum of a system of equations by SD in the Computational Toolkit under the topic "Steepest descent." Answer all questions.

---

[5]If the elements of $\mathbf{H}$ are complex, then a Hermitian matrix is positive definite if $\mathbf{x}^* \mathbf{H} \mathbf{x} > 0$, in which $\mathbf{x}^*$ is the conjugate transpose of $\mathbf{x}$.

2. Find the global minimum of the 2D Rosenbrock function using the Levenberg-Marquardt method and a trust-region method in the Computational Toolkit under the topic "Steepest descent." Answer all questions.

Appendix 3A:
Levenberg-Marquardt regularization

In the Levenberg-Marquardt regularization method (Aster et al., 2005), a penalty term is added to the original objective function

$$f(\mathbf{x} + \alpha \Delta \mathbf{x})$$
$$= f(\mathbf{x}) + \mathbf{g}^T \Delta \mathbf{x} + \frac{1}{2}\Delta \mathbf{x}^T \mathbf{H} \Delta \mathbf{x} + \frac{\eta^2}{2}\Delta \mathbf{x}^T \Delta \mathbf{x}, \quad (3.30)$$

in which η^2 is the scalar damping parameter. Taking the gradient of the regularized functional yields the modified Newton formula

$$(\mathbf{H} + \eta^2 \mathbf{I})\Delta \mathbf{x} = -\mathbf{g}, \quad (3.31)$$

in which $\mathbf{I}$ is an $N \times N$ identity matrix and η^2 is some small positive scalar. The eigenvectors for $(\mathbf{H} + \eta^2 \mathbf{I})$ are the same as for $\mathbf{H}$, but the eigenvalues become $\beta_i + \eta^2 \gg 0$

if **H** is positive semidefinite. Therefore, the unstable move $\Delta x_i \rightarrow g_i/(\beta_i + \eta^2)$ is damped to a more reasonable value. In an iterative scheme, the value of the damping parameter is reduced gradually with increasing iteration number.

The Levenberg-Marquardt method approaches the Newton method as $\eta^2 \rightarrow 0$, i.e.,

$$\lim_{\eta^2 \rightarrow 0}(\mathbf{H} + \eta^2\mathbf{I})^{-1}\mathbf{g} = \mathbf{H}^{-1}\mathbf{g}, \qquad (3.32)$$

which is appropriate as the search gets closer to the desired model area of convergence. On the other hand, if $\eta^2 \rightarrow$ large, then the Levenberg-Marquardt method approaches the gradient or steepest-descent method, i.e.,

$$\lim_{\eta^2 \rightarrow \text{large}}(\mathbf{H} + \eta^2\mathbf{I})^{-1}\mathbf{g} = \frac{1}{\eta^2}\mathbf{g}. \qquad (3.33)$$

In this last case, the gradient move is along the steepest-descent direction or the direction perpendicular to the contour's tangent. If the contours are round, then the steepest-descent direction points to the bullseye.

These two limiting cases are shown in Figure 3.2, where the Levenberg-Marquardt direction is between the steepest descent and Newton directions (Lines and Treitel, 1984). In practice, the value of η^2 is set to be large (about 1.0% of the largest diagonal value of **H**) for the initial iteration, and then is reduced gradually as the iterations proceed until the average residual is about the same as the expected data error. Large values of the damping parameter tend to suppress the high-frequency components of the inverted slowness model. In later chapters, we will discuss other terms that can be used to regularize the solution, including difference terms that penalize 2D rough solutions, e.g., $\sum_{ij}[(x_{ij} - x_{i+1j})^2 + (x_{ij} - x_{ij+1})^2]$, or entropy terms that penalize "unsimple" models (Buck and Macauly, 1994). Here, x_{ij} is the parameter value at the ith row and jth column in the gridded model.

The Levenberg-Marquardt procedure also is known as Tikhonov regularization (Groetsch, 1993). Mathematically, we are replacing an ill-posed problem with a well-posed problem whose solution becomes closer to that of the original problem as $\eta^2 \rightarrow 0$. The stabilizing functional is used to guide the solution to be near some a priori estimate of the model.

Appendix 3B:
Choosing a value for the regularization parameter

How do you choose the value of the damping parameter η that arbitrates the compromise between reducing the data misfit function and the model norm? Trial and error usually seems to work, in which tests with synthetic data having realistic noise are used to determine the smallest value of η^2. The discrepancy principle of Morozov (Groetsch, 1993) assigns a value for the damping parameter η^2, inverts for the model $\mathbf{x}^{\text{est}}$ from the synthetic data $\mathbf{d}$, and from the estimated model generates the estimated data $\mathbf{d}^{\text{est}}$. Plotting η^2 vs $\|\mathbf{d}^{\text{est}} - \mathbf{d}\|$ allows for the damping parameter to be associated with the value $\|\mathbf{d}^{\text{est}} - \mathbf{d}\|$ that is equal to the estimated residual norm in the actual data (see Figure 3.5a). A more expensive modification of this approach is to experimentally choose η that minimizes the data residual (above the estimated data residual threshold) for each iteration in a nonlinear iterative method (Constable et al., 1987).

Another approach is to construct a log–log plot of the length of the model vector versus the length of the residual vector for different choices of the damping parameter; the optimal damping parameter corresponds to the point on the curve with maximum curvature (see Figure 3.5b). In this context, larger model vectors lead to smaller data

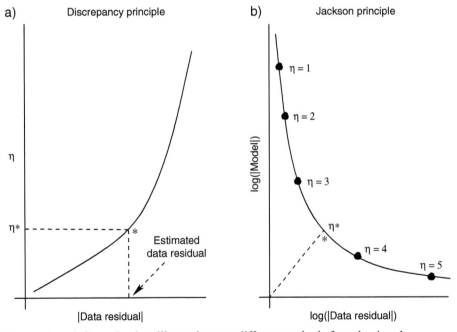

Figure 3.5. Schematic plots illustrating two different methods for selecting the optimal damping parameter η^*. (a) The discrepancy and (b) Jackson's (pick the elbow of the L-curve) principles. The discrepancy principle chooses the η that agrees with the estimated data residual, and Jackson's principle chooses the point on the curve with maximum curvature (at the elbow) near the origin in a log-log plot of the lengths of the model versus data residual vectors. Honoring the discrepancy principle ensures that the model is not fitted severely to the noise.

residuals, and vice versa. The point near the origin with the largest curvature is considered to be the optimal tradeoff between increasing data residual and decreasing model vector length, which is a heuristic choice in the absence of convergence criterion or error-level information.[6] This procedure selects the η on the *elbow* (or point of maximum curvature) of the L-shaped curve (Calvetti et al., 1999; Hansen, 1992; Hansen and O'Leary, 1993). However, there are limitations as pointed out by Hanke (1996).

Two other methods deserve mention. The first is the so-called truncated singular-value-decomposition method (or sometimes called truncated spectral factorization), which expands the solution in terms of the weighted singular-value eigenvectors, when the summation is truncated at singular values less than a small threshold value (Menke, 1984). Instead of a sharp truncation, smoothly attenuating these low eigenvalue contributions produces better results (Calvetti, 1999). Unfortunately, solving for the singular value decomposition is too computationally expensive for many realistic tomography problems. The other regularization method is that of the generalized cross-validation (GCV) method (Golub et al., 1979; Golub and van Matt, 1997), which can be used effectively for large-scale problems.

---

[6]Similarly, small values of η lead to small data residuals but at the expense of large model vectors; conversely, large values of η lead to small model vectors (or small model variance) but large data residuals (Jackson, 1972; Treitel and Lines, 1982; Meyer et al., 2004).

Chapter 4: Conjugate-Gradient and Quasi-Newton Methods

We now will discuss two gradient-optimization methods commonly used in geophysical inversion: the conjugate-gradient (CG) method and the quasi-Newton (QN) method. Unlike the Newton method, these two methods do not explicitly compute the inverse to the Hessian; instead, they iteratively move along descent directions that reduce the data residual. Each iteration costs only $O(N^2)$ operations of a matrix-vector multiply. Another strength is that, in the case of CG and low-memory QN methods, no Hessian matrix needs to be stored or inverted explicitly. Their weakness is that fast convergence is not guaranteed. However, they are generally faster than the nonpreconditioned steepest-descent method.

4.1 Conjugate-gradient method

The CG method of Hestenes and Stiefel (1952) is an efficient line-minimization method that searches along mutually conjugate directions. It is more attractive than Newton's method because it costs only $O(N^2)$ algebraic operations per iteration, usually achieves useful convergence in far fewer than N iterations for a well-conditioned SPD $\mathbf{H}$, is simple to program, and requires only $O(N)$ storage locations per iteration.

Conjugacy definition

Two vectors $\mathbf{u}$ and $\mathbf{v}$ are conjugate with respect to the matrix $\mathbf{H}$ if $(\mathbf{u}, \mathbf{Hv}) = 0$. Appendix 4A shows that N mutually conjugate vectors are linearly independent and span an N-dimensional Euclidean space. Thus, any $N \times 1$ solution vector can be expanded as a linear combination of N independent conjugate vectors. To understand the physical meaning of a conjugate direction, we first define the quasi-Newton formula.

Quasi-Newton formula

A finite-difference approximation to the second derivative of a function is proportional to the difference between the first derivatives at neighboring points

$$\frac{d^2 f(x)}{dx^2} \Delta x \approx \frac{df(x + \Delta x)}{dx} - \frac{df(x)}{dx}, \qquad (4.1)$$

in which Δx is the spatial increment between the evaluation points. This equation is a special case of the quasi-Newton formula, which relates the Hessian (associated with second derivatives of a quadratic misfit function) to the difference between the misfit gradient at neighboring points.

The quasi-Newton (QN) formula is defined as

$$\mathbf{H}(\mathbf{x}^{(k+1)} - \mathbf{x}^{(k)}) = \mathbf{g}^{(k+1)} - \mathbf{g}^{(k)}, \qquad (4.2)$$

which can be derived by forming the gradient of equations 2.9:

$$\nabla f(\mathbf{x}_o + \Delta \mathbf{x}) = \overbrace{\mathbf{g}(\mathbf{x}_o)}^{\mathbf{g}^{(k)}} + \mathbf{H}\Delta \mathbf{x}. \qquad (4.3)$$

where $\overbrace{\nabla f(\mathbf{x}_o + \Delta \mathbf{x})}^{\mathbf{g}^{(k+1)}}$

Defining $\mathbf{x}_o \to \mathbf{x}^{(k)}$ and $\Delta \mathbf{x} \to \mathbf{x}^{(k+1)} - \mathbf{x}^{(k)}$ and rearranging equation 4.3 gives equation 4.2.

If $\mathbf{x}^{(k+1)} - \mathbf{x}^{(k)}$ is normalized to be a unit vector, the curvature of the functional along this direction is given by $(\mathbf{x}^{(k+1)} - \mathbf{x}^{(k)})^T \mathbf{H}(\mathbf{x}^{(k+1)} - \mathbf{x}^{(k)})$. The QN formula is used next to derive the conjugate-gradient method.

Geometric interpretation of a conjugate vector

For an SPD Hessian, the conjugate vector is interpreted as pointing towards the misfit bullseye on the plane spanned by the vectors $\mathbf{d}^{(k-1)}$ and $\mathbf{g}^{(k)}$ in Figure 4.1b.

To prove this statement, note that the previous search direction $\mathbf{d}^{(k-1)}$ and its associated gradient[1] $\mathbf{g}^{(k)}$ are perpendicular to one another so that

$$(\mathbf{d}^{(k-1)}, \mathbf{g}^{(k)}) = 0. \qquad (4.4)$$

The vectors $\mathbf{g}^{(k)}$ and $\mathbf{d}^{(k-1)}$ span the hyperplane shown in Figure 4.1b, where the misfit contours on this plane form a local bullseye, which is the perpendicular projection of

---

[1] The associated gradient is evaluated at the endpoint of the vector $\mathbf{d}^{(k-1)}$.

the global minimum at $\mathbf{x}^*$. If the gradient $\mathbf{g}^{(k+1)}$ at the $k+1$ iteration is defined to be at the local bullseye, then it has no component along the plane spanned by $\mathbf{g}^{(k)}$ and $\mathbf{d}^{(k-1)}$, so $\mathbf{g}^{(k+1)}$ is perpendicular to any vector in this plane. That is,

$$(\mathbf{d}^{(k-1)}, \mathbf{g}^{(k+1)}) = 0. \qquad (4.5)$$

Taking the inner product of $\mathbf{d}^{(k-1)}$ with the quasi-Newton formula in equation 4.2 gives

$$(\mathbf{d}^{(k-1)}, \mathbf{H}\mathbf{d}^{(k)}) = \overbrace{(\mathbf{d}^{(k-1)}, \mathbf{g}^{(k+1)})}^{\text{eq. 4.5}} - \overbrace{(\mathbf{d}^{(k-1)}, \mathbf{g}^{(k)})}^{\text{eq. 4.4}} = 0, \quad (4.6)$$

in which $\mathbf{x}^{(k+1)} - \mathbf{x}^{(k)} \to \mathbf{d}^{(k)}$. This equation says that a search direction $\mathbf{d}^{(k)}$ with an endpoint at the local bullseye is conjugate to the previous search direction $\mathbf{d}^{(k-1)}$, where the bullseye is in the plane spanned by $\mathbf{g}^{(k)}$ and $\mathbf{d}^{(k-1)}$, as illustrated in Figure 4.1b.

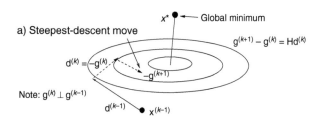

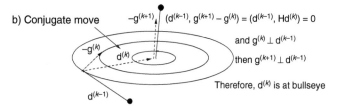

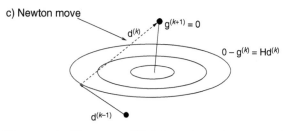

Figure 4.1. The vector $\mathbf{d}^{(k)}$ defines the update vector for the (top) steepest-descent (middle) conjugate-gradient and (bottom) Newton methods, where $\mathbf{x}^*$ denotes the global minimum point. The Newton update points to the global minimum, while the CG update points towards the misfit bullseye in the plane spanned by $\mathbf{g}^{(k)}$ and $\mathbf{d}^{(k-1)}$. If the above misfit function defines a narrow valley, then the steepest-descent iterations will follow a crisscross pattern inefficiently across the valley, and the CG and Newton methods will move directly to the minimum.

4.1.1 Conjugate-gradient algorithm

We now can construct a series of mutually conjugate search vectors that minimize a quadratic misfit function with an SPD $\mathbf{H}$. The following iterative solution, known as the conjugate-gradient method, uses the steepest-descent direction as the initial search direction to find the optimal solution.

1. Define the initial guess model to be $\mathbf{x}^{(k-1)} \to \mathbf{x}^{(0)}$ (see Figure 4.1b) with $k = 1$, and define the initial descent vector as $\mathbf{d}^{(k-1)} \to \mathbf{d}^{(0)} = -\mathbf{g}^{(0)}$. The updated solution $\mathbf{x}^{(k)}$ is given as

$$\mathbf{x}^{(k)} = \mathbf{x}^{(k-1)} + \alpha \mathbf{d}^{(k-1)}. \qquad (4.7)$$

Here, α is found by a line-minimization method that minimizes $f(\mathbf{x}^{(k-1)} + \alpha \mathbf{d}^{(k-1)})$. From equation 3.10, α is given by

$$\alpha = -\frac{(\mathbf{d}^{(k-1)}, \mathbf{g}^{(k-1)})}{(\mathbf{d}^{(k-1)}, \mathbf{H}\mathbf{d}^{(k-1)})}. \qquad (4.8)$$

2. Starting from $\mathbf{x}^{(k)}$, the next move $\mathbf{d}^{(k)}$ is required to be conjugate to $\mathbf{d}^{(k-1)}$ and is in the plane spanned by $\mathbf{g}^{(k)} = \nabla f(\mathbf{x}^{(k)})$ and $\mathbf{d}^{(k-1)}$, i.e.,

$$\mathbf{d}^{(k)} = -\mathbf{g}^{(k)} + \beta \mathbf{d}^{(k-1)}, \qquad (4.9)$$

in which β is chosen to ensure that $\mathbf{d}^{(k)}$ is conjugate to $\mathbf{d}^{(k-1)}$. Enforcing conjugacy by taking the inner product of equation 4.9 with $\mathbf{d}^{(k-1)^T}\mathbf{H}$ and setting the result to zero gives β as

$$\beta = \frac{(\mathbf{d}^{(k-1)}, \mathbf{H}\mathbf{g}^{(k)})}{(\mathbf{d}^{(k-1)}, \mathbf{H}\mathbf{d}^{(k-1)})}. \qquad (4.10)$$

Using equation 4.7, $\mathbf{H}\mathbf{d}^{(k-1)} = (\mathbf{g}^{(k)} - \mathbf{g}^{(k-1)})/\alpha$ and the QN condition in equation 4.2 allows equation 4.10 to be rewritten as

$$\begin{aligned} \beta &= (\mathbf{g}^{(k)} - \mathbf{g}^{(k-1)}, \mathbf{g}^{(k)})/(\alpha \mathbf{d}^{(k-1)}, \mathbf{H}\mathbf{d}^{(k-1)}), \\ &= (\mathbf{g}^{(k)} - \mathbf{g}^{(k-1)}, \mathbf{g}^{(k)})/(\mathbf{d}^{(k-1)}, \mathbf{g}^{(k)} - \mathbf{g}^{(k-1)}), \\ &= (\mathbf{g}^{(k)} - \mathbf{g}^{(k-1)}, \mathbf{g}^{(k)})/(\mathbf{g}^{(k-1)}, \mathbf{g}^{(k-1)}), \qquad (4.11) \end{aligned}$$

in which the denominator in the last equation follows by using $\mathbf{d}^{(k-1)} = -\mathbf{g}^{(k-1)} + \beta' \mathbf{d}^{(k-2)}$ and observing in Figure 4.1b that the kth gradient is perpendicular to the $k - 1$ search direction. β is the scalar that ensures $\mathbf{d}^{(k-1)}$ is conjugate to $\mathbf{d}^{(k-2)}$.

Equations 4.7–4.11 can be summarized (Scales, 1985) by the following CG formulas for minimizing $f(\mathbf{x})$:

$$\alpha^{(k)} = -\frac{(\mathbf{d}^{(k)}, \mathbf{g}^{(k)})}{(\mathbf{d}^{(k)}, \mathbf{H}\mathbf{d}^{(k)})}, \qquad (4.12)$$

$$\mathbf{x}^{(k+1)} = \mathbf{x}^{(k)} + \alpha^{(k)}\mathbf{d}^{(k)}, \qquad (4.13)$$

$$\mathbf{g}^{(k+1)} = \nabla f(\mathbf{x}^{(k+1)}), \qquad (4.14)$$

$$\mathbf{d}^{(k+1)} = -\mathbf{g}^{(k+1)} + \beta\mathbf{d}^{(k)}, \qquad (4.15)$$

and

$$\beta = \frac{(\mathbf{g}^{(k+1)} - \mathbf{g}^{(k)}, \mathbf{g}^{(k+1)})}{(\mathbf{g}^{(k)}, \mathbf{g}^{(k)})}. \qquad (4.16)$$

The geometric interpretation of the CG method is given in Figure 4.1b, in which the conjugate direction $\mathbf{d}^{(k)}$ is in the local plane spanned by $\mathbf{d}^{(k-1)}$ and $\mathbf{g}^{(k)}$, and this conjugate vector points towards the bullseye. Here, the bullseye is not the global minimum – it is the local minimum in the local plane.

Equations 4.13 to 4.16 describe the Polak-Ribiere CG method (Gill et al., 1981). It is clear from Figure 4.1b and by definition of $\mathbf{g}^{(k+1)}$ that $\mathbf{g}^{(k)}$ and $\mathbf{g}^{(k+1)}$ are orthogonal (Nocedal and Wright, 1999), so that β in equation 4.16 becomes

$$\beta = \frac{(\mathbf{g}^{(k+1)}, \mathbf{g}^{(k+1)})}{(\mathbf{g}^{(k)}, \mathbf{g}^{(k)})}. \qquad (4.17)$$

Replacing equation 4.16 by equation 4.17 results in the Fletcher-Reeves CG method (Gill et al., 1981).

An alternate form of α known to Hestenes and Stiefel (1952) is

$$\alpha^{(k)} = -\frac{(\mathbf{g}^{(k+1)}, \mathbf{g}^{(k+1)})}{(\mathbf{g}^{(k+1)}, \mathbf{H}\mathbf{g}^{(k)})}. \qquad (4.18)$$

For strictly quadratic functions and infinite precision arithmetic, the Polak-Ribiere and Fletcher-Reeves CG methods are identical. However, Scales (1985) shows that with non-quadratic functions, $\mathbf{d}^{(k)}$ can become almost orthogonal to $\mathbf{g}^{(k)}$, so it cannot make much progress. (The cause of the loss of orthogonality on a computer is arithmetic roundoff errors.) In this case, $\mathbf{g}^{(k+1)} \approx \mathbf{g}^{(k)}$, so the Polak-Ribiere formula in equation 4.16 yields $\beta = 0$ and $\mathbf{d}^{(k)} = -\mathbf{g}^{(k)}$; hence, Scales (1985) shows that the Polak-Ribiere CG algorithm resets to the steepest-descent direction when it is making little progress, making it a more stable method.

For example, if the algorithm is making little progress, then $\mathbf{g}^{(k)} \approx \mathbf{g}^{(k+1)}$ so that $\beta \approx 0$ and equation 4.15 becomes $\mathbf{d}^{(k+1)} = -\mathbf{g}^{(k+1)}$; thus, the algorithm automatically resets to the steepest-descent direction. Nocedal and Wright (1999) confirm the superiority of Polak-Ribiere CG over Fletcher-Reeves CG.

4.1.2 Conjugate-gradient method and linear systems of equations

The CG method also can be used to solve an $N \times N$ linear system of equations. Let an SPD system of equations be represented by

$$\mathbf{L}\mathbf{x} = \mathbf{t}, \qquad (4.19)$$

in which $\mathbf{t}$ is an $N \times 1$-vector, $\mathbf{x}$ is an $N \times 1$-vector, and $\mathbf{L}$ is an $N \times N$ matrix that is SPD. The solution to the above system of equations is the same as that which minimizes the misfit function

$$f(\mathbf{x}) = \frac{1}{2}\mathbf{x}^T\mathbf{L}\mathbf{x} - \mathbf{x}^T\mathbf{t}, \qquad (4.20)$$

in which the gradient is given by

$$\nabla f(\mathbf{x}) = \mathbf{L}\mathbf{x} - \mathbf{t}. \qquad (4.21)$$

The stationary vector $\mathbf{x}^*$ that minimizes equation 4.20 also satisfies $\nabla f(\mathbf{x}) = \mathbf{L}\mathbf{x} - \mathbf{t} = 0$, and it is the solution to the linear system of equations 4.19. Thus, $\mathbf{L}\mathbf{x} = \mathbf{t}$ can be solved by iteratively minimizing the misfit function along mutually conjugate directions.

4.1.3 MATLAB conjugate-gradient code

The MATLAB® code for solving a square SPD system of equations by a CG method is given below.

```
%
% CG Iterations to solve SPD  eqn Lx=t
%  where gradient gk = L*xk-t;
%  and iterate soln xk1 = xk + alpha*dk1
%
clear all;
L     = [400 1; 1 4];          % Simple 2x2
t     = [5 2]';                % problem
[m,n] = size(L);
nit   = 3;
%
xk    = zeros(n,1);            % Starting point at origin
gk    = (L*xk-t);dk=-gk;
%
for q = 1:nit;
alpha = -dk'*gk/(dk'*L*dk);
xk1   = xk + alpha*dk;         % Compute new iterate
gk1   = gk+alpha*L*dk;         % Find new gradient
beta  = gk1'*gk1/(gk'*gk);     % Fletcher-Reeves
beta  = gk1'*(gk1-gk)/(gk'*gk); % Polak-Ribiere
dk1   = -gk1+beta*dk;          % Find new conj. direction
dk    = dk1;                   % Refresh iterates
gk    = gk1;
xk    = xk1
end
%
```

If the system of equations is overdetermined, then the problem is to find $\mathbf{x}$ that satisfies the normal equations $\mathbf{L}^T\mathbf{L}\mathbf{x} = \mathbf{L}^T\mathbf{t}$. Similar to the steepest-descent solution of an overdetermined system of equations, the solution $\mathbf{x}$ is found that minimizes the misfit function given by the sum of the squared residuals:

$$f(\mathbf{x}) = \frac{1}{2}(\mathbf{Lx} - \mathbf{t})^T(\mathbf{Lx} - \mathbf{t}) = \frac{1}{2}\mathbf{x}^T\mathbf{L}^T\mathbf{Lx} - \mathbf{t}^T\mathbf{Lx} + \frac{1}{2}\mathbf{t}^T\mathbf{t}.$$

(4.22)

Here, $f(\mathbf{x})$ is a quadratic functional in $\mathbf{x}$, and the right side of equation 4.22 can be viewed as the first three terms of a Taylor series in $\mathbf{x}$ expanded about the origin. The gradient is given by

$$\nabla f(\mathbf{x}) = \mathbf{L}^T(\mathbf{Lx} - \mathbf{t}),$$

(4.23)

and the solution can be found by iteratively minimizing along mutually conjugate directions.

The matrix product in the gradient should be computed by first calculating the residual $\mathbf{r}$ (i.e., $\mathbf{r} = \mathbf{Lx} - \mathbf{t}$), and then multiplying it by $\mathbf{L}^T$. This minimizes the computational expense by carrying out only matrix-vector multiplication (rather than the matrix-matrix $\mathbf{L}^T\mathbf{L}$ multiplication), and it also minimizes round-off error. Scales (1987) applied the CG solver to some traveltime tomography problems and reports that the linear CG solver performs at least as well as a SIRT (simultaneous iterative reconstruction tomography) method.

Below is a conjugate-gradient MATLAB code for solving an overdetermined system of linear equations.

```
%
% CG Iterations to solve overdetermined eqns Lx=b
%   where gradient gk = L'*(L*xk-b);
%   and iterate soln xk1 = xk + alpha*dk1
%
clear all;
L      = [400 1; 1 4; 0 1];     % Simple 3x2
b      = [5 2 .5]';             % problem
[m,n]  = size(L);
nit    = 3;
%
xk = zeros(n,1);                % Starting point at origin
gk = L'*(L*xk-b);dk=-gk;
%
for q = 1:nit;
  res  = L*dk;
  res1 = L'*res;
  alpha = -dk'*gk/(res'*res);
  xk1  = xk + alpha*dk;         % Compute new iterate
  gk1  = gk+alpha*res1;         % Find new gradient
  beta = gk1'*gk1/(gk'*gk);     % Fletcher-Reeves
  beta = gk1'*(gk1-gk)/(gk'*gk);% Polak-Ribiere
  dk1  = -gk1+beta*dk;          % Find new conj. direction
  dk   = dk1;                   % Refresh iterates
  gk   = gk1;
  xk   = xk1
end
```

If the $N \times N$ matrix $\mathbf{L}$ is characterized by eigenvalues λ_i, then $\mathbf{L}^T\mathbf{L}$ has eigenvalues λ_i^2. This means that the condition number for $\mathbf{L}^T\mathbf{L}$ will be squared compared to that for

$\mathbf{L}$, which can result in slower convergence; hence the need for preconditioning. An alternative is the iterative LSQR method, which is a more reliable algorithm when the system of equations is ill-conditioned (Paige and Saunders, 1982).

An example of the Polak-Ribiere conjugate-gradient method applied to the Rosenbrock functional $f(x, y) = 100(y - x^2)^2 + (1 - x)^2$ is given in Figure 3.4. The CG method significantly outperforms the steepest-descent algorithms in this case, but not that of the Newton method. For a nonlinear functional, the CG direction always should be reset to the gradient direction at or before the Nth iteration, in which N is the dimension of the vector $\mathbf{x}$. For a nonlinear functional, the CG direction always should be reset to the steepest-descent direction every few iterations because the search directions quickly lose mutual conjugacy.

4.1.4 Convergence rate

For a linear problem, if the $N \times N$ Hessian is SPD then the CG algorithm is guaranteed to converge in N steps at most. But this convergence rate is accelerated if the eigenvalues of $\mathbf{H}$ are clustered about one value. Theorem 5.4 in Nocedal and Wright (1999) says that if there are r distinct eigenvalues associated with $\mathbf{H}$, then the CG iterations will terminate in r iterations at most. For example, if the eigenvalues for a 5×5 matrix $\mathbf{H}$ are given as $(5, 5, 2, 2, 2)$, then only two iterations will be needed. More realistically, the eigenvalue distribution might be $(5, 5.1, 4.8, 2, 2)$, and it might take three iterations for acceptable convergence, two iterations centered about the eigenvalue of 5, and one iteration for the other cluster with eigenvalue equal to 2. The intuitive explanation for this is that misfit contours associated with the clustered eigenvalues form a hypersphere, where one search direction points to the general center of this sphere.

Another property is Theorem 5.5 in Nocedal and Wright (1999), which says that the difference between the CG iterate $\mathbf{x}^{(k+1)}$ and the solution $\mathbf{x}^*$ is given by

$$||\mathbf{x}^{(k+1)} - \mathbf{x}^*|| \approx \epsilon ||\mathbf{x}^{(0)} - \mathbf{x}^*||,$$

(4.24)

in which $\epsilon = \sigma_{N-k} - \sigma_1$ is the difference between the $N - k$ and first eigenvalues (i.e., smallest) of $\mathbf{H}$ arranged in ascending order. For a small value of ϵ, this formula says that the CG solution will provide a good estimate of the solution after only a few iterations. Figure 4.2 schematically illustrates this convergence rate for four distinct eigenvalues and the rest clustered about a point.

The convergence rate of the conjugate-gradient method increases with smaller condition numbers of the Hessian matrix. In fact, if the Hessian is SPD and has only r distinct eigenvalues, the CG iteration will terminate at the

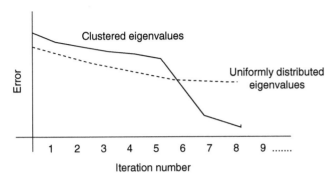

Figure 4.2. Convergence rate versus iteration number for clustered eigenvalues (solid line) and uniformly distributed eigenvalues (dashed line). After Nocedal and Wright (1999).

solution in r iterations at most (Theorem 5.4 in Nocedal and Wright, 1999). If the eigenvalues of the Hessian are equal to one another, then the misfit function's contours are round, so the first iterate of the CG method moves along the steepest-descent path pointing to the center of the bullseye. For highly elliptical contours, convergence can be slow so that either preconditioning or regularization should be used.

4.1.5 Preconditioned and regularized conjugate gradients

If some of the eigenvalues of $\mathbf{H}$ are zero, or nearly zero then the condition number of $\mathbf{H}$ is large and can lead to slow convergence of CG. Therefore, a preconditioner matrix $\mathbf{M}^{-1}$ is used to transform the ill-conditioned system into one with a condition number close to the value one.

Preconditioned conjugate gradient

We choose an easy-to-compute SPD $\mathbf{M}^{-1}$ that approximates the inverse of $\mathbf{H}$, so $\mathbf{x}$ is found by solving the preconditioned equations $\mathbf{M}^{-1}\mathbf{H}\mathbf{x} = \mathbf{M}^{-1}\mathbf{g}$. However, $\mathbf{M}^{-1}\mathbf{H}$ might not be SPD (even if both $\mathbf{M}^{-1}$ and $\mathbf{H}$ are SPD) as required by CG or SD, so an alternative system of preconditioned equations should be defined with the SPD property. Such a system is given by Cholesky factorization of $\mathbf{M} = \mathbf{E}\mathbf{E}^T$, in which $\mathbf{E}$ is a lower triangular matrix chosen so that the condition number of $(\mathbf{E}\mathbf{E}^T)^{-1}\mathbf{H}$ is small. Therefore, multiplying $\mathbf{H}\mathbf{x} = \mathbf{g}$ by $\mathbf{E}^{-1}$ gives

$$\overbrace{\mathbf{E}^{-1}\mathbf{H}\mathbf{E}^{-T}}^{\mathbf{R}}\hat{\mathbf{x}} = \mathbf{E}^{-1}\mathbf{g}, \qquad (4.25)$$

in which $\hat{\mathbf{x}} = \mathbf{E}^T\mathbf{x}$ is the solution to the transformed SPD system of equations (Shewchuk, 1994). The symmetric matrix $\mathbf{R} = \mathbf{E}^{-1}\mathbf{H}\mathbf{E}^{-T}$ has the same well-conditioned eigenvalues as $\mathbf{M}^{-1}\mathbf{H}$ because $\mathbf{E}^{-T}\mathbf{R}\mathbf{E}^T = \mathbf{M}^{-1}\mathbf{H}$ (see Exercise 4.1.1.5). This means that the SPD equation 4.25

can be solved efficiently for $\hat{\mathbf{x}}$ by a CG method, and then $\mathbf{x}$ can be found by back substitution of $\hat{\mathbf{x}} = \mathbf{E}^T\mathbf{x}$.

The MATLAB code for solving the preconditioned equation 4.25 is as before, except to replace $\mathbf{H}$ by $\mathbf{E}^{-1}\mathbf{H}\mathbf{E}^{-T}$ and $\mathbf{g}$ by $\mathbf{E}^{-1}\mathbf{g}$. This gives rise to the transformed preconditioned conjugate-gradient method (Shewchuk, 1994):

$$\hat{\mathbf{d}}^{(0)} = \hat{\mathbf{r}}^{(0)} = \mathbf{E}^{-1}\mathbf{g} - \mathbf{E}^{-1}\mathbf{H}\mathbf{E}^{-T}\hat{\mathbf{x}}^{(0)},$$

$$\alpha^{(i)} = \frac{(\hat{\mathbf{r}}^{(i)}, \hat{\mathbf{r}}^{(i)})}{(\hat{\mathbf{d}}^{(i)}, \mathbf{E}^{-1}\mathbf{H}\mathbf{E}^{-T}\hat{\mathbf{d}}^{(i)})}; \quad \hat{\mathbf{x}}^{(i+1)} = \hat{\mathbf{x}}^{(i)} + \alpha^{(i)}\hat{\mathbf{d}}^{(i)},$$

$$\hat{\mathbf{r}}^{(i+1)} = \hat{\mathbf{r}}^{(i)} - \alpha^{(i)}\mathbf{E}^{-1}\mathbf{H}\mathbf{E}^{-T}\hat{\mathbf{d}}^{(i)}; \quad \beta^{(i+1)} = \frac{(\hat{\mathbf{r}}^{(i+1)}, \hat{\mathbf{r}}^{(i+1)})}{(\hat{\mathbf{r}}^{(i)}, \hat{\mathbf{r}}^{(i)})},$$

$$\hat{\mathbf{d}}^{(i+1)} = \hat{\mathbf{r}}^{(i+1)} + \beta^{(i+1)}\hat{\mathbf{d}}^{(i)}. \qquad (4.26)$$

The problem with this approach is that $\mathbf{E}$ can be expensive to compute by Cholesky factorization and store for dense matrices $\mathbf{M}$, especially for typical 3D imaging problems.

To avoid the explicit calculation of $\mathbf{E}$ and its inverse, we can arrange the algorithm so that only vector multiplications by $\mathbf{M}^{-1}$ are computed. Setting $\hat{\mathbf{r}}^{(i)} = \mathbf{E}^{-1}\mathbf{r}^{(i)}$ and $\hat{\mathbf{d}}^{(i)} = \mathbf{E}^T\mathbf{d}^{(i)}$, and using the identities $\hat{\mathbf{x}}^{(i)} = \mathbf{E}^T\mathbf{x}^{(i)}$ and $\mathbf{E}^{-T}\mathbf{E}^{-1} = \mathbf{M}^{-1}$, we get the untransformed preconditioned CG method (Shewchuk, 1994) for solving $\mathbf{H}\mathbf{x} = \mathbf{g}$:

$$\mathbf{r}^{(0)} = \mathbf{g} - \mathbf{H}\mathbf{x}^{(0)}; \quad \mathbf{d}^{(0)} = \mathbf{M}^{-1}\mathbf{r}^{(0)},$$

$$\alpha^{(i)} = \frac{(\mathbf{r}^{(i)}, \mathbf{M}^{-1}\mathbf{r}^{(i)})}{(\mathbf{d}^{(i)}, \mathbf{H}\mathbf{d}^{(i)})}; \quad \mathbf{x}^{(i+1)} = \mathbf{x}^{(i)} + \alpha^{(i)}\mathbf{d}^{(i)},$$

$$\mathbf{r}^{(i+1)} = \mathbf{r}^{(i)} - \alpha^{(i)}\mathbf{H}\mathbf{d}^{(i)}; \quad \beta^{(i+1)} = \frac{(\mathbf{r}^{(i+1)}, \mathbf{M}^{-1}\mathbf{r}^{(i+1)})}{(\mathbf{r}^{(i)}, \mathbf{M}^{-1}\mathbf{r}^{(i)})},$$

$$\mathbf{d}^{(i+1)} = \mathbf{M}^{-1}\mathbf{r}^{(i+1)} + \beta^{(i+1)}\mathbf{d}^{(i)}. \qquad (4.27)$$

For large seismic problems, $\mathbf{M}^{-1}$ is not stored explicitly as a matrix. Instead, a row vector associated with $\mathbf{M}^{-1}$ is multiplied by the vector $\mathbf{r}$. If $\mathbf{M}^{-1}$ is computed by a limited memory quasi-Newton method, then these vector-vector multiplications are carried out by the outer-product vectors that form the quasi-Newton matrix.

Given the matrix $\mathbf{H}$, the convergence rate of the CG method is (Nocedal and Wright, 1999):

$$\frac{\|\mathbf{x}^* - \mathbf{x}^{(i)}\|_H}{\|\mathbf{x}^* - \mathbf{x}^{(0)}\|_H} \leq \left(\frac{\sqrt{\kappa(\mathbf{H})} - 1}{\sqrt{\kappa(\mathbf{H})} + 1}\right)^{2i}, \qquad (4.28)$$

in which $\|\mathbf{x}\|_H = (\mathbf{x}, \mathbf{H}\mathbf{x})$, i is the iteration index, and $\kappa(\mathbf{H})$ is the condition number of $\mathbf{H}$. Therefore, a good preconditioner which drives the condition number $\kappa(\mathbf{H}) \to 1$ will provide very fast convergence.

Practical preconditioners

The simplest approximate inverse is a diagonal matrix in which the diagonal elements are the reciprocals of the diagonal elements of **H**. Another possibility is to use a limited-memory quasi-Newton method to compute $\mathbf{M}^{-1}$ (Gill et al., 1981). The matrix $\mathbf{M}^{-1}$ is never computed explicitly; the limited number of vectors that form the rank-deficient inverse matrix are used to perform vector-vector multiplies. Alternatively, an incomplete Cholesky factorization can be used to get an approximate inverse for $\mathbf{H} = \mathbf{LL}^T$ by solving for an approximate factor $\tilde{\mathbf{L}}$ that is sparser than **L**. Then, we have $\mathbf{H} \approx \tilde{\mathbf{L}}\tilde{\mathbf{L}}^T$ and choose $\mathbf{E} = \tilde{\mathbf{L}}$ for the Cholesky factorized matrix.

Exercise 4.1.1

1. The nonlinear CG method resets the search direction to that of the steepest-descent direction every few iterations. This is because the Hessian matrix might change rapidly every few iterations. Use MATLAB scripts to find points that minimize the Rosenbrock function by both a steepest-descent and CG method, with and without preconditioning. Graph out contours of the Rosenbrock function and the iterative solutions for each step of CG, preconditioned steepest-descent, and steepest-descent methods.
2. Compare the benefits and pitfalls of the CG and SD methods for minimizing the Rosenbrock function.
3. Write a preconditioned CG MATLAB routine to solve an overdetermined system of equations. Use the approximation to the diagonal as the preconditioner. Compare the performance of CG with a preconditioning in finding the least-squares solution.
4. Tridiagonal solvers are computationally efficient for solving tridiagonal systems of equations. Let **W** be the tridiagonal approximation to **H**. Write a MATLAB code that uses a canned tridiagonal solver to precondition **H** without explicitly computing the inverse matrix $\mathbf{T}^{-1}$.
5. Prove that $\mathbf{R} = \mathbf{E}^{-1}\mathbf{HE}^{-T}$ has the same eigenvalues as $\mathbf{M}^{-1}\mathbf{H}$ when $\mathbf{E}^{-T}\mathbf{RE}^T = \mathbf{M}^{-1}\mathbf{H}$.

Regularized conjugate gradient

Solving the consistent system of equations given by

$$\begin{bmatrix} \mathbf{L} \\ \eta\mathbf{I} \end{bmatrix} \mathbf{x} = \begin{bmatrix} \mathbf{t} \\ \mathbf{0} \end{bmatrix}, \tag{4.29}$$

is equivalent to minimizing the functional given by

$$f(\mathbf{x}) = \frac{1}{2}(\mathbf{Lx} - \mathbf{t})^T(\mathbf{Lx} - \mathbf{t}) + \eta^2\mathbf{x}^T\mathbf{x}, \tag{4.30}$$

similar to the regularized steepest-descent method discussed in the previous chapter. Therefore, regularized CG is equivalent to solving the system of equations given by equation 4.29.

Exercise 4.1.2

Compare the performance of preconditioned CG and regularized CG in finding the point that minimizes the Rosenbrock function. The penalty term should be $\Delta\mathbf{x}^T\Delta\mathbf{x}$, in which $\Delta\mathbf{x}$ is the difference between the iterate and the bias point at $(1.2, 1.2)$. Graph out contours of the Rosenbrock function and the iterative solutions for each method.

4.2 Quasi-Newton methods

The main drawback to Newton's method is that the second derivatives of $f(\mathbf{x})$ can be difficult or expensive to compute, or the inverse Hessian computation is prohibitively expensive. To avoid these problems, the quasi-Newton iterative formula

$$\mathbf{x}^{(k+1)} = \mathbf{x}^{(k)} - \mathbf{H}_k^{-1}\mathbf{g}^{(k)}, \tag{4.31}$$

can be used, where $\mathbf{H}_k^{-1}$ is an approximation to $\mathbf{H}^{-1}$ and is updated iteratively from first, not second, derivatives of $f(\mathbf{x})$. For an $N \times N$ SPD Hessian, it can be shown (Scales, 1985) that

$$\lim_{k \to N} \mathbf{H}_k^{-1} = \mathbf{H}^{-1}. \tag{4.32}$$

The advantages of the quasi-Newton (QN) method, relative to Newton's method, are that each update requires only $O(N^2)$ algebraic operations and only first derivatives are computed; and unlike the CG method, there is no need to restart the iterations periodically. However, there still is the requirement for $O(N^2)$ memory locations compared to $O(N)$ locations for the CG method. One way to overcome this is to use a limited-memory QN method (Nocedal and Wright, 1999) in which only a few vectors are stored to form an implicit approximation to the inverse of **H**.

We will now describe the quasi-Newton optimization procedure in detail.

Rank-one quasi-Newton method

In the rank-one method, we set the starting approximation to $\mathbf{H}^{-1}$ as $\mathbf{H}_0^{-1} = \mathbf{I}$ in equation 4.31, to get

$$\mathbf{x}^{(1)} = \mathbf{x}^{(0)} - \alpha\mathbf{H}_0^{-1}\mathbf{g}^{(0)}, \tag{4.33}$$

in which α is computed by a line-search method to minimize $f(\mathbf{x})$.

We then update $\mathbf{H}_0^{-1}$ by requiring that the updated inverse $\mathbf{H}_1^{-1}$ satisfies the quasi-Newton formula associated with equation 4.2:

$$\mathbf{x}^{(1)} - \mathbf{x}^{(0)} = \mathbf{H}_1^{-1}(\mathbf{g}^{(1)} - \mathbf{g}^{(0)}). \tag{4.34}$$

Note that $\mathbf{H}_0^{-1}$ does not satisfy the quasi-Newton formula because it is only an approximation to the Hessian inverse. To ensure that equation 4.34 is satisfied, we construct $\mathbf{H}_1^{-1}$ by a rank-one update, i.e.,

$$\mathbf{H}_1^{-1} = \mathbf{H}_0^{-1} + a\mathbf{u}\mathbf{u}^T, \qquad (4.35)$$

in which $\mathbf{u}$ is an $N \times 1$ vector and a is a constant. The constant a and $\mathbf{u}$ are determined by plugging equation 4.35 into equation 4.34 to get

$$\Delta\mathbf{x}^{(0)} = (\mathbf{H}_0^{-1} + a\mathbf{u}\mathbf{u}^T)\Delta\mathbf{g}^{(0)}. \qquad (4.36)$$

Rearrangement gives

$$a\mathbf{u}\mathbf{u}^T\Delta\mathbf{g}^{(0)} = \Delta\mathbf{x}^{(0)} - \mathbf{H}_0^{-1}\Delta\mathbf{g}^{(0)}, \qquad (4.37)$$

in which $\Delta\mathbf{x}^{(0)} = \mathbf{x}^{(1)} - \mathbf{x}^{(0)}$ and $\Delta\mathbf{g}^{(0)} = \mathbf{g}^{(1)} - \mathbf{g}^{(0)}$. A matrix of the form $\mathbf{u}\mathbf{u}^T$ is termed a matrix of rank one with only one linearly independent row vector. Every column of $\mathbf{u}\mathbf{u}^T$ is a multiple of the vector $\mathbf{u}$, and every row is a multiple of the vector $\mathbf{u}^T$. A matrix of the form $\mathbf{I} + \alpha\mathbf{u}\mathbf{u}^T$ is termed an elementary matrix.

In the above equation, there are $N + 1$ unknowns and only N equations. Therefore, one possible solution (Gill et al., 1981) is

$$\mathbf{u} = \Delta\mathbf{x}^{(0)} - \mathbf{H}_0^{-1}\Delta\mathbf{g}^{(0)} \qquad (4.38)$$

and

$$a = \frac{1}{\mathbf{u}^T\Delta\mathbf{g}^{(0)}}, \qquad (4.39)$$

which can be plugged into equation 4.35 to give $\mathbf{H}_1^{-1}$. Generalizing to an iterative solution, equations 4.35, 4.38, and 4.39 become

$$\mathbf{H}_{k+1}^{-1} = \mathbf{H}_k^{-1} + \frac{(\Delta\mathbf{x}^{(k)} - \mathbf{H}_k^{-1}\Delta\mathbf{g}^{(k)})(\Delta\mathbf{x}^{(k)} - \mathbf{H}_k^{-1}\Delta\mathbf{g}^{(k)})^T}{(\Delta\mathbf{x}^{(k)} - \mathbf{H}_k^{-1}\Delta\mathbf{g}^{(k)})^T\Delta\mathbf{g}^{(k)}}, \qquad (4.40)$$

and

$$\mathbf{x}^{(k+1)} = \mathbf{x}^{(k)} - \alpha\mathbf{H}_k^{-1}\mathbf{g}^{(k)}. \qquad (4.41)$$

The rank-one quasi-Newton scheme suffers from two problems. First, $\mathbf{g}^{(k)}$ does not in general maintain the positive-definite property, so we don't always go downhill. Second, the denominator in equation 4.40 might be near or equal to zero, leading to stability problems (Fletcher, 1980).

Rank-two quasi-Newton method

The rank-one quasi-Newton method can be improved by a rank-two update, i.e.,

$$\mathbf{H}_{k+1}^{-1} = \mathbf{H}_k^{-1} + a\mathbf{u}\mathbf{u}^T + b\mathbf{v}\mathbf{v}^T, \qquad (4.42)$$

in which the $N \times 1$ vectors $\mathbf{u}$ and $\mathbf{v}$ and constants a and b are chosen to satisfy the quasi-Newton formula in equation 4.34. Plugging equation 4.42 into equation 4.34 gives

$$(a\mathbf{u}\mathbf{u}^T + b\mathbf{v}\mathbf{v}^T)\Delta\mathbf{g}^{(k)} = \Delta\mathbf{x}^{(k)} - \mathbf{H}_k^{-1}\Delta\mathbf{g}^{(k)}. \qquad (4.43)$$

Obvious choices for $\mathbf{u}$ and $\mathbf{v}$ are

$$\mathbf{u} = \Delta\mathbf{x}^{(k)}, \qquad (4.44)$$

$$\mathbf{v} = -\mathbf{H}_k^{-1}\Delta\mathbf{g}^{(k)}, \qquad (4.45)$$

and for a and b are

$$a = \frac{1}{\mathbf{u}^T\Delta\mathbf{g}^{(k)}}, \qquad (4.46)$$

$$b = \frac{1}{\mathbf{v}^T\Delta\mathbf{g}^{(k)}}, \qquad (4.47)$$

which yields the rank-two quasi-Newton formula

$$\mathbf{H}_{k+1}^{-1} = \mathbf{H}_k^{-1} + \frac{\Delta\mathbf{x}^{(k)}\Delta\mathbf{x}^{(k)T}}{\Delta\mathbf{x}^{(k)T}\Delta\mathbf{g}^{(k)}} - \frac{\mathbf{H}_k^{-1}\Delta\mathbf{g}^{(k)}(\Delta\mathbf{g}^{(k)}\mathbf{H}_k^{-1})^T}{\Delta\mathbf{g}^{(k)T}\mathbf{H}_k^{-1}\Delta\mathbf{g}^{(k)}}. \qquad (4.48)$$

The above equation describes the Davidon-Fletcher-Powell (DFP) formula. With exact line searches, Fletcher (1980) shows the DFP formula outperforms steepest-descent methods and operates with more efficiency than conjugate-gradient approaches. If $\mathbf{H}_0^{-1} = \mathbf{I}$, then the DFP formula reduces to a CG method. According to Nocedal and Wright (p. 197, 1999), "The DFP updating formula is quite effective, but it was soon exceeded by the BFGS formula, which is presently considered to be the most effective of all quasi-Newton updating formulae."

For a large number of unknowns, storing the QN approximation to $\mathbf{H}^{-1}$ is untenable. In this case, a limited-memory QN method is used (Nocedal, 1980; Zhu et al., 1997), which maintains a history of the position vectors and gradients at no more than about 10 iterations. Only vector-vector operations are used to update the operations requiring the $\mathbf{H}_k$-vector product.

4.3 Nonlinear functionals

The quadratic model assumes that the curvature (i.e., elements of $\mathbf{H}$) is constant everywhere. In actual seismic problems, the functional is highly nonlinear and so the curvature values depend on the location in the model space. This means that the linear CG or QN methods, both of which assume a purely quadratic functional, lose their convergence guarantee in N iterations. The typical cure is nonlinear CG or QN with reset where, in the case of CG, the new search direction is along the local gradient direction.

For example, use the CG method until the misfit decrease begins to stall, then reset the search direction to the steepest descent to start a new round of CG iterations. A similar resetting can be carried out for the QN method.

Mackie and Madden (1993) approximate the Newton solution by a truncated CG method, in which the CG iterations are stopped early. At each iteration, the Hessian components remained unchanged. Once an incomplete solution was found, this was used as a new starting model to find a new incomplete solution. AlTheyab and Wang (2013) adopt a similar strategy successfully for full-waveform inversion. In contrast, the nonlinear CG (NLCG) method simply applies the CG algorithm to the functional, where the Hessian matrix values and curvature values implicitly change at each iteration. Conjugacy is weakened because one move is not conjugate to *all* of the previous moves. Rodie and Mackie (2001) show that NLCG and the Mackie-Madden method enjoy similar performance features when applied to magnetotelluric (MT) data. Experience with waveform inversion (AlTheyab et al., 2013) and traveltime tomography (Nemeth et al., 1997) suggests that using a truncated CG to compute the Hessian inverse, and then updating the background velocity model after a few iterations, provides a faster convergence than the NLCG method.

4.4 What really works?

Practical seismic-imaging problems are plagued mainly by strongly nonlinear misfit functions with many local minima and a weak global minimum. Moreover, the physics of the actual wave propagation is not fully modeled in predicting the observed data. These pathologies inhibit the nice convergence properties of the gradient-optimization methods. In the context of full-waveform inversion (FWI), this nonlinearity is equivalent to the cycle-skipping mismatch between the predicted and observed seismic traces.

Therefore, further tricks need to be developed and used to accelerate convergence. For example, Nemeth et al. (1997) successfully use the preconditioned steepest-descent method in conjunction with a multigrid-like method to avoid getting stuck in a local minimum. Using smooth low-wavenumber models in the initial iterations often seems to yield a smooth misfit function with fewer local minima and a global minimum in the general vicinity of the actual model. A similar multigrid-like method, also known as a multiscale method, is used now for waveform inversion (Bunks et al., 1995) to mitigate the local minima problem. For mathematicians, a general multigrid procedure for solving nonlinear optimization problems is described by Kornhuber (1998), who notes that monotone multigrid methods begin by choosing a neighborhood of the smoothed iterate that allows linearization. The coarse-grid correction is constrained to that neighborhood. This type of local linearization allows local corrections to be made at every coarse-grid node, so the energy functional decreases monotonically.

My empirical experience with both traveltime and waveform tomography suggests numerical line-search methods are always superior to the exact formulas for step-length calculations. Specifying trust regions (by trial and error) for step-length calculations seems to be mandatory for efficient convergence. Reweighted least squares is probably the right thing to use when data are polluted with large outliers, and regularization terms obtained from a priori information about the model are very useful. Preconditioning the original problem for waveform inversion is a necessity for at least doubling the convergence rate; for example, using the diagonal preconditioning matrix with $[\mathbf{M}]_{ii}^{-1}$ equal to the reciprocal of the Hessian diagonals corrects for geometric spreading and doubles the convergence rate of the CG method (Luo and Schuster, 1991a). Empirical evidence[2] suggests that the quasi-Newton method can more than double the rate of convergence when applied to CG for least-squares migration. Eliminating events not modeled by the computer simulations is very important. The above blend of methods is my current approach to solving practical seismic imaging problems.

4.5 Summary

An overview of the CG and QN gradient-optimization methods is given for solving nonlinear and linear systems of equations. The conjugate-gradient method is similar to the steepest descent method, except each direction of descent is along a mutually conjugate direction such that $(\mathbf{d}^{(i)}, \mathbf{H}\mathbf{d}^{(j)}) = (\mathbf{g}^{(i)}, \mathbf{g}^{(j)}) = 0$ if $i \neq j$. The descent direction $\mathbf{d}^{(k)}$ at the kth iteration is chosen to be along the plane spanned by the previous descent direction $\mathbf{d}^{(k-1)}$ and the gradient $\mathbf{g}^{(k)}$ at the kth solution. This new descent direction points to the misfit bullseye in this plane, where $\mathbf{g}^{(k+1)} \perp \mathbf{d}^{(k)}$. This is the consequence of $\mathbf{d}^{(k)}$ being conjugate to $\mathbf{d}^{(k-1)}$. Each iterative solution minimizes the functional in the subspace spanned by all the previous moves.

In practice, CG methods are used widely by geophysicists because of their minimal $O(N)$ memory and $O(N^2)$ algebraic operations per iteration, and their friendly convergence properties. The convergence rate for an SPD Hessian is linear. An alternative is the quasi-Newton method, which iteratively estimates the Hessian inverse; the drawback is that the inverse Hessian matrix must be stored using $O(N^2)$ memory locations unless a limited-memory approach is used. The convergence rate for a QN method with an SPD

---

[2]Personal communication with W. Dai, 2012.

Hessian is superlinear, and typically is better than that of CG.

Major problems in seismic gradient optimization include the following issues.

- Misfit functions are characterized by many local minima in practical tomography problems. A partial remedy is a multiscale regularization in which coarse models are first determined to explain the data, and then the models are refined iteratively with smaller grid spacing (Bunks et al., 1995). Apparently, coarse grid spacing leads to smoother misfit functions so the initial iterations avoid the many local minima present in a misfit function parameterized on a finer grid.
- Incomplete data from limited source-receiver coverage can lead to long, narrow, misfit valleys and nonuniqueness in the solution. Equivalently, many models nearly explain the same data. A partial remedy is to incorporate more data and other types of data into the misfit function, e.g., including both transmission and reflection traveltimes in traveltime tomography.

4.6 Exercises

1. Use MATLAB scripts to find points that minimize the Rosenbrock function by a QN method. Graph out contours of Rosenbrock function and the iterative solutions for each step of CG, preconditioned steepest-descent, and steepest-descent methods.
2. Compare the above performance of the QN to the other methods in minimizing the Rosenbrock function.
3. For a nonlinear functional, the elements of the Hessian matrix change with iteration. Is the Hessian matrix SPD for each iteration in the Rosenbrock minimization? Would this make a difference in the convergence rate? For nonsymmetric positive-definite Hessians, the biconjugate-gradient method is recommended (Press et al., 2007).
4. Derive a rank-three QN method.
5. Is the curvature a function of position for the functional $f(x) = x^2 - 3x + 3$? If $\mathbf{x}$ is an N-vector and $f(\mathbf{x}) = \mathbf{x}^T \mathbf{H} \mathbf{x}$ is a strictly quadratic functional, is the curvature of $f(\mathbf{x})$ a function of position? Explain your reasoning.
6. Show $[\mathbf{X}^T \mathbf{H} \mathbf{X}]_{ij} = \sigma_i \delta_{ij}$, where the ith column of $\mathbf{X}$ is the orthonormal eigenvector $\mathbf{x}_i$.
7. It is often too expensive to compute the exact eigenvectors of the $N \times N$ matrix $\mathbf{H}$ for large values of N. Describe how you might find the eigenvectors for a reduced-size tomography problem (coarser and fewer cells, but same number of shots and receivers), and use interpolation to find the approximate $N \times 1$ eigenvectors. Describe how you might use these approximate eigenvectors in an alternating eigenvector method.

Why would you want to choose only the eigenvectors associated with the largest eigenvalues?

4.7 Computational labs

1. Apply preconditioning to the CG algorithm in the Computational Toolkit under the topic "Conjugate Gradient."

Appendix 4A:
Successive line-minimization methods

The steepest-descent method successively moves along sequential gradient directions. As illustrated in Figure 3.1, the method works well for well-conditioned Hessians (Figure 3.1a) but not as well for ill-conditioned Hessians (Figure 3.1b). The same would be true if we successively moved along sequential coordinate directions $\mathbf{e}_i$. These successive search algorithms belong to the class of line-minimization methods, sometimes referred to as *direction set* methods (Press et al., 2007). That is, to specify a direction of descent $\mathbf{d}^{(k)}$, use a line minimization procedure to find the appropriate step length, and then repeat this procedure with a new direction of descent $\mathbf{d}^{(k+1)}$. Examples include the methods of alternating coordinates, eigenvector direction, and conjugate direction.

Successive-eigenvector and conjugate-direction methods

We define an orthogonal transformation that rotates the coordinate axes so they are lined up with the principle axes of the ellipse, then successively moving along the transformed coordinate directions will converge in N steps (see dashed coordinate system in Figure 3.1a). Such a transformation diagonalizes the Hessian, as will be shown below.

As an example, assume an SPD $N \times N$ Hessian, so that the solution can be expanded into a set of N orthonormal basis vectors $\mathbf{x}_i$ that are eigenvectors of $\mathbf{H}$:

$$\mathbf{x} = \sum_i \alpha_i \mathbf{x}_i, \qquad (4.49)$$

in which

$$\mathbf{x}_j^T \mathbf{x}_i = \delta_{ij},$$

and α_i represents the unknown coefficients. The vector $\mathbf{x}_i$ is an eigenvector of $\mathbf{H}$ so $\mathbf{H} \mathbf{x}_i = \sigma_i \mathbf{x}_i$, where σ_i is the ith eigenvalue. Plugging equation 4.49 into $\mathbf{H} \mathbf{x} = -\mathbf{g}$ gives

$$\sum_i \alpha_i \sigma_i \mathbf{x}_i = -\mathbf{g}, \qquad (4.50)$$

and multiplying both sides by $\mathbf{x}_j^T$ yields

$$\sum_i \alpha_i \sigma_i \mathbf{x}_j^T \mathbf{x}_i = -\mathbf{x}_j^T \mathbf{g}. \qquad (4.51)$$

The basis vectors are orthonormal so the above equation becomes

$$\alpha_j \sigma_j = -\mathbf{x}_j^T \mathbf{g}, \qquad (4.52)$$

and solving for α_j gives

$$\alpha_j = -\mathbf{x}_j^T \mathbf{g}/\sigma_j. \qquad (4.53)$$

Thus, successively moving along eigendirections with step lengths of $-\mathbf{x}_j^T \mathbf{g}/\sigma_j$ will lead to the bullseye in N moves or less. Such eigenvectors diagonalize the Hessian because $[\mathbf{X}^T \mathbf{H} \mathbf{X}]_{ij} = \sigma_i \delta_{ij}$, where the ith column of the $N \times N$ matrix $\mathbf{X}$ consists of the eigenvectors $\mathbf{x}_i$. Unfortunately, diagonalization by, e.g., Jacobi-type methods (Press et al., 2007), is still too expensive for large imaging problems.

Are there nonorthogonal coordinate systems that diagonalize the Hessian? Yes: these systems feature basis vectors that are conjugate to another such that

$$(\mathbf{x}_j, \mathbf{H}\mathbf{x}_i) = \mathbf{x}_j^T \mathbf{H} \mathbf{x}_i = \mathbf{x}_j^T \mathbf{H} \mathbf{x}_i \delta_{ij}. \qquad (4.54)$$

It can be shown for an SPD $\mathbf{H}$ that any arbitrary vector in $\mathbb{R}^N$ can be expanded into a weighted sum of N linearly independent conjugate vectors. Similar to the procedure for getting eigenvector coefficients in equation 4.53, we can show that the jth step length for the search direction is

$$\alpha_j = -\mathbf{x}_j^T \mathbf{g}/(\mathbf{x}_j^T \mathbf{H} \mathbf{x}_j), \qquad (4.55)$$

which is equal to that in equation 4.8 for the conjugate-gradient method. The conjugacy property defined in equation 4.54 says that $\mathbf{X}^T \mathbf{H} \mathbf{X}$ is a diagonal matrix, in which the columns of the $N \times N$ matrix $\mathbf{X}$ are conjugate to one another.

The problem with either the eigendirection or conjugate-direction methods is that they will cost $O(N^3)$ algebraic operations to compute all of the basis vectors. An alternative approach is the conjugate-gradient method, which is similar to the conjugate-direction methods, except it costs only $O(N^2)$ operations per iteration.

Part II

Traveltime Tomography

Chapter 5: Raypath Traveltime Tomography

As discussed in Chapter 1, geophysical traveltime tomography is the procedure for inverting traveltimes of specified body waves for the velocity distribution of the earth. It has been the primary means for earthquake imaging of the Earth's interior from the early 1970s (Aki et al., 1977; Dziewonski and Anderson, 1984; Humphreys et al., 1984; Bishop et al., 1985; Nolet, 1987; Iyer, 1989; Zelt and Smith, 1992; Iyer and Hirahara, 1993). Until recently, it was implemented mostly using the high-frequency approximation of ray tracing, but there is a growing tendency to use finite-frequency tomography (Harlan, 1990; Luo and Schuster, 1991a; Woodward, 1992; Marquering et al., 1999; Montelli et al., 2004), in which traveltime residuals are back projected along wavepaths rather than raypaths. Finite-frequency wave-equation tomography, also known as wave-equation tomography (Woodward, 1992) or wave-equation traveltime tomography (Luo and Schuster, 1991a; Marquering et al., 1999), can be more accurate than raypath tomography. However, it is at least an order of magnitude more costly because the wave equation must be solved numerically for each source. Traveltime tomography also is used in a variety of other fields, such as medical imaging (Duric et al., 2007), nondestructive evaluation (Leonard et al., 2002), and meteorology (Ostashev et al., 2009).

In this chapter, we introduce the raypath traveltime-tomography method. Ray theory is used to compute raypaths between the sources and receivers, and the weighted traveltime residuals are smeared along these raypaths to update the model. The velocity tomogram is the starting model for the next iteration, and rays typically are recomputed because the model variations perturb the rays.

5.1 Perturbed traveltime integral

The three-dimensional (3D) eikonal equation (see equation 5.43)

$$|\nabla t(\mathbf{x})|^2 = \left|\frac{\partial t(\mathbf{x})}{\partial x}\right|^2 + \left|\frac{\partial t(\mathbf{x})}{\partial y}\right|^2 + \left|\frac{\partial t(\mathbf{x})}{\partial z}\right|^2 = s(\mathbf{x})^2 \quad (5.1)$$

can be used to derive the traveltime integral associated with a perturbed slowness medium. Here, $t(\mathbf{x})$ is the traveltime

for an event to propagate from a source to a specified receiver, and $s(\mathbf{x})$ is the slowness distribution.

The traveltime integral is the keystone equation by which the slowness model can be updated efficiently in traveltime tomography. Its derivation starts with defining the slowness perturbation $\delta s(\mathbf{x})$ from a background slowness field $s(\mathbf{x})$. The corresponding perturbed traveltime field is defined as $t(\mathbf{x}) + \delta t(\mathbf{x})$, in which $t(\mathbf{x})$ is the unperturbed traveltime field in the background model and $\delta t(\mathbf{x})$ is the traveltime perturbation arising from the slowness perturbation. The perturbed traveltime field honors the eikonal equation[1]

$$|\nabla t(\mathbf{x}) + \nabla \delta t(\mathbf{x})|^2 = |\nabla t(\mathbf{x})|^2 + 2\nabla \delta t(\mathbf{x}) \cdot \nabla t(\mathbf{x}) + |\nabla \delta t(\mathbf{x})|^2,$$
$$= [s(\mathbf{x})]^2 + 2\delta s(\mathbf{x})s(\mathbf{x}) + [\delta s(\mathbf{x})]^2. \quad (5.2)$$

Subtracting the unperturbed eikonal equation 5.1 from equation 5.2, we get

$$2\nabla t(\mathbf{x}) \cdot \nabla \delta t(\mathbf{x}) + |\nabla \delta t(\mathbf{x})|^2 = 2\delta s(\mathbf{x})s(\mathbf{x}) + [\delta s(\mathbf{x})]^2. \quad (5.3)$$

Neglecting the second-order terms in the perturbation parameters, this becomes

$$\nabla t(\mathbf{x}) \cdot \nabla \delta t(\mathbf{x}) = |\nabla t(\mathbf{x})| \, d\hat{\mathbf{l}} \cdot \nabla \delta t(\mathbf{x})$$
$$= \delta s(\mathbf{x})s(\mathbf{x}), \quad (5.4)$$

in which $d\hat{\mathbf{l}}$ is defined to be the unit vector parallel to the unperturbed ray direction, so $\nabla t(\mathbf{x}) = |\nabla t(\mathbf{x})| \, d\hat{\mathbf{l}}$.

Defining the directional derivative along $d\hat{\mathbf{l}}$ to be $d/dl = d\hat{\mathbf{l}} \cdot \nabla$ (this directional derivative is determined by the background slowness distribution, not the perturbed medium), and dividing equation 5.4 by $|\nabla t(\mathbf{x})| = s(\mathbf{x})$ gives

$$d\delta t(\mathbf{x})/dl = \delta s(\mathbf{x}), \quad (5.5)$$

---

[1]An eikonal equation has the general form $|\nabla u| = F(\mathbf{x})$, $\mathbf{x} \in \Omega$, and $u|_{\partial\Omega} = 0$, in which $F > 0$ usually is given and $\partial\Omega$ defines the boundary points that enclose the volume Ω. The solution $u(\mathbf{x})$ usually is interpreted as the shortest time it takes for a wave to travel from the boundary to the point $\mathbf{x}$ inside the volume Ω.

or by rearrangement, gives the Fréchet derivative of the traveltime perturbation with respect to the slowness variation

$$d\delta t(\mathbf{x})/\delta s = dl. \qquad (5.6)$$

The Fréchet derivative is used to assess the sensitivity of the data with respect to perturbations in the slowness.

Multiplying both sides of equation 5.5 by dl and integrating along the old raypath from the source to the listener at $\mathbf{x}$ yields the perturbed traveltime integral

$$\delta t(\mathbf{x}) = \int_{\text{raypath}} \delta s(\mathbf{x}')dl', \qquad (5.7)$$

which is first-order correct in the perturbation parameters. The integration path denoted by the term raypath is an implicit function of the source location and the listener located at $\mathbf{x}$.

Equation 5.7 says that the traveltime perturbation arising from a slowness perturbation is given by an integration over the old raypath weighted by the slowness perturbation. This can be a cost-efficient computation because the traveltime perturbation calculation uses the old raypaths and does not require retracing of rays through the perturbed slowness model.

5.2 Raypath traveltime tomography

An overdetermined system of linear equations has more equations than unknowns. For example, the 4×2 system of equations symbolized by $\mathbf{Ls} = \mathbf{t}$ is given by

$$\begin{bmatrix} 0 & 1 \\ 0 & 1 \\ 1 & 1 \\ 0.7 & 1 \end{bmatrix} \cdot \begin{pmatrix} s_1 \\ s_2 \end{pmatrix} = \begin{pmatrix} 0.5 \\ 0.4 \\ 1 \\ 1 \end{pmatrix}. \qquad (5.8)$$

These equations are *inconsistent* when no solution can simultaneously satisfy all of the equations. For example, the first and second equations conflict with each other.

A physical example related to equation 5.8 is the tomographic imaging experiment shown in Figure 5.1. The traveltime for each ray is governed by equation 5.7, and the velocity model is discretized into N cells of unknown constant slowness. The traveltime integral can be approximated by a weighted summation

$$t_i = \sum_{j=1}^{N} l_{ij} s_j, \qquad (5.9)$$

over the segment lengths l_{ij} of the ith ray that intersect the jth cells, where we assume M traveltime picks in the data set. This results in an $M \times N$ system of equations,

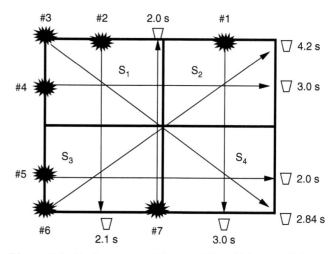

Figure 5.1. Each square cell has a width of 1 km, straight rays are denoted by thin arrows and traveltimes are associated with direct waves traveling from sources (stars) to receivers (buckets), respectively.

denoted in matrix-vector notation as $\mathbf{Ls} = \mathbf{t}$, in which $\mathbf{t}$ represents the measured $M \times 1$ traveltime data vector, and $\mathbf{s}$ is the $N \times 1$ vector of unknown slownesses in the cells. The $M \times N$ matrix $\mathbf{L}$ contains the segment lengths of the rays.

The goal is to solve the system of equations 5.9 and find the unknown slowness value s_j in each cell, which is illustrated by the velocity tomogram in Figure 1.1. Geometrically, equations 5.8 plot as the dashed straight lines shown in Figure 5.2, and no common intersection point means that the equations are inconsistent. In practice, this inconsistency is caused by traveltime picking errors and/or because the physics used to model the data is incomplete. Inexistence of a solution violates one of the Hadamard (1902) criteria for a well-posed solution discussed in Chapter 1.

Although there is no *exact* solution to equation 5.8, we would be happy with an approximate solution "near" the densest intersection of lines. Such a compromise is the least-squares solution which minimizes the objective functional denoted[2] as ϵ:

$$\epsilon = \frac{1}{2} [\mathbf{Ls} - \mathbf{t}]^T [\mathbf{Ls} - \mathbf{t}],$$

$$= \frac{1}{2} \sum_{i=1}^{4} \sum_{j=1}^{2} (l_{ij} s_j - t_i)^2,$$

$$= \frac{1}{2} \sum_{i=1}^{4} r_i^2, \qquad (5.10)$$

in which $r_i = \sum_j l_{ij} s_j - t_i$ is the ith residual, i.e., the difference between the ith component of the predicted traveltime and the observed traveltime. If the rays bend, then the

---

[2]In previous chapters, we used $f(\mathbf{x})$ to denote the objective functional, but we now will switch to the ϵ notation often used in geophysical literature.

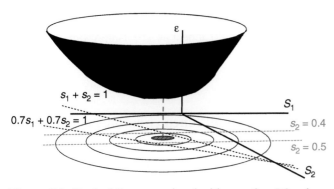

Figure 5.2. Dashed lines associated with equation 5.8, where the equations are inconsistent and there is no common intersection point. Above the least-squares solution (red oval) is the error surface described by ϵ. Note, the contours are elongated along the $\hat{s}_1$ direction so that many models along the oval valley nearly fit the same data.

matrix elements in equation 5.8 depend on the unknowns **s**. In this case, the traveltime equations are nonlinear and the rays must be recomputed for the new slowness model after each iteration.

Plotting the misfit value against s_1 and s_2 yields the error bowl shown in Figure 5.2. The bottom of this error bowl is directly over the optimal solution $\mathbf{s}^*$, which is also the least-squares solution. There is a bottom to this error bowl, so we know a least-squares solution exists.

Finding the optimal solution by examination of Figure 5.2 might be convenient for systems of equations with just a few unknowns, but it is impractical for many unknowns. A more systematic approach is to recognize that at the bottom of the error bowl, the partial derivatives $\partial\epsilon/\partial s_k = 0$ are simultaneously zero for all values of k:

$$\partial\epsilon/\partial s_k = \sum_{i=1}^{4}\sum_{j=1}^{2}\left[(l_{ij}s_j - t_i)l_{ij}\frac{\partial s_j}{\partial s_k} + (l_{ij}s_j - t_i)s_j\frac{\partial l_{ij}}{\partial s_k}\right],$$

$$\approx \sum_{i=1}^{4}\sum_{j=1}^{2}(l_{ij}s_j - t_i)l_{ij}\delta_{jk}, \qquad (5.11)$$

in which the Kronecker delta function $\delta_{jk} = 1$ if $j = k$, otherwise it is equal to zero. The far-right term $s_j\,\partial l_{ij}/\partial s_k(\sum_j l_{ij}s_j - t_i)$ in equation 5.11 often is neglected, partly because it is too expensive to compute and partly because $\partial l_{ij}/\partial s_k$ can be quite small when the background slowness model is sufficiently close to the actual model. Of course, if the ray geometry does not change with slowness variations, then $\partial l_{ij}/\partial s_k$ would be identically zero. Equation 5.11 gives rise to the Gauss-Newton method (Gill et al., 1981) for solving an overdetermined system of equations. If $|s_j\,\partial l_{ij}/\partial s_k|$ is of the same order as $|l_{ij}\,\partial s_j/\partial s_k|$, then retaining the second term leads to the Gauss-Newton

method of large residuals (Gill et al., 1981). See exercises 13 and 14 and Chapter 26.

Therefore,

$$\partial\epsilon/\partial s_k = \sum_{i=1}^{4}(l_{ik}s_k - t_i)l_{ik},$$

$$= [\mathbf{L}^T(\mathbf{Ls} - \mathbf{t})]_k = 0 \quad k = 1, 2, \qquad (5.12)$$

is the gradient for the Gauss-Newton method (Gill et al., 1981). Here, the kth component of the gradient vector is denoted by $[\mathbf{L}^T(\mathbf{Ls} - \mathbf{t})]_k$.

5.2.1 Normal equations

Equation 5.12 can be written more compactly as

$$\mathbf{L}^T\mathbf{Ls} = \mathbf{L}^T\mathbf{t}, \qquad (5.13)$$

and represents the normal equations. In this case, $\mathbf{L}^T\mathbf{L}$ is a symmetric 2×2 matrix and the two unknowns s_1 and s_2 can be solved by inverting the above matrix to give the least-squares solution denoted as $\mathbf{s}^*$.

For a general $M \times N$ system of linear equations, equation 5.13 is used to solve for the least-squares solution that minimizes the sum of the squared residuals. Equation 5.13 is called the normal system of equations because the equations can be rearranged and multiplied by $\mathbf{s}^T$ to give

$$(\mathbf{Ls}, \overbrace{\mathbf{Ls} - \mathbf{t}}^{\mathbf{r}}) = 0, \qquad (5.14)$$

which says that the optimal solution $\mathbf{s}^*$ is the one in which the residual vector $\mathbf{r} = \mathbf{Ls} - \mathbf{t}$ is normal to the predicted traveltime vector $\mathbf{Ls}$, as illustrated in Figure 5.3.

What kind of matrix $\mathbf{L}$ is associated with the diagram in Figure 5.3? For $\mathbf{s} = (s_1, s_2)$, $\mathbf{L} = [a\ b; c\ d; 0\ 0]$, because $\mathbf{Ls} = \mathbf{t}$ can be expressed as a sum of column vectors

$$\begin{bmatrix} a \\ c \\ 0 \end{bmatrix}s_1 + \begin{bmatrix} b \\ d \\ 0 \end{bmatrix}s_2 = \begin{pmatrix} t_1 \\ t_2 \\ t_3 \end{pmatrix}, \qquad (5.15)$$

in which each column vector is one of the column vectors in $\mathbf{L}$, and a, b, c, and d are the matrix coefficients. The last component of these column vectors is zero, so no weighted linear combination of them can create a component that lives in the t_3 dimension shown in Figure 5.3. In other words, the columns of $\mathbf{L}$ only span the horizontal plane formed by the $\hat{t}_1$ and $\hat{t}_2$ basis vectors.

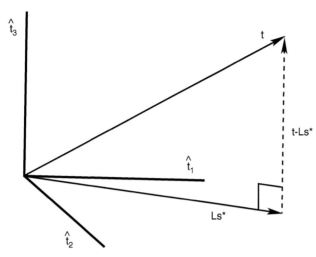

Figure 5.3. The least-squares solution finds the optimal $\mathbf{s}^*$ so that the residual $\mathbf{t} - \mathbf{Ls}^*$ is orthogonal to the predicted traveltimes given by $\mathbf{Ls}^*$.

Exercises 5.2.1

1. Write the 7×4 system of traveltime equations $\mathbf{Ls} = \mathbf{t}$ associated with the traveltime data in Figure 5.1.
2. From the traveltime equations generated in the previous problem, find the least-squares solution $\mathbf{s}$ in MATLAB® by typing $s = inv(L' * L) * L' * t$. Form the squared length of the residual vector (i.e., $||t^{predict} - t^{observed}||^2$) by typing $e = (L * s - t)' * (L * s - t)$. Are the equations consistent or inconsistent? Why?
3. There are nonunique solutions to $\mathbf{Ls} = \mathbf{t}$ if any column vector in $\mathbf{L}$ is a linear combination of the other column vectors, otherwise the column vectors are linearly independent. Are the columns in $\mathbf{L}$ linearly independent? A numerical check for a poorly conditioned system of SPD equations is to determine the condition number (maximum eigenvalue/mininimum eigenvalue) by typing $cond(L' * L)$. Large values of the condition number indicate that the columns are nearly linearly independent.
4. Find the least-squares solution for $L = [1\ 2; 2\ 1; 4\ 1]$ and $t = [3;\ 3;\ 5]$. Are the equations consistent or inconsistent? Why? Plot out each of the equations with the following commands.

```
s=inv(L'*L)*L'*t;
x=[-5:5];
for i=1:3;
   plot(x,(t(i)-L(i,1)*x)/L(i,2));
   hold on;
end
xlabel('x');ylabel('y');
plot(s(1),s(2),'*');
hold off;
axis([-5 5 -5 5]);
```

Does the least-squares solution (labeled as * in the MATLAB graph) appear as a best approximate solution to all three equations?

5.2.2 Poorly conditioned equations and regularization

The condition number of $\mathbf{L}^T\mathbf{L}$ can be large, and therefore, many different solutions can yield nearly the same value of ϵ in equation 5.10. This is an example of an *unstable* or ill-conditioned inverse problem. To clarify this statement, consider the system of equations

$$\begin{bmatrix} \kappa_1 & 0 \\ 0 & \kappa_2 \\ \kappa_1 & 0 \end{bmatrix} \cdot \begin{pmatrix} s_1 \\ s_2 \end{pmatrix} = \begin{pmatrix} 1 \\ 1 \\ 3 \end{pmatrix}, \qquad (5.16)$$

in which $\kappa_2 \gg \kappa_1 \approx 0$. The corresponding normal equations are

$$\begin{bmatrix} 2\kappa_1^2 & 0 \\ 0 & \kappa_2^2 \end{bmatrix} \cdot \begin{pmatrix} s_1 \\ s_2 \end{pmatrix} = \begin{pmatrix} 4\kappa_1 \\ \kappa_2 \end{pmatrix}, \qquad (5.17)$$

in which the condition number (i.e., maximum eigenvalue/minimum eigenvalue = $0.5\kappa_2^2/\kappa_1^2$) is very large. This means that quite different values of s_1 give about the same value for the objective function ϵ. Equivalently, the objective function, similar to the one shown in Figure 5.2, is characterized by a long, narrow valley along the s_1 axis, where ϵ is somewhat insensitive to large changes in the parameter value of s_1.

In fact, if $\kappa_1 = 0$, then the null space of $\mathbf{L}^T\mathbf{L}$ is nonempty and is spanned by the null-space vector $(1\ \ 0)^T$. Any scaled value of this null-space vector will not change the residual value, and therefore can contaminate the solution with unrealistic model features. This is an example of nonuniqueness in the inverse problem and violates one of Hadamard's conditions for a well-posed solution.

To avoid nonuniqueness, we add a model penalty function into the objective function, i.e.,

$$\epsilon = 1/2||\mathbf{Ls} - \mathbf{t}||^2 + 1/2\eta^2||\mathbf{s} - \mathbf{s}^0||^2, \qquad (5.18)$$

in which η^2 is a small damping parameter and $\mathbf{s}^0$ is an a priori guess to the solution. The constraint says that we wish to find $\mathbf{s}$ that minimizes the sum of the squared residuals and is close to the a priori guess at $\mathbf{s}^0$. The degree of closeness is determined by the value of η^2. For traveltime tomography, this regularization term can be estimated to ensure errors are not fitted into the smoothed model (Lizarralde and Swift, 1999).

The normal equations associated with this constrained objective function are obtained by differentiating ϵ to give

$$\partial \epsilon / \partial s_k = \sum_i \sum_j (l_{ij} s_j - t_i) l_{ij} \delta_{jk} + \eta^2 (s_k - s_k^0) = 0,$$

$$(5.19)$$

or more compactly,

$$[\mathbf{L}^T \mathbf{L} + \eta^2 \mathbf{I}] \mathbf{s} = \mathbf{L}^T \mathbf{t} + \eta^2 \mathbf{s}^0. \qquad (5.20)$$

The solution to this system of equations

$$\mathbf{s} = [\mathbf{L}^T \mathbf{L} + \eta^2 \mathbf{I}]^{-1} (\mathbf{L}^T \mathbf{t} + \eta^2 \mathbf{s}^0) \qquad (5.21)$$

is known by a variety of names: the Levenberg-Marquardt, damped least-squares, or the regularized least-squares solution. In the case of equation 5.17, the solution becomes $s_1 = 4\kappa_1/(2\kappa_1^2 + \eta^2)$ and $s_2 = \kappa_2/(\kappa_2^2 + \eta^2)$ if $\mathbf{s}^0 = 0$. Note that the condition number $(\kappa_2^2 + \eta^2)/(2\kappa_1^2 + \eta^2)$ is improved with damping at the cost of somewhat diminished accuracy. There are several ways to select the optimal value for η^2, as illustrated in Figure 3.5.

Other constraint equations include a roughness penalty function $R(s(\mathbf{x}))$ that employs nth-order derivatives of the slowness function

$$R(s(\mathbf{x})) = \int \left[\left(\frac{\partial^n s(\mathbf{x})}{\partial x^n} \right)^2 + \left(\frac{\partial^n s(\mathbf{x})}{\partial y^n} \right)^2 + \left(\frac{\partial^n s(\mathbf{x})}{\partial z^n} \right)^2 \right] d\mathbf{x},$$

$$(5.22)$$

in which rough solutions are discouraged in favor of smoother solutions. Zhang and Toksöz (1998) compare the performance of these roughness constraints and show for their examples that $n = 2$ or $n = 4$ provide superior performance compared to $n = 0$ or $n = 1$. Their empirical tests suggest the superiority of using a weighted sum of two misfit functions: one is denoted as the average slowness misfit $\sum_i (t_i - t_i^{\text{obs}})^2 / l_i^2$ inversely weighted with squared raypath lengths l_i^2, and the other one $\sum_i (dt_i/dx - dt_i^{\text{obs}}/dx)^2$ consists of the slopes of traveltime curves. The former tends to emphasize reconstruction of shallow velocities because it equalizes the magnitudes of both long and short traveltimes, although the latter requires fitting the slopes of a traveltime curve rather than the absolute traveltimes. They claim that this emphasizes the inversion of longer wavelength features at deeper depths.

Exercises 5.2.2

1. For the system of equations $\mathbf{Ls} = \mathbf{t}$, $\mathbf{L} = [1\ 2; 2\ 1; 4\ 1]$, and $\mathbf{t} = [3; 3; 5]$, assume that the RHS of the first equation contains strong errors with a variance of 22. To correct for this error, one strategy might be to premultiply the system of equations by a diagonal-like matrix $\mathbf{W} = [1/22\ 0\ 0; 0\ 1\ 0; 0\ 0\ 1]$, in which the first equation has been downweighted by the inverse variance. Try downweighting other rows by adjusting values of W and then rerun the MATLAB script below.

```
W=[1/22 0 0;0 1 0; 0 0 1];
L=W*L;t=W*t;
s=inv(L'*L)*L'*t;
x=[-5:5];
for i=1:3;
   plot(x,(t(i)-L(i,1)*x)/L(i,2));
   hold on;
end
xlabel('x');
ylabel('y');
plot(s(1),s(2),'*');
hold off;
axis([-5 5 -5 5]);
```

Explain how the solution changes as you downweight an equation.

2. Plot the misfit function for a range of $(s(1), s(2))$ values for the system of equations defined below.

```
L=[1 2; 2 4; 3 7];
t= [3 ; 6 ; 9];
xstart=-30;
xend=30;
hold off;
for i=xstart:xend;
   ii=i-xstart+1;
   for j=xstart:xend
      jj=j-xstart+1;
      xx=[i j];
      eps(ii,jj)=(L*xx'-t)'*(L*xx'-t);
   end;
end
imagesc([xstart:xend],[xstart:xend],eps');
colorbar;
hold on;
x=[xstart:xend];
for m=1:3;
   plot(x,(-L(m,1)*x+t(m))/L(m,2),'-w');
end;
title('Sum of Squared Error Misfit Function')
xlabel('x');ylabel('y')
```

Are the equations consistent or inconsistent? Why? Are the lines nearly parallel? Why should nearly parallel lines lead to an ill-posed system of equations?

3. Solve the previous problem by a damped least-squares method for different values of η^2.

5.2.3 Reweighted least squares

Some traveltime picks might be unreliable, which suggests that the noisy traveltime equations should be downweighted relative to the reliable ones. The weighting values can be selected by assuming the picking error for the ith traveltime is a random variable with zero mean and a standard deviation σ_i. Then, the noisiest traveltime equations might be downweighted with $w_{ii} = 1/\sigma_i^2$, so the weighted objective function in equation 5.18 becomes

$$\epsilon = 1/2||\mathbf{W}^{1/2}(\mathbf{Ls} - \mathbf{t})||^2 = 1/2 \sum_{i=1}^{M} \left(\frac{r_i}{\sigma_i}\right)^2, \quad (5.23)$$

in which the ith component of the $M \times 1$ residual vector is $r_i = (\mathbf{Ls} - \mathbf{t})_i$ and $\mathbf{W}$ is the $M \times M$ diagonal matrix[3] with elements $w_{ij} = \delta_{ij}/\sigma_i^2$.

Equation 5.23 is the data misfit function for the weighted least-squares method (Press et al., 2007), in which the kth component of the gradient is

$$\partial\epsilon/\partial s_k = \sum_{i=1} w_{ii} r_i(\mathbf{x}) \partial r_i/\partial s_k,$$

$$= \sum_i w_{ii}(l_{ik} s_k - t_i) l_{ik},$$

$$= [\mathbf{L}^T \mathbf{W}(\mathbf{Ls} - \mathbf{t})]_k. \quad (5.24)$$

Setting the above equation to zero and solving for $\mathbf{s}$ gives the linearized Newton solution

$$\mathbf{s} = [\mathbf{L}^T \mathbf{W}\mathbf{L}]^{-1} \mathbf{L}^T \mathbf{W}\mathbf{t}. \quad (5.25)$$

If the starting model $\tilde{\mathbf{s}}$ predicts the traveltimes $\tilde{\mathbf{t}} = \tilde{\mathbf{L}}\tilde{\mathbf{s}} \neq \mathbf{t}$, then the data residual is $\delta\mathbf{t} = \tilde{\mathbf{t}} - \mathbf{t}$ and

$$\mathbf{s} = \tilde{\mathbf{s}} - [\mathbf{L}^T \mathbf{W}\mathbf{L}]^{-1} \mathbf{L}^T \mathbf{W}\delta\mathbf{t}, \quad (5.26)$$

in which $\mathbf{L} = \tilde{\mathbf{L}}$ is assumed.

For a nonlinear problem in which the ray trajectories in the $\mathbf{s}$ model are significantly different than those in the $\tilde{\mathbf{s}}$ model, we have the iterative nonlinear method known as the weighted Gauss-Newton solution

$$\mathbf{s}^{(k+1)} = \mathbf{s}^{(k)} - \alpha[(\mathbf{L}^T\mathbf{W}^{(k)}\mathbf{L})^{(k)}]^{-1}\mathbf{L}^{(k)T}\mathbf{W}^{(k)}\delta\mathbf{t}^{(k)}, \quad (5.27)$$

in which $\delta\mathbf{t}^{(k)}$ is the traveltime residual vector at the kth iteration. The raypath lengths in $\mathbf{L}^{(k)}$ depend on the slowness

value $\mathbf{s}^{(k)}$ and should be updated every iteration. In practice, the Hessian inverse is too expensive to compute, so a linear steepest-descent (SD), conjugate-gradient (CG), or quasi-Newton (QN) method is used for five or so iterations to approximate the update direction. With the linear CG method, the raypath trajectories are not updated for about five iterations, and then at, say, the sixth iteration, the raypaths and their segment lengths are used to update $\mathbf{L}^{(k)}$. In this case, the CG iterations are restarted every sixth iteration with the initial search direction parallel to the misfit gradient. This hybrid strategy is used in waveform inversion (AlTheyab and Wang, 2013), and also is known as the truncated Newton method (Gill et al., 1981). Preconditioning is important here because we hope to move downhill quickly in about five steps, which is more likely with a well-conditioned set of equations.

The problem with equation 5.27 is that the variance of traveltime picks is not well known, which can be disastrous if large outliers are included in the inversion. To alleviate this problem, we allow the algorithm to weight each traveltime with the absolute reciprocal of the residual at each iteration. This adaptive strategy is known as the reweighted least-squares (RLS) algorithm, in which the diagonal elements of $\mathbf{W}$ in equation 5.27 are assigned to be

$$w_{ii} = \begin{cases} 1/|r_i|^{2-p} & if \ |r_i| > \beta \\ 1/\beta^{2-p} & if \ |r_i| \leq \beta \end{cases}, \quad (5.28)$$

where $|r_i|$ is the data residual at the kth iteration. Here, β acts as a damping term that avoids unstable divides by zero when the residual is close to zero.[4] This choice of weighting is sufficient to guarantee the convergence of iterative, reweighted least squares. If $p = 1$, Appendix 5B shows that the above weighting scheme leads to the RLS solution that minimizes the l_1 normed misfit function

$$\epsilon = \sum_i |r_i|. \quad (5.29)$$

If $p = 2$, the weights are unity so that equation 5.23 reduces to that of unweighted least squares. The l_1 norm solution downweights large picking errors because $w_{ii} \approx 0$ for $r_i \gg 0$, although the l_2 solution is highly sensitive to such large outliers. One strategy is to set $1 < p < 2$ so that both stability and unique solubility (Scales and Gersztenkorn, 1988; Bube and Langan, 1994) can be achieved.

---

[3]The motivation for choosing $w_{ii} = 1/\sigma_i^2$ can be traced to maximum likelihood estimators (Press et al., 2007), when the most probable model is the one that maximizes the normal distribution function $P(d|m) \approx e^{-\epsilon}$, in which ϵ is the expression in equation 5.23. Therefore, the most probable model is the one that minimizes ϵ, which is the weighted least-squares solution.

[4]As described in Scales and Gersztenkorn (1988), one should normalize the elements of w_{ii} to lie between β/r_{max} and 1 to improve convergence (Gersztenkorn et al., 1986).

Example 5.2.1. Reweighted least squares and straight-ray tomography

The reweighted least-squares method is applied to traveltimes generated by straight raytracing in the Figure 5.4a and 5.4b models. The example is that of a transmission experiment in which the model is gridded into a 20×20 grid of cells with 400 unknown slowness. There are 20 sources evenly distributed along the bottom boundary of the model, and each source shoots a straight ray into each of the 20 evenly distributed receivers along the top boundary of the model. This gives rise to 400 traveltimes that are used as input data into the least-squares Gauss-Newton method. The model and data are linearly related because the raypaths are fixed as straight rays.

The damped least-squares solution results in the reconstructed models shown in Figures 5.4c and 5.4d. In this case, the vertical-layered model is best resolved, and the horizontal layered model is least resolved. This is because the best resolution is achieved for rays that are perpendicular to the direction of velocity variations, so that the nearly vertical rays are best at resolving layered models with nearly vertical interfaces. See Chapters 6 and 14 for a mathematical treatment of the resolution problem.

For example, simply dividing the raypath length by the traveltime for a vertical ray passing through one vertical layer will yield the exact velocity of that layer. Hence, the velocity values in a sequence of vertical layers (i.e., a model with strictly horizontal velocity variations) can be reconstructed uniquely by inverting traveltimes associated with vertical rays. Conversely, if the model consists of horizontal layers with equal thickness, then the raypath lengths divided by the traveltimes will yield only the average velocity of the layers. In fact, the layer velocities can be exchanged with one another and still yield the same predicted traveltimes. Thus, the solution is nonunique when there is more than one slowness model that satisfies the same data.

The least-squares solution can handle Gaussian noise adequately, but it will have difficulty with large outliers in the traveltime errors. As an example, Figure 5.5 depicts the tomograms for standard and reweighted least-squares inversion when the traveltime data are contaminated with noise. The noise consists of zero-mean, 1% Gaussian noise added to the traveltimes, and six picks have more than 500% error. The reweighted least-squares method gives the Figure 5.5b tomogram with less than half the errors in the standard tomogram shown in Figure 5.5a. It is obvious that the influence of the large outliers is suppressed by the reweighted least-squares method.

5.3 Iterative steepest-descent solution

Setting $\mathbf{W}$ to be the identity matrix in equation 5.27 yields the least-squares Gauss-Newton formula

$$\mathbf{s}^{(k+1)} = \mathbf{s}^{(k)} - \alpha[\mathbf{L}^T\mathbf{L} + \eta^2\mathbf{I}]^{-1}\mathbf{L}^T\delta\mathbf{t}, \qquad (5.30)$$

in which the k superscript is taken conveniently to be silent in the residual vector and raypath matrix. The problem with realistic tomography problems is that there can be anywhere from tens of thousands to more than a million unknowns. This means that the cost of matrix storage and directly

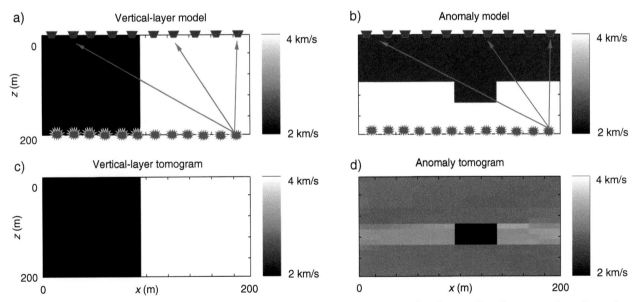

Figure 5.4. (a) Vertical layer and (b) anomaly models and tomograms in (c) and (d). The ray directions are oriented mostly along the vertical axis, so the vertical-layer model with layering parallel to the rays is best resolved (courtesy of G. Waite).

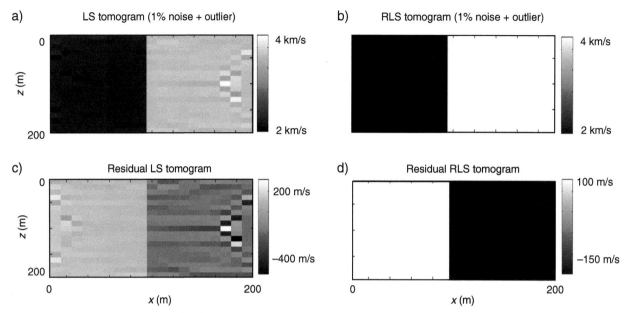

Figure 5.5. Velocity tomograms obtained by (a) damped least squares and (b) reweighted damped least squares (RLS) for the vertical-layer model. The input traveltimes are corrupted by 1% random noise, and six outlier traveltimes are corrupted with more than 500% traveltime error. The corresponding residual tomograms (courtesy of G. Waite), i.e., difference between actual and estimated velocity models, are shown in (c) and (d).

inverting $[\mathbf{L}^T\mathbf{L}]$ is prohibitive. Thus, an iterative indirect method such as conjugate gradients (Nolet, 1987) is used, where only vector-vector multiplications are needed.

The preconditioned and regularized steepest-descent formula for traveltime tomography is obtained by approximating the inverse to $[\mathbf{L}^T\mathbf{L}]$ by

$$[\mathbf{L}^T\mathbf{L} + \eta^2\mathbf{I}]_{ij}^{-1} \approx \frac{\delta_{ij}}{[\mathbf{L}^T\mathbf{L} + \eta^2\mathbf{I}]_{jj}}. \quad (5.31)$$

Substituting this approximation into equation 5.30 yields the preconditioned+regularized steepest-descent formula for the estimate of s_j:

$$s_j^{(k+1)} = s_j^{(k)} - \alpha \frac{[\mathbf{L}^T\delta\mathbf{t}]_j}{[\mathbf{L}^T\mathbf{L} + \eta^2\mathbf{I}]_{jj}}. \quad (5.32)$$

Note, matrix-vector multiplication in the above equation costs only $O(N^2)$ algebraic operations for $M = O(N)$ compared to the $O(N^3)$ cost for finding the inverse Hessian matrix. Preconditioners other than the diagonal matrix can be used, as will be discussed in Chapter 15.

The denominator of $1/[\mathbf{L}^T\mathbf{L}]_{jj} = 1/\sum_i l_{ij}^2$ is the sum of the squared segment lengths of rays that visit the jth cell. Thus, infrequently visited cells are given more weight than frequently visited cells, as will be explained in the following two examples.

Example 5.3.1. One ray and only one slowness perturbation

Assume a single ith ray and a constant slowness anomaly in the jth cell so that equation 5.32 becomes

$$s_j^{(k+1)} = s_j^{(k)} - \alpha l_{ij}\delta t_i/(l_{ij}^2 + \eta^2). \quad (5.33)$$

This equation says that the estimate for s_j is updated by smearing the weighted residual δt_i into the jth cell visited by the ith ray, in which the weight is $\alpha l_{ij}/(l_{ij}^2 + \eta^2) \approx 1/l_{ij}$ for small η^2 and $\alpha = 1$. The slowness update $\delta s_j = -\delta t_i/l_{ij}$ makes sense if the only slowness error in the model is in the jth cell. However, this residual is smeared mistakenly into any other cell visited by the ith ray. Further iterations and more data (i.e., rays) are needed to correct for these mistakes, and if we are lucky, the regularized preconditioned steepest-descent method should converge to the correct answer.

Example 5.3.2. Many rays and many slowness perturbations

Now assume that many rays visit the jth cell so that

$$[\mathbf{L}^T\delta\mathbf{t}]_j = \sum_i l_{ij}\delta t_i \approx \tilde{l}\sum_i \delta t_i \quad (5.34)$$

and

$$[\mathbf{L}^T\mathbf{L}]_{jj} = \sum_i l_{ij}^2 \approx M_j \tilde{l}^2, \qquad (5.35)$$

in which $\tilde{l}$ is the effective value of a ray's segment length in a cell, and M_j is the number of rays that visit the jth cell. With these approximations, the preconditioned+regularized SD formula becomes

$$s_j^{(k+1)} \approx s_j^{(k)} - \alpha\tilde{l} \sum_i \frac{\delta t_i}{M_j\tilde{l}^2 + \eta^2}, \qquad (5.36)$$

in which the summation is over the rays that visit the jth cell. Comparing this equation to the steepest-descent formula

$$s_j^{(k+1)} = s_j^{(k)} - \alpha\tilde{l} \sum_i \delta t_i \qquad (5.37)$$

says that the M_j term in the equation 5.36 denominator acts as a normalization factor so that, no matter how infrequent the jth cell is visited, its slowness update will have nearly the same importance (or weighting) as the more frequently visited cells. Such preconditioning will warp the long valleys of the misfit contours into more rounded ones, and so it will promote faster convergence than the unweighted steepest-descent formula.

For example, if all the sources and receivers in an experiment are on the earth's surface, then the shallow cells are visited much more frequently by rays than the deeper ones. In this case, equation 5.37 will update the slownesses in the deeper cells weakly, compared to the much stronger updates in the shallower cells. In contrast, the preconditioning factor in equation 5.36 avoids such bias by almost equally weighting all of the slowness updates.

5.4 Reflection tomography

Traditional reflection traveltime tomography (Bishop et al., 1985) requires the parameterization of both the velocity in each cell and the unknown locations of the reflecting boundaries. This increases both the number of unknowns (i.e., reflector locations) and the complexity of the problem.

To avoid the parameterization of the reflector boundary, Billette et al. (1998) introduce stereotomography, in which the ray directions for the downgoing source ray and upgoing reflection ray are found by a local slant stack of the traces (Sword, 1987). The intersection of the source and receiver rays defines the location of the reflector boundary, and the velocity is updated by smearing the traveltime residual along the reflection ray, or its associated Fresnel zone. This procedure is repeated, except the background velocity model is updated at each iteration. Similarly, wavepath migration (Sun, 2001) employs local slant stacks of the traces to determine the shooting angles of the source and receiver rays, except the reflection energy is smeared around the reflection Fresnel zone to define the reflector locations.

According to Lambarè (2008, VE28), "The... theoretical frame of stereotomography can reconcile, very satisfactorily and efficiently, most methods proposed for velocity-macromodel estimation for depth imaging. Moreover, an extension of the method to full-waveform inversion already exists and opens the way for very interesting developments." Indeed, some groups claim that stereotomography is much more robust than full-waveform inversion and can sometimes produce velocity images as useful as FWI.

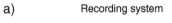

a)   Recording system   b)   Accelerated weight drop

Figure 5.6. (a) Recording system and (b) accelerated weight-drop source with Paul Gettings. Photographs by Sherif Hanafy. Used by permission.

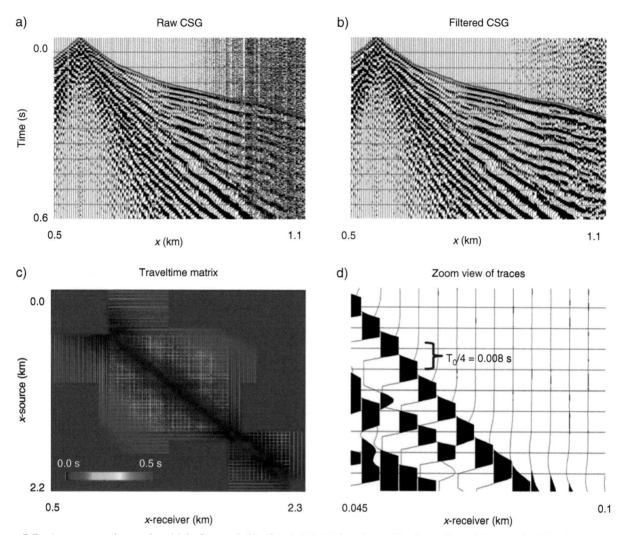

Figure 5.7. A common shot gather (a) before and (b) after 5-100 Hz bandpass filtering. The red lines coincide with the picked traveltimes of the first arrivals, and bandpass filtering is not needed for traces with a source-receiver offset less than three-hundred meters. (c) The traveltime matrix of traveltime picks and (d) a zoom view of some near-offset traces. Here, T_o is the dominant period estimated from the data.

At the very least, it can provide a good low-wavenumber starting model for FWI.

5.5 Field-data example

This section demonstrates the effectiveness of preconditioned multiscale tomography applied to refraction traveltimes picked from seismic field data.

Vertical-component geophones are used to record seismic data from a land survey in the desert shown in Figures 5.6a and 5.6b. The geology consists of poorly consolidated soil overlying a bedrock formation that is of economic interest. The goal is to use both refraction traveltime tomography and migration of refraction arrivals to map the sediment-bedrock boundary. A secondary goal is to detect the location of buried faults.

The seismic survey is characterized by shot and receiver intervals of 20 m and 5 m, respectively, and a typical shot gather is shown in Figure 5.7. The seismic source is the elastic weight-drop device shown in Figure 5.6b. A recording line with a length of 600 m (120 receivers at a 5-m sampling interval) is deployed sequentially at three line locations denoted as A, B, and C (see colored bars in Figure 5.8a). These three nonoverlapping lines run from west to east and form a continuous east-west line with a length of 1800 m.

There are three stages of recording. In the first stage, line A is employed and 102 shots at 20-m intervals from $0 < x < 2020$ m are used to generate 102 shot gathers over a 2020-m line. Next, the geophones are redeployed

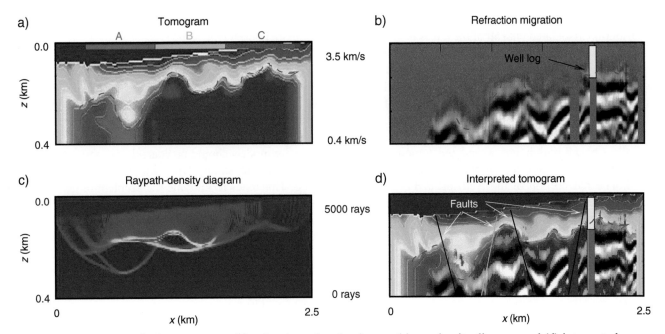

Figure 5.8. (a) P-wave velocity tomogram, (b) refraction migration image, (c) ray-density diagram, and (d) interpreted tomogram and migration image. The sediment-bedrock boundary interpreted from the tomogram is denoted by the blue dashed line. The tilted black and green lines in (d) are the tomogram-interpreted and field-conjectured faults, respectively. The three colored bars in (a) denote the locations for the three receiver lines, each 600 m long. Illustrations courtesy of Naoshi Aoki. Used by permission.

to the location of line B, and 70 shot gathers are collected at 20-m shot intervals. The geophones then are moved to the location of line C, but now only 20 shot gathers are collected with a 40-m shot interval.

Picked traveltimes of the first arrivals are plotted with respect to the source and receiver offsets in Figure 5.7c, where approximately 23,000 first-arrival traveltimes are picked from 192 shot gathers. Traveltimes are eliminated if they did not honor the reciprocity condition $|t_{ij} - t_{ji}| < T_o/2 = 0.004\ s$, in which T_o is the dominant period of the source wavelet and t_{ij} is the picked traveltime for a source and receiver with locations indexed by i and j, respectively. Fewer than 8% of the picked traveltimes failed the reciprocity test and are not used for inversion. Figure 5.7d depicts a zoom view of some near-offset traces that are pickable easily out to a source-receiver offset of about 330 m.

The picked first-arrival traveltimes are inverted with a multiscale tomography method (Nemeth et al., 1997), in which the velocity model is initially a coarse grid of cells with unknown slownesses. The starting model is a layered model with velocity values increasing with depth.[5] The convergence rate typically stalls after about five iterations,

and so the iterations are stopped. Then, the cell size is halved and the velocity model at the last iterate is projected and smoothed onto the refined grid[6] to give the new starting model for a new stage of iterations.

The velocity tomogram inverted from about 21,500 traveltimes is shown in Figure 5.8a. Forty iterations of preconditioned steepest descent are used with eight stages of inversion (five iterations/stage). The final stage uses a smoothing filter with 10 gridpoints (50 m) in the offset coordinate and five gridpoints (25 m) in the depth coordinate. The smallest averaging filter is about the same scale as the estimated minimum wavelength of 25 m, and a finite-difference solution to the eikonal equation (Qin et al., 1992) is used to compute the predicted traveltimes. The RMS residual error is about 0.8 ms at the last iteration.

The tomogram in Figure 5.8a is used to migrate the refraction arrivals to their place of origin, i.e., the refractor boundary. The refraction migration section in Figure 5.8b provides an estimate of the bedrock topography in this

---

[5]The shallowest velocity of 600 m/s is estimated from the slope of the near-offset direct arrivals and the deepest velocity of 3500 m/s is estimated from the slope of the far-offset arrivals.

[6]Instead of explicitly constructing a coarse-grid model, a coarse-smoothing filter can be applied to a fine-grid velocity model. For example, the traveltimes can be inverted iteratively using a fine-grid velocity model, but the coarse-grid model can be approximated at each iteration by smoothing the fine-grid tomogram by an averaging filter with area much greater than the area of a grid cell.

area. To assess the depth of ray penetration, the ray density distribution associated with all of the traces is plotted in Figure 5.8c. This diagram allows for a qualitative estimate of which parts of the tomogram are reliable (high density of rays) or unreliable (low density of rays). Obviously, the sides and the deepest parts of the tomogram are of least reliability because they have the fewest number and least angular diversity of raypaths.

Finally, the migration image and the tomogram are combined together to give the interpreted section in Figure 5.8d. The red portion of the well log in Figure 5.8d indicates the bedrock, and so the tomogram accurately predicts the sediment-bedrock depth at the well location to within about 5 m. Also, the green normal fault surmised from field observations coincides with a significant change in the tomogram velocity and a discontinuity in the reflectivity image. The tilted black lines are conjectured faults interpreted from the image in Figure 5.8d.

5.6 Summary

The theory of traveltime tomography is presented in which the objective function is taken to be a sum of a model-based regularization term and a data misfit function. Typically, the data misfit is a sum of weighted traveltime residuals raised to some power. The predicted traveltimes are computed by the high-frequency method of ray tracing, which requires that the velocity model is much smoother than the wavelength λ_{src} of the source wavelet. According to Bleistein (1984), this means that the minimum wavelength of the slowness model λ_{slow} must satisfy $\lambda_{slow} > 3\lambda_{src}$.

The traveltime equations are nonlinear, so a nonlinear optimization method such as the steepest-descent (equation 5.32), CG, or QN method is used along with regularization and preconditioning. If the Hessian $\mathbf{L}^T\mathbf{L}$ is poorly conditioned, then many different models can account for the same data to give an unstable solution. The partial remedy is to impose equations of constraint to regularize the system of equations. If the system of equations is highly inconsistent because of large errors in the traveltime picks, then an l_1 minimization method can be used. It can be implemented in the same fashion as an iterative least-squares solution except the ith residual r_i at the kth iteration is weighted by $1/|r_i|$. This procedure is known as reweighted least squares.

One of the main problems with traveltime tomography is getting stuck in a local minimum. Some partial remedies include the following:

- Find the solution for different starting models to see if they converge to the same model. Also, the data can be sprinkled with random noise for many different

simulations to determine the variance of the slowness estimate in each cell.
- Use a priori knowledge about the model, e.g., sonic logs in nearby wells, to constrain the tomogram.
- Parameterize the model so that it does not violate the wavelength restrictions imposed by a finite-frequency source.
- A multiscale approach can be used in which the initial-velocity models should be coarsely discretized, although later iterations should have a more refined model gridding. This tends to mitigate the problem of getting stuck in the local minima of the objective function (Nemeth et al., 1997).
- The number of unknowns should be significantly less than the number of traveltime equations. Our empirical rule of thumb for refraction surveys is that the ratio of the number of equations to number of unknowns should be at least equal to 3:1.

5.7 Exercises

1. Set up the 7×4 system of traveltime equations $\mathbf{Ls} = \mathbf{t}$ associated with the traveltime data shown in Figure 5.1.
2. The column span of the $M \times N$ matrix $\mathbf{L}$ is the ensemble of $M \times 1$ vectors that are linear combinations of the $\mathbf{L}$ column vectors. What plane is spanned by the 3×1 column vectors in $\mathbf{L} = [1\ 1;\ 1\ 0;\ 1\ 0]$? Is that plane closer to the observed 3×1 vector $\mathbf{t}$ than the $t_1 - t_2$ plane in Figure 5.3? The $M \times 1$ $\mathbf{t}$ vector represents data, so the column vectors of $\mathbf{L}$ are said to span a region of data space.
3. Can every region in three-dimensional space be spanned by the column vectors in $\mathbf{L} = [1\ 1;\ 1\ 0;\ 1\ 0]$? Prove your answer.
4. What geometrical object, line, or plane, is spanned by the column vectors in $\mathbf{L} = [1\ 2;\ 1\ 2;\ 1\ 2]$? Are these two column vectors in data space linearly independent?
5. Linear combinations of slowness vectors span a model space. For the example $\mathbf{L} = [1\ 2;\ 1\ 2;\ 1\ 2]$, show that there is more than one 2×1 slowness vector $\mathbf{s}$ that yields the same predicted traveltime equations. This means that the solution is nonunique.
6. The non-zero vector $\mathbf{s}_o$ such that $\mathbf{Ls}_o = (0\ 0\ 0)^T$ is known as a null-space vector. Any null-space vector added to a solution of $\mathbf{L}(\mathbf{s} + \mathbf{s}_0) = \mathbf{t}$ also will satisfy the traveltime equations. In other words, there are nonunique solutions. The space spanned by these null vectors defines the model null space. What geometrical object is spanned by the model null-space vectors for $\mathbf{L} = [1\ 2;\ 1\ 2;\ 1\ 2]$? This space is known as the model null space, and it is characterized by zero eigenvalues of $\mathbf{L}^T\mathbf{L}$.

7. Show that the model null-space vector for $\mathbf{L} = [1\ 2; 1\ 2; 1\ 2]$ is the same as the eigenvector of $\mathbf{L}^T\mathbf{L}$ associated with a zero eigenvalue.

8. Insert a new ray that is parallel to ray 3 in Figure 5.1, and call it ray 4. Show that the three traveltime equations associated with rays 2, 3, and 4 in Figure 5.1 give rise to a nonempty null space. What does this say about the ability of a straight-ray crosswell experiment to resolve lateral velocity variations? A crosswell experiment is one in which the receivers are along a vertical well and the sources are along another vertical well offset from the receiver well.

9. Show that, if the most probable model is the one that maximizes the normal distribution function $P(d|m) \approx e^{-\epsilon}$, then this also minimizes the data misfit function. Here, ϵ is the expression in equation 5.23.

10. Assume the data misfit function $\epsilon = 1/2 \sum_{i=1}^{M} r_i^2$, in which the ith residual is given by $r_i = [\mathbf{Ls} - \mathbf{d}]_i$ and $\mathbf{s}$ is the $N \times 1$ vector of unknown slownesses. If the variations of $\mathbf{L}$ with respect to slowness variations are significant, then the kth component of the misfit gradient $\mathbf{g}_k$ is

$$g_k = \frac{\partial \epsilon}{\partial s_k} = \frac{\partial (\mathbf{s}^T \mathbf{L}^T)}{\partial s_k} \mathbf{r},$$

$$= \mathbf{e}_k^T \mathbf{L}^T \mathbf{r} + \mathbf{s}^T \frac{\partial \mathbf{L}^T}{\partial s_k} \mathbf{r}, \qquad (5.38)$$

in which $\mathbf{e}_k$ is the kth unit vector. The second derivatives of the objective function that form the H_{kl} components of the Hessian are given by

$$H_{kl} = \frac{\partial^2 \epsilon}{\partial s_k \partial s_l} = \frac{\partial^2 (\mathbf{s}^T \mathbf{L}^T)}{\partial s_k \partial s_l} \mathbf{r} + \frac{\partial (\mathbf{s}^T \mathbf{L}^T)}{\partial s_k} \frac{\partial (\mathbf{Ls})}{\partial s_l}. \quad (5.39)$$

The Newton formula in equation 2.14 is $\mathbf{H}\Delta\mathbf{s}' = -\mathbf{g}$, in which $\Delta\mathbf{s}' = \mathbf{s}^{\text{true}} - \mathbf{s}$. Show that this formula reduces to the normal equations $\mathbf{L}^T\mathbf{L}\Delta\mathbf{s} = \mathbf{L}^T\mathbf{r}$ if the first and second derivatives of $\mathbf{L}$ with respect to slowness are negligible and $\Delta\mathbf{s} = -\Delta\mathbf{s}'$.

11. The normal equations in equation 5.20 were obtained by assuming that the gradient is evaluated at the bottom of the error bowl. At this point $\mathbf{s}$, the gradient in equation 5.19 is taken to be zero and leads to a simple derivation of the normal equations compared to the Taylor expansion in the previous exercise, in which the starting model $\mathbf{s}$ is far from the minimum. Explain the advantages and disadvantages of each derivation of the normal equations.

12. The Gauss-Newton method of large residuals (Gill et al., 1981) assumes that the first and second derivatives of $\mathbf{L}$ with respect to s_i cannot be neglected. Derive the steepest-descent formula for large residuals.

Show how to compute these derivatives efficiently for ray-based traveltime tomography.

13. The interpretation of the kth component of the gradient $[\mathbf{L}^T\mathbf{r}]_k$ is that the s_k slowness is updated by summing the weighted residuals associated with the rays that visit the kth cell. What is the interpretation of the slowness update for the component $\mathbf{s}^T \dfrac{\partial \mathbf{L}^T}{\partial s_k} \mathbf{r}$ in equation 5.38?

14. What is the connection between the Gauss-Newton method of large residuals and the method of generalized image domain inversion in Chapter 26, in which the objective function in equation 26.3 is

$$\epsilon = \frac{1}{2} \Delta\mathbf{d}^T \mathbf{L} \mathbf{H}^T \mathbf{H} \mathbf{L}^T \Delta\mathbf{d}? \qquad (5.40)$$

Here, $\Delta\mathbf{d}$ represents the data residual, $\mathbf{H}$ is a diagonal matrix (not the Hessian matrix) whose elements depend on the velocity model, and $\mathbf{L}$ is the forward-modeling operator.

15. Assume $\phi(\mathbf{x})_i = x_1 e^{-t_i/x_2}$, in which decay rates are calculated to fit the observations d_i (Fletcher, 1980). Find x_1 and x_2 that fit the data values $(d_1, d_2, d_3, d_4) = (2.7, 1, 0.4, 0.1)$ for $(t_1, t_2, t_3, t_4) = (-1, 0, 1, 1)$. Use the nonlinear Gauss-Newton method and the nonlinear Newton method of large residuals, and compare their convergence rates.

5.8 Computational labs

1. Review linear algebra for overdetermined systems of equations under the topic "Basic MATLAB tomography" in the Computational Toolkit.

2. Perform straight-ray tomography with the "Straight-ray MATLAB tomography" exercise in the Computational Toolkit under the topic "Traveltime tomography." Answer all questions.

3. Repeat the previous exercise, except employ the "Curved-ray MATLAB tomography" exercise.

4. Employ the KAUST or Qademah "Field Data" exercises.

5. Generate the traveltime data for the Figure 5.4 model. Use the code in the previous exercise except rewrite it so to give a RLS solution for $1 < p < 2$. Which value of p provides the best RLS solution for data with large outliers?

Appendix 5A:
Eikonal equation derivation

A zoom view of a bent raypath in a smoothly varying medium would reveal a straight ray, in which the associated wavefronts are straight and perpendicular to this straight ray. Consequently, for small wavelengths (much smaller than the characteristic wavelength of the velocity distribution), the harmonic wave equation is solved by the plane wave solution $e^{i\omega(k_x x + k_y y - \omega t)}$. At a small neighborhood around (x, y), the medium is effectively homogeneous $c(x, y) = \omega/k$ for very high frequencies f so that the following dispersion relationship is locally true:

$$k_x^2 + k_y^2 = (2\pi/cT)^2, \qquad (5.41)$$

in which T is the period of the source wavelet. Recalling that $k_x = 2\pi/\lambda_x$ and $k_y = 2\pi/\lambda_y$, in which λ_x and λ_y are the horizontal and vertical apparent wavelengths, respectively, equation 5.41 becomes, after multiplying by $(.5T/\pi)^2$,

$$(T/\lambda_x)^2 + (T/\lambda_y)^2 = (1/c)^2. \qquad (5.42)$$

For a plane wave, $T/\lambda_x = \partial t(x, y)/\partial x$ and $T/\lambda_y = \partial t(x, y)/\partial y$, so the above equation reduces to the eikonal equation

$$\left(\frac{\partial t(x, y)}{\partial x}\right)^2 + \left(\frac{\partial t(x, y)}{\partial y}\right)^2 = (1/c)^2, \qquad (5.43)$$

in which $t(x, y)$ is the traveltime for a direct wave to propagate from the specified source point to the listener at (x, y). The eikonal equation is expressed more compactly as $|\nabla t(x, y)| = 1/c(x, y)$, in which $\nabla t(x, y)$ is the gradient of the traveltime field, which points perpendicular to the wavefront. We can replace this compact representation by the directional derivative

$$|\nabla t(x, y)| = dt(x, y)/dl = 1/c(x, y), \qquad (5.44)$$

in which the direction perpendicular to the wavefront is denoted by $\hat{l}$ and a small incremental change of raypath length along this direction is denoted by dl. Multiplying through by dl and integrating the raypath length from the source to the observation point (x, y) yields the traveltime integral

$$t(x, y) = \int_{\text{raypath}} dl/c(x, y),$$
$$= \int_{\text{raypath}} s(x, y) dl, \qquad (5.45)$$

which is the high-frequency modeling equation for traveltime tomography. Note that this is a nonlinear integral

equation with respect to slowness $s(x, y)$ because both the integrand and raypath geometry depend on $s(x, y)$.

More generally, the eikonal equation can be derived directly from the elastic wave equation given by

$$\rho \frac{\partial^2 u_i}{\partial t^2} = \frac{\partial \tau_{ij}}{\partial x_j}, \qquad (5.46)$$

in which

$$\tau_{ij} = \lambda \delta_{ij} \frac{\partial u_k}{\partial x_k} + \mu \left(\frac{\partial u_i}{\partial x_j} + \frac{\partial u_j}{\partial x_i} \right). \qquad (5.47)$$

Here, repeated indices indicate summation from 1 to 3, u_k corresponds to the kth particle displacement, ρ is density, and λ and μ are Lame's constants.

For a harmonic plane-wave source oscillating at angular frequency ω and a scatterer embedded in a homogeneous medium, it is reasonable to assume that scattered far-field first arrivals can be approximated by a free-space Green's function, i.e.,

$$\mathbf{u}(\mathbf{r}, \omega) \sim \mathbf{A}(\mathbf{r}) e^{i\omega \tau_{so}}, \qquad (5.48)$$

in which the scatterer is at the origin, τ_{so} is the traveltime from the scatterer to the interrogation point $\mathbf{r}$, and $\mathbf{A}(\mathbf{r})$ is a displacement vector that accounts for scattering and geometrical-spreading losses.

Equation 5.48 can be used as an ansatz, or trial solution to the wave equation. The unknowns $\mathbf{A}$ and τ can be found by plugging equation 5.48 into equation 5.46 to yield a quadratic equation in ω. At high frequencies, the geometrical-spreading term is governed by the transport equation

$$-\rho \mathbf{A} + (\lambda + \mu)(\mathbf{A} \cdot \nabla \tau) \nabla \tau + \mu |\nabla \tau|^2 \mathbf{A} = 0. \qquad (5.49)$$

Equation 5.49 is satisfied either by 1) choosing $\mathbf{A} \cdot \nabla \tau = 0$ which implies or 2) choosing $\nabla \tau$ to be parallel to $\mathbf{A}$ to give

$$|\nabla \tau|^2 = \rho/\mu,$$
$$:= v_S^{-2}, \qquad (5.50)$$
$$|\nabla \tau|^2 = \rho/(\lambda + 2\mu),$$
$$:= v_P^{-2}, \qquad (5.51)$$

in which $v_P^2 = \frac{\lambda + 2\mu}{\rho}$ and $v_S^2 = \frac{\mu}{\rho}$.

Equations 5.50 and 5.51 are the S- and P-wave eikonal equations, respectively, whose solutions yield the traveltimes of the first P- and S-wave arrivals everywhere in a smoothly varying velocity medium. They also lead to the traveltime integral, which is used to calculate the traveltimes of the associated rays.

Appendix 5B:
l_p misfit gradient

I now will show that setting $p = 1$ in equation 5.28 reduces to finding the solution that minimizes the misfit function in the l_1 norm. Consider the misfit function in the general l_p norm:

$$\epsilon = \frac{1}{p} \sum_i \left| \sum_j l_{ij} s_j - t_i \right|^p . \qquad (5.52)$$

Defining $\mathrm{sgn}(r_i) = r_i / |r_i|$ and $\partial |r_i| / \partial r_i = \mathrm{sgn}(r_i)$, the gradient of ϵ is given as

$$\frac{\partial \epsilon}{\partial s_k} = \frac{1}{p} \sum_i \frac{\partial |\sum_j l_{ij} s_j - t_i|^p}{\partial s_k},$$

$$= \sum_i |r_i|^{p-1} \frac{\partial |r_i|}{\partial r_i} \frac{\partial r_i}{\partial s_k},$$

$$= \sum_i \mathrm{sgn}(r_i) |r_i|^{p-1} l_{ik},$$

$$= \sum_i r_i |r_i|^{p-2} l_{ik},$$

$$= [\mathbf{L}^T \mathbf{W} (\mathbf{L}\mathbf{s} - \mathbf{t})]_k, \qquad (5.53)$$

and $\mathbf{W}$ is a diagonal matrix in which the diagonal element values can be approximated by equation 5.28. Setting $p = 1$ gives the l_1 gradient, which can be used in formula 5.27 to give the model that minimizes the l_1 norm misfit function.

Chapter 6: Traveltime Tomography: Assessing model accuracy

The previous chapters discussed procedures for reconstructing velocity tomograms from traveltime data. Now we discuss how to assess the accuracy of the reconstructed traveltime tomogram.

6.1 Introduction

A tomogram $\mathbf{m} \approx \mathbf{L}^{-1}\mathbf{d}$ estimated from field data always has an uncertainty associated with any of its velocity values. As illustrated in Figure 6.1, these model errors $\delta\mathbf{m}$ can be attributed to a number of causes:

1. Noise in the overdetermined set of equations and data $\delta\mathbf{d}$ leads to model errors $\delta\mathbf{m} = \mathbf{L}^{-1}\delta\mathbf{d}$ and an inconsistent set of traveltime equations. The partial remedy is to find the best solution in some sense, e.g., a least-squares inverse $\mathbf{m} + \delta\mathbf{m} = [\mathbf{L}^T\mathbf{L}]^{-1}\mathbf{L}^T(\mathbf{d} + \delta\mathbf{d})$. In this case, the model covariance matrix presented in section 6.2 can be used to assess how the data errors are mapped into model errors for data that are linearly related to the model.

2. Data are incomplete, so there is more than one model that satisfies or nearly satisfies the data, i.e., there is a nonunique solution. Incompleteness can arise because, e.g., the data are collected discretely over a narrow recording aperture with a limited source-frequency band. To ameliorate this problem, an approximate solution might be obtained using a least-squares inverse solution with regularization, i.e., $\mathbf{m} = [\mathbf{L}^T\mathbf{L} + \lambda\mathbf{I}]^{-1}\mathbf{L}^T\mathbf{d}$. As discussed in section 6.3, the corresponding resolution loss in the model can be quantified numerically with the model resolution matrix $\mathbf{R}$. Here, stronger off-diagonal components of $\mathbf{R}$ lead to increased spatial blurring in the final image.

   The model artifacts that arise from incomplete source and receiver coverage are sometimes referred to as the acquisition footprint. For traveltime tomography with straight rays, section 6.6 presents the projection-slice theorem, which shows how a restricted source-receiver coverage limits the range of wavenumbers that can be reconstructed in the model spectrum. A similar theorem, sometimes known as the diffraction-slice or the Fourier diffraction theorem (Wu and Toksöz, 1987), is applicable to velocity models reconstructed from wavefields. It is restricted to scatterers embedded in homogeneous background velocity models, but its asymptotic extension to inhomogeneous background models is provided by the generalized Radon transform (Beylkin, 1984) discussed in Chapter 14. Limiting the range of reconstructed wavenumbers by a limited source-receiver coverage and source bandwidth means less resolution and more artifacts in the final image.

3. The forward-modeling operator does not honor all of the physics in the data, and this operator error is denoted by $\delta\mathbf{L}$. Therefore, $\delta\mathbf{m} = [(\mathbf{L} + \delta\mathbf{L})^{-1} - \mathbf{L}^{-1}]\mathbf{d}$. An example is not taking into account phase delays from attenuation in traveltime tomography. Another example is using ray-based traveltime tomography inappropriately when the high-frequency assumption is invalid. In these cases, a sensitivity study might be used to identify the important physics that strongly affect the data. For example, synthetic data with attenuation can be modeled and the associated traveltimes can be inverted with a tomography code that does not account for attenuation. An ensemble of reasonable attenuation models are used and the model errors that result from incomplete physics can be assessed statistically for their importance. For example, Chapter 15 presents the sensitivity of least-squares migration with respect to not accounting for attenuation in the data. As discussed in Chapter 12, analyzing the Fréchet derivative also can be used to assess the sensitivity of data to the variation of physical parameters.

4. The inversion problem is nonlinear so the global minimum is difficult to find amidst a sea of local minima. To recognize the severity of this problem, a variety of starkly different starting models can be used to generate different sets of synthetic data. If inversion of these data lead to dramatically different final models with about the same data residual, then there is a severe local-minima problem with nonunique solutions. The partial remedy is to record a more comprehensive data set and impose reasonable constraints on the solution.

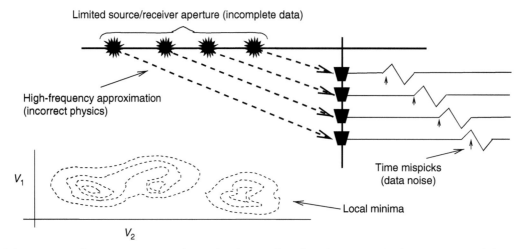

Figure 6.1. Major sources of tomogram errors: data noise, incomplete data, incorrect physics, and local minima as a result of the nonlinear relationship between data and model. The dashed contours represent the values of the misfit function plotted with respect to the two model parameters V_1 and V_2.

In this chapter, we will show how the special form of the model covariance matrix $[\mathbf{L}^T\mathbf{L}]^{-1}$ relates the data errors $\delta\mathbf{d}$ to the model errors $\delta\mathbf{m}$, i.e., items 1 and 2. It also will be shown how the acquisition geometry affects the magnification of data errors into model errors, for both reflection and transmission traveltimes. Finally, the projection-slice theorem is derived to show how the reconstructed model is restricted by the source-receiver geometry.

Terminology

To clarify terminology, the word uncertainty is used for either data measurements or model-parameter estimates, and it refers to the range of values that the true value will fall within. As an example, data recorded with uncertainty to one standard deviation says that 68.2% of the measured (or estimated) values fall within the mean value. If the standard deviation is large, then the measured data are said to be highly uncertain. The word resolution usually is restricted to estimates of model parameters. Highly resolved model parameters in velocity tomograms mean that most of the significant wavenumbers, especially the high ones, in the model spectrum are reconstructed accurately. Poorly resolved models are ones in which significant wavenumbers in the model spectrum are missing or determined inaccurately.

6.2 Model covariance matrix

The model covariance matrix is a compact expression for representing the second-order statistics of multivariate random variables. It can be used to estimate the reliability of the solution (Menke, 1984), as a row-scaling matrix to guide us optimally toward the solution (Tarantola, 1984), or as a preconditioner for least-squares migration

(Hu et al., 2001; Guitton, 2004; Yu et al., 2006) and full-waveform inversion. We now will define the data and model covariance matrices.

Let δt_i be a continuous random variable corresponding to the traveltime pick error associated with the ith ray. If there are M distinct source-receiver pairs, then there will be M distinct raypaths that give rise to M distinct traces and picked transmission traveltimes. The associated set of continuous random variables for picking errors δt_i with $i = 1, 2, \ldots M$ is governed by the probability density function (PDF) $P(\delta t_i)$ such that

$$\int_{-\infty}^{+\infty} P(\delta t_i)d(\delta t_i) = 1, \tag{6.1}$$

for all i. The interpretation of $P(\delta t_i)d(\delta t_i)$ is that it gives the probability of the random variable taking on the value δt_i within the range $d\delta t_i$.

The expectation or average value of δt_i is defined as

$$\overline{\delta t_i} = E(\delta t_i) = \int_{-\infty}^{+\infty} P(\delta t_i)\delta t_i d(\delta t_i), \tag{6.2}$$

the joint PDF $P(\delta t_1, \delta t_2, \ldots, \delta t_M)$ honors

$$\int_{-\infty}^{+\infty} \ldots \int_{-\infty}^{+\infty} P(\delta t_1, \delta t_2, \ldots, \delta t_M)d(\delta t_1) \ldots d(\delta t_M) = 1, \tag{6.3}$$

and the joint expectation value is defined as

$$E(\delta t_1, \ldots, \delta t_M) := \int_{-\infty}^{+\infty} \ldots \int_{-\infty}^{+\infty} P(\delta t_1, \delta t_2, \ldots, \delta t_M)$$
$$\times \, \delta t_1 \ldots \delta t_M d(\delta t_1) \ldots d(\delta t_M). \tag{6.4}$$

If δt_i is a statistically independent random variable (Cadzow, 1987) for all values of i, then $P(\delta t_1, \delta t_2, \ldots, \delta t_M) = P(\delta t_1)P(\delta t_2) \ldots P(\delta t_M)$.

The second-order statistics of the random variables δt_i are determined by the covariance function

$$E([\delta t_i - \overline{\delta t_i}][\delta t_j - \overline{\delta t_j}])$$

$$:= E(\delta t_i \delta t_j) - \overbrace{[\overline{\delta t_j} E(\delta t_i) + \overline{\delta t_i} E(\delta t_j)]}^{2\overline{\delta t_i}\,\overline{\delta t_j}} + \overbrace{E(\overline{\delta t_j}\,\overline{\delta t_i})}^{\overline{\delta t_i}\,\overline{\delta t_j}},$$

$$= E(\delta t_i \delta t_j) - \overline{\delta t_i}\,\overline{\delta t_j},$$

$$= \sigma_{ij}^2, \qquad (6.5)$$

in which σ_{ij}^2 is known as the covariance of the random variables δt_i and δt_j. If the data errors have zero mean, then $\sigma_{ij}^2 = E(\delta t_i \delta t_j)$, and if δt_j and δt_i are independent random variables, then

$$i \neq j; \quad \sigma_{ij}^2 = \int_{-\infty}^{+\infty} \int_{-\infty}^{+\infty} P(\delta t_i, \delta t_j) \delta t_i \delta t_j \, d(\delta t_i) d(\delta t_j),$$

$$= \int_{-\infty}^{+\infty} P(\delta t_i) \delta t_i d(\delta t_i) \int_{-\infty}^{+\infty} P(\delta t_j) \delta t_j d(\delta t_j) = 0.$$
$$(6.6)$$

The data covariance is a measure of the correlation between the ith and jth random variables, and reduces to the variance σ_{ii}^2 of δt_i when $i = j$. A large positive value of σ_{ij}^2 means that the ith and jth random variables are highly correlated with one another, as illustrated by the Figure 6.2a plot of trial outcomes. In contrast, trial outcomes for a pair of uncorrelated random variables in which $\sigma_{ij}^2 \approx 0$ for $i \neq j$ plot out as a cloud of uncorrelated points, as shown in Figure 6.2b.

If there are M random variables δt_i for $i = 1, 2, 3 \ldots M$, then they can be assembled into an $M \times 1$ random vector $\delta \mathbf{t}$, which can be used to form the $M \times M$ data matrix $\delta \mathbf{t} \delta \mathbf{t}^T$. Applying the expectation operator to each of the elements in this matrix gives the $M \times M$ data covariance matrix

$$\mathbf{C}_d := E(\delta \mathbf{t} \delta \mathbf{t}^T) - \overline{\delta \mathbf{t}}\,\overline{\delta \mathbf{t}}^T, \qquad (6.7)$$

in which the ij component of $\mathbf{C}_d$ is given by

$$[\mathbf{C}_d]_{ij} := E(\delta t_i \delta t_j) - \overline{\delta t_i}\,\overline{\delta t_j} = \sigma_{ij}^2, \qquad (6.8)$$

and the variance value σ_{ii}^2 occupies the ith diagonal element position. Each element in the i,j position of $\mathbf{C}_d$ is the covariance between the ith and jth elements of the random vector $\delta \mathbf{t} - \overline{\mathbf{t}}$. If the variances are all equal to the same value σ^2 and the zero-mean data are uncorrelated, then $\mathbf{C}_d$ becomes a weighted identity matrix

$$\mathbf{C}_d = E(\delta \mathbf{t} \delta \mathbf{t}^T) = \sigma^2 \mathbf{I}, \qquad (6.9)$$

in which $\mathbf{I}$ is the $M \times M$ identity matrix.

Example 6.2.1. Traveltime picking errors and random variables

Consider the vertical seismic profiling (VSP) experiment in Figure 6.1, in which traces are recorded along the well, and the ith traveltime pick $t_i + \delta t_i$ is associated with the ith ray. The ith traveltime pick is the outcome of one trial experiment for the specified ith shot-receiver pair. Repeating this experiment for the same source-receiver pair gives a new trace in which the ith traveltime can be picked again, except that it has a new picking error. The kth experiment is denoted by attaching the superscript (k) to the random variable δt_i so it becomes $\delta t_i^{(k)}$. The collection (i.e., ensemble) of these traveltimes (i.e., outcomes) for N trials can be used to estimate the mean traveltime pick for the ith ray

$$\overline{t_i} \approx \frac{1}{N} \sum_{k=1}^{N} \overbrace{(t_i + \delta t_i^{(k)})}^{t_i^{(k)}} = t_i + \frac{1}{N} \sum_{k=1}^{N} \delta t_i^{(k)}, \quad (6.10)$$

in which t_i is the noise-free traveltime for the ith ray, and $t_i^{(k)}$ for the same ray is the picked traveltime from the kth experiment. The estimated data covariance is given by

$$\sigma_{ij}^2 \approx \frac{1}{N} \sum_{k=1}^{N} (\overline{t_i} - t_i^{(k)})(\overline{t_j} - t_j^{(k)}). \qquad (6.11)$$

Ideally, the traveltime errors are uncorrelated so $\sigma_{ij}^2 = 0$ for $i \neq j$, but in the real world, there could be coupling of picking errors between neighboring geophones. For example, some geophones might be planted in the same washout zone, so there is weak coupling between these geophones and the earth. This poor coupling will lead to similar errors in traveltime picking. Noise in a land survey also can be caused by wind that vibrates the cable and geophones, and so it introduces correlated noise into neighboring traces.

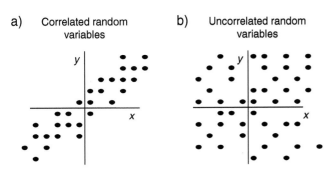

a) Correlated random variables   **b)** Uncorrelated random variables

Figure 6.2. Plots of (a) correlated and (b) uncorrelated random variables x and y for the outcomes of different trials.

In practice, it is too expensive to repeat experiments as a means for estimating the statistics of picking errors[1].

If the data are linearly related to the model, the mapping between data and model errors can be estimated by the model covariance matrix $\mathbf{C}_m$, which for zero-mean data becomes

$$
\begin{aligned}
\mathbf{C}_m &= E[\delta\mathbf{s}\delta\mathbf{s}^T], \\
&= E[[\mathbf{L}^T\mathbf{L}]^{-1}\mathbf{L}^T\delta\mathbf{t}\delta\mathbf{t}^T\mathbf{L}[\mathbf{L}^T\mathbf{L}]^{-1}], \\
&= [\mathbf{L}^T\mathbf{L}]^{-1}\mathbf{L}^T E[\delta\mathbf{t}\delta\mathbf{t}^T]\mathbf{L}[\mathbf{L}^T\mathbf{L}]^{-1}, \qquad (6.12)
\end{aligned}
$$

where the matrix $\mathbf{L}$ does not contain random variables, so it can be treated as a constant with respect to the expectation operator. Here, we conveniently assume that the slowness model is related linearly to the data vector by the least-squares inverse $[\mathbf{L}^T\mathbf{L}]^{-1}\mathbf{L}^T$ and $[\mathbf{L}^T\mathbf{L}]^{-1}$ exists. Unfortunately, if the data and model are nonlinearly related, then a model covariance matrix with small variances *can mislead tomographers into thinking their tomograms are accurate!* At best, this says that their estimated model might be accurate.

For zero-mean uncorrelated data errors with identical variance values σ^2, equation 6.9 says that equation 6.12 becomes

$$
\mathbf{C}_m = \sigma^2[\mathbf{L}^T\mathbf{L}]^{-1}. \qquad (6.13)
$$

For a slowness model parameterized into cells of constant slowness, $[\mathbf{C}_m]_{ii} = \sigma^2[\mathbf{L}^T\mathbf{L}]_{ii}^{-1}$ is the slowness variance for the ith cell. For $i \neq j$, $[\mathbf{C}_m]_{ij}$ is the slowness covariance associated with the ith and jth cells, where large values suggest an undesirable large coupling of slowness errors between the ith and jth cells. Therefore, examining the element values of $[\mathbf{L}^T\mathbf{L}]^{-1}$ (especially the diagonal components) will reveal the uncertainty in the estimated model parameters caused by data errors. Examples in section 6.4 show that narrower source-receiver apertures and fewer terminating rays in a layer lead to increased values of $[\mathbf{L}^T\mathbf{L}]^{-1}$ and larger model errors.

6.2.1 Numerical estimation of the model covariance matrix

The direct inverse to the $N \times N$ matrix $[\mathbf{L}^T\mathbf{L}]$ in equation 6.13 is too expensive to compute if $N \geq 10^6$. As an inexpensive alternative, Squires and Cambois (1992) estimate the values of the model covariance matrix using a linear filter that annihilates parts of the model that are estimated to be in the null space of $[\mathbf{L}^T\mathbf{L}]$. However, certain

parts of the model are very close to the null space and must be suppressed in some ad hoc manner. Another approach is suggested by Tarantola and Valette (1982), in which they assume a Gaussian covariance function

$$
C_m(\mathbf{r}, \mathbf{r}') = \tilde{\sigma}^2 exp\left(-\frac{1}{2}\frac{||\mathbf{r}-\mathbf{r}'||^2}{\zeta^2}\right). \qquad (6.14)
$$

Here $\mathbf{r}$, $\mathbf{r}'$ are position vectors anywhere in the model, $\tilde{\sigma}^2$ is the model variance, and ζ is the correlation length of the unknown model parameters. The correlation length and variance usually are estimated in an ad hoc manner. For example, ζ can be assigned to be equal to the minimum wavelength of the source wavelet.

Another means for inexpensively estimating $\mathbf{C}_m$ is to 1) generate a set of random traveltime picking errors with zero mean, 2) add these random timing errors to the actual traveltimes for the true model, and 3) invert these noisy traveltimes by an iterative solver to get the kth slowness model $\mathbf{s}^{(k)}$. The true model is the one inverted from the noiseless synthetic data for a specified true model. 4) Repeating steps 1–3 for N different realizations of the random picking errors, the average slowness vector $\bar{\mathbf{s}} \approx \frac{1}{N}\sum_k^N \mathbf{s}^{(k)}$ and its variance

$$
[\mathbf{C}_m]_{ii} \approx \frac{1}{N}\sum_{k=1}^N (s_i^{(k)} - \bar{s}_i)^2, \qquad (6.15)
$$

can be calculated. If $\bar{s}_i$ is replaced by the true model value s_i, then the variance reveals model uncertainty because of traveltime errors and the limitations of traveltime tomography with a restricted source-receiver geometry. Implicit in this procedure is that the slowness model is "close enough" to the correct one and the finite number of realizations is sufficient to give a good approximation to the model variance.

As an example, Figure 6.3a and 6.3b depict a shot gather and the traveltime tomogram associated with a small-scale field experiment, respectively. Using the four steps above, the slowness variance for each pixel is computed and shown in Figure 6.3c. The hotter colors correspond to larger variance values, and therefore, worse reliability. In this example, the areas of poor resolution can be attributed partly to poor ray coverage because of a limited source-receiver coverage.

Instead of using the tomogram inverted from the recorded data as the ground-truth model, the trial slowness distribution can be a checkerboard model (Lévêque et al., 1993; Tryggvason et al., 2002) of slowness anomalies. Here, the checkerboard model is a regular pixelization of alternating slowness perturbations superimposed on a smooth background slowness model. Each pixel is several wavelengths or more in size, and the background model should be characteristic of the actual velocity distribution

---

[1] For most surveys conducted at the University of Utah and KAUST, we conveniently assigned the standard deviation of the traveltime pick error to be $T/4$, in which T is the dominant period of the source wavelet.

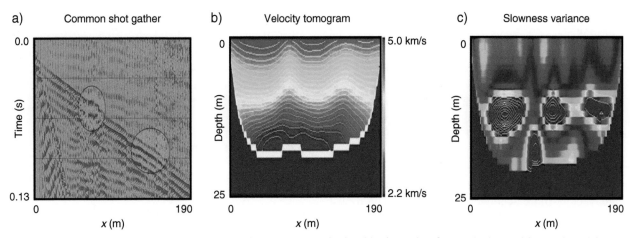

Figure 6.3. (a) Common shot gather and (b) velocity tomogram obtained by inverting first-arrival traveltimes picked from 48 common shot gathers; contour bumps in the shallow depths correspond to high-velocity gravel deposits. Calculating the tomograms for 50 different realizations of traveltime picking errors and using equation 6.15 gives the slowness variance estimate in (c). Images courtesy of F. Ravanelli and M. Almubarak. Used by permission.

(Kissling et al., 2001). One choice for the background model might be a smoothed version of the tomogram obtained by inverting the picked traveltimes. Another consideration is that ray tracing is a high-frequency approximation that assumes a model smoother than the source wavelength, so the back projection of the traveltime residual should be along a fat ray (Harlan, 1986; 1990) or a wavepath (Woodward, 1989; Luo, 1991; Woodward, 1992; Schuster and Quintus-Bosz, 1993; Vasco and Majer, 1993; Vasco et al., 1995; Vasco et al., 1998). This is somewhat similar to smoothing the velocity model after each iteration (Nemeth et al., 1997), so that the slowness wavenumbers greater than about half that of the dominant source wavenumber are not admitted into the tomogram.

As a critique, Vasco et al. (1998) point out that the damped least-squares method will fortuitously show good resolution, because of the regularization, in regions poorly visited by rays in the checkerboard model. Another problem is that the slowness resolution capabilities are revealed mostly at small wavelengths, but not at large wavelengths for pixels with small size.

Sometimes computing the ray density/pixel image is an acceptable means for approximately estimating the illumination in a pixel (Kissling, 1988). An even better metric is to include the diversity of angular ray coverage. Soldati and Boschi (2005) conclude that for their example, synthetic checkerboard tests do not provide much more information than a simple plot of ray densities in each pixel. To avoid solution artifacts arising from poor ray coverage (e.g., sparse ray density in a cell or a small diversity of crossing rays), several cells can be combined into a larger cell with one unknown slowness in that cell (Kissling, 1988; Kissling et al., 2001). Cell size also can be adjusted according to hit count (Bijwaard et al., 1998) and the volume

of the Fresnel zone (Williamson, 1991; Williamson and Worthington, 1993; Woodward, 1989; Woodward, 1992).

Finally, inexpensive estimates of the important components of $[\mathbf{L}^T\mathbf{L}]^{-1}$ can be obtained with a few iterations of, e.g., conjugate-gradient solver (Zhang and McMechan, 1995, 1996; Fomel et al., 2002) or by computing local nonstationary filters (Guitton, 2004; Aoki and Schuster, 2009) that relate the actual reflectivity image $\mathbf{m}$ to the migration image $\mathbf{m}' = \mathbf{L}^T\mathbf{d}$. It seems reasonable that these inexpensive methods also can be used for traveltime tomograms by specifying the slowness tomogram to be $\mathbf{m}' = \mathbf{L}^T\mathbf{d}$, with $\mathbf{d}$ as the traveltime data, and $\mathbf{m}$ as the actual slowness model.

6.3 Model resolution matrix

The model resolution matrix is another means for assessing solution reliability. If the estimated model is $\mathbf{m}' = [\mathbf{L}^T\mathbf{L} + \eta^2\mathbf{I}]^{-1}\mathbf{L}^T\mathbf{d}$, then substituting $\mathbf{d} = \mathbf{L}\mathbf{m}$ gives

$$\mathbf{m}' = \mathbf{R}\mathbf{m}, \qquad (6.16)$$

in which $\mathbf{R} = [\mathbf{L}^T\mathbf{L} + \eta^2\mathbf{I}]^{-1}[\mathbf{L}^T\mathbf{L}]$ is the model resolution matrix. Equation 6.16 says that the estimated model $\mathbf{m}'$ is a weighted linear combination of actual model parameters (Menke, 1984). A well-resolved estimate of the model is desired so $\mathbf{R}$ ideally should be an identity matrix in which there is no spatial averaging of the components of $\mathbf{m}$. If, for example, η^2 is too big or the acquisition geometry is limited in source-receiver sampling, then $\mathbf{R}$ will have large off-diagonal values and lead to a strong acquisition footprint in the tomogram.

Undesirable averaging can be identified by plotting the off-diagonal values of $\mathbf{R}$, and therefore, pinpoint unreliable parts in the tomogram. For example, Soldati and Boschi (2005) assess slowness reliability by computing the model resolution matrix $[\mathbf{L}^T\mathbf{L} + \eta^2\mathbf{I}]^{-1}\mathbf{L}^T\mathbf{L}$ by Cholesky factorization of matrices associated with P, PKP, and PcP traveltimes picked from earthquake records.

Zhang and Thurber (2007) report that software packages now can efficiently estimate the singular values and vectors associated with $\mathbf{Lm} = \mathbf{d}$ when there are tens of thousands of model parameters and hundreds of thousands of traveltime measurements. This software uses Lanczos bidiagonalization and is able to estimate the singular values and eigenvectors more accurately than LSQR. The robust portion of the estimated velocity model then can be reconstructed by using only the eigenvectors associated with singular values above a specified cutoff value. This is similar to specifying a damping parameter in a regularized least-squares solution.

6.4 Analytic model covariance matrices

The model covariance matrix $\sigma^2[\mathbf{L}^T\mathbf{L}]^{-1}$ in equation 6.13 is estimated typically by a numerical computation, which does not provide general insights into how the acquisition geometry influences the model errors. Such insights, however, can be achieved with an analytic formula for the model covariance matrix.

We now derive the analytic formulas for $[\mathbf{L}^T\mathbf{L}]^{-1}$ associated with vertical seismic profile (VSP) and common-midpoint (CMP) acquisition geometries and a 1D layered velocity model. The resulting formulas contain diagonal terms with a form similar to

$$[\mathbf{C}_m]_{ii} = \sigma^2[\mathbf{L}^T\mathbf{L}]_{ii}^{-1} \approx \frac{\sigma^2}{N_t l_i^2 + N_r L_i^2}, \quad (6.17)$$

which says that the slowness variance $[\mathbf{C}_m]_{ii}$ of the ith layer decreases with an increase in the number N_t (N_r) of

transmission (reflection) rays that terminate (reflect) in a layer. It also predicts decreasing slowness variance as the segment lengths l_i (L_i) of the transmission (reflection) rays increase with source-geophone offset. These rules of thumb also seem to be applicable to general velocity models with nearly horizontal layering.

6.4.1 VSP transmission data

Assume straight rays, homogeneous layers with equal thickness, and the two-source VSP experiment shown in Figure 6.4a. Let l_i be the segment length of the ith transmission ray within a layer; this ray originates at the near-offset source and terminates at the ith interface. The segment length of this ray within any layer is the same if the ray is straight and the layers are of equal thickness.

The slowness in the ith layer is denoted by s_i, and t_i represents the traveltime of a first arrival recorded by the geophone at the ith layer interface. Traveltimes and segment lengths associated with the far-offset source will be primed, and the traveltime equations for the Figure 6.4a experiment with two sources are represented by

$$\mathbf{Ls} = \begin{bmatrix} l_1 & 0 & 0 \\ l_2 & l_2 & 0 \\ l_3 & l_3 & l_3 \\ l'_1 & 0 & 0 \\ l'_2 & l'_2 & 0 \\ l'_3 & l'_3 & l'_3 \end{bmatrix} \begin{pmatrix} s_1 \\ s_2 \\ s_3 \end{pmatrix} = \begin{pmatrix} t_1 \\ t_2 \\ t_3 \\ t'_1 \\ t'_2 \\ t'_3 \end{pmatrix}. \quad (6.18)$$

Here, the raypath matrix $\mathbf{L}$ can be decomposed into $\mathbf{L} = [\mathbf{L}_1 ; \mathbf{L}_2]$, in which $\mathbf{L}_1$ and $\mathbf{L}_2$ are the top and bottom 3×3 block matrices in equation 6.18, respectively. The block matrix $\mathbf{L}_i$ is a product of a 3×3 diagonal scaling matrix $\mathbf{D}_i$ and a 3×3 quadrature matrix $\mathbf{Q}$. For example, $\mathbf{L}_1$ can be

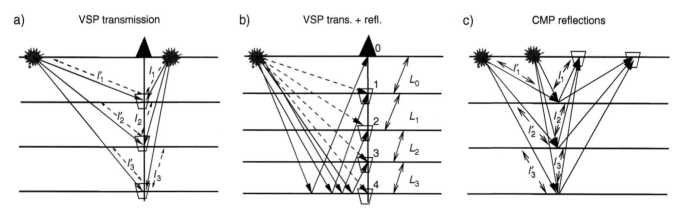

Figure 6.4. Raypaths for (a) VSP transmission, (b) VSP transmission + reflection, and (c) CMP reflection arrivals. The segment length of the transmission (reflection) raypath that terminates (reflects) in the ith layer is denoted by l_i (L_i), where a ray's segment length is the same in each layer.

decomposed as

$$\mathbf{L}_1 = \mathbf{D}_1\mathbf{Q} = \begin{bmatrix} l_1 & 0 & 0 \\ 0 & l_2 & 0 \\ 0 & 0 & l_3 \end{bmatrix} \begin{bmatrix} 1 & 0 & 0 \\ 1 & 1 & 0 \\ 1 & 1 & 1 \end{bmatrix}, \quad (6.19)$$

in which $\mathbf{Q}$ is interpreted as a quadrature matrix because it is the discrete representation of the traveltime integral for a zero-offset VSP experiment. Therefore, it is not surprising to recognize that $\mathbf{Q}^{-1}$ is the first-order difference matrix

$$\mathbf{Q}^{-1} = \begin{bmatrix} 1 & 0 & 0 \\ -1 & 1 & 0 \\ 0 & -1 & 1 \end{bmatrix}. \quad (6.20)$$

Similar to equation 6.19, $\mathbf{L}_2$ can be decomposed into a product of a 3×3 diagonal scaling matrix $\mathbf{D}_2$ (with diagonal elements $[\mathbf{D}_2]_{ii} = l_i'$) and the quadrature matrix $\mathbf{Q}$.

Therefore, $\mathbf{L}^T\mathbf{L}$ can be expressed as

$$\mathbf{L}^T\mathbf{L} = \sum_{i=1}^{2} \mathbf{L}_i^T\mathbf{L}_i = \sum_{i=1}^{2} \mathbf{Q}^T\mathbf{D}_i^2\mathbf{Q} = \mathbf{Q}^T\left[\sum_{i=1}^{2} \mathbf{D}_i^2\right]\mathbf{Q}. \quad (6.21)$$

Equation 6.21 allows for a straightforward derivation of the inverse (which is proportional to the slowness covariance matrix in equation 6.13) as

$$[\mathbf{L}^T\mathbf{L}]^{-1} = \mathbf{Q}^{-1}\left[\sum_{i=1}^{2} \mathbf{D}_i^{-2}\right]\mathbf{Q}^{-T}$$

$$= \begin{bmatrix} \dfrac{1}{l_1^2 + l_1'^2} & -\dfrac{1}{l_1^2 + l_1'^2} & 0 \\ -\dfrac{1}{l_1^2 + l_1'^2} & \dfrac{1}{l_1^2 + l_1'^2} + \dfrac{1}{l_2^2 + l_2'^2} & -\dfrac{1}{l_2^2 + l_2'^2} \\ 0 & -\dfrac{1}{l_2^2 + l_2'^2} & \dfrac{1}{l_2^2 + l_2'^2} + \dfrac{1}{l_3^2 + l_3'^2} \end{bmatrix}. $$

$$(6.22)$$

The above equation can be generalized for S source gathers by replacing the upper summation limit by S so that the $1/(l_i^2 + l_i'^2)$ terms are replaced by $1/(\sum_{s=1}^{S} l_i^{(s)2})$. Here, $l_i^{(s)}$ is the segment length of the ray originating at the sth source and terminating at the ith receiver.

Smaller values of the element $[\mathbf{L}^T\mathbf{L}]_{ii}^{-1}$, which is proportional to the variance of the ith slowness, lead to a more accurate estimate of s_i. Therefore, equation 6.22 suggests that more raypaths and longer raypath segments that terminate in a layer lead to a more accurate velocity estimate of that layer. Specifically, the following conclusions are obtained.

- Longer raypath segments lead to smaller values of the diagonal elements and better slowness accuracy in the layer in which the ray terminates. As illustrated in Figure 6.5b–6.5d, shallow layers (with long terminating ray segments) for a nonzero offset source are better resolved than deeper layers (with shorter terminating ray segments).
- Slowness variance depends explicitly on the number of rays that terminate in a layer, not on the number of rays that penetrate a layer. For example, many rays penetrate the first layer in Figure 6.4a, but only two rays terminate there. This is demonstrated in Figure 6.5d — accuracy increases by incorporating both transmission and reflection traveltimes.
- Wider source offsets also lead to better slowness accuracy because the segment length of a terminating ray increases with source offset, as illustrated in Figure 6.5b–6.5c.
- Incorporating extra traveltime equations by using traveltimes from more sources decreases the slowness variance in each layer by roughly $1/(Sl^2)$, in which l is the average segment length of a terminating ray and S is the number of sources. Better thickness resolution can be achieved by parameterizing the model into thinner layers (i.e., l becomes smaller) at the expense of increasing the variance of the slowness estimate.
- The matrix inverse $[\mathbf{L}^T\mathbf{L}]^{-1}$ should approximate that for curved-ray tomography with short source-well offsets and gently bending rays. Figure 6.6 shows the plot of the tridiagonal element values of $[\mathbf{L}^T\mathbf{L}]^{-1}$, calculated by a matrix inverse method for 88 transmission traveltimes for the Figure 6.5a model. Also plotted are the element values computed from an 87×87 analytic inverse matrix; this matrix is generalized from the 3×3 matrix in equation 6.22, except curved-ray segment lengths computed by ray tracing are substituted for the straight-ray segment lengths. There is excellent agreement between the actual and predicted element values of $[\mathbf{L}^T\mathbf{L}]^{-1}$.

6.4.2 VSP reflection data

Equation 6.22 suggests that increasing the number of rays that terminate at an interface will give better slowness accuracy. We now will show this to be true when both reflection and transmission traveltimes are inverted simultaneously. This is not surprising because the reflection raypath from an interface at depth z gives a reflection traveltime that is the same as that from a virtual transmission raypath, in which the virtual source is located $2z$ beneath the original source.

Figure 6.4b illustrates the reflected and transmission raypaths for a single source with VSP receivers. The associated traveltime equations are

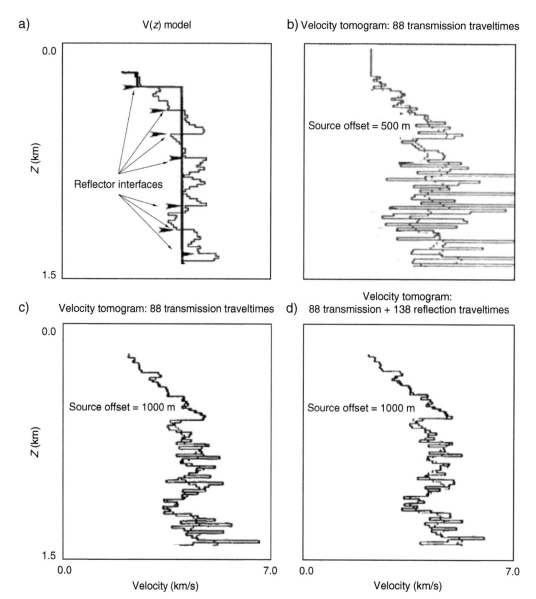

Figure 6.5. (a) An 87-layer velocity model (thick line is the starting model and arrows mark the reflector interfaces) and velocity tomograms reconstructed from 88 direct-arrival traveltimes with source offsets of (b) 500 m and (c) 1000 m. The velocity profile inverted from the combination of both 138 reflection and 88 transmission traveltimes is given in (d) (Salo and Schuster, 1990).

$$
\begin{bmatrix}
l_1 & 0 & 0 & 0 \\
l_2 & l_2 & 0 & 0 \\
l_3 & l_3 & l_3 & 0 \\
l_4 & l_4 & l_4 & l_4 \\
2L_0 & 2L_0 & 2L_0 & 2L_0 \\
L_1 & 2L_1 & 2L_1 & 2L_1 \\
L_2 & L_2 & 2L_2 & 2L_2 \\
L_3 & L_3 & L_3 & 2L_3
\end{bmatrix}
\cdot
\begin{pmatrix}
s_1 \\
s_2 \\
s_3 \\
s_4
\end{pmatrix}
=
\begin{pmatrix}
t_1 \\
t_2 \\
t_3 \\
t_4 \\
T_0 \\
T_1 \\
T_2 \\
T_3
\end{pmatrix}
, \quad (6.23)
$$

in which L_i (T_i) denotes the segment length (reflection time) of the reflection ray that reflects from the bottom and terminates at the ith interface. Unlike the transmission rays, one of the reflections terminate at the $i = 0$ interface, which is

the free surface. It can be shown (Schuster, 1988; Schuster et al., 1988) that for a near-offset source, the $[\mathbf{L}^T\mathbf{L}]^{-1} = [\mathbf{L}]_1^{-1} + [\mathbf{L}]_2^{-1}$ is composed of

$$
[\mathbf{L}]_1^{-1}
$$

$$
=
\begin{bmatrix}
\dfrac{1}{l_1^2 + L_1^2} & -\dfrac{1}{l_1^2 + L_1^2} & 0 & 0 \\
-\dfrac{1}{l_1^2 + L_1^2} & \dfrac{1}{l_1^2 + L_1^2} + \dfrac{1}{l_2^2 + L_2^2} & -\dfrac{1}{l_2^2 + L_2^2} & 0 \\
0 & -\dfrac{1}{l_2^2 + L_2^2} & \dfrac{1}{l_2^2 + L_2^2} + \dfrac{1}{l_3^2 + L_3^2} & -\dfrac{1}{l_3^2 + L_3^2} \\
0 & 0 & -\dfrac{1}{l_3^2 + L_3^2} & \dfrac{1}{l_3^2 + L_3^2}
\end{bmatrix},
$$

$$
(6.24)
$$

Covariance element values versus row number

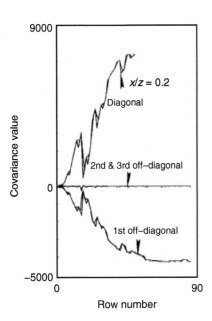
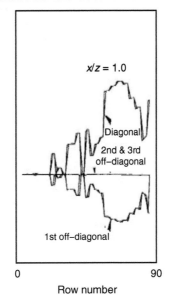
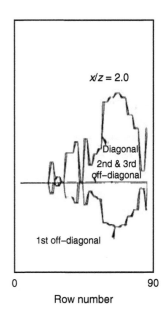

Figure 6.6. Element values of $[\mathbf{L}^T\mathbf{L}]^{-1}$ plotted against row number for transmission traveltime data associated with an 87-layer model for different ratios of $x/z =$ source-offset/well-depth; segment lengths and traveltimes are computed by curved-ray tracing. The elements of $[\mathbf{L}^T\mathbf{L}]^{-1}$ are computed in two different ways: 1) compute the actual inverse and 2) substitute curved-ray segment lengths into the analytic formula for $[\mathbf{L}^T\mathbf{L}]^{-1}$ (Schuster et al., 1988a).

and $\mathbf{L}_2^{-1}$ is a dense coupling matrix:

$$[\mathbf{L}]_2^{-1} = \frac{1}{\beta} \begin{bmatrix} \Delta_{10}^2 & \Delta_{21}\Delta_{10} & \Delta_{32}\Delta_{10} & \Delta_{43}\Delta_{10} \\ \Delta_{10}\Delta_{21} & \Delta_{21}^2 & \Delta_{32}\Delta_{21} & \Delta_{43}\Delta_{21} \\ \Delta_{10}\Delta_{32} & \Delta_{21}\Delta_{32} & \Delta_{32}^2 & \Delta_{43}\Delta_{32} \\ \Delta_{10}\Delta_{43} & \Delta_{21}\Delta_{43} & \Delta_{32}\Delta_{43} & \Delta_{43}^2 \end{bmatrix}.$$

$$(6.25)$$

Here, the coupling terms are given by:

$$\Delta_{i,i-1} = 2\left(\frac{L_i^2}{l_i^2 + L_i^2} - \frac{L_{i-1}^2}{l_{i-1}^2 + L_{i-1}^2}\right); \quad \text{for } i = 2, 3 \quad (6.26)$$

$$\Delta_{10} = \frac{2L_1^2}{l_1^2 + L_1^2}; \quad \Delta_{43} = 1 - \frac{2L_3^2}{l_3^2 + L_3^2}. \quad (6.27)$$

$$\beta = l_4^2 + 3L_0^2 + 3\sum_{i=1}^{3} \frac{l_i^2 L_i^2}{l_i^2 + L_i^2}. \quad (6.28)$$

These terms become small when the segment lengths are nearly the same or when β is large (i.e., the total raypath length is large with respect to the segment length). Therefore, $[\mathbf{L}^T\mathbf{L}]^{-1} \approx [\mathbf{L}_1]^{-1}$ is effectively a tridiagonal matrix

for deep-imaging VSP experiments. The above equation can be generalized to S CSGs by replacing the $1/(l_i^2 + L_i^2)$ terms by $1/(\sum_{s=1}^{S}[l_i^{(s)^2} + L_i^{(s)^2}])$. Here, $l_i^{(s)}$ ($L_i^{(s)}$) is the segment length of the transmission (reflection) ray originating at the sth source and terminating at the ith receiver.

Notice that the diagonal terms in $[\mathbf{L}_1]^{-1}$ are inversely proportional to the sum of squared segment lengths for the reflection and transmission rays. This implies that the tomogram inverted from just one CSG of reflection + transmission traveltimes should be about as accurate as that computed from two CSGs of transmission traveltimes.

As an example of inverting transmission + reflection traveltimes, Figure 6.5d depicts the velocity profile reconstructed from 88 transmission traveltimes and 138 reflected traveltimes per source. Here, the source is offset 1000 m from the well. As predicted by equation 6.25, the accuracy of the reconstructed profiles increases with an increase in the number of rays reflecting from a layer.

6.4.3 CMP reflection data

If the VSP raypaths in Figure 6.4a are replaced by the CMP reflection raypaths in Figure 6.4c, then the reflection raypath matrix $\mathbf{L}_R$ is related to the transmission raypath matrix $\mathbf{L}$ in equation 6.18 by $\mathbf{L}_R = 2\mathbf{L}$. Therefore, $[\mathbf{L}_R^T\mathbf{L}_R]^{-1} = \frac{1}{4}[\mathbf{L}^T\mathbf{L}]^{-1}$, and the dependence of slowness uncertainty on source-receiver geometry is the same for both VSP and CDP data.

Exercises 6.4.1

1. For a simple two-layer model, assume that the data consist of direct-wave and head-wave traveltimes (see Grant and West, 1965, for a description of head waves) for sources and receivers on the surface. Assume that interface depths are known but slownesses are unknown. Find the associated analytic expression for $[\mathbf{L}^T\mathbf{L}]^{-1}$. Comment on how the reconstructed slowness model is sensitive to the source-receiver geometry.

2. For a simple two-layer model, assume that the data consist of direct and reflection traveltimes for sources and receivers on the surface. Assume that both the interface depths and the layer slownesses are unknown. Find the associated analytic expression for $[\mathbf{L}^T\mathbf{L}]^{-1}$. Comment on how the reconstructed slowness model depends on the source-receiver geometry. How does this dependence compare to that for the VSP examples in which only the slownesses are assumed to be unknown.

6.4.4 Uncertainty principle

For a 1D slowness model, the slowness uncertainty Δs is proportional to the square root of $[\mathbf{L}^T\mathbf{L}]_{ii}^{-1}$ so its product with the thickness uncertainty[2] Δz (i.e., the layer thickness) is

$$\Delta z \Delta s \approx \Delta z \Delta t \sqrt{\frac{1}{l_i^2} + \frac{1}{l_{i-1}^2}} > C, \qquad (6.29)$$

in which C is a positive constant that depends on the single-source VSP geometry and the uncertainty[3] in the traveltime pick is denoted as Δt. Equation 6.29 can be proven by noting that $\sqrt{\frac{1}{l_i^2} + \frac{1}{l_{i-1}^2}} \propto 1/\Delta z$ for small source offsets from the well; hence, $\sqrt{\frac{1}{l_i^2} + \frac{1}{l_{i-1}^2}} \Delta z$ is a constant. The product of uncertainties $\Delta z \Delta s$ represents the tradeoff between slowness and depth uncertainties (Pan, 1993); smaller receiver intervals will lead to smaller uncertainties Δz in thickness, but the slowness uncertainty will get larger because the ray segments get shorter. Figure 6.7 shows the tradeoff between slowness and depth uncertainty for various offsets; such graphs can aid in the design of source and receiver offsets for VSP experiments.

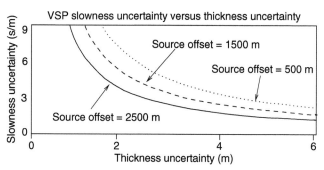

Figure 6.7. Slowness uncertainty versus thickness uncertainty for a single-source VSP experiment and an assumed traveltime uncertainty of $\Delta t = 0.001 s$; the geophone is at a depth of 1.5 km. A better knowledge of Δz leads to more uncertainty in slowness Δs. As the source offset becomes larger, the velocity uncertainty decreases because the raypath segment lengths increase (see equation 6.24).

6.5 Null space of $\mathbf{L}^T\mathbf{L}$ for 2D velocity models

The ill-posed nature of the traveltime tomography problem now is examined for 2D velocity models[4]. We will assume the Figure 6.8 configuration for straight rays, a continuous distribution of sources and receivers on the left and right sides of the model, respectively, and a slowness parameterization into an $N \times N$ grid of square pixels. This VSP + crosswell geometry is identical to a crosswell configuration except receivers are distributed continuously along the top of the model.

We will now list some important properties of the $\mathbf{L}^T\mathbf{L}$ matrix.

Property 1

$\mathbf{L}^T\mathbf{L}$ *is a full-rank matrix for transmission traveltime equations for the Figure 6.8 crosswell + VSP experiment.*

Argument: In Figure 6.8a, ray AZ (which connects the rightmost source position to the shallowest surface receiver) can be used to find the velocity (i.e., $v_1 = l_1/t_1$) in the upper rightmost pixel. Knowing the velocity in this pixel, ray BZ then can be used to find the velocity in the next pixel to the left. This procedure can be continued until all of the velocities in the top-row pixels are determined (see Figure 6.8b).

---

[2]We will conveniently assume that the uncertainty in the interface depth is proportional to the separation between adjacent geophones.

[3]As mentioned at the beginning of this chapter, the uncertainty can be equated to the standard deviation of the estimated or recorded variable.

[4]Early contributions to theorems related to the null-space properties of $\mathbf{L}^T\mathbf{L}$ can be attributed to Bishop et al. (1985), Bube et al. (1985), Ivansson (1985), and Bube and Meadows (1998). One of the key discoveries is that crosswell artifacts typically are characterized by vertical stripes, which are components of the null-space vectors of the partial derivative matrix (see Appendix 6A). Later clarifications are found in Calnan (1989) and Berryman (1991). It is important to recognize that there is the ambiguity in estimating reflector position and the value of the velocity anomaly (Stork and Clayton, 1986; Stork, 1991).

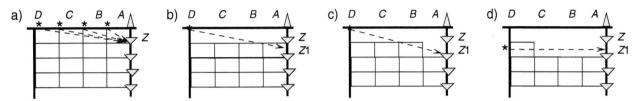

Figure 6.8. VSP and crosswell geometries. (a) The slowness in the top right pixel can be determined (or stripped) by dividing the traveltime associated with ray *AZ* by its pathlength. (b) Then, the next left pixel can be stripped by inverting the traveltime associated with ray *BZ*, and this procedure can be continued until all of the pixels are stripped as shown in (c) and (d). This configuration assumes a sufficiently dense distribution of sources along the top surface and along the left well, and a dense distribution of receivers along the right well.

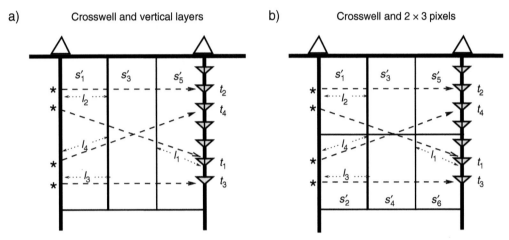

Figure 6.9. Crosswell geometry with (a) three vertical layers and (b) a 2×3 matrix of slowness cells. For (a), the traveltime equation for any crosswell ray is proportional to the equation $t = ls_1 + ls_2 + ls_3$; hence, the traveltime equations are not linearly independent.

Now that the first row of pixels have been stripped, the velocities in the second row of pixels can be reconstructed in a similar fashion as shown in Figures 6.8b–6.8d. Each underlying row can be stripped sequentially until the very bottom row; this process is similar to solving, row by row, a lower triangular system of equations. Note that a dense distribution of sources must be placed in the leftmost crosswell and along the surface for all the pixels to be stripped.

Property 2

The null-space dimension of $\mathbf{L}^T\mathbf{L}$ for a 1D model with N vertical layers (see Figure 6.9a) is equal to $N - 1$ for transmission traveltimes from a crosswell data set with a sufficiently dense distribution of sources and receivers.

Argument: Referring to Figure 6.9a, the associated traveltime equations $\mathbf{Ls} = \mathbf{t}$ are expressed as

$$\begin{bmatrix} l_1 & l_1 & l_1 \\ l_2 & l_2 & l_2 \\ l_3 & l_3 & l_3 \\ l_4 & l_4 & l_4 \end{bmatrix} \begin{pmatrix} s_1 \\ s_2 \\ s_3 \end{pmatrix} = \begin{pmatrix} t_1 \\ t_2 \\ t_3 \\ t_4 \end{pmatrix}. \qquad (6.30)$$

Here, we see that three column vectors of the 4×3 ray-path matrix $\mathbf{L}$ are linearly dependent so that the column null space of the 3×3 $\mathbf{L}^T\mathbf{L}$ matrix has a dimension of two. This dimension remains the same for any increase in the number of rays (or traveltime equations). In general, for a velocity model with N vertical layers, $N - 1$ of the column vectors of $\mathbf{L}$ will be linearly dependent so the column null space of $\mathbf{L}$ will have a dimension of $N - 1$ for a crosswell geometry.

Two null-space eigenvectors of $[\mathbf{L}^T\mathbf{L}]$ are $\mathbf{s}_1 = (1, -1, 0)$, and $\mathbf{s}_2 = (0, 1, -1)$. This says that the traveltime data are unchanged if the velocities of any two vertical layers are exchanged with each other. For example, the traveltime data will be identical to each other for the two slowness models $(s_1, s_2, s_3) = (1, -1, 3)$ and $(s_1, s_2, s_3) = (3, 1, -1)$.

Property 2 highlights an important characteristic of crosswell traveltime tomography: horizontal-like layers[5]

---

[5] A horizontally layered modeled will lead to crosswell traveltime equations with full rank. That is, the slowness of the ith layer is computed by t_i/l_i if the source and receiver associated with the t_i traveltime are at the same depth.

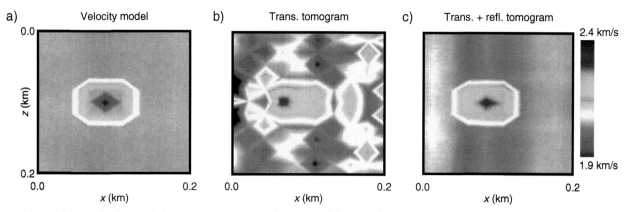

Figure 6.10. (a) 2D velocity model and reconstructed velocity model using (b) 144 transmission traveltimes and (c) 144 and 288 transmitted and reflected traveltimes, respectively, for 12 sources in the left well and 12 receivers in the right well (Calnan, 1989). Here there are two reflectors, one at the top and the other at the bottom. Note the vertical stripes in the reconstructed model are artifacts associated with the nonempty null space or singular vectors with small singular values. Ray bending associated with both the transmission and reflection arrivals can mitigate null-space artifacts.

are well resolved although vertical layers are poorly resolved. More generally, it can be said that parallel rays best resolve the velocity gradient perpendicular to the ray direction (Fawcett and Clayton, 1984). A mathematical restatement of this idea is the projection-slice theorem, derived in the next section.

As an example, the horizontal layer model in Figure 6.4a (i.e., vertical velocity gradient) can be reconstructed perfectly for a crosswell configuration because the crosswell rays are mostly horizontal, at least one ray per layer. This idea also is illustrated in Figure 5.4, except the layers and rays mostly are oriented vertically.

In contrast, if the velocity gradient is mostly parallel to the layers, then the reconstruction will be incomplete. To partly overcome this problem, velocity gradients in the layers will bend crosswell rays away from the horizontal, especially if traveltimes of crosswell reflections are employed. This is demonstrated in the Figure 6.10 tomograms reconstructed with curved-ray tomography for a crosswell experiment with 12 equally spaced sources in the left well and 12 equally spaced receivers in the right one; there are two horizontal reflectors, one at the top boundary and the other at the bottom. Figure 6.10b and Figure 6.10c show the tomograms which use 144 transmission traveltimes in Figure 6.10b and 144 transmission and 288 reflection traveltimes in Figure 6.10c as the input data. The combination transmission and reflection data largely have eliminated much of the null space associated with $\mathbf{L}^T\mathbf{L}$. Consequentially, there are many fewer artifacts in the transmission and reflection tomogram compared to the transmission tomogram. However, there is still some vertical striping in Figure 6.10c which is consistent with Property 2 and indicates the presence of eigenvectors with small singular values. Appendix 6A reviews several other important properties of $\mathbf{L}^T\mathbf{L}$ for crosswell traveltime data.

6.6 Projection-slice theorem: Traveltime tomography

The previous section discussed how the covariance matrix maps data noise into model errors. We now present a variation of the projection-slice theorem (Bracewell, 1990), which shows that traveltimes associated with parallel rays can be inverted for velocity gradients perpendicular to the rays. This theorem is valid for straight rays and is consistent with the rule of thumb that for traveltime tomography, rays best resolve velocity gradients perpendicular to the ray.

The starting point for the derivation of this theorem is the Radon transform (Nolet, 1987), which maps a function $m(\mathbf{x})$ on $\mathbf{x} \in \mathcal{R}^M$ into its set of integrals over a hyperplane in $\mathcal{R}^M$. If the integral is over a line or a hyperplane, then it is the Radon transform; integrals with a weight function over more general hypersurfaces represent the generalized Radon transform (Beylkin, 1984). A simple example of a Radon transform is a dental X-ray measurement $d(\theta, x)$, described by

$$d(\theta, x) = \int_{-\infty}^{\infty} m(x + t\theta)dt, \qquad (6.31)$$

in which the integral of $m(x)$ is over the straight line, and the function $m(x + t\theta)$ is related to the tooth density at a position indicated by $x + t\theta$. Here, $x + t\theta$ describes a line with intercept x and slope θ, and the goal is to measure the X-ray intensity $d(\theta, x)$ exterior to the tooth, and invert equation 6.31 to estimate the density variations inside the tooth.

Similarly, many geophysical measurements can be described as a Radon transform of an earth model. A geophysical example (Nolet, 1987) is the straight-ray

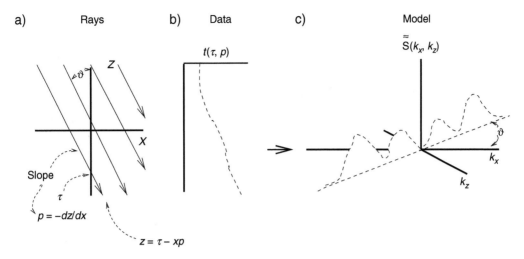

Figure 6.11. (a) Straight rays in (x, z) with slope $dz/dx = -p$, (b) associated traveltime data, and (c) associated slice in (k_x, k_z).

traveltime integral from Chapter 5

$$t(x', z') = \int_{\text{raypath}} s(x, z)dl, \qquad (6.32)$$

in which $s(x, z)$ is the slowness model at (x, z) and the traveltime for energy to propagate from the source to the receiver at (x', z') is defined as $t(x', z')$.

If the rays are straight, as in Figure 6.11, then their z-coordinates can be parameterized as $z = \tau - px$ with the slope $dz/dx = -p$ and z-intercept τ. In this case, the length of a ray segment is $dl = dx\sqrt{1 + (dz/dx)^2} = dx\sqrt{1 + p^2}$ and the traveltime integral becomes

$$t(\tau, p) = \sqrt{1 + p^2} \int_{-\infty}^{\infty} s(x, \overbrace{\tau - px}^{z})dx, \qquad (6.33)$$

or dividing by $\sqrt{1 + p^2}$ yields

$$t(\tau, p)' = \int_{-\infty}^{\infty} s(x, z = \tau - px)dx. \qquad (6.34)$$

The scaled traveltime measurement is defined as the projection $t(\tau, p)' = t(\tau, p)/\sqrt{1 + p^2}$, in which each projection is a traveltime measurement produced by a weighted integration of the slowness field along a line.

Applying a Fourier transform in τ to equation 6.34 yields

$$\mathcal{F}(t(\tau, p)') = \tilde{T}(k_z, p)$$

$$= \int_{-\infty}^{\infty} \left[\int_{-\infty}^{\infty} e^{-ik_z\tau} s(x, z = \tau - px)d\tau \right] dx, \qquad (6.35)$$

in which k_z has units of radians/distance. Substituting $\tau' = \tau - px$ in the above equation gives

$$\tilde{T}(k_z, p) = \int_{-\infty}^{\infty} e^{-ipk_zx} \left[\int_{-\infty}^{\infty} e^{-ik_z\tau'} s(x, \tau')d\tau' \right] dx,$$

$$= \int_{-\infty}^{\infty} e^{-ipk_zx} \tilde{S}(x, k_z)dx,$$

$$= \tilde{\tilde{S}}(pk_z, k_z). \qquad (6.36)$$

The arguments of $\tilde{\tilde{S}}(pk_z, k_z)$ can be equated to (k_x, k_z), in which $k_x = pk_z$ traces out the spectral line with slope $dk_z/dk_x = 1/p$ in the (k_x, k_z) domain. This equation says that the transform of a common-angle gather of traveltimes is equal to the slice of the model spectrum, and defines the projection slice theorem for straight-ray tomography:

PROJECTION-SLICE THEOREM

$$\tilde{T}(k_z, p) = \tilde{\tilde{S}}(k_x = pk_z, k_z)$$

Tilted rays reconstruct layers tilted at the same angle.

Therefore, the transformed common-angle-gather (CAG) traveltimes $\tilde{T}(k_z, p)$ provide a slice $\tilde{\tilde{S}}(pk_z, k_z)$ of the model spectrum along the line given by $k_x = pk_z$. This spectral line has the slope $dk_z/dk_x = 1/p$ in (k_x, k_z), compared to the slope $dz/dx = -p$ of the common-angle rays in (x, z). They are orthogonal to one another if the x- and y-axes are aligned with the k_x- and k_z-axes.

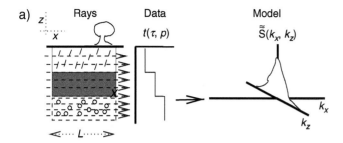

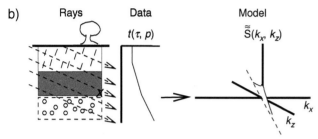

Figure 6.12. Straight rays in (x, z) (a) parallel and (b) subparallel to the interfaces. Rays with a common tilt angle provide a good "view" of the velocity variations perpendicular to the tilt angle.

As an example, traveltimes from horizontal rays can reconstruct the purely vertical velocity variations exactly in the slowness model shown for the top model in Figure 6.12. More generally, traveltime data with constant p can be used to reconstruct the velocity variations perpendicular to these rays.

Resolution limits imposed by the crosswell geometry

The previous analysis implicitly assumed vertical geophone and source wells extended to infinity in the z-direction. To account for vertical wells truncated to length Z and separated by the distance L, define the unit rectangle function as $h(x, z) = 1$ for any (x, z) inside this rectangle and $h(x, z) = 0$ otherwise. Equation 6.34 then can be defined for a finite-aperture crosswell configuration by setting $s(x, z) = h(x, z)s(x, z)'$, in which $s(x, z)'$ describes the layered model with infinite extent. Therefore, the modified projection-slice theorem for a finite-aperture crosswell configuration becomes[6]

$$\tilde{T}(k_z, p) = \tilde{\tilde{S}}(k_x = pk_z, k_z) * \tilde{\tilde{H}}(k_x, k_z), \quad (6.37)$$

in which $\underset{\sim}{*}$ denotes 2D convolution of the 2D sinc function $\tilde{H}(k_x, k_z)$ with the slowness spectrum. For horizontal layers, the 2D sinc function has a main lobe width (height) proportional to $1/L$ $(1/Z)$, and so the reconstructed slowness spectra is a blurred version of the actual slowness spectra. This blurring introduces the uncertainties $\Delta k_x \propto 1/L$ and $\Delta k_z \propto 1/Z$ into the reconstructed slowness spectrum.

Spectrum slices = tilted layers

A tilted slice in the model spectrum is proportional to the Fourier transform of a tilted-layer model in (x, z). This follows from the fact that a tilted-layer model can be represented by $s(x, z) = g(x + pz)$, in which the slope of the tilted layers is equal to $dz/dx = -1/p$. It is straightforward to show that the Fourier transform of $s(x, z)$ is proportional to $\tilde{G}(k_x)\delta(k_z - pk_x)$, in which $\tilde{G}(k_x)$ is the Fourier spectrum of $g(x)$. The function $\delta(k_z - pk_x)$ describes a slice in (k_x, k_z) that tilts with the slope p, and so is perpendicular to the layer tilt in (x, z)[7]. Figure 6.12 illustrates that rays parallel to the layer interfaces will provide projections that yield a good "view" of these layer velocities.

As an example of how the crosswell geometry restricts model resolution, consider the crosswell geometry with two parallel wells offset by a distance X and each having a vertical length L. According to the projection-slice theorem, the straight-ray traveltime data will be unable to reconstruct layers tilted at an angle greater than $\arctan(L/X)$ with respect to the horizontal. It is best to reconstruct models in which the layers are mostly horizontal because the crosswell rays are mostly horizontal and therefore parallel to the horizontal layers.

Radon transform and CDP geometry

The previous section applied the projection-slice theorem to transmission traveltime data. This theorem is also applicable to common-depth-point (CDP) traveltime data by noting that the reflected rays associated with the CDP experiment in Figure 6.13a yield traveltimes equal to those for the mirror-transmission experiment depicted in Figure 6.13b. Here, the transmission experiment is for a horizontal receiver well at the surface and a horizontal source well at twice the depth of the reflector. From this equivalency and the projection-slice theorem, we conclude that near-offset CDP data associated with vertical rays reconstruct velocity models with a lateral velocity gradient.

---

[6]Recall that the product of $f(x)$ with a boxcar function $b(x)$ of width L yields a Fourier transform that is the spectral convolution $\tilde{B}(k_x) * \tilde{H}(k_x)$, where $\tilde{H}(k_x)$ is a sinc function with a main lobe width proportional to $1/L$.

[7]As before, this assumes the x- and z-axes are aligned with the k_x- and k_z-axes.

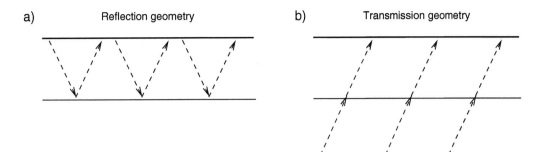

Figure 6.13. (a) Reflection and (b) equivalent mirror-transmission raypaths.

6.7 Summary

The model uncertainty in a traveltime tomogram can be attributed to a combination of problems: data noise, limited source-receiver coverage, incorrect or incomplete physics in the modeling operator, and the possibility of getting stuck in a local minimum of the misfit function. Understanding the nature of these problems can lead to strategies for mitigating their harmful effects.

A mathematical tool for understanding how data errors map to model errors is the model covariance matrix, which implicitly assumes a linear relationship between model and data. Analysis of $[\mathbf{L}^T\mathbf{L}]^{-1}$ for 1D and 2D models provides the following insights into how slowness uncertainty depends on data errors and source-receiver geometry.

1. Analysis of the covariance matrix $[\mathbf{C}_m]$ for layered velocity models says that longer raypath segment lengths and more terminating rays increase the accuracy of slowness estimates for a VSP, crosswell, or CMP acquisition geometry. The assumes a straight-ray approximation, but empirical results suggest that the analytic $[\mathbf{L}^T\mathbf{L}]^{-1}$ can be appropriate for some bending in the rays. Therefore, wider offsets, shallower layers, more reflection traveltimes, and more sources will lead to less slowness uncertainty.

2. Theoretical considerations show that a gridded $N \times N$ crosswell model yields an $\mathbf{L}^T\mathbf{L}$ matrix with a null-space dimension equal to $N - 1$. Here, transmission traveltime data with a dense distribution of sources+receivers and straight rays are assumed, and N is the number of pixels in a row of the slowness model. The null-space vectors resemble vertical stripes in the model. Traveltimes from dipping reflectors and curved rays can lead to an empty null space for $[\mathbf{L}^T\mathbf{L}]^{-1}$.

3. The projection-slice theorem validates the following rule of thumb for straight-ray traveltime tomography: velocity gradients perpendicular to the ray are best resolved, and gradients parallel to rays are worst resolved. This suggests that wider apertures of source-receiver configurations should be used to maximize the angular diversity of rays that visit any one pixel. Maximizing the range of incidence angles to enhance slowness resolution is consistent with the model resolution formulas derived from the generalized Radon transform (Beylkin, 1984; Sheng and Schuster, 2003) discussed in Chapter 14.

4. The model covariance matrix might yield a model with small variance values, even if the iterations have stalled at a local minimum far from the actual slowness model. This alarming possibility might lure the unsuspecting geophysicist into falsely believing in the accuracy of the tomogram. A sanity test is needed where dramatically different starting models are used to invert the recorded data. If each starting model leads to about the same final tomogram, then this increases the confidence that we are at or near the global minimum.

5. The modeling operator $\mathbf{L}$ might not account for the important physics associated with the data, and yet the covariance matrix is blind to this disturbing fact. For example, the high-frequency assumption of ray tracing might be invalid for some traveltime data which does not honor the high-frequency assumption of ray tracing. Another example is that significant traveltime shifts in the arrivals might be caused by something other than slowness variations in an isotropic model; for example, attenuation, anisotropy, or scattering losses can cause phase delays. Such shifts should be accounted for in $\mathbf{L}$, otherwise the covariance matrix will not be a reliable indicator of model error. The high-frequency assumption is avoided if finite-frequency wavepaths (Woodward, 1992) replace the raypaths, which will be discussed in Chapters 12, 14, and 20.

6.8 Exercises

1. Sometimes static delays[8] at a geophone are severe. A possible remedy is to subtract the unprimed traveltime equations in equation 6.18 from the primed ones to give

---

[8]A static delay is a time shift arising from, for example, wave propagation through a localized velocity anomaly just beneath the receiver.

the interferometric traveltime equations:

$$[\mathbf{L}_1 - \mathbf{L}_2]\mathbf{s} = \begin{bmatrix} l_1 - l_1' & 0 & 0 \\ l_2 - l_2' & l_2 - l_2' & 0 \\ l_3 - l_3' & l_3 - l_3' & l_3 - l_3' \end{bmatrix} \begin{pmatrix} s_1 \\ s_2 \\ s_3 \end{pmatrix}$$

$$= \begin{pmatrix} t_1 - t_1' \\ t_2 - t_2' \\ t_3 - t_3' \end{pmatrix}. \tag{6.38}$$

Find the associated $[(\mathbf{L}_1 - \mathbf{L}_2)^T(\mathbf{L}_1 - \mathbf{L}_2)]^{-1}$ and discuss how the variance of the solution is affected. What are some acquisition strategies for minimizing variance? See Zhou and Schuster (2000).

2. Assume a severe source static in the traveltimes represented by equation 6.18. Devise an interferometric strategy for eliminating the source static, and derive the associated model covariance matrix. What is the best acquisition strategy for minimizing slowness variance and source statics?

3. Assume both source and receiver statics in the data. What subtraction strategy can eliminate both source and receiver statics. Find the associated model covariance matrix and comment on how this affects slowness variance.

4. Find the model covariance matrix in which closure phase is applied to the traveltime data (Zhou and Schuster, 2000). Comment on how this affects slowness covariance.

5. Use the method of Aoki and Schuster (2009) to estimate the diagonal components of $[\mathbf{L}^T\mathbf{L}]^{-1}$ for traveltime tomography, with the traveltime data generated for a simple velocity model. Compare the actual components of $[\mathbf{L}^T\mathbf{L}]^{-1}$ to the estimated components. Comment on the possibility of using this estimate as a preconditioner.

Appendix 6A:
Null-space properties of $\mathbf{L}^T\mathbf{L}$

We now discuss the null-space properties (3 and 4) of $\mathbf{L}^T\mathbf{L}$ for reflection and transmission crosswell data. Unless stated otherwise, the slowness model is assumed to be gridded into square pixels of the same size and each pixel is homogeneous.

Property 3

For a sufficiently dense distribution of crosswell sources and receivers, the minimum null-space dimension of $\mathbf{L}^T\mathbf{L}$ for a 2D model with $N \times N$ pixels is equal to $N - 1$ for transmission traveltimes. This also is true for transmission and reflection data, as long as the reflection data are from horizontal reflectors.

Example 6.8.1. VSP transmission traveltimes

The transmission-traveltime equations for the 2×3 pixel model in Figure 6.9b are given by

$$\overbrace{\begin{bmatrix} l_1 & 0 & .5l_1 & .5l_1 & 0 & l_1 \\ l_2 & 0 & l_2 & 0 & l_2 & 0 \\ 0 & l_3 & 0 & l_3 & 0 & l_3 \\ 0 & l_4 & .5l_4 & .5l_4 & l_4 & 0 \end{bmatrix}}^{\mathbf{L}_{2d}} \begin{pmatrix} s_1' \\ s_2' \\ s_3' \\ s_4' \\ s_5' \\ s_6' \end{pmatrix} = \begin{pmatrix} t_1 \\ t_2 \\ t_3 \\ t_4 \end{pmatrix}, \tag{6.39}$$

in which the 4×6 raypath matrix is denoted as $\mathbf{L}_{2d}$. Let us reparameterize the 2×3 model into the 1×3 model in Figure 6.9a, in which $s_1' = s_2' = s_1$ and the leftmost pixels in the model have the same slowness. This constraint can be incorporated into equation 6.39 by vectorially adding the two leftmost column vectors and replacing the two unknowns s_1' and s_2' by s_1 to get

$$\begin{bmatrix} l_1 & .5l_1 & .5l_1 & 0 & l_1 \\ l_2 & l_2 & 0 & l_2 & 0 \\ l_3 & 0 & l_3 & 0 & l_3 \\ l_4 & .5l_4 & .5l_4 & l_4 & 0 \end{bmatrix} \begin{pmatrix} s_1 \\ s_3' \\ s_4' \\ s_5' \\ s_6' \end{pmatrix} = \begin{pmatrix} t_1 \\ t_2 \\ t_3 \\ t_4 \end{pmatrix}. \tag{6.40}$$

Thus the leftmost column of pixels in Figure 6.9b is reparameterized into a single vertical column. In a similar fashion, the middle column of pixels can be constrained to have the same slowness (i.e., reparameterized into a single vertical column), and then the slownesses in the last column of pixels can be equated to one another as well. This yields the system of traveltime equations

$$\overbrace{\begin{bmatrix} l_1 & l_1 & l_1 \\ l_2 & l_2 & l_2 \\ l_3 & l_3 & l_3 \\ l_4 & l_4 & l_4 \end{bmatrix}}^{\mathbf{L}_{1d}} \begin{pmatrix} s_1 \\ s_2 \\ s_3 \end{pmatrix} = \begin{pmatrix} t_1 \\ t_2 \\ t_3 \\ t_4 \end{pmatrix}, \tag{6.41}$$

in which the raypath matrix is denoted as $\mathbf{L}_{1d}$, and s_2 and s_3 are the slownesses, respectively, for the middle and right columns in Figure 6.9a.

Formula 6.41 represents the traveltime equations for the model with three vertical columns of slowness in Figure 6.9a, in which the null-space dimension of $\mathbf{L}_{1d}$ is $N - 1$ for $N = 3$ in this example. In general, any $N \times N$ pixelated model can be reduced to a model of N homogeneous columns of slownesses in which the resulting $\mathbf{L}_{1d}$ matrix has a null-space dimension of $N - 1$. This, of course, assumes a sufficiently dense distribution of sources and receivers.

But each of the 4×1 linearly dependent column vectors of $\mathbf{L}_{1d}$ is a vectorial sum of two distinct column vectors of $\mathbf{L}_{2d}$. It follows that the ensemble of the column vectors in $\mathbf{L}_{2d}$ has a null-space dimension greater than or equal to $N - 1$. In general, each column vector of $\mathbf{L}_{1d}$ for a model of N equi-thick vertical layers always can be constructed by a vectorial sum of distinct column vectors in $\mathbf{L}_{2d}$, in which $\mathbf{L}_{2d}$ is associated with the grid of $N \times N$ pixels. Hence, the previous property implies that the null-space dimension of $\mathbf{L}_{2d}$ is at least equal to or larger than $N - 1$.

In fact, the null-space dimension of $\mathbf{L}_{2d}$ is exactly equal to $N - 1$ for a dense distribution of sources and receivers. To prove this last statement, simply replace the top row of N pixels in the $N \times N$ model by a long homogeneous layer as in Figure 6.8b. Algebraically, the associated raypath matrix can be obtained by adding together N column vectors in the original $\mathbf{L}_{2d}$ matrix, which is the same as constraining all the slownesses in the top row of pixels to be equal to one another. By the pixel-stripping argument illustrated in Figure 6.8, the deflated matrix now has full rank. Hence, the null-space dimension of the original $\mathbf{L}_{2d}$ matrix for the $N \times N$ model must be exactly equal to $N - 1$ for a dense source-receiver distribution.

As an example, transmission crosswell traveltimes are generated for a 6×6 grid model with 144 traveltime equations (12 sources on the left and 12 receivers on the right). All 36 singular values of $\mathbf{L}^T\mathbf{L}$ are plotted in Figure 6.14, in which there are $N - 1 = 6 - 1 = 5$ near-zero eigenvalues as predicted by Property 3. Indeed, the five null-space eigenvectors plotted in Figure 6.15 resemble vertical columns of homogeneous velocity.

The null-space dimension of $\mathbf{L}^T\mathbf{L}$ also is equal to $N - 1$ for both transmission and reflection data in models with horizontal reflectors. This is true because the image ray of a reflected ray is just another transmitted ray. Figure 6.10 illustrates this idea for a 2D slowness model and a crosswell geometry consisting of 12 sources (receivers) along the left (right) side of the model. The vertical stripes in the reconstructed model are associated with eigenvectors having small or zero eigenvalues.

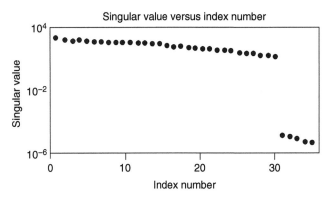

Figure 6.14. Singular values of the 36×36 $\mathbf{L}^T\mathbf{L}$ matrix plotted against the index number of the ordered eigenvalues (Calnan, 1989). The associated slowness model has 36 unknown slownesses in an evenly spaced 6×6 grid model, and there are 144 transmission traveltimes in the data. A singular value is equal to the square root of an eigenvalue of $\mathbf{L}^T\mathbf{L}$.

Property 4

$\mathbf{L}^T\mathbf{L}$ *can be full rank when both transmission traveltime equations and reflection traveltime equations from a dipping layer are used to compute* $\mathbf{L}$.

This property can be proved by considering the simple two-layer model in Figure 6.16a and the associated raypath matrix

$$\mathbf{L} = \begin{bmatrix} l_1 & l'_1 \\ l_2 & l'_2 \end{bmatrix}, \qquad (6.42)$$

in which $l'_2 \neq l_2$ and $l_1 \neq l'_1$. Hence, $\mathbf{L}$ has full rank. An example with many more pixels is illustrated in Figure 6.16b and 6.16c, in which the reflection traveltime equations are associated with reflections from the dipping layer.

As an example, Figure 6.16c displays the singular values of $[\mathbf{L}^T\mathbf{L}]$ for 288 reflection and transmission

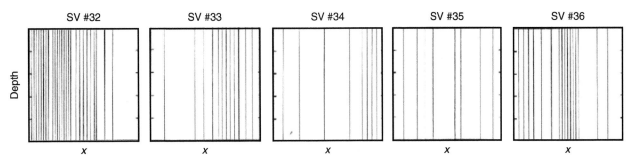

Figure 6.15. Null-space singular vectors (SV) associated with $\mathbf{L}^T\mathbf{L}$ for the 6×6 slowness model (Calnan, 1989); the axis labels are those for the crosswell depth and horizontal coordinates. The element value of each SV (or eigenvector) is inserted into the appropriate pixel in the 6×6 grid, and these values are contoured as above. All of the vectors plot as vertical stripes similar to the vertical layer model in Figure 6.9a.

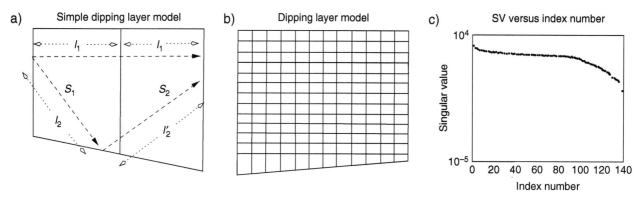

Figure 6.16. (a) Two-pixel and (b) 144-pixel dipping-layer models. The 144-pixel model is 200-m wide and 200-m deep along the right side, and (c) displays the associated singular values (i.e., square root of eigenvalues of $L^T L$), for 12 sources in the left well and 12 receivers in the right well. The input data were 144 transmission traveltimes and 144 reflection traveltimes (Calnan, 1989).

traveltime equations. In this case, the dipping reflector is along the bottom of the model and there are 12 sources in the left well and 12 receivers in the right well. This property is consistent with the Figure 6.10c

tomogram, in which the reflection traveltimes associated with the horizontal reflectors eliminated most of the artifacts seen in the Figure 6.10b transmission tomogram.

Part III

Numerical Modeling

Chapter 7: Traveltime Calculation by Solution of the Eikonal Equation

This chapter presents the numerical solution of the eikonal equation (see Appendix 5A) by a finite-difference method, in which the output is the first-arrival traveltime field for a smoothly varying inhomogeneous velocity model. These traveltimes can be used for either traveltime tomography or reflection migration.

7.1 Finite-difference solution of the eikonal equation

The traveltime field can be computed by a finite-difference solution to the eikonal equation (Vidale, 1988; Podvin and Lecomte, 1991; Qin et al., 1992; Sethian and Popovici, 1999). We will follow the expanding-wavefront scheme proposed by Qin et al. (1992), which is based partly on Huygen's principle (Saito, 1990).

1. Project the slowness field $s(\mathbf{x})$ onto a rectangular grid of nodes, and assume a constant slowness value s_i in the ith cell. The grid interval h must be smaller than $1/10$ the shortest wavelength λ^{source} in the source field, and the minimum velocity variation[1] $\lambda^{\text{velocity}}$ should satisfy $3\lambda^{\text{velocity}} > \lambda^{\text{source}}$ (Bleistein, 1984).

2. Calculate the approximate first-arrival traveltime from the source point to its nearest eight neighboring nodes by straight-ray tracing. In the Figure 7.1a example, the traveltime t_{B1} at gridpoint $B1$ is calculated by $t_{B1} = \Delta x s(B1)$, where Δx is the distance between the source and the point $B1$, and $s(B1)$ is the slowness at point $B1$. The other seven gridpoints are timed in a similar fashion. The outer ring of timed gridpoints represents the computational wavefront at a particular iteration, and the computational wavefront expands along with the physical wavefront of first arrivals. Straight-ray tracing is used until the computational wavefront is at about five points from the source point (see Qin et al., 1992).

3. Approximate the eikonal equation by a finite-difference formula (Vidale, 1988); e.g., in Figure 7.1b, the finite-difference approximation centered at gridpoint c becomes

$$((t_e - t_w)/2h)^2 + ((t_n - t_s)/2h)^2 = s(c)^2. \qquad (7.1)$$

If the known traveltimes are at gridpoints w, n, and s, then the unknown traveltime at point e can be found from the above equation to give

$$t_e = t_w + 2h\sqrt{(\bar{s}^2 - (t_n - t_s)^2/4h^2)}, \qquad (7.2)$$

in which $\bar{s}$ is the slowness at the center of the stencil. The gridpoints at or next to the corner points are timed by the stencils shown in Figure 7.1b.

4. Search for the minimum traveltime point along the computational wavefront (see dashed contour in Figure 7.2a). From this minimum traveltime point, expand the solution to its nearest outer neighbor. For example, the red disk in Figure 7.2a is assumed to be the minimum traveltime along the dashed contour, so the solution is expanded (using a formula similar to that in equation 7.2) from there to its nearest neighbors (red and green disks along the dashed contour in Figure 7.2b). Update the computational wavefront by including the three newly timed points and time the red disk in Figure 7.2c. Now all the points along the dashed contour have almost identical traveltimes.

5. Step 4 is repeated until all of the gridpoints in the model have been timed. Expanding outward from the minimum traveltime point ensures that the computational wavefront stays nearly coincident with the physical wavefront of first arrivals. This prevents violation of causality (Qin et al., 1992).

Note, the above procedure times new points along an "expanding wavefront," which is superior to the "expanding-square" strategy that violates causality (see Figure 7.3) for models with moderate-to-large velocity contrasts. For large velocity contrasts, the expanding-square method can violate the causality rule "the time for the part of the ray path leading to a point must be known before

---

[1]The shortest source wavelength is computed by dividing the minimum velocity in the model by the maximum frequency in the source wavelet. The minimum wavelength in the velocity model is found by taking a spatial Fourier transform of the model, and setting $\lambda^{\text{velocity}}$ to be inversely proportional to the maximum wavenumber.

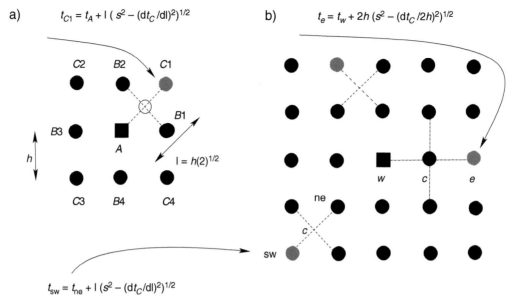

a) $t_{C1} = t_A + l (s^2 - (dt_C/dl)^2)^{1/2}$

b) $t_e = t_w + 2h (s^2 - (dt_C/2h)^2)^{1/2}$

$l = h(2)^{1/2}$

$t_{sw} = t_{ne} + l (s^2 - (dt_C/dl)^2)^{1/2}$

Figure 7.1. The finite-difference grid and differencing stencils associated with the discrete approximation to the eikonal equation. The stencils are shown (a) around the source-point region and (b) away from the source-point region. The solid square at point A is the source point and the points shown as red disks are about to be timed.

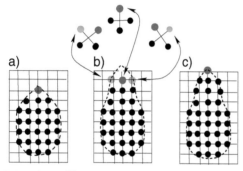

Figure 7.2. Figure illustrating the "expanding wavefront" method. (a) The solution region (black disks) and the red disks (next minimum traveltime) to be timed. The dashed curve represents the actual wavefront. (b) The solution region is expanded to the next minimum traveltime points (red and green disks). The finite-difference stencils used to time the new points are shown above the solution region. (c) Next minimum time point (red disks) to be timed.

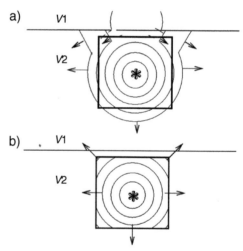

Figure 7.3. A sketch to show the differences between (a) the actual wavefront and (b) the wavefront calculated by the expanding-square method for a two-layer model. Note that the expanding-square wavefront is incorrect if the critical angle θ_c is less than $\sin^{-1}(V_1/V_2) = 45°$ (or $V_1/V_2 < 0.7071$).

the time of the point can be found" (Vidale, 1988). This can lead to negative values inside the square root. Figure 7.3 is a sketch to show the difference between the actual wavefronts and those calculated by the expanding-square method, in which the miscalculation of the head-wave traveltime is seen clearly. The above procedure can be quite expensive because each gridpoint will initiate a minimum travel-time search along its associated computational wavefront of $O(N)$ points. Thus, the computational cost to time the entire grid can be quite high.

To reduce this cost, Qin et al. (1992) suggest that the perimeter search for the minimum traveltime point be reinitiated only after the computational wavefront expands over some fixed time interval, say δt. Prior to the next perimeter search at $t + \delta t$, the solution is expanded in the same pointwise order as determined by the previous perimeter search at t. Larger δt values will lead to less traveltime accuracy, so there is a tradeoff between accuracy and computational efficiency. The traveltimes need to be reordered from minimum to maximum values every $K\delta t$ for some specified integer K. An efficient alternative is the fast marching method of Sethian and Popovici (1999), and the

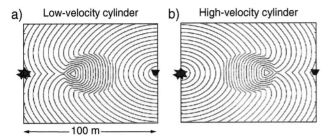

Figure 7.4. First-arrival traveltime contours for a source located on the left side of (a) a low-velocity cylinder and (b) high-velocity cylinder model. All traveltimes are computed by a finite-difference solution to the eikonal equation.

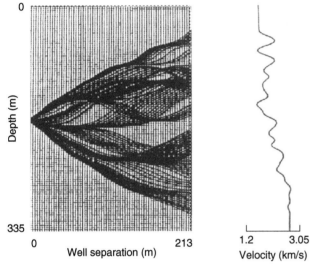

Figure 7.5. Langan velocity model adapted from a Southern California well log and rays computed by a shooting method. Note the failure of rays to penetrate into the shadow zones.

algorithm described in Appendix 7A costs only $O(N^2)$ for an $N \times N$ grid.

The advantages of calculating traveltimes by a finite-difference method compared to ray tracing are that traveltime fields can be computed in shadow zones, some multipathing events are included and the entire grid is timed efficiently (Vidale, 1988). Knowing the traveltimes at all gridpoints can facilitate applying traveltime tomography to the data (Nolet, 1987). The disadvantage is that only first arrivals can be computed easily, but there are procedures (e.g., Podvin and Lecomte, 1991) for computing other arrivals such as the direct arrival (Mo and Harris, 2002) that can be used for migration. See Figure 7.4 for an example of traveltime contours computed by a finite-difference solution of the eikonal equation both for high- and low-velocity cylinder models. For the low-velocity cylinder model, the raypaths for first-arrivals will mostly go around, not through, the cylinder. This is similar to the layered model in Figure 7.5, where rays computed by a shooting

method fail to penetrate into the shadow zone around the depth of 160 m.

The raypaths associated with the traveltime integral in equation 5.45 are computed by tracing rays normal to a wavefront, or by invoking the traveltime reciprocity equation (Saito, 1990)

$$\tau_{rs} = \tau_{rx} + \tau_{xs}, \qquad (7.3)$$

in which τ_{xs}, τ_{rx} and τ_{rs} are the first-arrival traveltimes from the source point **s** to **x**, from the receiver point **r** to **x**, and from the source point to the receiver point, respectively. The first-arrival raypath between **s** and **r** is described by the locus of points **x** that satisfy equation 7.3.

7.2 Summary

A numerical scheme for the finite-difference solution to the eikonal equations is presented, in which traveltimes of specified events are computed at every gridpoint of the slowness model. The first-arrival traveltimes can be used for refraction tomography, and the direct arrival traveltimes can be used for migration. To satisfy the high-frequency approximation, the characteristic wavelength of the velocity fluctuations must be more than three times longer than the source wavelength (Bleistein, 1984).

7.3 Exercises

1. Sketch out a rough MATLAB® code that solves the 2D eikonal equation for first arrivals.
2. Sketch out a rough MATLAB code that solves the 2D eikonal equation for direct arrivals (Mo and Harris, 2002).
3. Using Fermat's principle, sketch out the MATLAB procedure for finding reflection traveltimes from a specified reflection interface. Assume the direct-arrival times have been calculated by an eikonal solver.
4. Same as previous question, except find the traveltimes of the free-surface related multiples.

Appendix 7A:
Efficient sorting of traveltimes

Yonghe Sun (personal communication, 2013) shows that $O(N^2)$ algebraic operations can be used to compute the traveltimes in an $N \times N$ gridded model. Assume that the current wavefront has $M = O(N)$ gridpoints, and the next wavefront needs to be computed. The traveltimes of gridpoints at the current wavefront are nearly the same, but not identical. Let the minimum and maximum traveltimes of the current wavefront points be T_{min} and T_{max}, respectively. Let $\Delta T = T_{max} - T_{min}$. Divide this span ΔT into M buckets with each spanning the time interval $\delta t = \Delta T/M$. The traveltime for the ith bucket has all the points with traveltimes nearest $T_{\min} + i\delta t$. Some buckets have few gridpoints, and some have no gridpoints. The buckets contain gridpoints sorted with resolution of $\delta t/2$. The $i = 0$ bucket has the minimum traveltimes, and the $i = M$ bucket has the largest traveltimes. The algorithm is sketched below.

1. Initialize a new array of buckets for sorting the next wavefront.
2. For each gridpoint in the buckets starting with $i = 0$ to $i = M$ in the old array of buckets, compute the traveltimes at untimed neighbors, and drop them into the new array of buckets.

3. Repeat steps 1 and 2 until all $N \times N$ points are timed.

The new wavefront and new buckets for one wavefront are computed with $O(M)$ operations, so the cost is no more than $O(N)$ operations. Because we have $O(N)$ wavefronts, the total operation is on the order of $O(N^2)$. Because δt is so small, further sorting within each bucket is unnecessary.

For example, let $N = 1000$, $\Delta T = 0.005$s, $M = 1000$, $\delta t = 0.000005$s, and assume the total traveltime to be 5 s. All gridpoints in a bucket have essentially the same traveltime. Further sorting will improve the accuracy by a small fraction of δt, which is not practically meaningful.

Chapter 8: Numerical Solutions to the Wave Equation

This chapter introduces some popular numerical methods for approximating solutions to the acoustic and elastic wave equations. Such solutions include all events from primary and multiple scattering, and so are used for reverse time migration and waveform inversion. We will give an overview of the finite-difference method on regular grids (Kelly et al., 1976) and on staggered grids (Virieux, 1984 and 1986; Levander, 1988). Higher-order stencils are needed for better accuracy, so spectral collocation methods have been developed that are more accurate than the finite-difference method. Trefethen (2000) writes "If one wants to solve an ODE or PDE to high accuracy on a simple domain, and if the data defining the problem are smooth, then spectral methods are usually the best tool. They can often achieve ten digits of accuracy where a finite-difference or finite element method would get two or three. At lower accuracies, they demand less computer memory than the alternatives." Therefore, this chapter also describes the pseudospectral and the spectral element methods. The pseudospectral method (Kosloff and Baysal, 1982; Kosloff et al., 1984) has the highest accuracy, but can suffer from significant numerical errors at interfaces with large impedance contrasts. This problem can be mostly overcome with the spectral element method (Komatitsch et al., 2005; Kudela et al., 2007), and still retain high-order accuracy and reasonable efficiency in the solution.

8.1 Finite-difference method

Table 8.1 contains finite-difference (FD) approximations to derivative operators (Dablain, 1986; Fornberg, 1988), whose order of accuracy can be estimated by using a Taylor series expansion. For example, the forward FD approximation can be expanded in a Taylor series

$$\frac{f(x + \Delta x) - f(x)}{\Delta x} = \frac{1}{\Delta x}\left[f(x) + \frac{df(x)}{dx}\Delta x \right.$$
$$\left. + \frac{1}{2}\frac{d^2f(x)}{dx^2}(\Delta x)^2 + \cdots - f(x)\right],$$

$$= \frac{df(x)}{dx} + 1/2\frac{d^2f(x)}{dx^2}\Delta x + \cdots ,$$
$$= \frac{df(x)}{dx} + O(\Delta x), \qquad (8.1)$$

which says that this FD approximation with the pivot point at x is first-order accurate in the sampling interval Δx, where the term $O(\Delta x)$ is denoted as the truncation error. Similarly, the central FD approximation to a second-order derivative $d[df(x)/dx]/dx$ can be derived by applying a forward FD approximation that is first-order accurate for the term in brackets and a backward FD approximation that is first-order accurate for the outer term.

8.1.1 Finite-difference approximation to the wave equation

The 2D acoustic wave equation for a medium with no density variations is given by

$$\frac{\partial^2 p(\mathbf{x}, t')}{\partial x^2} + \frac{\partial^2 p(\mathbf{x}, t')}{\partial z^2} - \frac{1}{c(x,z)^2}\frac{\partial^2 p(\mathbf{x}, t')}{\partial t'^2} = f(\mathbf{x}, t'),$$
$$(8.2)$$

in which $c(x, z)$ is the velocity model, $p(\mathbf{x}, t')$ is the pressure field, and $f(\mathbf{x}, t')$ is the inhomogeneous source term. The continuous wave equation and its solution can be discretized onto an evenly sampled grid in the space and time domains such that

$$(x, z, t') \longleftrightarrow (i\Delta x, \ j\Delta z, \ t\Delta t),$$
$$\text{in which } i, j, \text{ and } t \text{ are integers}$$
$$p(x, z, t') \longleftrightarrow p_{ij}^t, \qquad (8.3)$$
$$f(x, z, t') \longleftrightarrow f_{ij}^t,$$
$$c(x, z) \longleftrightarrow c_{ij},$$

and for convenience, we will assume that the vertical grid-point spacing Δz is the same as the horizontal spacing Δx. The discrete solution can be visualized with a 3D-data cube (see Figure 8.1) with the x, z, and t axes. The depth of the

Table 8.1. Finite-difference (FD) formulas for first-, second-, fourth-, and eighth-order approximations to derivatives, in which Δx is the difference interval.

Derivative	FD approximation	FD name	Order of accuracy
$df(x)/dx$	$[f(x+\Delta x) - f(x)]/\Delta x$	Forward FD	$O(\Delta x)$
$df(x)/dx$	$[f(x) - f(x-\Delta x)]/\Delta x$	Backward FD	$O(\Delta x)$
$df(x)/dx$	$[f(x+\Delta x) - f(x-\Delta x)]/(2\Delta x)$	Central FD	$O[(\Delta x)^2]$
$df(x)/dx$	$[8(f(x+\Delta x) - 8f(x-\Delta x))$ $\quad -(f(x+2\Delta x) - f(x-2\Delta x))]/(12\Delta x)$	Central FD	$O[(\Delta x)^4]$
$df(x)/dx$	$1/\Delta x \sum_{i=-4}^{4}[c_i f(x+i\Delta x)]$ $c_0 = 0; c_1 = 4/5; \; c_2 = -1/5$ $c_3 = 4/105; \; c_4 = -1/280; c_i = -c_{-i}$	Central FD	$O[(\Delta x)^8]$
$d^2f(x)/dx^2$	$[f(x+\Delta x) - 2f(x) + f(x-\Delta x)]/(\Delta x)^2$	Central FD	$O[(\Delta x)^2]$
$d^2f(x)/dx^2$	$1/(\Delta x)^2 \sum_{i=-2}^{2}[c_i f(x+i\Delta x)]$ $c_0 = -5/2; \; c_1 = 4/3; \; c_2 = -1/12; c_i = c_{-i}$	Central FD	$O[(\Delta x)^4]$
$d^2f(x)/dx^2$	$1/(\Delta x)^2 \sum_{i=-4}^{4}[c_i f(x+i\Delta x)]$ $c_0 = -205/72; \; c_1 = 8/5; \; c_2 = -1/5$ $c_3 = 8/315; \; c_4 = -1/560; c_i = c_{-i}$	Central FD	$O[(\Delta x)^8]$

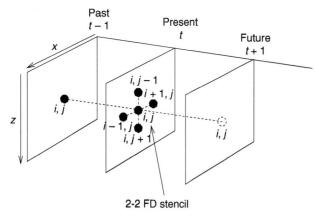

Figure 8.1. Depiction of 2-2 FD stencil for the 2D acoustic wave equation. The future value of the pressure at the (i, j) node (open dashed circle) is computed from the present and past values of the pressure that neighbor the (i, j) node at the present time t. The stencil can be shifted within the t plane to compute all of the pressure values within the $t + 1$ plane. The pressure values at the boundaries of these planes must be specified.

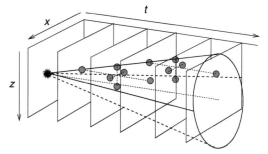

Figure 8.2. Depiction of forward light cone generated by a FD solution (several stencils are depicted) to the wave equation for a point source at depth. The numerical domain of dependence for the point source is alive within the conical boundaries, but is quiescent outside the cone. Note that the physical propagation velocity should be slower than the cone velocity for the FD solution to accurately emulate the actual wave phenomenon.

data cube is given by $M\Delta z = D$, the width is $N\Delta x = X$, and the temporal extent is $L\Delta t = T$, where M, N and L are integers.

Pivoting (i.e., evaluating) the pressure field at (i, j, t) and approximating the second-order derivatives in equation 8.2 by second-order correct central-difference approximations gives

$$\frac{\partial^2 p}{\partial t^2} \longleftrightarrow [p_{ij}^{t+1} - 2p_{ij}^{t} + p_{ij}^{t-1}]/(\Delta t)^2,$$

$$\frac{\partial^2 p}{\partial x^2} \longleftrightarrow [p_{i+1j}^{t} - 2p_{ij}^{t} + p_{i-1j}^{t}]/(\Delta x)^2, \quad (8.4)$$

$$\frac{\partial^2 p}{\partial z^2} \longleftrightarrow [p_{ij+1}^{t} - 2p_{ij}^{t} + p_{ij-1}^{t}]/(\Delta x)^2,$$

yields the discretized wave equation and its associated stencil is shown in Figure 8.1. The time-stepping scheme for these discrete equations is given by

$$\textit{for } t = 2 : nt$$
$$p_{ij}^{t+1} = 2p_{ij}^{t} - p_{ij}^{t-1} + a[p_{i+1j}^{t} - 2p_{ij}^{t} + p_{i-1j}^{t}]$$
$$\qquad + a[p_{ij+1}^{t} - 2p_{ij}^{t} + p_{ij-1}^{t}] - (\Delta x)^2 a f_{ij}^{t},$$
$$\textit{end} \qquad\qquad\qquad\qquad\qquad\qquad (8.5)$$

where $a = (c_{ij}\Delta t/\Delta x)^2$. Here, we assume that the initial conditions are $p(\mathbf{x}, t' = 0)$ and $\partial p(\mathbf{x}, t' = 0)/\partial t'$ for all (x, z), so that the source wavefield is generated by the body-force term f_{ij}^{t}.

A transformation of coordinates from $t' \rightarrow -t'$, i.e., time reversal, will leave the form of the wave equation 8.2

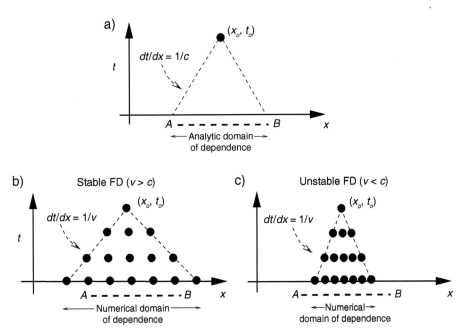

Figure 8.3. (a) The dashed triangle outlines the region that influences the pressure value at (x_0, t_0), and the heavy dashed horizontal line AB at $t = 0$ defines the domain of dependence (DOD) for the analytic solution. Here, the physical propagation velocity is defined as c. The dotted triangular region in (b) defines the region that influences the pressure field at (x_0, t_0) computed by a FD scheme. This FD scheme is conditionally stable because, the numerical propagation velocity $\Delta x / \Delta t$ is faster than the actual velocity c, or equivalently, the numerical domain of dependence is wider than the analytical domain of dependence AB. This is not true for the illustration in (c).

unchanged. This means that the response of the time-reversed wave equation will be the same as the original one, except for a change in the sign of the temporal variable. In this case, the forward light cone in Figure 8.2 will become a backward light cone. The important point is that backward light cones can be generated with the finite-difference equations by solving backward in time rather than forward in time. Such backward cones are used to recreate the earlier history of wavefields from later data, which are known as backward-extrapolated wavefields (Chapter 11).

8.1.2 Stability and accuracy analysis

The accuracy of the 2-2 (i.e., second-order accurate in time and space) scheme is found empirically (Kelly et al., 1976) to be acceptable in a homogeneous medium if there are at least 10 points per minimum wavelength, and the propagation distance is no more than a dozen or so wavelengths. In heterogeneous media, 15–20 points per wavelength usually are used. A higher-order FD scheme such as a 2-4 scheme requires about five points/wavelength in a homogeneous medium (Levander, 1988), but 10 to 15 points per wavelength are needed in a heterogeneous medium. If the gridpoint spacing is too coarse, dipping interfaces appear as stair steps, where the edge of each step acts as a strong diffractor. If the

waves propagate more than 30 wavelengths, empirical evidence suggests higher-order schemes of 2–8 or higher are needed. In fact, Stork (2013) claims that the waves should suffer no more than a quarter of a period in timing error after propagating 50 wavelengths, otherwise iterative waveform inversion will suffer from unacceptable errors.

The CFL (Courant-Friedrichs-Lewy) stability condition can be determined by noting that an FD solution satisfying both the wave equation and the initial conditions at $t = 0$ must have a numerical domain of dependence (DOD) (shown in Figure 8.3) larger than the analytical DOD (Mitchell and Griffiths, 1980). Otherwise, the FD solution will be ignorant of some initial conditions that influenced the solution at (x_0, t_0). This ignorance will lead to an unstable FD solution.[1] To avoid such ignorance, the numerical propagation velocity (defined by $\Delta x / \Delta t$ in 1D) must be faster than the actual propagation velocity c.

---

[1] An unstable FD scheme is one where the errors grow with increasing iterations in the time index. For example, suppose that the solution to the first-order hyperbolic wave equation is a normalized exponential $p_j^t = e^{ikx_j}$ at a specified time step denoted by the index t. Plugging this exponential into the FD approximation to the 1D wave equation gives a solution at a future time as $p_j^{t+p} = \lambda^p e^{ikx_j}$, in which λ is a magnification factor that depends on the sampling intervals in time and space. If the magnification factor $|\lambda| > 1$, the solution is unstable. Otherwise it is a stable solution.

This condition is equivalent to the 1D CFL stability criterion

$$\frac{1}{c} > \frac{\Delta t}{\Delta x},$$ (8.6)

which, in a higher spatial dimension, takes the form

$$\frac{1}{\sqrt{N}} > \frac{c\Delta t}{\Delta x},$$ (8.7)

in which $N = 1, 2, 3$ denotes the spatial dimension number. Therefore, Δx is selected to satisfy the accuracy condition and Δt is selected to satisfy the conditional stability condition.

8.1.3 MATLAB code for FD solution of the acoustic wave equation

The following MATLAB® code computes the 2-2 FD solutions to the 2D acoustic wave equation with constant density.

No absorbing boundary conditions have been included in the above code so strong reflections will emanate from the sides of the model, as if there is a free surface on each side with zero pressure conditions. These unwanted reflections can be attenuated partly by applying a sponge zone and/or absorbing boundary conditions (see Appendix 8A) to the bottom and side boundaries.

8.2 Pseudospectral solution of the wave equation

A significant problem with finite-difference solutions to the wave equation is that they suffer from numerical dispersion errors for long propagation distances. To decrease these errors the finite-difference stencil must become higher order, which leads to longer stencils and computation times. A method that effectively increases the extent of the discrete

```
%%%%%%%%%%%%%%%%%%%%%%%%%%%%%%%%%%%%%%%%%%%%%%%%%%%%%%%%%%%%%%%%%%%%%%%%%%%%%
% (NX,NZ,NT) - input- (Horizontal,Vertical) gridpt dimens. of vel
% model & # Time Steps
% FR          - input- Peak frequency of Ricker wavelet
% BVEL        - input- NXxNZ matrix of background velocity model
% (dx,dt)     - input- (space, time) sample intervals
% (xs,zs)     - input- (x,z) coordinates of line source
% RICKER(NT)  - input- NT vector of source time histories
% (p2,p1,p0) - calc.- (future,present,past) NXxNZ matrices of
% modeled pressure field
% (p0,p1)     -output- Old and present pressure panels at time NT.
% REALDATA(NX,NT) -output- CSG seismograms at z=2
%%%%%%%%%%%%%%%%%%%%%%%%%%%%%%%%%%%%%%%%%%%%%%%%%%%%%%%%%%%%%%%%%%%%%%%%%%%%%
c=4.0;FRE=20;
NX=300;NZ=NX; dx=c/FRE/20;dt=.5*dx/c;
xs=round(NX/2.3); zs=round(NX/2);NT=600;
t=[0:1:NT-1]*dt-0.95/FRE;RICKER=zeros(length(t));
RICKER= (1-t .*t * FRE^2 *pi^2 ) .*exp(- t.^2 * pi^2 * FRE^2 ) ;
plot([0:NT-1]*dt,RICKER);
title('Ricker Wavelet');xlabel('Time (s)')
BVEL=ones(NX,NZ)*c;
BVEL(NX-round(NX/2):NX,:)= BVEL(NX-round(NX/2):NX,:)*1.2;
REALDATA=zeros(NX,NT);
p0=zeros(NX,NZ);p1=p0;p2=p0;
cns=(dt/dx*BVEL).^2;
NX=200;NZ=NX;

%for it=NT:-1        %Reverse Time Looping
for it=1:1:NT        %Forward Time Looping
  p2 = 2*p1 - p0 + cns.*del2(p1);
  p2(xs,zs) = p2(xs,zs) + RICKER(it);
  REALDATA(:,it) = p2(xs,:)';
  p0=p1;p1=p2;
  if round(it/20)*20==it;p00=p0/max(abs(p0(:))+.001);
    imagesc([1:NX]*dx,[1:NX]*dx,(p00+BVEL)); colorbar;
    pause(.1);
  end
end;

p1=p0;p0=p2;
title('Snapshot of Acoustic Waves')
xlabel('X (km)')
ylabel('Z (km)')
```

derivative operator to the width of the computational grid is the pseudospectral method (Kreiss and Oliger, 1972; Kosloff and Baysal, 1982; Kosloff et al., 1984), in which the spatial derivatives are computed in the Fourier domain. In theory, only two points per wavelength are needed for an accurate solution in a smooth medium.

The key elements of the pseudospectral solution to the 1D wave equation

$$\frac{\partial^2 p}{\partial t^2} = \rho c^2 \frac{\partial}{\partial x}\left(\frac{1}{\rho}\frac{\partial p}{\partial x}\right), \tag{8.8}$$

are now presented, in which ρ is density.

1. The spatial derivative $\frac{1}{\rho}\partial p/\partial x$ is computed in the Fourier domain by first taking a fast Fourier transform (FFT) of the pressure field to get P, and multiplying P by ik_x.
2. Take the inverse FFT of $ik_x P$, and multiply the result by $1/\rho$ to get $1/\rho \partial p/\partial x$. This Fourier procedure then is applied to $1/\rho \partial p/\partial x$ to get its spatial derivative $\partial(1/\rho \partial p/\partial x)/\partial x$.

3. The second-order time derivative in the wave equation is approximated by a second-order accurate finite-difference approximation. The future wavefield can be estimated from the current and past values of the wavefield.
4. The time step is incremented by one sample, and steps 1 to 4 are repeated until the total duration of the wavefield is computed.

Because the FFT represents the derivative in the wavenumber domain by the exact multiplication of ik_x, its spatial representation is equivalent to a discrete derivative operator that is as wide as the computational domain. It requires a periodic boundary condition, but if the absorbing boundary conditions are effective (see Appendix 8A and Liu and Sen, 2010; 2012), this should not be a problem.

8.2.1 MATLAB code for pseudospectral solution of the acoustic wave equation

A MATLAB code is described below for forward modeling of the 1D acoustic wave equation with constant density.

```
%%%%%%%%%%%%%%%%%%%%%%%%%%%%%%%%%%%%%%%%%%%%%%%%%%%%%%%%%%%%%%%%%%%%%%%%
% Pseudospectral solution of 1D acoustic  wave equation  by Kai Lu
% method=1     pseudospectral method
% method=2     finite difference method
%%%%%%%%%%%%%%%%%%%%%%%%%%%%%%%%%%%%%%%%%%%%%%%%%%%%%%%%%%%%%%%%%%%%%%%%
clear all; hold off;
method=1;

c=4.0;FRE=20;nx=2000;
dx=c/FRE/10;      %set dx
dt=.3*dx/c;       %set dt
nt=2000;
sx=nx/2;
thick=300;        % sponge thickness
alpha=pi/5/thick;
factor=9;         % sponge factor

% generate wavelet
t=(-200:1:nt-201)*dt-0.95/FRE;
ricker=(1-t.*t*FRE^2*pi^2).*exp(-t.*t*pi^2*FRE^2/2);
plot((0:nt-1)*dt,ricker);title('Ricker Wavelet');xlabel('Time (s)');
pause(1);

% initiate wavefield
p2=zeros(1,nx); p1=p2;p0=p2;

% calculate wavenumber
k=zeros(1,nx);
for i=1:nx
    k(i)=2*pi*(i-1)/nx/dx;
end;
for i=nx/2+2:nx
    k(i)=k(i)/(i-1)*(i-nx-1);
end;

% extrapolate wavefield
for it=1:nt;
    if method==1;
```

```
%  pseudo-spectral method
   P1=fft(p1); DP1=-k.^2.*P1; dp1=real(ifft(DP1));
   p2=2*p1-p0+c^2*dt^2*dp1;
   elseif method==2
%  finite difference method
   p2(2:nx-1)=2*p1(2:nx-1)-p0(2:nx-1)+(c*dt/dx)^2*(p1(3:nx)-2*p1(2:nx-1)+p1(1:nx-2));
   end;

%  add source
   if (it==1);
       p2(sx)=p2(sx)+ricker(it);
   else
       p2(sx)=p2(sx)+ricker(it)-ricker(it-1);
   end;

%  sponge ABC
   for i=1:thick
       p2(i)=p2(i)*(cos(alpha*(thick+1-i))^0.5+factor)/(factor+1);
   end;
   for i=nx-thick+1:nx;
       p2(i)=p2(i)*(cos(alpha*(i-nx+thick))^0.5+factor)/(factor+1);
   end;
%  free surface ABC
%      p2(nx)=0;
%      p2(1)=0;

%  update wavefield
   p0=p1;p1=p2;

   plot((0:nx-1-2*thick),real(p2(thick+1:nx-thick)));
   axis([0 nx-1-2*thick -2.5 2.5]);
   title('Pressure snapshot');
   xlabel('Distance');
pause(0.01);
end;
```

The main drawback of the pseudospectral method is that there are Gibbs-like errors for waves propagating across interfaces with sharp impedance contrasts. This problem seems to have tempered the widespread use of pseudospectral methods in geophysics unless the velocity model is smooth, but the principle of spectral accuracy plays an important role in spectral element methods.

8.2.2 Stability and accuracy analysis

The CFL stability condition is a necessary condition for stability but not sufficient. Therefore, we need to analyze stability further with von Neumann stability analysis. The first step is to assume a discrete plane-wave solution to the 1D wave equation as $p_j = e^{i(kj\Delta x - n\omega\Delta t)}$, in which j and n are the space and time indices. The second-order derivative in x computed by the FFT method gives the second-order derivative as

$$\frac{\partial^2 p_j}{\partial x^2} = -k^2 e^{i(kj\Delta x - n\omega\Delta t)}, \qquad (8.9)$$

and plugging the plane-wave solution into the central difference approximation to the second-order time derivative

in equation 8.4 gives

$$\frac{\partial^2 p_j}{\partial t^2} = -\frac{4}{(\Delta t)^2}\sin^2(\omega\Delta t/2)e^{i(kj\Delta x - n\omega\Delta t)}. \qquad (8.10)$$

Substituting these expressions into the wave equation yields the discrete numerical dispersion relation $k = \frac{2}{c\Delta t}\sin\frac{\omega\Delta t}{2}$, whose reciprocal is

$$\omega = \frac{2}{\Delta t}\sin^{-1}\left(\frac{kc\Delta t}{2}\right). \qquad (8.11)$$

This relation closely approximates the actual dispersion relationship $\omega = kc$ if $\Delta t \ll 1$ and if the argument is smaller than one

$$\frac{k_{\max}c\Delta t}{2} < 1, \qquad (8.12)$$

where $k_{\max} = \pi/\Delta x$ is the maximum wavenumber associated with an unaliased plane wave. In this case, there is very little dispersion and the method is stable for a homogeneous medium with $c\Delta t/\Delta x < 2/\pi \approx 0.636$. Unfortunately, if the velocity variations are not smooth with sharp impedance boundaries, there will be significant errors in the reflected wavefields (Trefethen, 2000).

8.3 Spectral element solution of the wave equation

The spectral element solution to the wave equation is a type of finite element method that is becoming popular among earthquake seismologists for 2.5D and 3D elastic modeling of the Earth (Komatitsch et al., 2005). Its advantages over the standard finite-difference methods are that its irregular grids can be adjusted to conform to irregular free-surface topography and to subsurface interfaces so there are no artificial stair-step diffractions. Similar to the FD with a spatially wide stencil, it can yield solutions that have very little dispersion[2] if the order of the integration is high enough. It is more accurate than the standard finite element method with a lumped-mass approximation (Marfurt, 1984) because the mass matrix is naturally diagonal. The spectral element method also is more accurate than pseudospectral modeling for models with irregular interfaces because the spectral element boundaries can be adapted to the interface geometry.

There are three steps in implementing the spectral element method for efficient wavefield modeling.

1. Expand the solution of the, e.g., 1D wave equation into a sum of $N + 1$ weighted basis functions $N_i(x)$,

$$p(x) = \sum_{i=1}^{N+1} p_i N_i(x), \qquad (8.13)$$

such that these basis functions satisfies the fundamental property

$$N_i(x_j) = \delta_{ij}, \qquad (8.14)$$

for the quadrature points $[x_1, x_2, \ldots, x_{N+1}]$ shown in Figure 8.4 (Kudela et al., 2007). Here, p_i are the pressure values at the quadrature points (also known as nodal points) that are computed at each time step, and the time variable is silent. The basis functions $N_i(x)$ also are known as shape functions, and Figure 8.4 shows several Lagrange polynomials of $N + 1$ order, described by the Lagrange formula

$$N_i(x) = \frac{\prod_{j=1, j \neq i}^{N+1} (x - x_j)}{\prod_{j=1, j \neq i}^{N+1} (x_i - x_j)}. \qquad (8.15)$$

---

[2]Trefethen (2000) writes about "the connection between the smoothness of a function and the rate of decay of its Fourier transform, which determines the size of the aliasing errors introduced by discretization; these connections explain how the accuracy of spectral methods depends on the smoothness of the functions being approximated."

2. Integration of $p(x)$ over the element in Figure 8.4 is approximated by a weighted sum of integrands (each evaluated at a quadrature point)

$$\int p(x)dx \approx \sum_j w_j p(x_j), \qquad (8.16)$$

in which w_j is the quadrature weight. For example, the nodal points in Figure 8.4 are the Gauss-Lobatto-Legendre points ($x_1 = -1$, $x_2 = -0.8717401$, $x_3 = -0.591700$, $x_4 = -0.209299$), $x_5 = -x_4$, $x_6 = -x_3$, $x_7 = -x_2$, $x_8 = -x_1$, and the weights w_j can easily be calculated (Kudela et al., 2007).

Integration of the product of two shape functions and the discrete orthogonality property in equation 8.14 leads to

$$\int N_i(x)N_j(x)dx \approx \sum_k w_k N_i(x_k)N_j(x_k) = \delta_{ij} w_i. \quad (8.17)$$

This property is important because it leads to the diagonal form of the mass matrix so that an explicit time-stepping scheme can be formulated without the use of the lumped-mass approximation.

3. Assume the time-discretized wave equation is represented by $L(x, t)$. Multiply the time-discretized 1D wave equation by the basis function $N_i(x)$, integrate over $0 \leq x \leq 1$, and then integrate by parts, which gives

$$\int L(x, t)N_i(x)dx = \int N_i(x) \left[\frac{d^2 p(x)^t}{dx^2} - \frac{1}{(\Delta t)^2 c^2} \right.$$
$$\left. \times \{p(x)^{t+1} - 2p(x)^t + p(x)^{t-1}\} \right] dx,$$

$$= \left[N_i(x) \frac{dp(x)^t}{dx} \right]_0^1$$

$$+ \int \left[-N_i(x)' \frac{dp(x)^t}{dx} - \frac{N_i(x)}{(\Delta t)^2 c^2} \right.$$
$$\left. \times \{p(x)^{t+1} - 2p(x)^t + p(x)^{t-1}\} \right] dx,$$

$$= \int \left[-N_i(x)' \frac{dp(x)^t}{dx} - \frac{N_i(x)}{(\Delta t)^2 c^2} \right.$$
$$\left. \times \{p(x)^{t+1} - 2p(x)^t + p(x)^{t-1}\} \right] dx.$$
$$(8.18)$$

Here, $N_j(x)'$ is the spatial derivative of $N_j(x)$ evaluated at the nodal point x and zero boundary conditions are assumed, for convenience, at the end points $x = 0$ and $x = 1$ of the element. For further convenience, we take $t + 1$ to be the time that is one time step Δt greater

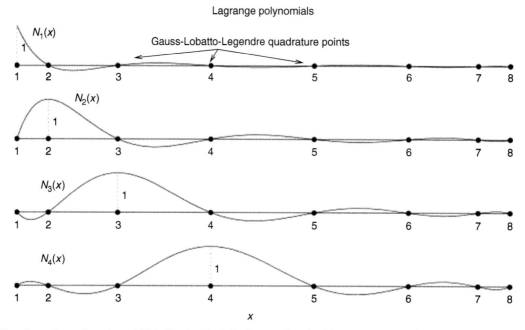

Figure 8.4. First four shape functions $N_j(x)$ (for $j = 1, 2, 3, 4$) associated with a Lagrange polynomial of 7th order, with eight shape functions for this range of x-values. The zero-crossing points x_i are the unevenly spaced Gauss-Lobatto-Legendre quadrature points in which the shape functions $N_j(x_i)$ are zero at these points, except when $i = j$. This range of x-values defines that of a single element. Figure adapted from Kudela et al. (2007).

than the time at t. The integration by parts gives the weak formulation in which only a first-order spatial derivative is used rather than the second-order derivative seen in equation 8.18. Higher-order derivatives of the shape function reduce the order of accuracy, so the weak formulation in equation 8.18 is preferred.

Insert equation 8.13 into the above equation and approximate the integration by a Gauss-Lobatto-Legendre quadrature, which gives

$$\int L(x,t)N_i(x)dx$$

$$\approx -\sum_j w_j \left[\overbrace{N_i(x_j)'N_j(x_j)'}^{\text{non-orthogonal}} p(x_j)^t \right.$$

$$\left. + \frac{\overbrace{N_i(x_j)N_j(x_j)}^{\text{orthogonal}}}{(\Delta t)^2 c^2} \{p(x_j)^{t+1} - 2p(x_j)^t + p(x_j)^{t-1}\} \right],$$

$$= -\sum_j w_j N_i(x_j)'N_j(x_j)'p(x_j)^t$$

$$- \frac{w_i}{(\Delta t)^2 c^2} \{p(x_i)^{t+1} - 2p(x_i)^t + p(x_i)^{t-1}\},$$

$$= 0, \tag{8.19}$$

in which $N_j(x_j)'$ is the spatial derivative of $N_j(x)$ evaluated at the nodal point x_j. Rearranging equation 8.19 gives the formula for the explicit time-stepping scheme

$$p(x_i)^{t+1} = 2p(x_i)^t - p(x_i)^{t-1}$$

$$- \frac{c^2(\Delta t)^2}{w_i} \sum_j w_j N_i(x_j)'N_j(x_j)'p(x_j)^t,$$

$$= 2p(x_i)^t - p(x_i)^{t-1} - \sum_j C_{ij}p(x_j)^t, \tag{8.20}$$

in which $C_{ij} = \frac{c^2 w_j (\Delta t)^2}{w_i} N_i(x_j)'N_j(x_j)'$ represent the spectral element weights for the explicit time-stepping solution of the 1D wave equation. In general, there will be a contiguous series of elements that represent the model space, and so there will be an extra summation in equation 8.19 over the contiguous element values. This does not increase the complexity of the problem because the local basis functions for an element are orthogonal to those from another element.

The above formulation can be extended to higher dimensions by the use of curved spectral elements shown in Figure 8.5. In this case, the quadrature points $\mathbf{x}_i$ in a curved element are mapped to those in a unit square by the formula $\mathbf{x} = \sum_{i=1}^{M_p} N_i(\eta, v)\mathbf{x}_i$, in which $N_i(\eta, v)$ is a two-dimensional Lagrange interpolation function that is zero at the M_p nodal points in the

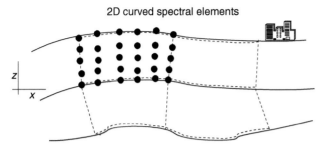

Figure 8.5. Earth model discretized into four curved spectral elements denoted by dashed lines. Each element borders an interface (thick lines) of strong impedance contrast and the material properties can be heterogeneous inside each element. The quadrature points $\mathbf{x}_i$ in one element, i.e., the dashed quadrilateral, are denoted by the filled circles.

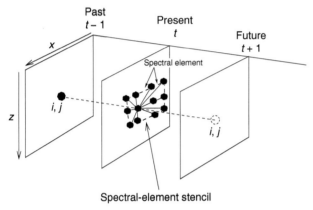

Figure 8.6. Spectral element stencil associated with a time-stepping scheme that is second-order correct in time. There are 12 unevenly-spaced quadrature points in the stencil if the pivot point is in the element's interior.

square except at the (η_i, ν_i) point, where $-1 \leq \eta \leq 1$ and $-1 \leq \nu \leq 1$. The 2D shape function $N_i(\eta, \nu)$ is a product of 1D Lagrange polynomials. The 2D spectral element stencil for the 2D wave equation is shown in Figure 8.6, where it is asymmetrical in space compared to the symmetrical FD stencil in Figure 8.1.

In summary, the spectral element method has very high accuracy and does not suffer from large errors at reflecting boundaries if the spectral element boundaries are parallel to the interfaces. This makes spectral elements ideal for modeling land data with large topographic variations of the free surface. The spectral element (SE) method differs from the standard finite element in that its nodes are at the unevenly spaced quadrature points, and it eliminates the need to make the lumped-mass approximation. However, generating a suitable mesh can require significant computation time and an extensive effort in coding.

8.4 Staggered-grid FD solution of the wave equation

The FD solution to the first-order acoustic and isotropic wave equations (Virieux, 1984 and 1986; Levander, 1988) on a staggered grid now are presented. Its advantage over an FD solution to the second-order equations of motion is that it is more stable for large impedance contrasts in the model because there are no explicit spatial derivatives of material properties. The disadvantage of a staggered-grid FD method is that it requires about 33% more memory if the standard 3D stress-velocity scheme is used. This problem can be eliminated if a parsimonious formulation is used (Luo and Schuster, 1990).

8.4.1 Staggered-grid FD of the first-order acoustic equations

The first-order equations of motion in a 2D acoustic medium

$$\frac{\partial p}{\partial t} = -\kappa \left(\frac{\partial \dot{u}}{\partial x} + \frac{\partial \dot{w}}{\partial z} \right),$$

$$\rho \frac{\partial \dot{u}}{\partial t} = -\frac{\partial p}{\partial x}, \tag{8.21}$$

$$\rho \frac{\partial \dot{w}}{\partial t} = -\frac{\partial p}{\partial z},$$

can be discretized on a staggered grid so there are no explicit spatial derivatives of the bulk modulus or density. The standard staggered-grid scheme (Virieux, 1984) assigns the particle-velocity (u, w) and pressure components to the open gridpoints shown in Figure 8.7 and the pressure component is restricted to the filled gridpoints. The first-order spatial derivatives of pressure and particle velocity in equation 8.21 now can be approximated by second-order correct central-difference approximations, e.g.,

$$\frac{\partial \dot{u}((i+1/2)\Delta x, j\Delta x, t)}{\partial x} \approx \frac{\dot{u}^t_{i+1j} - \dot{u}^t_{ij}}{\Delta x},$$

$$\frac{\partial p(i\Delta x, j\Delta x, t)}{\partial x} \approx \frac{p^t_{i+1/2\,j} - p^t_{i-1/2\,j}}{\Delta x}. \tag{8.22}$$

The time derivatives in equation 8.21 are replaced by centered differences in time, except the pressure time derivatives are centered at time t and the velocity time derivatives are centered at time $t + 1/2$, e.g.,

$$\frac{\partial \dot{u}(i\Delta x, j\Delta x, t+1/2)}{\partial t} \approx \frac{\dot{u}^{t+1}_{ij} - \dot{u}^t_{ij}}{\Delta t},$$

$$\frac{\partial p(i\Delta x, j\Delta x, t)}{\partial t} \approx \frac{p^{t+1/2}_{ij} - p^{t-1/2}_{ij}}{\Delta t}. \tag{8.23}$$

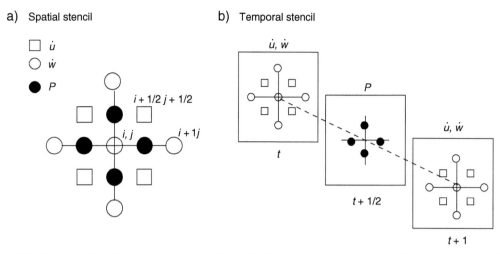

Figure 8.7. The gridpoints at which the pressure and particle-velocity components are spatially staggered. The $\dot{w}$ components are restricted to the (i,j) gridpoints, the $\dot{u}$ components are restricted to the $(i + 1/2, j + 1/2)$ gridpoints, and the pressure p is restricted to the $(i, j + 1/2)$ and $(i + 1/2, j)$ gridpoints.

Here, the temporal variable t will be restricted to be an integer when referring to the finite-difference approximations. The differencing stencil for the z-velocity component in equation 8.21 is shown in Figure 8.7b, where the pressure panels are staggered temporarily with respect to the velocity panels for all time steps.

The free-surface boundary condition assumes that the pressure values at gridpoints just above and below the free surface are opposite and equal. This is an antisymmetric mirror-image boundary condition that ensures the average value of these pressure fields to be zero at the free surface.

8.4.2 Staggered-grid FD of the first-order elastodynamic equations

The first-order elastodynamic equations of motion in a 2D isotropic medium are given as

$$\rho \frac{\partial}{\partial t} \dot{u} - \left(\frac{\partial}{\partial x} \tau_{xx} + \frac{\partial}{\partial z} \tau_{xz} \right) = 0,$$

$$\rho \frac{\partial}{\partial t} \dot{w} - \left(\frac{\partial}{\partial z} \tau_{zz} + \frac{\partial}{\partial x} \tau_{xz} \right) = 0,$$

$$\frac{\partial}{\partial t} \tau_{xx} = (\lambda + 2\mu) \frac{\partial}{\partial x} \dot{u} + \lambda \frac{\partial}{\partial z} \dot{w} + S_{xx}, \qquad (8.24)$$

$$\frac{\partial}{\partial t} \tau_{zz} = (\lambda + 2\mu) \frac{\partial}{\partial z} \dot{w} + \lambda \frac{\partial}{\partial x} \dot{u} + S_{zz},$$

$$\frac{\partial}{\partial t} \tau_{xz} = \mu \left(\frac{\partial}{\partial x} \dot{w} + \frac{\partial}{\partial z} \dot{u} \right),$$

in which S_{xx} and S_{zz} represent the time histories of the body forces acting as "xx" and "zz" component stresses, and $\dot{u}$, $\dot{w}$, τ_{xx}, τ_{zz}, and τ_{xz} denote particle velocities

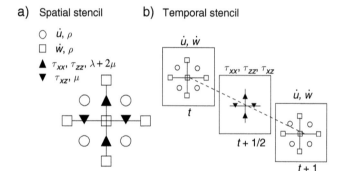

Figure 8.8. Spatial and temporal FD stencils for the first-order elastic equations of motion in an isotropic medium (concepts from Virieux, 1986 and Levander, 1988).

and stresses.[3] Figure 8.8 depicts the arrangement of the stress and particle-velocity variables for a 2-2 elastic FD scheme.

The implementation of the free-surface boundary condition also uses an anti-symmetric condition across the free surface. That is, if the actual free surface intersects the gridpoints for the normal stresses, the normal and shear stresses just above the free surface are set to be equal and opposite to those just below the free surface in Figure 8.8. In this way, the average stress at the free surface is zero.

---

[3]The staggered-grid method has been adapted by Chung and Engquist (2006) to finite elements for solving the acoustic wave equation. They present an energy conserving scheme that has optimal convergence with block diagonal matrices. In the case of rectangular meshes, the mass matrices are diagonal (Chung et al., 2013). Dispersion analysis shows that staggered-grid methods show dispersion errors smaller than the classical finite element or discontinuous Galerkin methods.

An alternative is to intersect the free surface with the node points of the shear stresses, so that similar anti-symmetric conditions are applied to the stresses just above this interface. Both of these formulations appear to give about the same accuracy for a 2-4 elastic staggered-grid scheme (Gottschammer and Olson, 2001).

8.4.3 MATLAB code for staggered-grid FD of the first-order elastic equations

Equations 8.24 can be approximated by an FD scheme on the 2-2 staggered grid (Virieux, 1984 and 1986) shown in Figure 8.8. In this case, the pressure variable becomes the stress variables and the bulk modulus is replaced by Lamé's constant and the shear modulus. A fragment of a MATLAB code for computing the solution to equation 8.24 is given below:

8.5 Modeling in the oil and gas industry

Numerical solutions to the 3D wave equation for reverse time migration and full-waveform inversion (FWI) are now widely used in the oil and gas industry. Therefore, it is important to select the optimal modeling method that minimizes computation time and numerical dispersion. Stork (2013) claims that numerical dispersion errors should be no more than $\pi/20$ after propagating more than 50 wavelengths, which is equivalent to a 0.05% phase error. Otherwise, there can be a fatal buildup of errors when iterative methods such as FWI or least-squares migration are used. He suggests that longer 25-point stencils using optimized coefficients (Zhang and Yao, 2013) are much better at controlling numerical dispersion than using similar-sized stencils with Taylor expansion coefficients (e.g., Table 1). Numerical dispersion is characterized by lower frequency

```
t=2:nt2
%
% Interior 2-2 FD of the Wave Equation (cns = 4*{c dt/dx}^2 )
%
it
k=[2:nz-1];
j=[2:nx-1];
u1(j,k)=u1(j,k)+ dtx./dens(j,k).*(px1(j,k)-px1(j-1,k)+xy1(j,k)-xy1(j,k-1));
%
v1(j,k)=v1(j,k)+ dtx./dens(j,k).*(pz1(j,k+1)-pz1(j,k)+xy1(j+1,k)-xy1(j,k));
%
% Compute Stress Components
%
au=u1(j+1,k)-u1(j,k);
av=v1(j,k)-v1(j,k-1);
px1(j,k)=px1(j,k)+dtx*( ca(j,k).*au+cl(j,k).*av);
pz1(j,k)=pz1(j,k)+dtx*( cl(j,k).*au+ca(j,k).*av);
xy1(j,k)=xy1(j,k)+(cm(j,k)*dtx).*(u1(j,k+1)-u1(j,k)+v1(j,k)-v1(j-1,k));
%
% Free-surface boundary condition at the top boundary
%
k=1;
for j=1:nx;
  xy1(j,k)=0.;
  pz1(j,k)=-pz1(j,k+1);
end;
%
% Add Source Term at nsp points to vertical particle velocity
%
if it<=r;
    for ns=1:nsp;
        v1(xxx(ns),yyy(ns))=v1(xxx(ns),yyy(ns))+ricker(it);
    end;
end
%
% Save Particle Velocity and tzz Seismograms at Free Surface.
%
seismo(1:nx,it)=u1(1:nx,3);seismoy(1:nx,it)=v1(1:nx,3);
seismotzz(1:nx,it)=pz1(1:nx,3);
if it/30 == round(it/30); plotit(dx,pz1+px1,nx,nz,it,dt); end
it
end;
```

waves traveling faster than higher frequency waves, and arises from numerical errors caused by a coarse sampling interval in the computational grid (Diet and Lailly, 1984).

Stork (2013, 3) makes the following claims:

> The improved accuracy of longer (i.e., higher-order accuracy) stencil operators significantly reduces cost. Going from 4 gridpoints per wavelength to 2.2 gridpoints per wavelength reduces computation cost by $(4/2.2)^4 = 11$ and reduces memory by $(4/2.2)^3 = 6$. We achieve this improved accuracy by increasing the stencil operator from 11 points to 25 points. Although this increases the number of floating point operations (FLOPs) by 25/11, the computer cost does not go up this much because this increase in FLOPs requires no additional DRAM memory transfers. Modern CPUs are very efficient at performing FLOPs but are often limited by memory transfer. Longer operators increase the ratio of computations to memory transfer if the algorithm uses CPU cache effectively.

One of the problems with longer operators is the generation of artificial diffractions from stair-step interfaces where dipping reflectors appear to be stair steps. In this case, there is a need for adaptive modeling methods such as the spectral element method, or coefficients optimized to reduce this problem.

8.6 Summary

Finite-difference schemes are widely used to simulate 3D wave propagation in models with arbitrary velocity and density distributions. Stability and accuracy conditions are described, and absorbing boundaries can be applied to the sides of the model to minimize unwanted reflections. Today's best practice is to use higher-order, finite-difference stencils, with recommendations of eighth-order in space and second-order in time. For media with strong contrasts in physical properties (water next to elastic sediments or air), the staggered grid scheme is recommended over the conventional FD solutions to the second-order elastic wave equation.

The spectral element method has very high accuracy and does not suffer from large errors at reflecting boundaries if the element boundaries are parallel to the interfaces. Thus, it is ideal for modeling land data with large topographic variations of the free surface. The SE method differs from the standard FE element in that its nodes are at the unevenly spaced quadrature points,[4] and therefore removes the need to make the lumped-mass approximation. However, generating a suitable mesh can require significant

computation time and an extensive effort in coding. In contrast, the highly accurate pseudospectral method does not require an unstructured mesh, but the conventional approach is only suitable for smooth velocity models.

This chapter concentrated on seismic modeling methods in exploration geophysics, but Virieux et al. (2012) provide a more comprehensive treatment. They review both space-time and space-frequency modeling methods used in exploration and earthquake seismology.

8.7 Exercises

1. Using a Taylor series, prove that $[p(i+1) - 2p(i) + p(i-1)]/(\Delta x)^2$ is a second-order correct approximation to the second-order derivative.

2. The Taylor series expansion can be used to give
$$\frac{f(x + \Delta x) - f(x - \Delta x)}{2\Delta x}$$
$$= \frac{df(x)}{dx} + \frac{(\Delta x)^2 d^3 f(x)}{3! dx^3} + O[(\Delta x)^4],$$
$$\frac{f(x + 2\Delta x) - f(x - 2\Delta x)}{4\Delta x}$$
$$= \frac{df(x)}{dx} + \frac{4(\Delta x)^2 d^3 f(x)}{3! dx^3} + O[(\Delta x)^4]. \quad (8.25)$$
Use these identities to derive the fourth-order approximation to the first-order derivative in Table 8.1.

3. Prove that $[-p(i+2) + 16p(i+1) - 30p(i) + 16p(i-1) - p(i-2)]/(12(\Delta x)^2)$ is a fourth-order-correct approximation to the second-order derivative.

4. Prove the 2D stability condition given by equation 8.7. This is a necessary condition for stability.

5. Prove that the stability condition for a 2-2 scheme in 3D is the same as that for the 2D case, except the square root of 2 is replaced by the square root of 3.

6. Write a MATLAB code that computes a fourth-order, finite-difference solution to the acoustic wave equation.

7. Show that the rightgoing propagating plane wave $p = e^{i\omega(x/c-t)}$ exactly satisfies the absorbing boundary condition $\partial p/\partial t + c^{-1}\partial p/\partial x = 0$. Show how a 1-1 FD approximation to this equation can be used to update the right-side boundary values of the $t + 1$ panel in Figure 8.1. Describe the absorbing boundary conditions that absorb upgoing or downgoing or leftgoing plane waves. See Keys (1985) for a generalization of these absorbing boundary conditions.

8. Apply a 40-point sponge zone to the 2-2 FD code. Find the value of α that optimizes absorption of waves that enter the sponge zone.

9. Derive the equation for a spectral-element solution of the 2D wave equation. Draw out the SE stencils for a pivot point at the boundary between two elements and a pivot point that joins four elements.

---

[4]In numerical analysis, a quadrature rule is used to determine the numerical value of a definite integral, usually stated as a weighted sum of function values at specified points within the domain of integration. These points are known as quadrature points.

10. Derive the strong form of the SE equation which does not require an integration by parts. This means that there is a second derivative of the shape function. What are the advantages and disadvantages of this approach compared to the weak formulation?

11. Does the strong form of the SE equation require an absorbing boundary condition at the sides of the computational grid?

12. Write a 2D SE code that solves the acoustic wave equation. Compare the wavefield accuracy to that computed by a 2-4 FD code. The different propagation distances should range from 0 to 50 wavelengths.

8.8 Computational labs

1. Compute the VSP seismograms in the Computational Toolkit under the topic "Modeling" and subtopic "1D FD VSP Acoustic Modeling."

2. Execute one of the 2D acoustic FD exercises in the Computational Toolkit under the topic Modeling.

3. Execute one of the 2D elastic FD exercises in the Computational Toolkit under the topic Modeling.

4. Compare the accuracy of the pseudospectral solution to that of a FD method for propagating 50 wavelengths. Use the MATLAB code in the text.

Appendix 8A:
Absorbing boundary conditions

The boundaries along the side of the model can reflect incident waves back into the model, and therefore interfere with the desired waves. To minimize these undesirable reflections, absorbing boundary conditions[5] are applied to the sides of the model that should only transmit, not reflect, incoming waves. There are three types of absorbing boundary conditions in general use today: partial differential equations (PDEs) at the boundaries that solve a one-way wave equation (Clayton and Engquist, 1977; Keys, 1985; Higdon, 1991), a sponge damping zone that is five to ten wavelengths in thickness (Cerjan et al., 1985), and the perfectly matched layer (PML) scheme (Berenger, 1994). I will discuss the first two, and then present a hybrid absorbing-boundary-condition scheme (Liu and Sen, 2010; 2012) that is simple and adaptable to any FD scheme, but also appears to be at least as effective as the more complicated PML scheme.

---

[5] An absorbing boundary condition at the side of the model is a boundary condition that the wavefield must satisfy so that incident waves from the interior do not reflect back inside.

8A.1 Sponge zone

The simplest absorbing boundary condition is that of a damping zone (Cerjan et al., 1985), also known as a sponge zone, with a thickness of about five to ten wavelengths located next to the sides of the model. Inside the left-side sponge region, the wavefield is multiplied by an exponential damping function $f(i)$ at each time step, in which i is the gridpoint index for the x-coordinate. Here, $i = 1$ on the innermost gridpoint of the left-side sponge zone and increases to the left until it is at the leftmost boundary point at $i = $ ndamp. The damping function on this left-side boundary takes the form

$$f(i) = e^{-|(i-1)log(\alpha)/\text{ndamp}|}, \qquad (8.26)$$

in which ndamp is the number of gridpoints that define the width of the damping zone and α is a specified damping parameter. The damping parameter α is selected to minimize boundary reflections, and empirical tests must be conducted to determine its optimal value. An example snapshot of a propagating wave in a two-layer medium is shown in Figure 8.9.

A modified damping function is proposed by Wang and Qin (1997):

$$f(i) = e^{-|(i-1)^2 log(\alpha)/\text{ndamp}^2|}, \qquad (8.27)$$

in which $\frac{df(x)}{dx}$ is zero at $x = 1$. This means that, unlike equation 8.26, the first derivative of the damping function in equation 8.27 is continuous at the inner boundary of the sponge zone. Numerical tests suggest that equation 8.27 provides better absorption properties than given by equation 8.26.

As an example, two different implementations of the damping functions are tested by Wang and Qin (1997). The model is a 3D homogeneous acoustic model with a P velocity equal to 4750 m/s. The model size is 191 ×

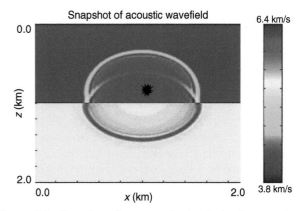

Figure 8.9. Snapshot of an acoustic simulation in a two-layer medium. The star denotes the location of the point source and the colorbar denotes velocity in km/s.

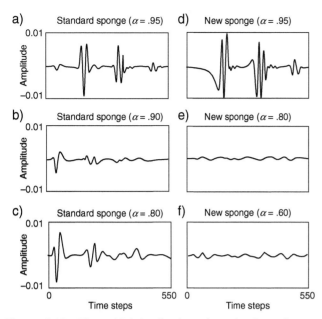

a) Standard sponge ($\alpha = .95$)
d) New sponge ($\alpha = .95$)

b) Standard sponge ($\alpha = .90$)
e) New sponge ($\alpha = .80$)

c) Standard sponge ($\alpha = .80$)
f) New sponge ($\alpha = .60$)

Figure 8.10. The artificial reflections that arise from the (a–c) standard and (d–f) equation 8.27 damping conditions. Exclusive damping of the particle-velocity variables yielded moderately worse results than simultaneous damping of both particle-velocity and stress variables. Plots redrawn from Wang and Qin (1997).

291×162 ($nx \times ny \times nz$), which includes a 20-gridpoint-thick damping zone along each boundary and a grid spacing of 50 m. An explosive point source with a peak source frequency of 10 Hz is placed at the gridpoint coordinate (95, 95, 100), and a receiver is placed at the gridpoint coordinate (95, 145, 40) which records the vertical particle velocity.

Figure 8.10a to 8.10c shows the artificial reflections from the boundary for different values of the old damping factor α. It is found that the artificial reflections first decrease then increase in amplitude when decreasing the damping factor α from 0.95 to 0.80. The optimum value of α is found to be 0.90 for this example. Figure 8.10d to 8.10f shows the artificial reflections using the damping function in equation 8.27. The values of the damping factor decrease from 0.95 to 0.60. The optimum value of the damping factor is smaller than that of the old damping function, and far fewer artificial reflections are generated for the same sized damping zone. The value $\alpha = 0.80$ provides very good damping for a damping width of 20 gridpoints.

Figure 8.11 depicts the artificial reflections in a trace recorded just outside the sponge zone in a homogeneous medium. In this case, a staggered-grid solution to the acoustic wave equation is used so there are two options for implementing the damping function: apply it exclusively to the particle-velocity components after each time step, or apply it to both the particle-velocity and stress components after each time step. The results show that damping

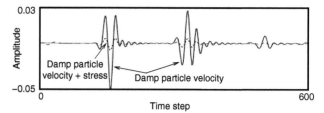

Damp particle velocity + stress
Damp particle velocity

Figure 8.11. Comparison between two damping schemes: 1) damping particle-velocity variables only (solid line), and 2) damping particle-velocity and stress variables simultaneously (dashed line). The second scheme provides a more effective ABC in this acoustic example. The direct wave is not included here. After Wang and Qin (1997). Reprinted by permission.

just the particle-velocity component after each time step is less effective than damping both the stress and particle-velocity components after each time step. However, an instability has been observed when both stress and velocity components are damped for the elastic wave equation.

8A.2 PDE absorbing boundary conditions

An important absorbing boundary condition (ABC) is obtained by factoring the wave equation into leftgoing and rightgoing component PDEs that are a weighted sum of first-order space and time derivatives (Keys, 1985; Higdon, 1991). That is, the 1D wave equation can be recast into the form

$$\overbrace{\left(\frac{\partial}{\partial x} + \frac{1}{c}\frac{\partial}{\partial t}\right)}^{\text{rightgoing waves}} \overbrace{\left(\frac{\partial}{\partial x} - \frac{1}{c}\frac{\partial}{\partial t}\right)}^{\text{leftgoing waves}} p = 0, \qquad (8.28)$$

in which a homogeneous velocity c is assumed and p is the solution to the wave equation. The left-bracketed term above is called a rightgoing wave annihilator because a rightgoing plane wave $p^+ = e^{i(kx-\omega t')}$ (for $k > 0$, $\omega > 0$) exactly satisfies this equation. That is,

$$\overbrace{\left(\frac{\partial}{\partial x} + \frac{1}{c}\frac{\partial}{\partial t}\right)}^{\text{rightgoing}} p^+ = i(k - \omega/c)p^+ = 0. \qquad (8.29)$$

In a similar fashion, the other bracketed term in equation 8.28 exactly annihilates leftgoing waves $p^- = e^{i(kx+\omega t')}$ such that

$$\overbrace{\left(\frac{\partial}{\partial x} - \frac{1}{c}\frac{\partial}{\partial t}\right)}^{\text{leftgoing}} p^- = i(k - \omega/c)p^- = 0. \qquad (8.30)$$

Therefore, we can apply the first-order rightgoing wave operator to the right-side boundary of the computational grid and expect perfect annihilation of a plane wave that is purely rightgoing. A similar procedure can be used for the left-side boundary, except we use an FD approximation to the leftgoing annihilation operator.[6] These operators can be approximated by one-sided FD approximations to the first-order spatial derivative. The one-sided nature of the FD approximation ensures that the FD stencil does not need field values outside the grid.

As an example, the FD approximation to the rightgoing operator in equation 8.28 is

$$\left(\frac{\partial}{\partial x} + \frac{1}{c}\frac{\partial}{\partial t}\right)p \approx \frac{p_{i+1}^t - p_i^t}{\Delta x} + \frac{1}{c}\frac{p_{i+1}^{t+1} - p_{i+1}^t}{\Delta t} = 0, \quad (8.31)$$

where the spatial pivot point is at the $i+1$ gridpoint along the x-axis. Here, a first-order forward differencing in time (pivoted at time t) is used along with a backward differencing in space (pivoted at spatial gridpoint $i+1$).

The unknown field value p_N^{t+1} at future time $t+1$ can be solved for at the rightside boundary labeled as $i+1 = N$ to get

$$p_N^{t+1} = -c\Delta t\frac{p_N^t - p_{N-1}^t}{\Delta x} + p_N^t. \quad (8.32)$$

Note that the field values at time t are assumed to be known everywhere within the computational model. Here, the spatial index numbers increase for points from left to the right with the last computational gridpoint number denoted as N. A similar argument shows that the leftgoing operator applied to the left-side boundary is given by

$$p_1^{t+1} = c\Delta t\frac{p_2^t - p_1^t}{\Delta x} + p_1^t, \quad (8.33)$$

except the first-order spatial derivative is replaced by a forward difference approximation pivoted at the number 1 gridpoint.

What happens if the wave, e.g., $p^+ = e^{i(k_x x + k_z z - \omega t')}$ is traveling obliquely to the horizontal axis? In this case, we see that the rightgoing operator does not exactly satisfy the wave equation:

$$\left(\frac{\partial}{\partial x} + \frac{1}{c}\frac{\partial}{\partial t}\right)p^+ = i(k_x - \omega/c)p^+ \neq 0. \quad (8.34)$$

The only way the equation can be satisfied at the boundary is if a left going wave with reflection strength R is generated at the boundary. That is, at the boundary, a combination of rightgoing and leftgoing waves

$$p^+ = \overbrace{e^{i(k_x x + k_z z - \omega t')}}^{\text{rightgoing}} + \overbrace{Re^{i(-k_x x + k_z z - \omega t')}}^{\text{leftgoing}}, \quad (8.35)$$

---

[6]For the bottom of the model, the downgoing wave annihilator is $(\partial/\partial x - 1/c\partial/\partial t')$ for decreasing z in the depth directions.

are superimposed to satisfy exactly the rightgoing wave operator. The value of R increases with increasingly oblique angles of incidence. This can be shown analytically by plugging equation 8.35 into equation 8.29 and solving for R.

To annihilate waves at several incidence angles, Keys (1985) shows that the wave equation can be decomposed into

$$\overbrace{\left(\nabla + \frac{\mathbf{a}}{c}\frac{\partial}{\partial t}\right)}^{\text{rightgoing waves}} \cdot \overbrace{\left(\nabla - \frac{\mathbf{a}}{c}\frac{\partial}{\partial t}\right)}^{\text{leftgoing waves}} p = 0, \quad (8.36)$$

in which the unit vector $\mathbf{a}$ is selected to absorb waves at several incidence angles. In this case, the rightgoing wave operator will annihilate a rightgoing plane wave $p^+ = e^{i(k_x x + k_z z - \omega t')}$ if $\omega\mathbf{a}/c$ is equal to $\mathbf{k} = (k_x, k_z)$. This can be seen easily because $\nabla p^+ = i\mathbf{k}p^+$, which when plugged into the rightgoing operator in equation 8.36 gives

$$\nabla p^+ + \frac{\mathbf{a}}{c}\frac{\partial p^+}{\partial t} = i\left(\mathbf{k} - \frac{\omega\mathbf{a}}{c}\right)p^+ = 0, \quad (8.37)$$

if $\omega\mathbf{a}/c = \mathbf{k}$. A slight adjustment of this ABC increases its capability to absorb plane waves in two directions parallel to either $\mathbf{k}_1$ and $\mathbf{k}_2$. This adjusted ABC is given by

$$[\mathbf{a}_1 + \mathbf{a}_2] \cdot \left(\nabla p^+ + \frac{\mathbf{a}_2}{c}\frac{\partial p^+}{\partial t}\right) = 0, \quad (8.38)$$

where one of the perfect absorption directions is parallel to the specified unit vector $\mathbf{a}_2$ and the other is parallel to the specified unit vector $\mathbf{a}_1$.

Figure 8.12a depicts the reflection magnitude $|R|$ plotted against the incidence angle for waves reflecting from a boundary with the second-order ABC in equation 8.38. Here, the ABC is designed to annihilate perfectly waves that are incident at angles of $\pm15°$ and $\pm30°$ with respect to the normal. Figure 8.12b and 8.12c depicts shot gathers before and after application of the first-order and second-order ABCs, respectively, along the side boundaries. Here, the model is a two-layer medium with the source and receivers along a horizontal line in the top layer. Region E in the Figure 8.12b shot gather corresponds to artificial reflections from the imperfect absorbing boundary conditions (ABCs). These unwanted reflections are extinguished in Figure 8.12c, and the reflections around the B region correspond to the desired primary reflections from the interface that separates the two layers. Note the improvement in reducing unwanted reflections from the model boundaries after application of the ABC.

Because waves typically are traveling in all directions at a model boundary, then some artificial reflections are generated for non-normal incidence angles, even for the equation 8.38 ABC. Thus, we get artificial unwanted reflections generated at the boundaries that propagate into the

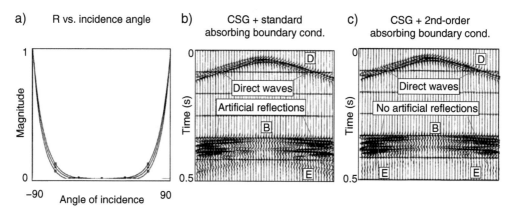

Figure 8.12. (a) R versus incidence-angle graph for incidence angles $|\theta|$ equal to 15° and 30° using the ABC in equation 8.38, (b) shot gather using the standard ABC along left and right sides of model where the normal incidence angle wave is annihilated. (c) Shot gather using the second-order ABC tuned to annihilate both the direct and reflection wavefields at the boundary. After Keys (1985). Used by permission.

interior part of the grid. If such artificial reflections are strong, then they can spoil the accuracy of the simulation. For this reason, a combination of first-order ABC's and absorbing sponges are used in some FD codes.

A cautionary note on the absorbing boundary conditions is that they might induce instabilities in the solution even if the interior scheme is stable. This fact is proven by Renaut and Petersen (1989, 1153), who show that for the Clayton-Engquist absorbing boundary conditions (Clayton and Engquist, 1977)

> there is a stability barrier on the Courant number specified by the coefficients of the boundary conditions. Thus, proving stability of the interior scheme is not sufficient. Furthermore, waves may radiate spontaneously from the boundary, causing instability, even if the stability bound on the Courant number is satisfied.

8A.3 Hybrid PDE absorbing boundary conditions

Liu and Sen (2010, 2012) introduce a hybrid ABC scheme in which they averaged the solutions to the one-way wave equation and the two-way equations within an outer shell of about 10 gridpoints. The key idea is that implementation of a one-way ABC results in unwanted reflections if it is implemented on gridpoints that are next to those where the two-way wave equation is solved. To mitigate this problem, they propose the hybrid scheme, which is a weighted average of the two solutions: the weighting is adjusted gradually until only the one-way wave equation is used.

Figure 8.13 illustrates the hybrid computational model in which the outer shell, labeled as region II, averages the solution of the one-way equation $\mathbf{L}^{one\text{-}way}$ with that

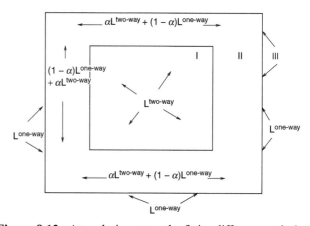

Figure 8.13. At each time step, the finite-difference solution is computed in region I for the two-way wave equation, and in region II, for a linear combination of one-way and two-way equations. The solution to the one-way equation is computed exclusively at the III boundary where $\alpha = 0$. Adapted from Liu and Sen (2010). Used by permission.

computed by the two-way wave equation $\mathbf{L}^{two\text{-}way}$ to give the updated solution at each time step. They set $\alpha = 1$ at the boundary between regions I and II, and $\alpha = 0$ at the boundary III: α is varied linearly between these two boundaries. The results of Liu and Sen (2012) show almost perfect absorption for waves propagating in a layered medium. This method appears to be effective for many different modeling schemes, it is easy to implement and code, and the computational cost is inexpensive compared to the PML scheme.

If a high-order stencil is used at the acoustic boundary, Liu and Sen (2012) use a mirroring of the fields across the absorbing boundaries. At the free surface for acoustic waves, they use an anti-mirror condition in which the mirror stress values are equal and opposite to one another.

Chapter 9: The Viscoacoustic Wave Equation

In this chapter, I derive the viscoacoustic wave equations and their representation by a staggered-grid, finite-difference approximation. The solutions to these equations will be used in subsequent chapters for least-squares migration and waveform inversion.

9.1 Introduction to linear viscoelasticity

Viscoelasticity[1] is the property of materials undergoing both viscous and elastic deformation (Meyers and Chawla, 1999). Under elastic loading, 100% of the mechanical energy is stored in the deformation. In contrast, viscoelastic materials dissipate some of the mechanical energy to friction and heating. This dissipation is known as a hysteresis loss, as illustrated in Figure 9.1a, in which the unloading stress is less than the loading stress for the same amount of strain. The ability to dissipate mechanical energy into other forms is the main reason why we use viscous shock absorbers and helmet padding.

Under a fixed strain, elastic materials will reach a fixed stress and stay at that level; they will return quickly to the original state once the strain is removed. In contrast, a viscoelastic material will relax its internal stress over time as shown in Figure 9.1b, until it asymptotically achieves a lower stress state. Under a fixed stress, the same material will creep and increase its stretch with time until it approaches the asymptotic strain value shown in Figure 9.1c. Whereas elasticity is often generated by bond stretching along crystallographic planes in an ordered solid, viscosity is associated with diffusion of atoms or molecules inside an amorphous material.

Dashpot model

The stress-strain relationship in a simple elastic medium can be modeled as a spring with elastic constant κ,

such that

$$\sigma = \kappa \epsilon_S. \qquad (9.1)$$

In this case, an instantaneous stress produces an instantaneous strain ϵ_S scaled by the proportionality constant κ. In contrast, the stress-strain relationship in a viscoelastic fluid can be approximated as a dashpot with viscosity G such that

$$\sigma = G \frac{d\epsilon_D}{dt}. \qquad (9.2)$$

Here, $\frac{d\epsilon_D}{dt}$ is the strain rate, and so a constant stress σ introduces a time-varying creep $\epsilon_D = \frac{\sigma}{G} t + \text{cnst}$. However, this is inappropriate behavior for a viscoelastic solid because linearly increasing strain does not asymptotically approach the finite-strain value illustrated in Figure 9.1c.

Maxwell model

The Maxwell model is a spring and dashpot in series (see Figure 9.2a), so that the total strain rate is a sum of their strain rates

$$\frac{d\epsilon}{dt} = \frac{d\epsilon_D}{dt} + \frac{d\epsilon_S}{dt} = \frac{\sigma}{G} + \frac{1}{\kappa} \frac{d\sigma}{dt}, \qquad (9.3)$$

in which σ is the stress. Under this model, if the material is put under a constant strain $\frac{d\epsilon}{dt} = 0$, then stresses gradually relax[2] as

$$\sigma = \sigma_0 e^{-t\kappa/G} = \sigma_0 e^{-t/\tau_R}. \qquad (9.4)$$

The characteristic relaxation time τ_R

$$\tau_R = \frac{G}{\kappa}, \qquad (9.5)$$

is a time scale in which the fluid's stress relaxes by e^{-1} over a time interval of τ_R; longer relaxation times mean a longer

---

[1] The introduction is adapted from http://en.wikipedia.org/wiki/viscoelasticity and http://www.umich.edu/~bme332/ch7consteqviscoelasticity/bme332consteqviscoelasticity.htm by Scott Hollister.

[2] A laboratory experiment might load a viscoelastic bar with a weight so that it initially compresses by 5% in height. As time increases, the bar will compress even more unless the load is decreased gradually with time to keep the strain constant, as shown in Figure 9.1c.

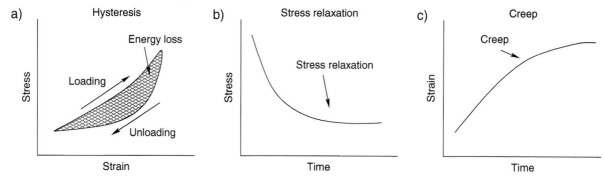

Figure 9.1. Plots of (a) hysteresis, (b) stress relaxation, and (c) creep for a viscoelastic solid. Assuming the strain is fixed, the internal stresses will relax with time for a viscoelastic solid (e.g., an aging rubber band stretched at a fixed length). If the external stress is fixed, then the viscoelastic strain will creep with time (e.g., slowly dripping honey). After Hollister (2014).

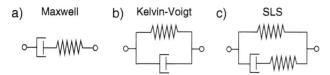

Figure 9.2. (a) Maxwell, (b) Kelvin-Voigt, and (c) standard-linear-solid (SLS) models of viscoelasticity.

time to relax. For a viscoelastic fluid, the Maxwell model predicts that stress decays exponentially to zero, which is accurate for a viscoelastic fluid, not a solid.

For a constant stress on the material, the strain solution of $d\epsilon/dt = \sigma/G$ is $\epsilon = \epsilon_0 + t\sigma/G$ and has two components. The first one is the elastic component ϵ_0, which occurs instantaneously with the spring, relaxing when the stress is released. The second one $t\sigma/G$ is a viscous component, corresponding to a dashpot, that grows with time as long as the stress is applied. This is not characteristic of a viscoelastic solid, because we expect that the creep will reach an asymptotic level after a certain time.

Kelvin-Voigt model

The Maxwell model is appropriate for viscoelastic fluids, but not solids. An alternative is the Kelvin-Voigt model that consists of a dashpot and spring in parallel (see Figure 9.2b), so the total stress is a sum of the spring and dashpot stresses

$$\sigma(t) = \overbrace{\kappa\epsilon}^{\text{spring}} + G\overbrace{\frac{d\epsilon}{dt}}^{\text{dashpot}}. \tag{9.6}$$

Here, the dashpot will be constrained to have the same strain as the spring so that $\epsilon_D = \epsilon_S = \epsilon$. This model represents a solid undergoing reversible, viscoelastic strain.

If the step strain $\epsilon = \epsilon_0 H(t)$ ($H(t)$ is the Heaviside function) is introduced into equation 9.6, then the stress

response

$$\sigma(t) = \overbrace{[\kappa H(t) + G\delta(t)]}^{\text{relaxation function}} \epsilon_0, \tag{9.7}$$

represents an instantaneous stress change. For example, instantly yanking the system to a fixed strain yields an instantaneous constant stress field after $t = 0$.

Upon application of a step stress $\sigma(t) = \sigma_0 H(t)$, the solution to equation 9.6 is

$$\epsilon(t) = \overbrace{\frac{1}{\kappa}[1 - e^{-t\kappa/G}]}^{\text{creep function}} H(t)\,\sigma_0, \tag{9.8}$$

and asymptotically approaches the steady-state strain value shown in Figure 9.1c. The creep function $J(t) = \frac{1}{\kappa}[1 - e^{-t\kappa/G}]H(t)$ says that no instantaneous elastic deformation is possible because of the restraint of the dashpot. Here, G/κ is the relaxation time for the response to a step-function stress.

Standard-linear-solid model

The standard-linear-solid model (SLS) is a spring and dashpot in series, which is in parallel with another system such as the spring in Figure 9.2c. In this case, the stress σ^M on the bottom Maxwell model (see equation 9.3) and the stress σ^S on the top spring system are related to the common strain ϵ by

$$\dot{\epsilon} = \frac{\sigma^M}{G} + \frac{\dot{\sigma}^M}{\kappa_1} \tag{9.9}$$

and

$$\sigma^S = \kappa_2\epsilon, \tag{9.10}$$

in which κ_1 (κ_2) is the stiffness coefficient for the Maxwell (spring) system. Substituting equation 9.10 into the total stress $\sigma = \sigma^M + \sigma^S$ of the SLS system gives

$$\sigma^M = \sigma - \kappa_2\epsilon. \tag{9.11}$$

Plugging equation 9.11 into equation 9.9 yields the differential equation for the SLS strain:

$$G\left(1 + \frac{\kappa_2}{\kappa_1}\right)\dot{\epsilon} + \kappa_2\epsilon = \sigma + \frac{G\dot{\sigma}}{\kappa_1}. \tag{9.12}$$

Applying a Fourier transform in time and rearranging gives the SLS stress-strain relationship

$$\sigma = \overbrace{\frac{G\kappa_1}{\kappa_1 + i\omega G}}^{\text{frequency-dependent modulus}}\left[(1 + \kappa_2/\kappa_1) + \frac{\kappa_2}{i\omega G}\right]i\omega\epsilon, \tag{9.13}$$

which says that in the time domain, the effective modulus is a function of time, and the stress is a convolution of it with the strain rate.

Setting σ to be the constant stress $\sigma_0 H(t)$ reduces equation 9.12 to

$$G\left(1 + \frac{\kappa_2}{\kappa_1}\right)\dot{\epsilon} + \kappa_2\epsilon = \sigma_0 H(t) + \frac{G\sigma_0\delta(t)}{\kappa_1}, \tag{9.14}$$

with the $t > 0$ solution

$$\epsilon(t) = \overbrace{\left[\frac{A}{\sigma_0}e^{-t\kappa_2/[G(1+\kappa_2/\kappa_1)]} + \frac{1}{\kappa_2}\right]}^{\text{SLS creep function}}H(t)\,\sigma_0, \tag{9.15}$$

in which A is a constant determined by the initial conditions. For $A < 0$, the SLS creep function behaves as the expected one in Figure 9.1c for a viscoelastic solid. Here, $\tau_\epsilon = G(1 + \kappa_2/\kappa_1)/\kappa_2$ is the relaxation time for the strain response to a step-function stress.

In a similar fashion, a constant strain $\epsilon(t) = \epsilon_0 H(t)$ can be applied to equation 9.12 to give the governing equation

$$\frac{G}{\kappa_1}\dot{\sigma} + \sigma = \epsilon_0\kappa_2 H(t) + G\left(1 + \frac{\kappa_2}{\kappa_1}\right)\epsilon_0\delta(t) \tag{9.16}$$

with the $t > 0$ solution

$$\sigma(t) = \overbrace{\left[\frac{B}{\epsilon_0}e^{-t\kappa_1/G} + \kappa_2\right]}^{\text{SLS relaxation function}}H(t)\,\epsilon_0. \tag{9.17}$$

For $B > 0$, the stress $\sigma(t)$ relaxes with increasing time as depicted in Figure 9.1b and $\tau_\sigma = G/\kappa_1$ is the relaxation time for a step-function strain. The relaxation parameters must honor the condition $\tau_\epsilon > \tau_\sigma$ to ensure that the equation 9.43 quality factor honors the condition $Q > 0$ (Morozov, 2014), which is satisfied by many proposed mechanisms that explain seismic attenuation.

Generalized relaxation and creep functions

The stress at time t depends on the relaxation response at both the current time and all previous times (Dahlen and Tromp, 1998). Assuming causality, linearity, and time invariance, this means that

$$\sigma(t) = \int_{-\infty}^{t} \mathcal{G}(t - \tau)\frac{d\epsilon(\tau)}{d\tau}d\tau, \tag{9.18}$$

in which $\mathcal{G}(t - \tau)$ is a generalized time-dependent viscoelastic modulus that is causal and time-shift invariant. As an example, assume a constant strain $\epsilon = \epsilon_0 H(t)$ imposed at $t = 0$ so the above equation becomes

$$\sigma(t) = \int_{-\infty}^{t} \mathcal{G}(t - \tau)\epsilon_0\delta(\tau)d\tau = \mathcal{G}(t)\epsilon_0, \tag{9.19}$$

in which $dH(t)/dt = \delta(t)$ and, analogous to equations 9.7 and 9.17, $\mathcal{G}(t)$ is the generalized relaxation function.

As an example, consider a car going over a bump. The viscous shock absorbers are compressed as the car passes over the bump, and then as they unload, you might come down hard on the seats to give the absorbers a new downward jolt. The net response of the shock absorbers will be a weighted sum of the relaxation response from going over the bump and the new response initiated by you landing on the car seat.

In summary, the general attenuation model can be a weighted summation of convolutional spring and dashpot models with time-dependent moduli (Christensen, 1982; Carcione et al. 1988; Blanch and Symes, 1995). This is the starting point for the viscoacoustic modeling equation derived in the next section.

9.2 Viscoacoustic wave equation

The relaxation function $\mathcal{G}(t)$ in equation 9.18 depends on the type of model. For a 1D SLS model with L standard linear solids connected in parallel, $\mathcal{G}(t)$ has the general form (Carcione et al., 1988; Robertsson et al., 1994)

$$\mathcal{G}(t) = K\left(1 - \sum_{l=1}^{L}\left(1 - \frac{\tau_{\epsilon l}}{\tau_{\sigma l}}\right)e^{-t/\tau_{\sigma l}}\right)H(t). \tag{9.20}$$

Here, K is the relaxed modulus of the medium. The terms $\tau_{\sigma l}$ and $\tau_{\epsilon l}$ are the stress and strain-relaxation times for the lth mechanism, respectively. See Appendix 9B for the derivation of this relaxation function.

From the definition of pressure and strain, we know that for a 1D medium,

$$\sigma = -p; \quad \frac{\partial u}{\partial x} = \dot{\epsilon}, \tag{9.21}$$

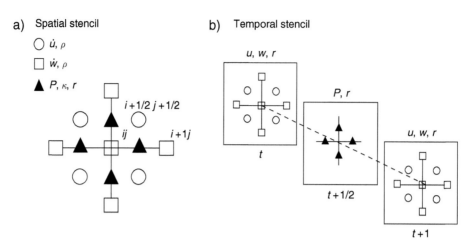

Figure 9.3. Same as the acoustic staggered-grid scheme in Figure 8.7, except now the stencil for the viscoacoustic staggered-grid scheme is shown with the memory variable r.

in which u is the particle velocity. Inserting equations 9.20 and 9.21 into equation 9.18 and taking the time derivative, we get

$$-\dot{p} = K\left(1 - \sum_{l=1}^{L}\left(1 - \frac{\tau_{\epsilon l}}{\tau_{\sigma l}}\right)\right)\frac{\partial u}{\partial x}$$
$$+ \left[K\left(\sum_{l=1}^{L}\frac{1}{\tau_{\sigma l}}\left(1 - \frac{\tau_{\epsilon l}}{\tau_{\sigma l}}\right)e^{-t/\tau_{\sigma l}}\right)H(t)\right] * \frac{\partial u}{\partial x}. \tag{9.22}$$

Carcione et al. (1988) simplified the convolution term here by introducing the so-called memory variable term r_l, so equation 9.22 becomes

$$-\dot{p} = K\left(1 - \sum_{l=1}^{L}\left(1 - \frac{\tau_{\epsilon l}}{\tau_{\sigma l}}\right)\right)\frac{\partial u}{\partial x} + \sum_{l=1}^{L}r_l, \tag{9.23}$$

where

$$r_l = \left[K\left(\frac{1}{\tau_{\sigma l}}\left(1 - \frac{\tau_{\epsilon l}}{\tau_{\sigma l}}\right)e^{-t/\tau_{\sigma l}}\right)H(t)\right] * \frac{\partial u}{\partial x}; \quad 1 \le l \le L. \tag{9.24}$$

Taking the time derivative of equation 9.24, we get

$$\dot{r}_l = -\left[\frac{1}{\tau_{\sigma l}}K\left(\frac{1}{\tau_{\sigma l}}\left(1 - \frac{\tau_{\epsilon l}}{\tau_{\sigma l}}\right)e^{-t/\tau_{\sigma l}}\right)H(t)\right] * \frac{\partial u}{\partial x}$$
$$+ \left[K\left(\frac{1}{\tau_{\sigma l}}\left(1 - \frac{\tau_{\epsilon l}}{\tau_{\sigma l}}\right)e^{-t/\tau_{\sigma l}}\right)\delta(t)\right] * \frac{\partial u}{\partial x},$$
$$= -\frac{1}{\tau_{\sigma l}}r_l + K\frac{1}{\tau_{\sigma l}}\left(1 - \frac{\tau_{\epsilon l}}{\tau_{\sigma l}}\right)\frac{\partial u}{\partial x}; \quad 1 \le l \le L. \tag{9.25}$$

From Newton's second law we have,

$$\dot{u} = -\frac{1}{\rho}\frac{\partial p}{\partial x}. \tag{9.26}$$

Equations 9.23, 9.25, and 9.26 together describe the first-order equations of motion in a 1D viscoacoustic medium represented by L sets of standard linear solids connected in parallel.

For higher dimensions, these equations can be written as

$$\frac{\partial \mathbf{u}}{\partial t} = -\frac{1}{\rho}\nabla p,$$
$$\frac{\partial p}{\partial t} = -K\left(1 - \sum_{l=1}^{L}\left(1 - \frac{\tau_{\epsilon l}}{\tau_{\sigma l}}\right)\right)\nabla \cdot \mathbf{u} - \sum_{l=1}^{L}r_l, \tag{9.27}$$
$$\frac{\partial r_l}{\partial t} = -\frac{1}{\tau_{\sigma l}}r_l + K\frac{1}{\tau_{\sigma l}}\left(1 - \frac{\tau_{\epsilon l}}{\tau_{\sigma l}}\right)\nabla \cdot \mathbf{u}, \quad 1 \le l \le L,$$

in which the particle-velocity vector is $\mathbf{u} = (u_x, u_y, u_z)$. Blanch and Symes (1995) show that only one relaxation mechanism is sufficient for numerical modeling purposes. Thus for a single relaxation mechanism, i.e., $l = 1$, we have

$$\frac{\partial \mathbf{u}}{\partial t} = -\frac{1}{\rho}\nabla p,$$
$$\frac{\partial p}{\partial t} = -K\frac{\tau_\epsilon}{\tau_\sigma}\nabla \cdot \mathbf{u} - r \tag{9.28}$$
$$\frac{\partial r}{\partial t} = -\frac{1}{\tau_\sigma}\left[r + K\left(\frac{\tau_\epsilon}{\tau_\sigma} - 1\right)\nabla \cdot \mathbf{u}\right].$$

The relaxation parameters $\tau_{\sigma 1} \to \tau_\sigma$ and $\tau_{\epsilon 1} \to \tau_\epsilon$, are related to the quality factor Q (see Appendix 9B), and the reference angular frequency f_w (usually chosen to be the central angular frequency) of the source wavelet (Robertsson et al., 1994), so that

$$\tau_\sigma = \frac{\sqrt{1 + \frac{1}{Q^2}} - \frac{1}{Q}}{f_w},$$

and

$$\tau_\epsilon = \frac{1}{f_w^2 \tau_\sigma}, \qquad (9.29)$$

in which Q is assumed to be constant over a limited frequency band (Blanch et al., 1995). The implementation of these equations by a staggered-grid, finite-difference method uses the finite-difference stencil shown in Figure 9.3.

9.3 Summary

The viscoacoustic wave equations are derived for the SLS model in Figure 9.4. An equation for updating the memory variable is used to avoid storing the time history of field values at every gridpoint. Solutions to the viscoacoustic wave equations will be important when using least-squares migration or waveform inversion in highly attenuative media.

9.4 Exercises

1. Derive the 1D viscoacoustic wave equations for the Kelvin-Voigt (KV) model. Physically interpret the meaning of the KV relaxation time and compare it to that for the 1D SLS viscoacoustic equations.
2. Same as the previous exercise except derive the 1D viscoacoustic wave equations for a dashpot model.
3. Write a 1D staggered-grid, finite-difference code for the viscoacoustic wave equations and the SLS model. Compare the viscoacoustic simulations to those computed by the 1D acoustic wave equation for $10 < Q < 100$ and propagation distances of up to 30 wavelengths.
4. Is causality honored in the numerical solutions to the KV, SLS, and dashpot models? Explain (see Morozov, 2014).

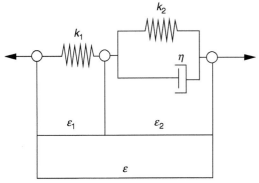

Figure 9.4. Zener model, also known as the standard-linear-solid model. After Carcione (2001).

5. Prove equations 9.32 and 9.33. Note that $\sigma = \kappa_1 \epsilon_1$, $\sigma = \eta \dot{\epsilon}_2 + \kappa_2 \epsilon_2$, and $\epsilon = \epsilon_1 + \epsilon_2$ are three equations in which ϵ_1 and ϵ_2 are to be eliminated.
6. Prove that equation 9.35 solves equation 9.34.

9.5 Computational labs

1. Execute the lab for 2D viscoacoustic modeling.

Appendix 9A:
Relaxation function

For the Zener SLS model shown in Figure 9.4, the stress-strain relation for the individual elements can be written as (Dutta, 2015):

$$\sigma = k_1 \epsilon_1; \quad \sigma_1 = \eta \frac{\partial \epsilon_2}{\partial t}; \quad \sigma_2 = k_2 \epsilon_2, \qquad (9.30)$$

and for the whole model as

$$\sigma = \sigma_1 + \sigma_2; \quad \epsilon = \epsilon_1 + \epsilon_2. \qquad (9.31)$$

The goal will be to find the general relaxation response $\mathcal{G}(t)$ so that $\sigma(t) = \mathcal{G}(t)\epsilon_0$ for a constant strain $\epsilon(t) = \epsilon_0 H(t)$.

From equations 9.30 and 9.31, we get the stress-strain relation as (see Exercise 5)

$$\sigma + \tau_\sigma \frac{\partial \sigma}{\partial t} = M_R \left(\epsilon + \tau_\epsilon \frac{\partial \epsilon}{\partial t} \right). \qquad (9.32)$$

Here M_R is the relaxed modulus, and τ_σ and τ_ϵ are the relaxation times given by

$$M_R = \frac{k_1 k_2}{k_1 + k_2}; \quad \tau_\sigma = \frac{\eta}{k_1 + k_2}; \quad \tau_\epsilon = \frac{\eta}{k_2}. \qquad (9.33)$$

The relaxation function $\mathcal{G}(t)$ for any medium can be obtained by measuring the stress after imposing a constant strain given by $\epsilon(t) = H(t)$. In this case, equation 9.19 says $\sigma(t) = \mathcal{G}(t)$ so that equation 9.32 becomes

$$\mathcal{G}(t) + \tau_\sigma \frac{\partial \mathcal{G}(t)}{\partial t} = M_R \left(H(t) + \tau_\epsilon \delta(t) \right), \qquad (9.34)$$

which has the solution

$$\mathcal{G}(t) = M_R \left(1 - \left(1 - \frac{\tau_\epsilon}{\tau_\sigma} \right) e^{-t/\tau_\sigma} \right) H(t). \qquad (9.35)$$

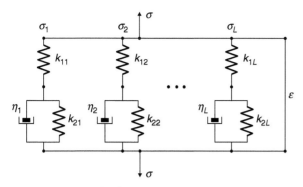

Figure 9.5. Generalized Zener model with L standard-linear-solid models connected in parallel. After Carcione (2001). Used by permission.

For a series of L standard linear solids connected in parallel, as shown in Figure 9.5, equation 9.35 has the general form

$$\mathcal{G}(t) = M_R \left(1 - \sum_{l=1}^{L} \left(1 - \frac{\tau_{\epsilon l}}{\tau_{\sigma l}} \right) e^{-t/\tau_{\sigma l}} \right) H(t). \quad (9.36)$$

Appendix 9B:
Relation between Q and τ's

Hooke's law in the lossless case (Pelissier et al., 2007) is given by

$$\sigma = M_e \epsilon, \quad (9.37)$$

in which M_e is the elastic modulus. For a lossy medium, the stress-strain relation becomes

$$\sigma = \mathcal{G} * \dot{\epsilon} = \dot{\mathcal{G}} * \epsilon, \quad (9.38)$$

where $\mathcal{G}(t)$ is the relaxation function that transforms a strain history $\epsilon(t)$ into the corresponding stress history $\sigma(t)$.

The Fourier transform of 9.38 gives

$$\mathcal{F}(\sigma(\omega)) = M(\omega)\mathcal{F}(\epsilon(\omega)), \quad (9.39)$$

where $\mathcal{F}$ represents the Fourier transform operation and $M(\omega) = \mathcal{F}(\dot{\mathcal{G}}(\omega))$. $M(\omega)$ also is known as the complex modulus and can be represented as

$$M(\omega) = M_1(\omega) + iM_2(\omega). \quad (9.40)$$

The time-averaged, strain-energy density can be written as

$$\langle V \rangle = \frac{1}{2} \langle Re(\epsilon)Re(M)Re(\epsilon) \rangle = \frac{1}{4} Re(\epsilon M \epsilon^*) = \frac{1}{4} M_1 |\epsilon|^2, \quad (9.41)$$

and similarly, the time-averaged dissipated-energy density is given by

$$\langle D \rangle = \frac{1}{2} M_2 |\epsilon|^2. \quad (9.42)$$

The quality factor Q quantifies dissipation and is defined as twice the time-averaged strain-energy density divided by the time-averaged dissipated-energy-density, i.e.,

$$Q = \frac{2 \langle V \rangle}{\langle D \rangle} = \frac{M_1}{M_2} = \frac{Re(M)}{Im(M)}. \quad (9.43)$$

For an SLS model with a single relaxation mechanism, the stress-strain relation is given by 9.32

$$\sigma + \tau_\sigma \frac{\partial \sigma}{\partial t} = M_R \left(\epsilon + \tau_\epsilon \frac{\partial \epsilon}{\partial t} \right), \quad (9.44)$$

in which $\sigma = M\epsilon$. Taking the Fourier transform of 9.44 gives

$$M(\omega) = \frac{M_R(1 + i\omega\tau_\epsilon)}{1 + i\omega\tau_\sigma}, \quad (9.45)$$

so that from equation 9.43, Q can be written as

$$Q(\omega) = \frac{Re(M)}{Im(M)} = \frac{1 + \omega^2 \tau_\sigma \tau_\epsilon}{\omega(\tau_\epsilon - \tau_\sigma)}. \quad (9.46)$$

This model has a relaxation peak at

$$\omega_0 = \frac{1}{\sqrt{\tau_\sigma \tau_\epsilon}}, \quad (9.47)$$

which can be verified by setting $\frac{dQ}{d\omega} = 0$ in equation 9.46. Here, ω_0 also is defined to be the center frequency of the source wavelet spectrum.

For our purposes, constant Q-models are used conveniently to parameterize attenuation in rocks because it is usually difficult to quantify the frequency dependence of Q. Also Q has been shown empirically to be constant in many frequency bands. Thus, a more physical parameterization of τ_σ and τ_ϵ can be obtained at the center frequency ω_0. From equation 9.46, at $\omega = \omega_0$, we get

$$Q = \frac{2}{\omega_0(\tau_\epsilon - \tau_\sigma)}, \quad (9.48)$$

where τ_σ and τ_ϵ can be obtained from equations 9.47 and 9.48 as

$$\tau_\sigma = \frac{\sqrt{1 + \frac{1}{Q^2}} - \frac{1}{Q}}{\omega_0}; \quad \tau_\epsilon = \frac{1}{\omega_0^2 \tau_\sigma}. \quad (9.49)$$

Part IV

Reflection Migration

Chapter 10: Forward and Adjoint Modeling Using Green's Functions

Forward modeling of the wave equation is defined as computing the propagating wavefields for a given source-receiver distribution, the source wavelet, and a velocity-density model. This chapter presents the forward-modeling approach with the Lippmann-Schwinger (LS) equation, a summation of weighted Green's functions over the model coordinates, in which the weights are the reflection-like coefficients in the model. Another name for this is diffraction-stack modeling under the weak scattering approximation, otherwise known as the Born approximation.

If the adjoint of the Green's function (complex conjugate of the Green's function for the acoustic wave equation) is used, then the estimate of the reflectivity model (commonly known as the migration image) is obtained by a summation of the weighted adjoint Green's functions over the data coordinates, where the weights are composed partly of the seismograms. Another name for this is *diffraction-stack migration* (French, 1974), which approximates the migration image by the summation of weighted CSG amplitudes along the appropriate diffraction-time curves.[1] If incidence-angle weighting based on Green's theorem is used, then this type of diffraction-stack migration is called Kirchhoff migration (Yilmaz, 2001). Asymptotically accounting for many of the geometrical and wavelet distortion effects of a complicated velocity model leads to a weighted diffraction-stack migration algorithm known as true-amplitude migration (Schleicher et al., 2007). As we will see in later chapters, the migration image is equivalent to the gradient of the data misfit function for iterative least-squares migration and iterative nonlinear waveform inversion.

10.1 Integral-equation forward modeling

The 3D Helmholtz equation is given by

$$(\nabla_{\mathbf{x}'}^2 + k^2)P(\mathbf{x}') = -F(\mathbf{x}'), \qquad (10.1)$$

---

[1] See Hagedoorn (1954) for a description of an early form of migration based purely on kinematics.

in which the differentiation $\nabla_{\mathbf{x}'}$ is with respect to the primed coordinates, the wavenumber $k = \omega/c(\mathbf{x}')$ is for an inhomogeneous medium with velocity $c(\mathbf{x}')$, $P(\mathbf{x}')$ is the associated pressure field, and $F(\mathbf{x}')$ represents the body-force term harmonically oscillating with angular frequency ω. To reduce notational complexity, the explicit dependence on the frequency variable is silent and density is assumed to be constant.

Given the source-receiver coordinates, the source wavelet, and the velocity model, our goal with forward modeling is to use Green's theorem to find the pressure field in the form of an integral equation. Towards this goal, we first define a Green's function and then use it to derive Green's theorem.

10.1.1 Green's functions

The response $G(\mathbf{x}'|\mathbf{x})$ of a medium arising from a harmonic point source at $\mathbf{x}$ oscillating at frequency ω is known as the 3D Green's function, which solves the 3D Helmholtz equation (Morse and Feshbach, 1953)

$$(\nabla_{\mathbf{x}'}^2 + k^2)G(\mathbf{x}'|\mathbf{x}) = -\delta(\mathbf{x}' - \mathbf{x}), \qquad (10.2)$$

in which $k = \omega/c(\mathbf{x}')$ and $\delta(\mathbf{x}' - \mathbf{x}) = \delta(x - x')\delta(y - y')\delta(z - z')$. Here, the density ρ is assumed to be constant and the spatial variations in velocity $c = \sqrt{\kappa/\rho}$ arise from variations in the bulk modulus κ.

There are two independent solutions to this second-order PDE: an outgoing Green's function $G(\mathbf{x}'|\mathbf{x})$ and its complex conjugate, the incoming Green's function $G(\mathbf{x}'|\mathbf{x})^*$. The outgoing Green's function (see Appendix 10A) for a homogeneous medium with velocity c is given by

$$G(\mathbf{x}'|\mathbf{x}) = \frac{e^{-ik|\mathbf{x}'-\mathbf{x}|}}{4\pi |\mathbf{x} - \mathbf{x}'|}, \qquad (10.3)$$

in which the wavenumber is $k = \omega/c$ and the denominator accounts for geometrical spreading between the observer at $\mathbf{x}'$ and the source point at $\mathbf{x}$.

For a homogeneous medium, the real part of the Green's function plots out as a series of concentric circles centered about $\mathbf{x}$ with wavelength $\lambda = 2\pi c/\omega$ (see

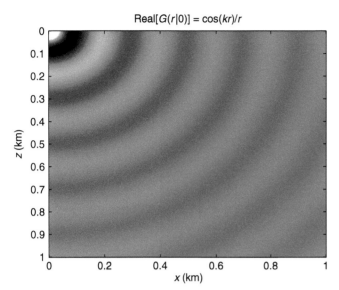

Figure 10.1. Snapshot of the real part of the harmonic Green's function.

Figure 10.1). Note that the source and receiver locations can be interchanged in equation 10.3 so $G(\mathbf{x}|\mathbf{x}') = G(\mathbf{x}'|\mathbf{x})$, which is consistent with the reciprocity principle (Morse and Feshbach, 1953). This says that a pressure trace recorded at position $\mathbf{x}'$ excited by a point-source at $\mathbf{x}$ will be the same as the trace located at $\mathbf{x}$ for a point-source excitation at $\mathbf{x}'$.

Appendix 10A shows that the inverse Fourier transform of $G(\mathbf{x}'|\mathbf{x})$ is proportional to $\delta(t - t_s - |\mathbf{x} - \mathbf{x}'|/c)/|\mathbf{x} - \mathbf{x}'|$. This means that if the excitation time t_s of the source is delayed by t_0, then the recorded trace will be the same as before except for a time shift of t_0. That is,

$$\frac{\delta(t - t_s - |\mathbf{x} - \mathbf{x}'|/c)}{|\mathbf{x} - \mathbf{x}'|}$$
$$= \frac{\delta([t - t_0] - [t_s - t_0] - |\mathbf{x} - \mathbf{x}'|/c)}{|\mathbf{x} - \mathbf{x}'|}. \quad (10.4)$$

This stationary property is true for an arbitrary acoustic-velocity model, and it can be expressed mathematically as $g(\mathbf{x}', t|\mathbf{x}, t_s) = g(\mathbf{x}', t - t_s|\mathbf{x}, 0)$. It says that the observed wavefield depends on the time difference between the source initiation time and the observation time, no matter when the source is initiated. For example, the shot gather obtained at noon ideally should be identical to the shot gather obtained at midnight, except for a source delay time of 12 hours.[2]

---

[2]The stationarity property also is true for any acoustic medium. A simple proof is given by multiplying equation 10.2 by a phase shift term $e^{-i\omega\tau_0}$. The right-side term now is $\delta(\mathbf{x}' - \mathbf{x})e^{-i\omega\tau_0}$, which is equivalent to delaying the source initiation time by the delay time τ_0. But the linearity of the wave equation says that the solution $G(\mathbf{x}'|\mathbf{x})e^{-i\omega\tau_0}$ is the same Green's function as before, except for the time shift of τ_0.

10.1.2 $(\nabla_{\mathbf{x}'}^2 + k^2)^{-1}$ by Green's theorem

We now derive Green's theorem that can be used to invert equation 10.1. Multiplying the Helmholtz equation (equation 10.1) by the Green's function $G(\mathbf{x}|\mathbf{x}')$ gives

$$G(\mathbf{x}|\mathbf{x}')(\nabla_{\mathbf{x}'}^2 + k^2)P(\mathbf{x}') = -G(\mathbf{x}|\mathbf{x}')F(\mathbf{x}'). \quad (10.5)$$

Inserting the identity $G\nabla_{\mathbf{x}'}^2 P = P\nabla_{\mathbf{x}'}^2 G + \nabla_{\mathbf{x}'} \cdot (G\nabla_{\mathbf{x}'}P - P\nabla_{\mathbf{x}'}G)$ (which can be proved by using differentiation by parts) into the above equation gives

$$P(\mathbf{x}')(\nabla_{\mathbf{x}'}^2 + k^2)G(\mathbf{x}|\mathbf{x}') + \nabla_{\mathbf{x}'} \cdot (G(\mathbf{x}|\mathbf{x}')\nabla_{\mathbf{x}'}P(\mathbf{x}')$$
$$- P(\mathbf{x}')\nabla_{\mathbf{x}'}G(\mathbf{x}|\mathbf{x}')) = -G(\mathbf{x}|\mathbf{x}')F(\mathbf{x}'). \quad (10.6)$$

Consider a closed surface S_o with the interior volume V_o. Integrating equation 10.6 over this volume gives

$$\int_{V_o} [P(\mathbf{x}')(\nabla_{\mathbf{x}'}^2 + k^2)G(\mathbf{x}|\mathbf{x}') + \nabla_{\mathbf{x}'} \cdot (G(\mathbf{x}|\mathbf{x}')\nabla_{\mathbf{x}'}P(\mathbf{x}')$$
$$- P(\mathbf{x}')\nabla_{\mathbf{x}'}G(\mathbf{x}|\mathbf{x}'))]dx'^3 = -\int_{V_o} G(\mathbf{x}|\mathbf{x}')F(\mathbf{x}')dx'^3,$$
$$(10.7)$$

in which $\mathbf{x}, \mathbf{x}' \in V_o$. Inserting equation 10.2 yields

$$\int_{V_o} P(\mathbf{x}')\delta(\mathbf{x}' - \mathbf{x})dx'^3 - \int_{V_o} \nabla_{\mathbf{x}'} \cdot (G(\mathbf{x}|\mathbf{x}')\nabla_{\mathbf{x}'}P(\mathbf{x}')$$
$$- P(\mathbf{x}')\nabla_{\mathbf{x}'}G(\mathbf{x}|\mathbf{x}'))dx'^3 = \int_{V_o} G(\mathbf{x}|\mathbf{x}')F(\mathbf{x}')dx'^3, \quad (10.8)$$

and by rearranging we get

$$P(\mathbf{x}) - \int_{S_o} (G(\mathbf{x}|\mathbf{x}')\nabla_{\mathbf{x}'}P(\mathbf{x}') - P(\mathbf{x}')\nabla_{\mathbf{x}'}G(\mathbf{x}|\mathbf{x}')) \cdot \hat{\mathbf{n}}dx'^2$$
$$= \int_{V_o} G(\mathbf{x}|\mathbf{x}')F(\mathbf{x}')dx'^3, \quad (10.9)$$

where the unit normal $\hat{\mathbf{n}}$ to the surface S_o is pointing outward from the integration volume.[3] The conversion from a volume integral to a surface integral follows from the divergence theorem (Morse and Feshbach, 1953). See the last appendix in this chapter for the generalized Green's theorem that is valid for differential operators that are

---

[3]A subtle feature of the volume integration is that it should not enclose a strong singularity such as the gradient of the Green's functions when $\mathbf{x} = \mathbf{x}'$. The classical remedy is to surround the singularity at $\mathbf{x}$ with a small void that is not part of the volume V_o. Then, the divergence theorem can be used to reduce the volume integration over the outer surface S_o and the surface of the small void. In the limit as the radius of the void decreases, the surface integration gives the finite-valued contribution of $P(\mathbf{x})$ on the left side of equation 10.9.

not self-adjoint. Rearranging gives the integral-equation solution to the Helmholtz equation:

$$P(\mathbf{x}) = \int_{S_o} (G(\mathbf{x}|\mathbf{x}')\nabla_{\mathbf{x}'}P(\mathbf{x}') - P(\mathbf{x}')\nabla_{\mathbf{x}'}G(\mathbf{x}|\mathbf{x}')) \cdot \hat{\mathbf{n}}dx'^2$$

$$+ \int_{V_o} G(\mathbf{x}|\mathbf{x}')F(\mathbf{x}')dx'^3. \quad (10.10)$$

The above integral is valid for $\mathbf{x}$ within the volume and the starting point for the boundary integral-equation modeling method (Brebbia, 1978).

If only outgoing waves are considered and the surface S_o is at infinity, then the surface integral is zero (see Sommerfeld radiation condition in Morse and Feshbach, 1953) in equation 10.10 to give

$$P(\mathbf{x}) = \int_{V_o} G(\mathbf{x}|\mathbf{x}')F(\mathbf{x}')dx'^3. \quad (10.11)$$

The physical interpretation of $P(\mathbf{x})$ for a homogeneous medium is that it represents the direct wave that travels from the source to the receiver. If the medium outside the boundary is inhomogeneous and the medium inside V_o is homogeneous where $G(\mathbf{x}|\mathbf{x}')$ is the associated Green's function, the boundary integral in equation 10.10 accounts for the external reflections that contribute to the field inside the volume.

This solution of the Helmholtz equation given by equation 10.11 is a weighted sum of the Green's functions, in which the weights are the source amplitudes at each point in the medium. This representation is valid for an arbitrary acoustic medium, and it shows that $-\int dx'^3 G(\mathbf{x}|\mathbf{x}')\cdot \equiv (\nabla_{\mathbf{x}'}^2 + k^2)^{-1}$ if the actual Green's function is used for the entire medium.[4] In other words, applying the appropriate Green's function to the Helmholtz equation and integrating over the volume is the inverse operator to the Helmholtz equation.

10.1.3 Lippmann-Schwinger solution

Equation 10.10 is expensive for the computation of the unknown field values $P(\mathbf{x})$ because they are on both the left and right sides, which means an expensive matrix inverse must be computed. To avoid this expense, we use the Lippmann-Schwinger equation under the Born approximation, as described below.

Assume a medium composed of the background slowness model $s(\mathbf{x}) = 1/c(\mathbf{x})$ and a perturbed slowness model given by $\tilde{s}(\mathbf{x}) = s(\mathbf{x})\sqrt{1 + 2s(\mathbf{x})\delta s(\mathbf{x})/s(\mathbf{x})^2}$, in which $\delta s(\mathbf{x})$ is the perturbation parameter. For example, Figure 10.2 shows the background medium as homogeneous and the perturbed region as potato shaped with a different velocity.

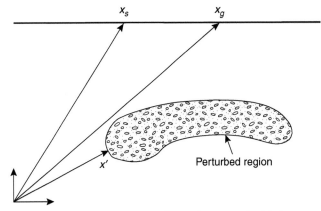

Figure 10.2. Background medium with an embedded potato-like perturbation with slightly different velocity.

The pressure field P in the perturbed medium is governed by

$$(\nabla_{\mathbf{x}'}^2 + \omega^2[s(\mathbf{x}')^2 + 2s(\mathbf{x}')\delta s(\mathbf{x}')])P(\mathbf{x}') = -F(\mathbf{x}'), \quad (10.12)$$

or by rearranging we get

$$(\nabla_{\mathbf{x}'}^2 + \omega^2 s(\mathbf{x}')^2)P(\mathbf{x}') = -2\omega^2 s(\mathbf{x}')\delta s(\mathbf{x}')P(\mathbf{x}') - F(\mathbf{x}').$$

$$(10.13)$$

The above Helmholtz equation can be inverted by applying $(\nabla_{\mathbf{x}'}^2 + \omega^2 s(\mathbf{x}')^2)^{-1} = -\int dx'^3 G(\mathbf{x}|\mathbf{x}')\cdot$ to both sides of the above equation to give the Lippmann-Schwinger equation

$$P(\mathbf{x}) = 2\omega^2 \int_{V_o} \overbrace{G(\mathbf{x}|\mathbf{x}')}^{\text{scatt}\rightarrow\text{geo}} \overbrace{s(\mathbf{x}')\delta s(\mathbf{x}')}^{\text{reflectivity}} \overbrace{P(\mathbf{x}')}^{\text{src}\rightarrow\text{scatt}} dx'^3$$

$$+ \int_{V_o} G(\mathbf{x}|\mathbf{x}')F(\mathbf{x}')dx'^3, \quad (10.14)$$

where the Green's function is that for the unperturbed medium and satisfies equation 10.2 for $k = \omega s(\mathbf{x}')$. The term $P(\mathbf{x}')$ in the integrand represents the total field on the potato excited by a neighboring source, so we call this the *source-to-scatterer field*. Similarly, the Green's function $G(\mathbf{x}|\mathbf{x}')$ takes the total field at $\mathbf{x}'$ on the potato and extrapolates it to the surface location $\mathbf{x}$ as the *scatterer-to-geophone field*; the strength of this upgoing field at the potato is proportional to the magnitude of the reflectivity-like[5] term $s(\mathbf{x}')\delta s(\mathbf{x}')$.

Note that the unknown field value $P(\mathbf{x}')$ is on both the left and right sides of equation 10.14, and therefore,

---

[4]Here, the dot symbol $\cdot$ indicates that the integral is an operator that requires an input function of $\mathbf{x}'$ to give an output function of $\mathbf{x}$.

[5]The pressure reflection coefficient associated with a plane wave vertically incident on a horizontal interface is given as $R = (v_2 - v_1)/(v_2 + v_1)$. Therefore, $s\delta s = -R\bar{v}/v_1^2 v_2$, in which $\bar{v} = (v_2 + v_1)$. Here, the density is constant and the upper- and lower-layer velocities are denoted as v_1 and v_2, respectively. In the context of slowness perturbations, v_1 is the smooth background velocity and v_2 is the updated velocity.

this equation is a Fredholm integral equation of the second kind.[6] The computational cost for inverting this equation for $P(\mathbf{x}')$ is prohibitive for large models. We now will examine two possible methods for finding an approximate solution: a series expansion and the Born approximation. The latter method often is used in seismic imaging.

10.1.4 Neumann series solution

An alternative to the direct inversion of equation 10.14 is an iterative solution (Morse and Feshbach, 1953; Schuster, 1985; Ramírez and Weglein, 2009), such as the Neumann series solution. A Neumann series solution is similar to the scalar geometric series

$$(1 - x)^{-1}y = (1 + x + x^2 + x^3 + \cdots)y \qquad (10.15)$$

that converges for $|x| < 1$, except x in this chapter will be treated as an operator applied to the input function y. Rearranging equation 10.14 so that the unknown $P(\mathbf{x}')$ is on the left side gives

$$\left[\iint_{V_o} dx'^3 \delta(\mathbf{x}' - \mathbf{x}) - 2\omega^2 \int_{V_o} dx'^3 G(\mathbf{x}|\mathbf{x}')s(\mathbf{x}')\delta s(\mathbf{x}') \right] P(\mathbf{x}')$$
$$= \int_{V_o} G(\mathbf{x}|\mathbf{x}')F(\mathbf{x}')dx'^3. \qquad (10.16)$$

The operator x in the Neumann series is identified in equation 10.16 as

$$x \to \overbrace{2\omega^2 \int_{V_o} dx'^3 G(\mathbf{x}|\mathbf{x}')s(\mathbf{x}')\delta s(\mathbf{x}')}^{\mathcal{G}_0 V} \cdot \qquad (10.17)$$

Therefore, the Neumann series solution to equation 10.14 is

$$P(\mathbf{x}) = \overbrace{\int_{V_o} G(\mathbf{x}|\mathbf{x}')F(\mathbf{x}')dx'^3}^{\psi_0} +$$

$$\overbrace{2\omega^2 \int_{V_o} G(\mathbf{x}|\mathbf{x}')s(\mathbf{x}')\delta s(\mathbf{x}') \int_{V_o} G(\mathbf{x}'|\mathbf{x}'')F(\mathbf{x}'')dx''^3 dx'^3}^{\mathcal{G}_0 V \psi_0} +$$

$$\overbrace{4\omega^4 \int_{V_o} G(\mathbf{x}|\mathbf{x}')s(\mathbf{x}')\delta s(\mathbf{x}') \int_{V_o} G(\mathbf{x}'|\mathbf{x}'')s(\mathbf{x}'')\delta s(\mathbf{x}'') \int_{V_o} G(\mathbf{x}''|\mathbf{x}''')F(\mathbf{x}''')dx'''^3 dx''^3 dx'^3}^{\mathcal{G}_0 V \mathcal{G}_0 V \psi_0} + \cdots$$

$$= \int_{V_o} G(\mathbf{x}|\mathbf{x}')F(\mathbf{x}')dx'^3 + \sum_{i=1}^{\infty} \overbrace{\left[2\omega^2 \int_{V_o} dx'^3 G(\mathbf{x}|\mathbf{x}')s(\mathbf{x}')\delta s(\mathbf{x}') \right]^i}^{[\mathcal{G}_0 V]^i} \overbrace{\int_{V_o} G(\mathbf{x}'|\mathbf{x}'')F(\mathbf{x}'')dx''^3}^{\psi_0}.$$

---

[6]If $\delta s(\mathbf{x}')$ is considered the unknown, then equation 10.14 is a nonlinear equation in $\delta s(\mathbf{x}')$ because $P(\mathbf{x}')$ also depends on $\delta s(\mathbf{x}')$.

The above equation can be represented in a more compact notation

$$P = \sum_{i=0}^{\infty} [\mathcal{G}_0 V]^i \psi_0 = P^{(0)} + P^{(1)} + P^{(2)} + \cdots, \qquad (10.18)$$

in which the nth term represents the nth order response of the perturbed medium. For example, the zeroth-order term $P^{(0)} = \int_{V_o} G(\mathbf{x}|\mathbf{x}')F(\mathbf{x}')dx'^3$ is the direct-wave response of the background medium, the first-order term $P^{(1)}$ is the primary-reflection response[7] between the potato and the background medium, the second-order term $P^{(2)}$ is its first-order multiple response, and so on. The first-order term $P^{(1)}$ also is known as the first Born approximation to the scattered wavefield, as discussed in the next section.

10.1.5 Born approximation

The first Born approximation, or simply the Born approximation, is obtained by approximating the scattered field $P - P^{(0)}$ by the first-order term of the Neumann series in equation 10.18

$$P - P^{(0)} \approx P^{(1)}, \qquad (10.19)$$

which is accurate for weak scatterers where the scattered field is much weaker than the incident field.[8] This means that the pressure field can be approximated by the first two terms on the right side of equation 10.18 to give the Born approximation

$$P(\mathbf{x}|\mathbf{s}) = 2\omega^2 \int_{V_o} G(\mathbf{x}|\mathbf{x}')s(\mathbf{x}')\delta s(\mathbf{x}')W(\omega)G(\mathbf{x}'|\mathbf{s})dx'^3$$
$$+ W(\omega)G(\mathbf{x}|\mathbf{s}), \qquad (10.21)$$

in which the first term on the right side accounts for the primary reflections from the slowness perturbation and the second term accounts for the incident field in the unperturbed medium. Here, the source term in equation 10.14 is replaced by $F(\mathbf{x}') = W(\omega)\delta(\mathbf{s} - \mathbf{x}')$ so that $\int_{V_o} G(\mathbf{x}|\mathbf{x}')F(\mathbf{x}')dx'^3$

---

[7]The wavefield from the background medium can contain multiples, but the primary-reflection response of the potato means that these multiples scatter just one time from its perturbations.

[8]Convergence of the Neumann series is guaranteed by the condition

$$I_1 = |2\omega^2 \int_{V_o} G(\mathbf{x}|\mathbf{x}')s(\mathbf{x}')\delta s(\mathbf{x}')W(\omega)G(\mathbf{x}'|\mathbf{s})dx'^3| < 1, \qquad (10.20)$$

and the Born approximation is accurate if $|s(\mathbf{x})\delta s(\mathbf{x})|$ is small enough. As an example, assume $ka < 1$ where a is the characteristic size of the scatterer or volume of integration. For the case of a homogeneous background and an incident plane wave $G(\mathbf{x}'|\mathbf{s}) = W(\omega)e^{i\mathbf{k}\cdot\mathbf{x}}$, the denominator in the Green's function of I_1 is of the order a so that I_1 is of the order $|k\omega W(\omega)a^2 \delta s(\mathbf{x}')|$. Therefore, the Born approximation is accurate if $|k\omega W(\omega)a^2 \delta s(\mathbf{x}')| \ll 1$, but this condition can be relaxed with the use of modified Born approximations (Saha and Sharma, 2005).

$= W(\omega)G(\mathbf{x}|\mathbf{s})$, in which $W(\omega)$ is the source spectrum and $\mathbf{s}$ is the source location. The Born approximation is valid if multiples inspired by δs can be neglected.

Subtracting the direct-wave term from both sides in equation 10.21 and defining the scattered field as $\delta P(\mathbf{x}|\mathbf{s})^{\text{scatt}} = P(\mathbf{x}|\mathbf{s}) - W(\omega)G(\mathbf{x}|\mathbf{s})$ gives

$$\delta P(\mathbf{x}|\mathbf{s})^{\text{scatt}} = 2\omega^2 \int_{V_o} G(\mathbf{x}|\mathbf{x}')s(\mathbf{x}')\delta s(\mathbf{x}')W(\omega)G(\mathbf{x}'|\mathbf{s})dx'^3.$$

(10.22)

Inserting $\delta s(\mathbf{x}') \rightarrow \delta(\mathbf{x}_o - \mathbf{x}')\delta s(\mathbf{x}_o)$, carrying out the integration, and dividing by $\delta s(\mathbf{x}_o)$ yields the Fréchet derivative

$$\frac{\delta P(\mathbf{x}|\mathbf{s})^{\text{scatt}}}{\delta s(\mathbf{x}_o)} = 2\omega^2 s(\mathbf{x}_o)G(\mathbf{x}|\mathbf{x}_o)W(\omega)G(\mathbf{x}_o|\mathbf{s}), \quad (10.23)$$

for the acoustic wave equation. Applying an inverse Fourier transform to the above formula gives the Fréchet derivative in the time domain

$$\frac{\delta p(\mathbf{x},t|\mathbf{s},0)^{\text{scatt}}}{\delta s(\mathbf{x}_o)} = -2s(\mathbf{x}_o)\ddot{g}(\mathbf{x},t|\mathbf{x}_o,0) \star p(\mathbf{x}_o,t|\mathbf{s},0),$$

$$= -2s(\mathbf{x}_o)\dot{g}(\mathbf{x},t|\mathbf{x}_o,0) \star \dot{p}(\mathbf{x}_o,t|\mathbf{s},0),$$

(10.24)

where we assume $p(\mathbf{x}_o,t|\mathbf{s},0) \approx g(\mathbf{x}_o,t|\mathbf{s},0) \star w(t)$ and $w(t)$ is the source wavelet in the time domain. Noting that $\partial p/\partial s = -c^2 \partial p/\partial c$, equation 10.24 becomes

$$\frac{\delta p(\mathbf{x},t|\mathbf{s},0)^{\text{scatt}}}{\delta c(\mathbf{x}_o)} = \frac{2}{c(\mathbf{x}_o)^3}\dot{g}(\mathbf{x},t|\mathbf{x}_o,0) \star \dot{p}(\mathbf{x}_o,t|\mathbf{s},0).$$

(10.25)

The Fréchet derivatives in equations 10.23 and 10.25 are used to compute the elements of the Jacobian matrix, and are a measure of the sensitivity of the trace at $\mathbf{x}$ arising from changes in the slowness at $\mathbf{x}_o$ (Marquering et al., 1999; de Hoop and van der Hilst, 2005; Liu et al., 2009; Xu and Xie, 2009). They will be used in Chapters 12 to 14 to estimate the resolution properties of migration and full-waveform inversion.

Rearranging equation 10.21 into a more compact notation gives

$$\mathbf{d} = \mathbf{L}\mathbf{m}, \quad (10.26)$$

in which the modeling operator $\mathbf{L}$, scattered data $\mathbf{d}$, and reflectivity model $\mathbf{m}$ are defined as

$$\mathbf{L} \rightarrow 2\omega^2 \int_{V_o} dx'^3 G(\mathbf{x}|\mathbf{x}')G(\mathbf{x}'|\mathbf{s})W(\omega)\cdot; \ \mathbf{d} \rightarrow P(\mathbf{x}|\mathbf{s})$$

$$- W(\omega)G(\mathbf{x}|\mathbf{s}); \ \mathbf{m} \rightarrow s(\mathbf{x}')\delta s(\mathbf{x}'). \quad (10.27)$$

Typically, the scattered data are the seismograms after the direct waves have been adaptively subtracted (or muted) from the recorded data. For migration or least-squares migration (Nemeth et al., 1999), the direct wave can be estimated by modeling the diving wave propagating through a smooth-background velocity model.

Example of nonzero offset modeling

Next we will derive the diffraction-stack modeling equation for a background velocity model restricted to smooth velocity variations, and each source shoots into receivers that have nonzero offset from the source.

Assume high frequencies so that the asymptotic Green's function can be used:

$$G(\mathbf{x}|\mathbf{s}) = \frac{e^{-i\omega\tau_{sx}}}{4\pi|\mathbf{x} - \mathbf{s}|}, \quad (10.28)$$

in which τ_{sx} is the time for energy to propagate from the source at $\mathbf{s}$ to the interrogation point at $\mathbf{x}$, and for notational simplicity we approximate the geometrical-spreading term by $1/|\mathbf{x} - \mathbf{s}|$.

Substituting equation 10.28 into equation 10.21, we get the diffraction-stack equation of forward modeling

$$P(\mathbf{x}|\mathbf{s})^{\text{scatt}} = \frac{\omega^2}{8\pi^2} \int_{V_o} \frac{s(\mathbf{x}')\delta s(\mathbf{x}')W(\omega)e^{-i\omega(\tau_{sx'}+\tau_{xx'})}}{|\mathbf{x}' - \mathbf{s}| \, |\mathbf{x} - \mathbf{x}'|}dx'^3,$$

(10.29)

in which the direct wave is subtracted from the total field to give the scattered field $P(\mathbf{x}|\mathbf{s})^{\text{scatt}}$. Applying $\frac{1}{2\pi}\int d\omega e^{i\omega t}$ to the above equation yields the time-domain diffraction-stack modeling formula

$$p(\mathbf{x},t|\mathbf{s},0)^{\text{scatt}} = -\frac{1}{8\pi^2} \int_{V_o} \frac{s(\mathbf{x}')\delta s(\mathbf{x}')\ddot{w}(t - \tau_{sx'} - \tau_{xx'})}{|\mathbf{x}' - \mathbf{s}| \, |\mathbf{x} - \mathbf{x}'|}dx'^3,$$

(10.30)

in which the double dot indicates double differentiation in time. This formula can be used to generate synthetic seismograms with primary reflections by setting $\delta s(\mathbf{x}) = 1$ along reflector boundaries, otherwise $\delta s(\mathbf{x}) = 0$.

A special case is for a point scatterer at $\mathbf{x}_o$ with $\delta s(\mathbf{x}') = \Delta s(\mathbf{x}_o)\delta(\mathbf{x}' - \mathbf{x}_0)$ and a geophone at $\mathbf{x} \rightarrow \mathbf{g}$, so that equation 10.30 becomes

$$p(\mathbf{g},t|\mathbf{s},0)^{\text{scatt}} = \frac{-s(\mathbf{x}_o)\Delta s(\mathbf{x}_o)\ddot{w}(t - \tau_{sx_o} - \tau_{gx_o})}{8\pi^2|\mathbf{x}_o - \mathbf{s}| \, |\mathbf{g} - \mathbf{x}_o|}, \quad (10.31)$$

in which $\Delta s(\mathbf{x}_o)$ represents the difference between the slownesses in the slowness models with and without the scatterer at $\mathbf{x}_o$. Here, $w(t - \tau_{sx_o} - \tau_{gx_o})$ is the source wavelet delayed by the amount of time it takes to propagate from the source

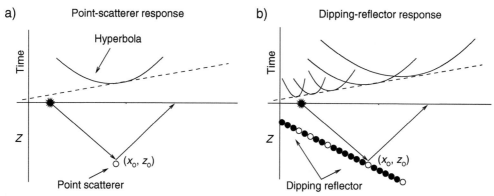

Figure 10.3. Shot gather of traces for (a) point scatterer at (x_o, z_o) and (b) dipping reflector, assuming an impulsive source wavelet. The reflectivity value $s(\mathbf{x}_o)\Delta s(\mathbf{x}_o) = 1$ is assumed to be one in this example for all point scatterers. Each reflectivity value is mapped (i.e., smeared) from the model-space point (x, z) into the data space along the appropriate hyperbola. Then, the amplitude values are summed together to give the traces. Each open circle is a scatterer that is associated with the hyperbola centered above it.

down to the scatterer and back up to the receiver. For an impulsive source wavelet, the support of $w(t - \tau_{sx_o} - \tau_{gx_o})$ exists along the hyperbola described by $t = \tau_{sx_o} + \tau_{gx_o} = \left[\sqrt{(x_s - x_o)^2 + z_o^2} + \sqrt{(x_g - x_o)^2 + z_o^2}\right]/c$, which traces out a hyperbola in data-space coordinates $(x_g, 0, t)$ for a fixed scatterer at (x_o, z_o). Thus, the point-scatterer response is obtained by smearing the reflectivity $\Delta s(\mathbf{x}_o)$ value along the appropriate hyperbola in data space (see Figure 10.3). If the wavelet is bandlimited and has a period T_0, then the hyperbola is spread out over the time duration of T_0.

For a string of contiguous point scatterers, the seismograms are obtained by smearing and summing the perturbation amplitudes along the appropriate hyperbolas, one for each scatterer as shown in Figure 10.3b.

Example of zero-offset modeling

The diffraction-stack modeling equation now is derived for computing a zero-offset (ZO) trace where the source and receiver are coincident with one another.[9]

When the source is coincident with the geophone, then $\tau_{sx_o} = \tau_{gx_o}$ and equation 10.31 becomes

$$p(\mathbf{s}, t|\mathbf{s}, 0)^{\text{scatt}} = -\frac{s(\mathbf{x}_o)\Delta s(\mathbf{x}_o)\ddot{w}(t - 2\tau_{sx_o})}{8\pi^2|\mathbf{x}_o - \mathbf{s}|^2}. \qquad (10.32)$$

In this case, the reflectivity term $s(\mathbf{x}_o)\Delta s(\mathbf{x}_o)$ is weighted and smeared along the hyperbola with its trough above the scatterer's position. More generally, a model with an interface can be approximated by a set of contiguous point scatterers, so that the data are given by the summed contribution

of all the point scatterers, i.e.,

$$p(\mathbf{s}, t|\mathbf{s}, 0)^{\text{scatt}} = \sum_{\mathbf{x}_o \in B} A(\mathbf{x}_o, \mathbf{s})s(\mathbf{x}_o)\Delta s(\mathbf{x}_o)$$

$$\times \ddot{w}\left(t - 2\sqrt{(x_o - x_s)^2 + z_o^2}/c\right), \qquad (10.33)$$

in which

$$A(\mathbf{x}_o, \mathbf{s}) = \frac{-1}{8\pi^2|\mathbf{s} - \mathbf{x}_o|^2}, \qquad (10.34)$$

and B denotes the set of coordinate points along the discretized interface boundary. This formula accounts for primary reflections, but it ignores multiples and angle-dependent reflection coefficients. Known as the Born diffraction-stack modeling formula, it can be described as smearing and summing the reflectivity values along the appropriate hyperbolas in the data space. For an inhomogeneous medium, ray tracing can be used to compute the propagation times, and the term $A(\mathbf{x}_o, \mathbf{s})$ accounts for geometrical spreading (Aki and Richards, 1980).

10.1.6 Matrix operator notation

Equation 10.30 gives the integral representation for Born forward modeling. We now will discretize the scattered pressure field, the slowness model, and the integral modeling operator to form a discrete system of equations.

In the 2D case, if the slowness field is discretized onto a $\sqrt{N} \times \sqrt{N}$ mesh of N square cells with a constant slowness perturbation Δs_i in the ith cell, the integral in equation 10.30 can be approximated by a Riemann sum to give

$$d_i = \sum_{j=1}^{N} l_{ij} m_j, \qquad (10.35)$$

---

[9]After normal-moveout correction of a common-midpoint gather and stacking, the resulting trace approximates the stacked ZO trace in Figure 1.11d.

for $i = 1 \ldots M$ and

$$m_j \leftrightarrow s(\mathbf{x}_j)\Delta s(\mathbf{x}_j), \qquad (10.36)$$

$$l_{ij} \leftrightarrow l_{gst,j} = -\ddot{\delta}(t - \tau_{jx_g} - \tau_{js})\frac{dx^2}{8\pi^2|\mathbf{x}_j - \mathbf{g}||\mathbf{x}_j - \mathbf{s}|}, \qquad (10.37)$$

and

$$d_i \leftrightarrow p_{gst} = p(\mathbf{g}, t|\mathbf{s}, 0)^{\text{scatt.}}, \qquad (10.38)$$

in which we have assumed an impulsive source wavelet and geometrical spreading approximated by the inverse distance terms; the delta function is that for a Kronecker delta function. Here, dx is the width of a square cell; $i \leftrightarrow (g, s, t)$ denotes the 1-1 mapping between the single data index i and the 3-tuple of data indices (g, s, t); and g, s, and t correspond to the integer indices associated with discretizing the geophone locations $\mathbf{g}$, source locations $\mathbf{s}$, and time values t, respectively. Here, the model indices are denoted by j. More compactly, the system of equations 10.35 can be represented by

$$\mathbf{d} = \mathbf{Lm}, \qquad (10.39)$$

in which $\mathbf{L}$ represents the $M \times N$ matrix with elements l_{ij}, $\mathbf{d}$ is the $M \times 1$ vector of scattered pressure data, and $\mathbf{m}$ is the $N \times 1$ vector of weighted slowness perturbations. In the following MATLAB® script, the matrix $\mathbf{L}$ is not formed explicitly; instead, each trace is computed by the summation indicated in equation 10.35.

A MATLAB code for zero-offset diffraction-stack modeling using equations 10.35–10.38 is given below, where an impulsive source wavelet is assumed.

```
%
% ZERO-OFFSET DIFFRACTION STACK MODELING of IMPULSE
    RESPONSE TRACES
% migi(ix,iz) = scaled reflection coefficient at
  (ix*dx,iz*dx)
  for ixtrace=1:ntrace; %LOOP OVER ALL TRACES
    for ix=1:nx    %LOOP OVER ROWS OF MODEL PIXELS
    for iz=1:nz;   %LOOP OVER COLUMNS OF MODEL
                        PIXELS
    r = sqrt((ixtrace*dx-ix*dx)^2+(iz*dx)^2);
    time = round( 1 + r/c/dt );
    d(ixtrace,time) = migi(ix,iz)/r^2 +
    d(ixtrace,time);
    end;
    end;
end;
```

The second time derivative of the source wavelet can be used to convolve each impulse response trace to give the bandlimited traces.

10.2 Integral-equation adjoint modeling

The reflectivity model $\mathbf{m}$ almost never exactly predicts the observed data in equation 10.39, so we seek the least-squares solution that minimizes the regularized sum of the squared data residuals

$$\epsilon = \frac{1}{2}\left\|\ \overbrace{\mathbf{Lm}}^{\text{predicted data}} - \overbrace{\mathbf{d}}^{\text{recorded data}}\ \right\|^2 + \frac{\eta^2}{2}||\mathbf{Cm}||^2. \qquad (10.40)$$

A linear iterative solution that minimizes the above misfit function also is referred to as the least-squares migration image (Gauthier et al., 1986; Nemeth et al., 1999; Duquet et al., 2000). Here, $||\mathbf{Cm}||^2$ is a model penalty function that avoids solutions with large values of $||\mathbf{Cm}||$ and η is a scalar damping parameter.

Minimizing equation 10.40 with respect to the components of the model vector $\mathbf{m}$ leads (see section 5.2.2) to the normal equations

$$[\mathbf{L}^\dagger\mathbf{L} + \eta^2\mathbf{C}^\dagger\mathbf{C}]\mathbf{m} = \mathbf{L}^\dagger\mathbf{d}, \qquad (10.41)$$

with the solution

$$\mathbf{m} = [\mathbf{L}^\dagger\mathbf{L} + \eta^2\mathbf{C}^\dagger\mathbf{C}]^{-1}\mathbf{L}^\dagger\mathbf{d}, \qquad (10.42)$$

known as least-squares migration (see Chapters 15 and 16). If both $\mathbf{m}$ and the background velocity in $\mathbf{L}$ are updated iteratively, then this is known as full-waveform inversion (see Chapters 19 to 23). Equation 10.42 reduces to that for standard migration if $[\mathbf{L}^\dagger\mathbf{L}]$ is approximated by an identity matrix and $\eta = 0$:

$$\mathbf{m}^{\text{mig}} = \mathbf{L}^\dagger\mathbf{d}, \qquad (10.43)$$

in which $\mathbf{d}$ is the recorded data with the direct waves muted from the traces. Typically, a preconditioning operator $\mathbf{P} \approx [\mathbf{L}^\dagger\mathbf{L} + \mathbf{C}^\dagger\mathbf{C}]^{-1}$ is applied to the migration image to correct for geometrical spreading, uneven illumination, and blurring by the source wavelet. If $\mathbf{m}^{\text{mig}} = \mathbf{L}^\dagger\mathbf{d}$ is inserted into equation 10.42, then $\mathbf{m} = [\mathbf{L}^\dagger\mathbf{L} + \eta^2\mathbf{C}^\dagger\mathbf{C}]^{-1}\mathbf{m}^{\text{mig}}$ is known as migration deconvolution (see Chapter 18) or generalized image-domain inversion if the velocity is updated iteratively (see Chapter 26).

Adjoint matrix and kernel

If the elements of $\mathbf{L}$ are defined as $[\mathbf{L}]_{ij} = l_{ij}$, then the elements of its Hermitian adjoint are given by $[\mathbf{L}^\dagger]_{ij} = l_{ji}^*$. For the integral equation 10.21, the forward-modeling kernel $\Gamma(\mathbf{g}|\mathbf{x}'|\mathbf{s})$ is

$$\mathbf{L} \rightarrow \Gamma(\mathbf{g}|\mathbf{x}'|\mathbf{s}) = 2\omega^2 W(\omega)G(\mathbf{g}|\mathbf{x}')G(\mathbf{x}'|\mathbf{s}), \qquad (10.44)$$

and its complex conjugate is the kernel of the migration operator $\mathbf{L}^\dagger$:

$$\mathbf{L}^\dagger \rightarrow \Gamma(\mathbf{g}|\mathbf{x}'|\mathbf{s})^* = 2\omega^2 W(\omega)^* G(\mathbf{g}|\mathbf{x}')^* G(\mathbf{x}'|\mathbf{s})^*. \quad (10.45)$$

The product $\mathbf{L}^\dagger\mathbf{L} \rightarrow \Gamma(\mathbf{g}|\mathbf{x}'|\mathbf{s})^*\Gamma(\mathbf{g}|\mathbf{x}_o|\mathbf{s})$ is interpreted as the point-scatterer response of the migration operator for a single source-receiver pair, in which the point scatterer is located at $\mathbf{x}_o$, the trial image point is at $\mathbf{x}'$, and the single trace is located at $\mathbf{g}$. It also is denoted as the migration Green's function (Schuster, 1997) for a single trace, and it is the starting point for approximating the Hessian inverse in Chapter 18.

According to equation 10.43, the migration image is formed by multiplying the conjugated kernel $\Gamma(\mathbf{g}|\mathbf{x}'|\mathbf{s})^*$ by the scattered data $P(\mathbf{g}|\mathbf{s})^{\text{scatt}}$. The product is integrated over all data coordinates (including frequency) to give

$$m(\mathbf{x})^{\text{mig}} = \int_{S_g} \int_{S_s} \int_{-\infty}^{\infty} \frac{\omega^2 P(\mathbf{g}|\mathbf{s})^{\text{scatt}} W(\omega)^* e^{i\omega(\tau_{sx}+\tau_{xg})}}{8\pi^2 |\mathbf{x} - \mathbf{s}|\,|\mathbf{x} - \mathbf{g}|} d\omega dx_g^2 dx_s^2,$$

$$(10.46)$$

$$= -\int_{S_g} \int_{S_s} \frac{[\ddot{p}(\mathbf{g}, t|\mathbf{s}, 0)^{\text{scatt}} \star w(-t)]|_{t=\tau_{sx}+\tau_{xg}}}{4\pi |\mathbf{x} - \mathbf{s}|\,|\mathbf{x} - \mathbf{g}|} dx_g^2 dx_s^2,$$

$$(10.47)$$

in which $m(\mathbf{x})^{\text{mig}}$ denotes the migration image, and the surface integration is over the free surface where the sources $\mathbf{s} \in S_s$ and geophones $\mathbf{g} \in S_g$ are restricted to the $z = 0$ plane.

Box 10.2.1 Adjoint of Integration

Forward modeling by Green's theorem is a causal operation in the sense that any current wavefield is represented by a weighted summation of present and past wavefields. In the simplest form, the causal linear operator can be represented by a real-valued lower-triangular matrix

$$\int_{-\infty}^{\infty} L(t|t')f(t')dt' \approx \begin{bmatrix} L_{11} & 0 & 0 & \cdots & 0 \\ L_{21} & L_{22} & 0 & \cdots & 0 \\ L_{31} & L_{32} & L_{33} & \cdots & 0 \\ \vdots & \vdots & \vdots & \ddots & \vdots \\ L_{N1} & L_{N2} & \cdots & L_{NN-1} & L_{NN} \end{bmatrix}$$

$$\times \begin{pmatrix} f_1 \\ f_2 \\ f_3 \\ \vdots \\ f_N \end{pmatrix}, \quad (10.48)$$

in which $L(t|t') = L_{tt'}$ is assumed to be real and there are no vibrations $L(t|t') = 0$ at $t' > t$ for observations at times t prior to the excitation time at t'. The adjoint of this causal linear operator is an acausal operator that is approximated by an upper-triangular matrix

$$\int_{-\infty}^{\infty} \mathcal{L}(t'|t)\hat{f}(t')dt' \approx \begin{bmatrix} L_{11} & L_{21} & L_{31} & \cdots & L_{N1} \\ 0 & L_{22} & L_{32} & \cdots & L_{N2} \\ 0 & 0 & L_{33} & \cdots & L_{N3} \\ \vdots & \vdots & \vdots & \ddots & \vdots \\ 0 & 0 & 0 & \cdots & L_{NN} \end{bmatrix}$$

$$\times \begin{pmatrix} \hat{f}_1 \\ \hat{f}_2 \\ \hat{f}_3 \\ \vdots \\ \hat{f}_N \end{pmatrix}, \quad (10.49)$$

in which $\mathcal{L}(t'|t) = L(t|t')$ and $\mathcal{L}(t'|t) = 0$ for $t' > t$. That is, the system is excited only before and at the source excitation time t. For the special case $\mathcal{L}(t'|t) = 1$ for $t' \geq t$, equation 10.48 represents the integration $\int_0^T f(t)dt$ forward in time and equation 10.49 represents the integration $\int_T^0 f(t)dt$ backward in time.

If an acausal system of real-valued equations is given by $\mathcal{L}\hat{\mathbf{f}} = \mathbf{d}$, the solution is found by starting at the last row to find $\hat{f}_N$, then proceeding to the next-to-last row to find $\hat{f}_{N-1}$, and repeating this procedure in reverse time until all values of $\hat{\mathbf{f}}$ are computed. This is equivalent to backpropagating the reflection traces by solving the wave equation in reverse time (see Chapter 11).

A causal Green's $g(\mathbf{x}, t|\mathbf{s}, 0) = A(\mathbf{x}, \mathbf{s})\delta(t - \tau_{xs})$ has a Fourier representation $G(\mathbf{x}|\mathbf{s}, 0) = A(\mathbf{x}, \mathbf{s})e^{i\omega\tau_{xs}}$. The inverse Fourier transform of its conjugate $G(\mathbf{x}|\mathbf{s}, 0)^*$ is $A(\mathbf{x}, \mathbf{s})\delta(t + \tau_{xs})$, which is an acausal Green's function. Weighting this acausal Green's functions with data and integrating over time will yield the wavefield at time t as a combination of weighted fields from later times $t' > t$. This is the essence of backward extrapolation of reflection data: reflections at an early time are constructed from these same reflections recorded at a later time.

10.2.1 Physical meaning of the migration equation

To interpret the physical meaning of equation 10.47, assume a source at $\mathbf{s}$, a receiver at $\mathbf{g}$, and a wide-band source so that $w(t) \to \delta(t)$ and equation 10.47 becomes

$$m(\mathbf{x})^{\text{mig}} = -\frac{\ddot{p}(\mathbf{g}, \tau_{sx} + \tau_{xg}|\mathbf{s}, 0)^{\text{scatt}}}{4\pi |\mathbf{x} - \mathbf{s}||\mathbf{x} - \mathbf{g}|}. \tag{10.50}$$

For a 2D homogeneous medium with velocity c, the term $\tau_{sx} + \tau_{xg} = \text{constant}$ describes an ellipse in model space coordinates $\mathbf{x} = (x, z)$ with foci at the source $\mathbf{s}$ and geophone $\mathbf{g}$. Thus, the migration image is formed by taking the reflection amplitude that arrives at $\tau_{sx} + \tau_{xg}$ and smearing it along the appropriate ellipse in the model coordinates $\mathbf{x}$ of Figure 10.4a.

The duration T of the source wavelet determines the thickness of the fat ellipse in (x, z) space, and its minimum thickness is $cT/2$. Somewhere along the ellipse is the green scatterer that gave rise to the event recorded at the receiver location $\mathbf{g}$. The scatterer's location can be estimated more accurately by stacking the "smears" from other traces into the model, as illustrated in Figure 10.4b. The intersection of the two fat ellipses forms a smaller area of uncertainty where the scatterer is located. A numerical example is shown in Figure 10.5b, which depicts the ZO migration image for a homogeneous velocity model with six scattering points. The migration images at (x, z) from each of the migrated traces are summed together to give the final stacked image seen in Figure 10.5b.

In standard diffraction-stack migration (French, 1974), the Green's functions $G(\mathbf{x}|\mathbf{s})$ and $G(\mathbf{x}|\mathbf{g})$ are computed by a model-based procedure such as ray tracing, or by a finite-difference solution to the wave equation. The Achilles heel of standard migration is that the estimated velocity model always contains inaccuracies which lead to errors in the computed Green's functions. Such mistakes manifest themselves as defocused migration images, as illustrated in Figures 15.2 to 15.4.

The MATLAB code for the main part of zero-offset diffraction-stack migration is given below.

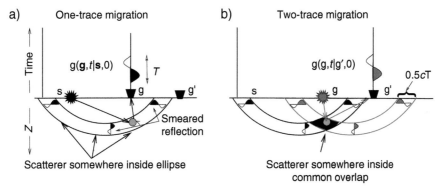

Figure 10.4. The migration image for each trace is computed by smearing and summing the trace amplitudes along the appropriate fat ellipses in (x, z) (Claerbout, 1992). (a) Migration of one trace, and (b) migration of two traces, which has better spatial resolution than (a). The minimum thickness of each fat ellipse is $0.5cT$, in which T is the dominant period of the source wavelet.

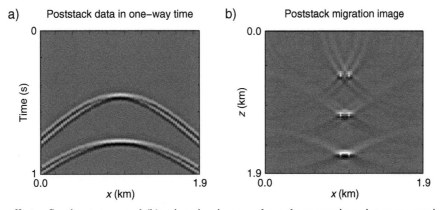

Figure 10.5. (a) Zero-offset reflection traces and (b) migration image where there are six point scatterers indicated by the white stars. Note the horizontal resolution of the image becomes better with decreasing depth of the scatterers.

Box 10.2.2 Adjoint of Derivatives

The Hermitian adjoint to the modeling operator $\mathbf{L}$ is defined such that the inner product $(\mathbf{d}, \mathbf{Lm})$ can be rewritten as

$$(\mathbf{d}, \mathbf{Lm}) = (\mathbf{L}^\dagger \mathbf{d}, \mathbf{m}). \qquad (10.51)$$

Here, $\mathbf{L}^\dagger$ is defined as the Hermitian adjoint operator that now maps functions in data space into model space. For a matrix-vector example, if $\mathbf{L}$ is an $M \times N$ matrix and $\mathbf{m}$ is an $N \times 1$ vector, then the inner product $(\mathbf{d}, \mathbf{Lm})$ can be written as

$$(\mathbf{d}, \mathbf{Lm}) = \sum_i d_i^* \sum_j L_{ij} m_j,$$
$$= \sum_j (\sum_i L_{ij}^* d_i)^* m_j = (\mathbf{L}^\dagger \mathbf{d}, \mathbf{m}), \quad (10.52)$$

in which $[\mathbf{L}]_{ji}^\dagger = L_{ij}^*$. For the examples below we assume that $\mathbf{L}$ is real so that the Hermitian adjoint of $\mathbf{L}$ is the same as the adjoint operator $\tilde{\mathbf{L}}$. The inner product definition also can be used to find the Hermitian adjoint of $\mathbf{L}$ that maps continuous functions $m(x)$ with finite support into the same space of continuous functions $d(x)$, in which x takes on values along the real line. For example, if $\mathbf{L} = \rho(x)^{-1} \partial/\partial x$ and $\rho(x)$ is real, then integration by parts says that equation 10.51 becomes

$$(\mathbf{d}, \mathbf{Lm}) = \int_{-\infty}^{\infty} d(x)^* \rho(x)^{-1} \frac{\partial m(x)}{\partial x} \, dx,$$
$$= \int_{-\infty}^{\infty} [\frac{\partial \{d(x)^* \rho(x)^{-1} m(x)\}}{\partial x}$$
$$- \frac{\partial \{d(x)^* \rho(x)^{-1}\}}{\partial x} m(x)] \, dx,$$
$$= -\int_{-\infty}^{\infty} \frac{\partial \{d(x)^* \rho(x)^{-1}\}}{\partial x} m(x) \, dx = (\mathbf{L}^\dagger \mathbf{d}, \mathbf{m}),$$
$$(10.53)$$

in which the adjoint of the first derivative $\rho(x)^{-1} \partial/\partial x$ is the negative derivative $-\partial \rho(x)^{-1}/\partial x$; here, finite support implies zero boundary conditions at infinity. If $\rho(x) = 1$ and the derivative is of even order, such as $\partial^2/\partial x^2$, then integration by parts twice will show that the adjoint operator, is $\partial^2/\partial x^2$ with the same sign as the original operator. In general, if the adjoint operator is equal to the original operator, then we say that these are self-adjoint operators. For a real matrix, this means that the matrix is symmetric.

This same rule of thumb can be deduced from a Fourier transform or matrix representations of differential operators. Recall, the Fourier transform of the derivative operator $\partial/\partial x$ is ik_x, of which the conjugate is $-ik_x$, so its inverse transform is $-\partial/\partial x$. For discrete approximations to derivatives, the backward finite-difference approximation $\mathbf{Lm} = \frac{\partial m(x)}{\partial x}|_{x=x_i} \approx [m(x_i) - m(x_{i-1})]/dx$ has the adjoint operation $\left[\frac{\partial m(x)}{\partial x}\right]^\dagger |_{x=x_i} \approx -[m(x_{i+1}) - m(x_i)]/dx$ for the real function $m(x)$:

$$\frac{\partial}{\partial x} \approx \begin{bmatrix} 1 & 0 & 0 & \cdots & 0 \\ -1 & 1 & 0 & \cdots & 0 \\ 0 & -1 & 1 & \cdots & 0 \\ \vdots & \ddots & \ddots & \ddots & \vdots \\ 0 & 0 & \cdots & -1 & 1 \end{bmatrix};$$

$$\left[\frac{\partial}{\partial x}\right]^\dagger \approx \begin{bmatrix} 1 & -1 & 0 & \cdots & 0 \\ 0 & 1 & -1 & \cdots & 0 \\ 0 & 0 & 1 & -1 & 0 \\ \vdots & \vdots & \ddots & \ddots & \ddots \\ 0 & 0 & 0 & 0 & 1 \end{bmatrix}, \quad (10.54)$$

in which dx is conveniently given the value of 1. It is recognized that $[\partial/\partial x]^\dagger$ is approximated by the negative of a forward differencing operator.

```
% ZERO-OFFSET ADJOINT MODELING OR
% ZERO-OFFSET DIFFRACTION STACK MIGRATION
%
for ixtrace=1:ntrace; %LOOP OVER ALL TRACES
    for ix=1:nx      %LOOP OVER ROWS OF MODEL PIXELS
    for iz=1:nz;     %LOOP OVER COLUMNS OF MODEL
                       PIXELS
        r = sqrt((ixtrace*dx-ix*dx)^2+(iz*dx)^2);
        time = round( 1 + r/c/dt );
        migi(ix,iz) = migi(ix,iz) + cdp3(ixtrace,
        time)/r;
    end;
    end;
end;
```

10.3 Summary

The space-time (space-frequency) Green's function is the point-source impulse (harmonic) response of the model. The model is any inhomogeneous acoustic medium where the wave motion approximates the acoustic wave equation. The Green's function $G(\mathbf{g}|\mathbf{s})$ in an arbitrary acoustic model is impossible to determine analytically, but can be approximated by the Born approximation to the Lippmann-Schwinger equation. Born modeling computes the single-scattered wavefields as a superposition of the primary reflections from the slowness perturbations. The primary reflections are a good approximation to the actual acoustic seismograms if the slowness perturbations are weak, i.e., multiple scattering events are negligible. The Hermitian adjoint modeling operator applied to the scattered data gives the migration image, and the reflectivity estimate that minimizes the sum of the squared residuals is the least-squares-migration image $[\mathbf{L}^\dagger\mathbf{L}]^{-1}\mathbf{L}^\dagger\mathbf{d}$. The direct inverse to $[\mathbf{L}^\dagger\mathbf{L}]$ is often too expensive to compute so an iterative solution method is used. Migration is the primary imaging tool used in seismic exploration.

10.4 Exercises

1. Prove the identity $G\nabla_{\mathbf{x}'}^2 P = P\nabla_{\mathbf{x}'}^2 G + \nabla_{\mathbf{x}'}\cdot(G\nabla_{\mathbf{x}'}P - P\nabla_{\mathbf{x}'}G)$. Show your work.

2. Show that if the Helmholtz Green's function at $k=0$ satisfies the Laplace's equation for a point source

$$\nabla_{\mathbf{x}'}^2 G(\mathbf{x}|\mathbf{x}') = -\delta(\mathbf{x}-\mathbf{x}'), \qquad (10.55)$$

then Green's theorem for Laplace's equation

$$\nabla_{\mathbf{x}'}^2 P(\mathbf{x}'|\mathbf{x}) = -F(\mathbf{x}') \qquad (10.56)$$

is given by equation 10.10, except now the Green's function is given by the solution to equation 10.55. Show the derivation.

3. Compute the movie of a propagating harmonic wave, as described by the MATLAB code below. Copy the MATLAB script and run it in MATLAB. We have omitted the geometrical-spreading term deliberately to avoid imbalanced amplitudes.

```
% Set up arrays of X and Y coordinates
x=[1:300]; y=[1:300]; [X,Y] = meshgrid(x,y);
k=.05;
% Compute the Green's Function for k=1;
R=sqrt(X.^2+Y.^2);G=cos(k*R);imagesc(G)
% Causal Green function if polarity=1; Acausal
Green Function if polarity=-1
polarity=1;
% Compute Movie of Propagating Wave as time
increases for j=1:100;
G=cos(k*R-polarity*j*.1);imagesc(G)
title([' Green Function t = ',num2str(j*.01)]);
colorbar
xlabel('X (m)');
ylabel('Y (m)');
pause(.01)
end
```

Look at the movie and script, and try to understand the script. For example, type help *meshgrid* to understand how *meshgrid* works. What is the period of this harmonic wave? What is the wavelength? What is the propagation velocity? What is the apparent velocity

in the x-direction? What is the apparent velocity in the y-direction. Change polarity to polarity $=-1$. Is the wave propagating toward or away from the origin? Change the code to make it propagate in the opposite direction.

4. The Helmholtz equation for a spherically symmetric Green's function is given by

$$\nabla_{\mathbf{x}}^2 G + k^2 G = \frac{1}{r^2}\frac{\partial}{\partial r}\left(r^2\frac{\partial G}{\partial r}\right) + k^2 G = 0 \quad (\text{for } r\neq 0).$$
$$(10.57)$$

Note that if the source point $\mathbf{x}'=0$ is at the origin, then $G(\mathbf{x}|\mathbf{x}')\propto e^{-ikr}/r$, in which $r=|\mathbf{x}-\mathbf{x}'|=|\mathbf{x}|$. Show that the Green's function for either an outgoing (equation 10.3) or incoming wave satisfies this equation as long as $r\neq 0$.

5. Recall the volume integral in spherical coordinates over a sphere of radius R is given by

$$\int_0^R\int_0^\pi\int_0^{2\pi} r^2 dr\,\sin\theta d\theta d\phi = \frac{4}{3}\pi R^3. \qquad (10.58)$$

Prove this. Also prove that the surface integral over the sphere is equal to the following:

$$\int_0^\pi\int_0^{2\pi} R^2\,\sin\theta d\theta d\phi = 4\pi R^2. \qquad (10.59)$$

Here, $d\Omega = \sin\theta d\phi d\theta$ is the differential of the solid angle, with the identity $\int d\Omega = 4\pi$.

6. Problem 4 asks you to show that the Green's function satisfies the Helmholtz equation when $r\neq 0$. Now you will show that integrating equation 10.2 over a small sphere that surrounds the source point $\mathbf{x}'=0$ centered at the origin yields

$$\int_{V_o}(\nabla^2 + k^2)G(\mathbf{x}'|\mathbf{x})\,r^2 dr\,\sin\theta d\theta d\phi$$

$$= \int_{V_o}\delta(\mathbf{x}-\mathbf{x}')dx^3 = 1.$$

The integration is in the observer space. The LHS of the above equation can be shown to be equal to 1 by using the following argument. Assume the integration is about a small spherical ball with radius ϵ. In this case, the volume integration over the k^2-like term becomes

$$\left|k^2\int_{V_o}Gr^2 dr\,d\Omega\right| = \left|\frac{k^2}{4\pi}\int_{V_o}e^{-ikr}r\,dr\,d\Omega\right|,$$

$$\leq \frac{k^2}{4\pi}\int_{V_o}r\,dr\,d\Omega,$$

$$= \frac{k^2\epsilon^2}{2}, \qquad (10.60)$$

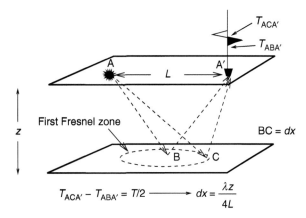

Figure 10.6. Trace with nonzero offset and a horizontal reflector. The minimum width dx of the horizontal Fresnel zone at the depth z for a ZO trace defines the horizontal spatial resolution of the migration image. The aperture width of the recording array is L.

which goes to zero as the volume radius $\epsilon \to 0$. The inequality follows from the property $\int f(x)dx \leq \max(|f(x)|) \int dx$.

The only remaining thing to do is to show that the integration of the Laplacian $\nabla^2 G$ goes to 1. This can be shown by using Gauss's theorem: $\int_{V_o} \nabla^2 G \, r^2 dr \, d\Omega = \int_{S_o} \partial G/\partial r \, r^2 d\Omega$, plugging in the Green's function $G = (4\pi)^{-1} e^{-ikr}/r$ and letting ϵ go to zero. (Hint: $\partial(1/r)/\partial r = -1/r^2$).

7. Figure 10.6 depicts the first Fresnel zone at the reflector depth of z. Show that the half-width dx of the Fresnel zone for ZO traces is $dx \approx \frac{\lambda z}{4L}$ under the far-field approximation (i.e., $z \gg L > \lambda$). For the ZO trace, L is the aperture width of the recording array. Discuss how this formula explains Figure 10.5, where dx increases with increasing depth of the scatterers.

8. From Figure 10.6, show that the vertical resolution dz below the geophone is $\lambda/4$ for a zero-offset trace. What is the vertical resolution for a trace with the source-receiver offset of L and a trial image point centered between the source and receiver at the depth z?

9. Transform the zero-offset forward-modeling code into a prestack modeling code in which the source and receiver positions are on the free surface but are not coincident. Demonstrate the effectiveness of this code by creating shot gathers for two earth models: a point-scatterer model and a single-reflector interface model.

10. Generate ZO data from the MATLAB forward-modeling code for a two-scatterer model. Migrate these traces and empirically validate the dx formula for horizontal resolution illustrated in Figure 10.6.

11. Derive the adjoint of $\frac{\partial^n}{\partial x^n}$ for n an integer.

12. Derive the adjoint of $\frac{\partial^n}{\partial x^n}$ for n a fraction. Hint: derive the adjoint in the Fourier domain, and inverse transform the result.

13. Derive the adjoint equation associated with the 1D wave equation with constant density: $\frac{\partial^2 P(x,t)}{\partial x^2} - \frac{1}{c(x)^2} \frac{\partial^2 P(x,t)}{\partial t^2} = 0$. Is this equation self-adjoint?

14. Derive the adjoint equation associated with the 1D wave equation: $\rho(x) \frac{\partial^2 u(x,t)}{\partial t^2} - \frac{\partial}{\partial x} \left[\kappa(x) \frac{\partial P}{\partial x} \right] = 0$. Is this equation self-adjoint?

15. Is the 1D Helmholtz equation $\left[\frac{\partial^2}{\partial x^2} + \frac{\omega^2}{c(x)^2} \right] \tilde{P}(x) = 0$ self-adjoint?

16. Using Green's theorem, prove reciprocity $G(\mathbf{x}|\mathbf{x}') = G(\mathbf{x}'|\mathbf{x})$, in which $G(\mathbf{x}|\mathbf{x}')$ is the Green's function for the Helmholtz equation. How is reciprocity connected to the self-adjoint property of the governing wave equation (see Morse and Feshbach, 1953)?

17. Is $\frac{\partial}{\partial x}(\kappa \frac{\partial u}{\partial x}) + \omega^2 \rho u = 0$ self-adjoint? How does the presence of both first-order and second-order derivatives in the PDE influence the adjoint properties of the governing equation? Is the reciprocity property valid for the solutions of this equation?

10.5 Computational labs

1. Carry out the labs under the topic "Modeling" in the Computational Toolkit. Answer all questions.

Appendix 10A:
Causal and acausal Green's functions

Causal Green's functions

Applying the inverse Fourier transform

$$\mathcal{F}^{-1} \cdot = \frac{1}{2\pi} \int_{-\infty}^{\infty} d\omega \, e^{i\omega(t-t_s)}, \qquad (10.61)$$

to equation 10.3 gives the causal Green's function

$$g_c(\mathbf{x}, t - t_s | \mathbf{x}', 0) = \mathcal{F}^{-1}(G(\mathbf{x}|\mathbf{x}')),$$

$$= \frac{1}{8\pi^2} \int_{-\infty}^{\infty} \frac{e^{-i\omega(|\mathbf{x}'-\mathbf{x}|/c - (t-t_s))}}{|\mathbf{x} - \mathbf{x}'|} d\omega,$$

$$= \frac{1}{4\pi} \frac{\delta(t - t_s - |\mathbf{x}' - \mathbf{x}|/c)}{|\mathbf{x} - \mathbf{x}'|}, \qquad (10.62)$$

in which

$$\delta(t - t_s - |\mathbf{x}' - \mathbf{x}|/c) = \begin{cases} \infty & \text{if } t - t_s = |\mathbf{x}' - \mathbf{x}|/c, \\ 0 & \text{if } t - t_s \neq |\mathbf{x}' - \mathbf{x}|/c, \end{cases}$$

$$(10.63)$$

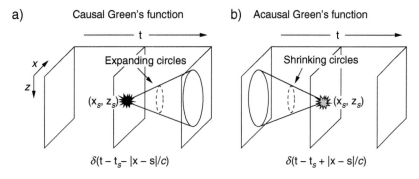

Figure 10.7. (a) Causal and (b) acausal Green's functions in *x-z-t* space.

More precisely, $\delta(t)$ is a generalized *delta function* which only can be defined in terms of an inner product with a sufficiently regular function (Zemanian, 1965). With this understanding, we symbolically denote its value to be ∞ for $t = 0$.

Equation 10.63 describes an expanding circle centered about the source point, where the initiation time of the impulsive source is at time t_s and the observation time is denoted by t. The radius of the expanding circle is equal to $c(t - t_s)$ as long as $t > t_s$. Equation 10.62 is a causal Green's function because the wave is not observed until after the excitation time of the source and after it has propagated from the source point to the observation point in the *retarded time* given by $|\mathbf{x}' - \mathbf{x}|/c$. Figure 10.7a shows the causal Green's function expanding as a "light cone" in *x-y-t* space.

Acausal Green's function

Equation 10.62 describes a causal Green's function in a homogeneous medium where the wavefield is observed only after the source initiation time τ_s. In contrast, the wavefield associated with the acausal Green's function is observed only prior to the initiation time of the source. It is represented by the adjoint kernel $G(\mathbf{x}|\mathbf{x}')^*$, which for a homogeneous medium is given as $\frac{1}{4\pi} e^{ik|\mathbf{x}-\mathbf{x}'|} / |\mathbf{x} - \mathbf{x}'|$.

Applying the inverse Fourier transform

$$\mathcal{F}^{-1} \cdot = \frac{1}{2\pi} \int_{-\infty}^{\infty} d\omega \, e^{i\omega(t-t_s)}, \qquad (10.64)$$

to $G(\mathbf{x}|\mathbf{x}')^*$ yields the time-domain acausal Green's function

$$g_a(\mathbf{x}, t - t_s|\mathbf{x}', 0) = \mathcal{F}^{-1}(G^*(\mathbf{x}|\mathbf{x}'))$$

$$= \frac{1}{8\pi^2} \int_{-\infty}^{\infty} \frac{e^{i\omega(|\mathbf{x}'-\mathbf{x}|/c+(t-t_s))}}{|\mathbf{x} - \mathbf{x}'|} d\omega,$$

$$= \frac{1}{4\pi} \frac{\delta(t - t_s + |\mathbf{x}' - \mathbf{x}|/c)}{|\mathbf{x} - \mathbf{x}'|}. \qquad (10.65)$$

The acausal Green's function describes a contracting circular wavefront centered at the source point and is extinguished at time t_s and later. It is acausal because it is alive and contracting (see Figure 10.7b) prior to the source initiation time t_s, and turns off just as the source turns on! This Green's function is important because it can be used for seismic migration which focuses wavefronts to their place of origin, compared to the causal Green's function that is used for forward modeling.

Appendix 10B: Generalized Green's theorem

The integral solution in equation 10.10 can be extended by a generalized Green's theorem (Morse and Feshbach, 1953) to the solution of a wide range of linear partial differential equations. The starting point is to recognize that the volume integrand in equation 10.8 can be expressed as

$$G(\mathbf{x}|\mathbf{x}')\nabla^2 P(\mathbf{x}') - P(\mathbf{x}')\nabla^2 G(\mathbf{x}|\mathbf{x}')$$

$$= \nabla_{\mathbf{x}'} \cdot \overbrace{(G(\mathbf{x}|\mathbf{x}')\nabla_{\mathbf{x}'}P(\mathbf{x}') - P(\mathbf{x}')\nabla_{\mathbf{x}'}G(\mathbf{x}|\mathbf{x}'))}^{\text{bilinear concomitant}},$$
$$(10.66)$$

where the argument of the divergence operator is defined as the bilinear concomitant vector. A generalization of this equation is

$$u(\mathbf{x})\mathcal{L}v(\mathbf{x}) - v(\mathbf{x})\tilde{\mathcal{L}}u(\mathbf{x}) = \tilde{\nabla} \cdot \mathbf{P}, \qquad (10.67)$$

where $\mathbf{P}$ is the general bilinear concomitant vector (Morse and Feshbach, 1953), $\mathcal{L}$ represents the operator for the linear partial differential equation of interest, and $\tilde{\mathcal{L}}$ denotes the adjoint of $\mathcal{L}$. If the coordinates of the PDE are (x, y, z, t), then $\tilde{\nabla} = (\partial/\partial x, \partial/\partial y, \partial/\partial z, \partial/\partial t)$.

If the coordinates of the PDE are (x, y, z), integration of equation 10.67 over the volume reduces it to a surface integral by Gauss' theorem. A special example is equation 10.10 where the solution to the Helmholtz equation is the sum of a surface integral and a weighted volume integral over the source distribution. If the PDE is self-adjoint then $\mathcal{L} = \tilde{\mathcal{L}}$, which is true for the Helmholtz equation. If the PDE is not self-adjoint, e.g. $\mathcal{L} = \partial^2/\partial x^2 + \partial/\partial x$, then the adjoint operator $\tilde{\mathcal{L}} = \partial^2/\partial x^2 - \partial/\partial x$ must be used to satisfy equation 10.67. In this case $\mathbf{P} \rightarrow u\partial v/\partial x - v\partial u/\partial x + uv$. It now becomes possible to solve the inhomogeneous problem $\mathcal{L}u = f$ as an integral solution with inhomogeneous conditions on the general boundary.

If $P(\mathbf{x}') \rightarrow \tilde{G}(\mathbf{x}''|\mathbf{x}')$ and $F(\mathbf{x}') \rightarrow -\delta(\mathbf{x}' - \mathbf{x}'')$ in equation 10.5, then equation 10.9 becomes

$$\tilde{G}(\mathbf{x}''|\mathbf{x}) - G(\mathbf{x}|\mathbf{x}'') = \int_{S_o} (G(\mathbf{x}|\mathbf{x}')\nabla_{\mathbf{x}'}\tilde{G}(\mathbf{x}''|\mathbf{x}')$$
$$- \tilde{G}(\mathbf{x}''|\mathbf{x}')\nabla_{\mathbf{x}'}G(\mathbf{x}|\mathbf{x}')) \cdot \hat{\mathbf{n}}dx'^2.$$
$$(10.68)$$

If $\tilde{G}$ and G both satisfy homogeneous boundary conditions on the surface (i.e. self-adjoint boundary conditions), then the surface integration vanishes and we get the generalized reciprocity condition $\tilde{G}(\mathbf{x}''|\mathbf{x}) = G(\mathbf{x}|\mathbf{x}'')$. Because the adjoint Helmholtz equation is identical to the Helmholtz equation, i.e. they are self-adjoint, then their Green's functions are the same so that reciprocity demands $G(\mathbf{x}''|\mathbf{x}) = G(\mathbf{x}|\mathbf{x}'')$.

In the time domain, the wave equation is self-adjoint but the initial conditions imposed by causality are asymmetric in time. Thus, reciprocity in the time domain is not a simple interchange of source and receiver space-time coordinates. Morse and Feshbach (1953) show that the space-time integration of the generalized Green's theorem (equation 10.67) for the space-time wave equation with self-adjoint initial/boundary conditions gives rise to the reciprocity condition in the space-time domain as

$$g(\mathbf{x}, t|\mathbf{x}', t') = g(\mathbf{x}', -t'|\mathbf{x}, -t). \qquad (10.69)$$

This condition can be validated with equation 10.4.

Chapter 11: Reverse Time Migration

In this chapter, we derive the equations for the reverse time migration (RTM) algorithm. This algorithm is used heavily by the oil industry for subsalt imaging of reflectors. It also is used to migrate residuals iteratively for both LSM and FWI. Compared to other migration methods such as diffraction-stack migration discussed in Chapter 10, RTM accounts for all the arrivals in the wavefield, including both primaries and multiples if the velocity model is sufficiently accurate. This can lead to much better resolution in the image, but it is at the cost of being more sensitive to errors in the migration velocity model. For frequencies less than 20 Hz, RTM is the migration method of choice for imaging below complex geology such as salt bodies.

We will derive the general imaging equations and discuss the practical applications of RTM.

11.1 Introduction

Chapter 10 introduced the concept of diffraction-stack migration (DM), which estimates the reflectivity distribution, i.e., migration image, by summing the weighted amplitudes of the recorded traces along the associated "moveout curve." For a general velocity distribution, the moveout curve in offset-time coordinates forms an irregular hyperbolic-like curve. The problem with standard DM is that typically it accounts for single-arrival imaging and does not model or properly migrate multiples. In fact, the single arrivals associated with the moveout curve may be quite weak relative to other reflections, so the DM image might be of low quality. This problem is particularly pernicious beneath salt bodies that tend to defocus the incident and reflection wavefields.

To partially overcome the defocusing problem caused by large velocity contrasts, Baysal et al. (1983), McMechan (1983), and Whitmore (1983) introduce the concept of reverse time migration. Instead of using ray tracing to compute the Green's functions, a finite-difference solution to the wave equation is used to estimate $G(\mathbf{x}|\mathbf{x}')$. If the velocity model is known accurately, then all arrivals are accounted for that might reflect off any trial image point, including multiples, diffractions, and converted waves. If the velocity

model is known accurately, the benefits can be a significant increase in signal-to-noise ratio (S/N) in the migration image, imaging of steep dips, and a greater ability to see beneath bodies with high-velocity contrast. However, the danger is that the migration velocity model has small errors that can lead to strong defocusing in the migration image. Thus, the more accurate the velocity model, the better the RTM image. The next section derives the equations for RTM in the context of a general imaging algorithm.

11.2 General imaging algorithm

The goals of seismic imaging and migration are to estimate, respectively, the slowness and reflectivity distributions of the earth from the recorded seismic data. Both algorithms are derived from the same gradient optimization method, as explained in the following steps.

1. Misfit function: Assume harmonic energy emanating from a source at $\mathbf{s}$ and recorded by a geophone at $\mathbf{g}$. For simplicity, assume the acoustic approximation so the observed pressure spectrums are denoted by $P(\mathbf{g}|\mathbf{s})^{\text{obs}}$, in which the unknown source wavelet $w(t)$ has the spectrum denoted by $W(\omega)$. The pressure misfit function ϵ is given by

$$\epsilon = 1/2 \int_{\omega} d\omega \sum_{g} \sum_{s} |\Delta P(\mathbf{g}|\mathbf{s})|^2, \qquad (11.1)$$

in which $\Delta P(\mathbf{g}|\mathbf{s})$ is the data residual defined by $\Delta P(\mathbf{g}|\mathbf{s}) = P(\mathbf{g}|\mathbf{s}) - P(\mathbf{g}|\mathbf{s})^{\text{obs}}$ and $P(\mathbf{g}|\mathbf{s})$ is the predicted pressure field obtained by a numerical solution to the acoustic wave equation. A starting velocity model is assumed to be known that is an accurate approximation to the actual earth model. The integration is over source frequencies and the summation is over the source and geophone coordinates. The predicted pressure is obtained by a finite-difference solution to the acoustic wave equation in either the space-time or space-frequency domain.

2. Slowness gradient and Fréchet derivative: Using a steepest-descent method, the slowness model $s(\mathbf{x})^{(i)}$ at

the ith iterate is updated by

$$s(\mathbf{x})^{(i+1)} = s(\mathbf{x})^{(i)} - \alpha\gamma(\mathbf{x})^{(i)}, \qquad (11.2)$$

in which α is the step length and $\gamma(\mathbf{x})^{(i)}$ is the misfit gradient defined as

$$\gamma(\mathbf{x})^{(i)} = \frac{\partial \epsilon_i}{\partial s(\mathbf{x})},$$

$$= \int_\omega d\omega \sum_g \sum_s Real\left[\Delta P(\mathbf{g}|\mathbf{s})_i \frac{\partial P(\mathbf{g}|\mathbf{s})_i^*}{\partial s(\mathbf{x})}\right],$$

$$(11.3)$$

where the ith data residual $\Delta P(\mathbf{g}|\mathbf{s})_i = P(\mathbf{g}|\mathbf{s})_i - P(\mathbf{g}|\mathbf{s})^{obs}$ is updated at each iteration. The operator $Real[\ ]$ refers to the real part of the complex number in brackets; from now on, the $Real$ notation will be dropped because the sum over frequencies is symmetrical and the imaginary part of the summand is antisymmetric in ω.

We recognize that the perturbation of P with respect to s is the Fréchet derivative in equation 10.23, so its substitution into 11.3 yields the expression for the gradient

$$\gamma(\mathbf{x})^{(i)} = 2s(\mathbf{x}) \int_\omega d\omega\omega^2 \sum_g \sum_s W(\omega)^*$$

$$\times \Delta P(\mathbf{g}|\mathbf{s})_i G(\mathbf{x}|\mathbf{g})_i^* G(\mathbf{x}|\mathbf{s})_i^*, \qquad (11.4)$$

in which $G(\mathbf{x}|\mathbf{x}')_i$ is the Green's function computed for the ith slowness model.

3. Slowness update: Substituting equation 11.4 into 11.2 yields the slowness update equation

$$s(\mathbf{x})^{(i+1)} = s(\mathbf{x})^{(i)} - \alpha 2s(\mathbf{x})^{(i)} \int_\omega d\omega\omega^2 \sum_g \sum_s$$

$$\times \Delta P(\mathbf{g}|\mathbf{s})_i W(\omega)^* G(\mathbf{x}|\mathbf{g})_i^* G(\mathbf{x}|\mathbf{s})_i^*, \quad (11.5)$$

and steps one to three are repeated until convergence to $s(\mathbf{x})$. The following five imaging algorithms can be derived from this formula.

- **Reflection migration.** If the smooth background slowness model does not generate reflections so that the data residual $\Delta P(\mathbf{g}|\mathbf{s})_i$ only contains the upgoing

reflections[1], then the gradient $\delta s(\mathbf{x}) = s(\mathbf{x})^{(1)} - s(\mathbf{x})^{(0)}$ at the first iterate is the migration image, an approximation to the earth's reflectivity distribution described by the footnote in section 10.1.3. If a finite-difference solution to the two-way wave equation is used, then this approximation is known as the reverse time migration image (Baysal et al., 1983; McMechan, 1983; Whitmore, 1983). Equation 11.5 is the formula for a one-way, wave-equation migration (OWEM) method if the two-way Green's functions are replaced by one-way Green's functions (Gazdag, 1978; Claerbout, 1992), and it reduces to diffraction-stack migration if an asymptotic ray-based Green's function is used. This asymptotic Green's function almost always is restricted to modeling primary reflections, although the Gaussian beam method (Hill, 1990; Hill, 2001; Nowack et al., 2003) can account for some multiple arrivals.

- **Least-squares migration.** If the smooth background slowness field is the same at every iteration, so that $G(\mathbf{x}|\mathbf{x}')_1 = G(\mathbf{x}|\mathbf{x}')_2 = G(\mathbf{x}|\mathbf{x}')_3 = \ldots$, then the final reflectivity image is known as the least-squares migration (LSM) image (Nemeth, 1996; Nemeth et al., 1999; Duquet et al., 2000). Least-squares migration also is known as linearized Born inversion (Lailly, 1983; Tarantola, 1984b) which is presented in Chapters 15 to 18.

- **Full-waveform inversion.** If both the high-wavenumber reflectivity and the smooth slowness model in the Green's function are updated after each iteration, then convergence yields the full-waveform inversion (FWI) tomogram (Tarantola and Valette, 1982; Tarantola, 1984a and 1987; Mora, 1987 and 1989), also known as the nonlinear inversion image (Pica et al., 1990). Theory and examples are presented in Chapters 19 to 23.

- **Traveltime tomography.** If the data residuals are something other than traces, such as traveltime residuals $\Delta\tau$, then adjustment of the Fréchet derivative leads to wave-equation tomography (Woodward, 1992) or wave-equation traveltime inversion (Luo and Schuster, 1991a, 1991b). See Chapters 20 to 21 for details.

- **Generalized FWI:** The generalized FWI algorithm starts with the objective function

$$\epsilon = \frac{1}{2}\Delta\mathbf{d}^\dagger \Delta\mathbf{T}^2 \Delta\mathbf{d}, \qquad (11.6)$$

where the gradient is given by

$$\frac{\partial\epsilon}{\partial s(\mathbf{x})} = \frac{\partial\Delta\mathbf{d}^\dagger}{\partial s(\mathbf{x})}\Delta\mathbf{T}^2\Delta\mathbf{d} + \Delta\mathbf{d}^\dagger\frac{\partial\Delta\mathbf{T}}{\partial s(\mathbf{x})}\Delta\mathbf{T}\Delta\mathbf{d}, \quad (11.7)$$

where, for convenience, vectors and matrices are assumed to be real, and $\Delta\mathbf{T}$ is a diagonal matrix of

---

[1]In practice, the recorded data contain multiples and downgoing reflections from the free surface. However, the data are preprocessed to eliminate (ideally) the multiples and downgoing reflections.

traveltime residuals. If $\Delta\mathbf{d} = \mathbf{L}\Delta\mathbf{m}$, then the gradient becomes

$$\frac{\partial\epsilon}{\partial s(\mathbf{x})} = \overbrace{\frac{\partial\Delta\mathbf{m}^\dagger}{\partial s(\mathbf{x})}\mathbf{L}^\dagger\Delta\mathbf{T}^2\Delta\mathbf{d}}^{\text{small-residual FWI}} + \overbrace{\Delta\mathbf{m}^\dagger\frac{\partial\mathbf{L}^\dagger}{\partial s(\mathbf{x})}\Delta\mathbf{T}^2\Delta\mathbf{d}}^{\text{large-residual FWI}}$$

$$+ \overbrace{\Delta\mathbf{d}^\dagger\frac{\partial\Delta\mathbf{T}}{\partial s(\mathbf{x})}\Delta\mathbf{T}\Delta\mathbf{d}}^{\text{WT}}, \qquad (11.8)$$

in which *WT* denotes wave-equation traveltime inversion discussed in Chapter 20. It is used to update the low-wavenumber components of the velocity model. The small-residual FWI gradient is similar to that for classical FWI and is valid for small data residuals. As discussed in Chapters 19 to 22, it can update both the low- and high-wavenumber components of the velocity model, but is biased towards the high wavenumbers at deeper depths. The large-residual FWI gradient is used in the Gauss-Newton method of large residuals (see Gill et al., 1981, and Exercise 12) when there are large data residuals. This procedure is equivalent to the Gauss-Newton method of large residuals applied to the image-doman inversion problem discussed in Chapter 26.

For $i = 0$, equation 11.5 can be rearranged to give the slowness residual

$$m(\mathbf{x})^{\text{mig}} = s(\mathbf{x})^{(1)} - s(\mathbf{x})^{(0)} = -\alpha 2s(\mathbf{x})\int_\omega d\omega\omega^2\sum_g\sum_s$$

$$\times \Delta P(\mathbf{g}|\mathbf{s})W(\omega)^* G(\mathbf{x}|\mathbf{g})^* G(\mathbf{x}|\mathbf{s})^*, \qquad (11.9)$$

where $m(\mathbf{x})^{\text{mig}}$, also known as the migration image, approximates the reflectivity distribution. Here, the i index is now silent on the RHS and $s(\mathbf{x})^{(0)} \to s(\mathbf{x})$. The interpretation of this formula was provided in section 10.1.5 for diffraction-stack migration. The next two sections interpret equation 11.9 in terms of the generalized diffraction migration and reverse time migration algorithms.

11.2.1 RTM = generalized diffraction-stack migration

The migration image described by equation 11.9 is purely real, so for a single shot gather, the complex conjugate can be taken to give

$$m(\mathbf{x})^{\text{mig}} = -2s(\mathbf{x})\int_\omega d\omega\sum_g\omega^2 W(\omega)\Delta P(\mathbf{g}|\mathbf{s})^* G(\mathbf{x}|\mathbf{g})G(\mathbf{x}|\mathbf{s}),$$

$$= 2\int_t dt\sum_g\overbrace{\ddot{d}(\mathbf{g},t|\mathbf{s},0)}^{\text{reflection data}}\overbrace{g(\mathbf{x},t|\mathbf{g},0)\star g(\mathbf{x},t|\mathbf{s},0)}^{\text{migration kernel}},$$

$$\qquad (11.10)$$

where, for notational convenience, $W(\omega) = 1/2\pi$, $\Delta p(\mathbf{g},t|\mathbf{s},0) \to d(\mathbf{g},t|\mathbf{s},0)$, $s(\mathbf{x}) \to 1$, $w(t) = \delta(t)$, and the subscript i has been dropped. Here, $d(\mathbf{g},t|\mathbf{s},0)$ represents the reflection trace for a shot at $\mathbf{s}$ and a receiver at $\mathbf{g}$ where the direct wave is muted.

Equation 11.10 is identical to that for generalized diffraction-stack migration (GDM), and the migration image is the same as that for reverse time migration (Schuster, 2002). If the Green's function only accounts for direct arrivals (e.g., $g(\mathbf{x},t|\mathbf{s},0) \approx \delta(t - |\mathbf{x} - \mathbf{s}|/c)/|\mathbf{x} - \mathbf{s}|)$, then the GDM formula reduces to that of a DM method described by, e.g., equation 10.47. As illustrated in Figure 11.1a, the migration kernel $g(\mathbf{x},t|\mathbf{g},0)\star g(\mathbf{x},t|\mathbf{s},0) = \delta(t - |\mathbf{x} - \mathbf{g}|/c - |\mathbf{x} - \mathbf{s}|/c)/|\mathbf{x} - \mathbf{g}||\mathbf{x} - \mathbf{s}|$ plots out as a single hyperbola in $x_g - t$ space for a specified trial image point at $\mathbf{x} = (0, d)$. In contrast, Figure 11.1b shows that the migration kernel plots out as multiple hyperbolas in data space if the Green's functions are computed by a finite-difference solution to the wave equation.

Unlike the primary migration kernel in Figure 11.1a, the dot product in $x_g - t$ space between the predicted multiple moveout curves (solid and dashed colored lines) and the actual moveout of the data (black hyperbolas) is negligible unless the trial image point is very close to the actual scatterer location at the star. Hence, the multiple migration image should have higher spatial resolution than the primary migration image.

The computation of the GDM image is similar to that of a DM image: $m(\mathbf{x})^{\text{mig}}$ is computed by a dot product between the recorded shot gather and the migration kernel $g(\mathbf{x},t|\mathbf{g},0)\star g(\mathbf{x},t|\mathbf{s},0)$ for a specified trial image point $\mathbf{x}$. Unlike DM, the GDM kernel accounts for both primaries and all multiple-scattered arrivals. See Chapter 13 for more details.

11.2.2 Reverse time migration

The gradient in equation 11.9 can be manipulated into a readily interpretable form

$$m(\mathbf{x})^{\text{mig}} = -\int_\omega d\omega\omega^2\sum_g[W(\omega)G(\mathbf{x}|\mathbf{s})]^* [G(\mathbf{g}|\mathbf{x})^*\tilde{d}(\mathbf{g}|\mathbf{s})],$$

$$= \overbrace{[w(t)\star g(\mathbf{x},t|\mathbf{s},0)]}^{D(\mathbf{x},t)=\text{downgoing source}}$$

$$\otimes \overbrace{\left[\sum_g g(\mathbf{g},-t|\mathbf{x},0)\star\ddot{d}(\mathbf{g},t|\mathbf{s},0)\right]}^{U(\mathbf{x},t)=\text{backpropagated upgoing refl.}}\bigg|_{t=0},$$

$$= \sum_t D(\mathbf{x},t)U(\mathbf{x},t), \qquad (11.11)$$

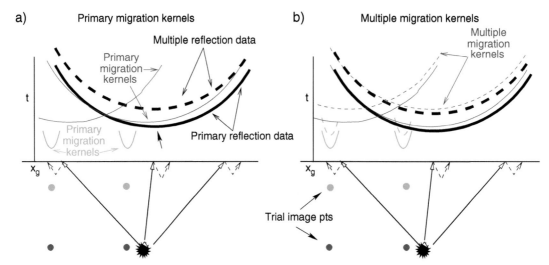

Figure 11.1. Data plotted as black hyperbolas and migration kernels plotted as green and purple hyperbolas in data space for (a) primary and (b) primary and multiple events associated with the shallow (green dots) and deep (purple dots) trial image points. The best match between the data (black hyperbolas) and migration curves (pink and green) is when the trial image point is near or at the scatterer's location.

in which $s(\mathbf{x})$ is conveniently taken to be $1/2\pi$, a single source at $\mathbf{s}$ is assumed, and $\tilde{d}(\mathbf{g}|\mathbf{s}) = \Delta P(\mathbf{g}|\mathbf{s})$ represents the trace that only contains upgoing reflected waves because the direct or diving waves have been eliminated. This equation says that the prestack RTM image $m(\mathbf{x})^{\text{mig}}$ is formed at the trial image point $\mathbf{x}$ by taking the zero-lag temporal correlation of the downgoing source field $D(\mathbf{x}, t)$ with the back-propagated reflections $U(\mathbf{x}, t)$ (McMechan, 1983; Whitmore, 1983).

The term $D(\mathbf{x}, t) = w(t) \star g(\mathbf{x}, t|\mathbf{s}, 0)$ represents the downgoing wavefield[2] and the upgoing back-propagated reflections are given by $U(\mathbf{x}, t) = \sum_g g(\mathbf{g}, -t|\mathbf{x}, 0) \star \ddot{\tilde{d}}(\mathbf{g}, t|\mathbf{s}, 0)$. For an impulsive source, these back-propagated reflections[3] coincide with $D(\mathbf{x}, t)$ only at $\mathbf{x} = \mathbf{x}_{\text{scatt}}$ in the space-time cube of Figure 11.2. Ideally, this means that the only nonzero dot product[4] of $\sum_t U(\mathbf{x}, t)D(\mathbf{x}, t)$ is at the scatterer's position, as it should be in an ideal migration image. In practice, however, migration artifacts will appear

because of the band-limited source wavelet, a limited source-receiver aperture, coarse geophone and source sampling intervals, an incorrect migration velocity, multiples and converted waves, and the fact that the back-propagated reflection wavefield appears below the scatterer as a defocused wavefield.

A preconditioning term can be included in the RTM formula by weighting the migration image by $I(\mathbf{x})$ at each trial image point

$$m(\mathbf{x})^{\text{mig}} = \frac{\sum_t D(\mathbf{x}, t)U(\mathbf{x}, t)}{I(\mathbf{x})}, \qquad (11.12)$$

to boost up relatively weak migration amplitudes. This term can be considered as an approximation to the inverse Hessian (see section 11.4) and can compensate for the weakening of both the downgoing source wavefield and upgoing reflections from geometric spreading and attenuation (Beydoun and Mendes, 1989). It also can be designed to deconvolve the source wavelet as well, in which case the division in the frequency domain is replaced in the time domain by a weighted deconvolution filter or by a banded matrix approximation to the Hessian inverse (Hu et al., 2001; Yu et al., 2006). If many shot gathers are available, then there is an extra integration over the source variables, i.e., shot gathers, to give the stacked RTM migration image. Of course, the quality of the RTM image depends on the accuracy of the migration velocity because strong velocity errors will lead to blurred stacking of $m(\mathbf{x})^{\text{mig}}$ computed from different shot gathers.

The following MATLAB® code implements equation 11.11 as 2D reverse time migration of the common

---

[2]In a homogeneous medium, the source wavefield is strictly a downgoing wave, but it consists of both upgoing and downgoing waves in a heterogeneous medium. Nevertheless, we will refer to it as a "downgoing" source wave.

[3]The $U(\mathbf{x}, t)$ term describes an upgoing reflection at $\mathbf{x}$ below the recording surface. That is, the multiplication of the recorded reflections $\tilde{d}(\mathbf{g}|\mathbf{s}) \approx e^{-i\omega\tau_{sx}^{\text{refl}}}$ by the conjugated Green's function $G(\mathbf{g}|\mathbf{x})^* \approx e^{i\omega\tau_{gx}}$ gives a decreased time in the exponent of $U(\mathbf{x}) \approx \tilde{d}(\mathbf{g}|\mathbf{s})G(\mathbf{g}|\mathbf{x})^* \approx e^{-i\omega[\tau_{sx}^{\text{refl}} - \tau_{gx}]}$. Thus, the back-propagated reflection $\tilde{d}(\mathbf{g}|\mathbf{s})G(\mathbf{g}|\mathbf{x})^*$ arrives increasingly earlier in time as $\mathbf{x}$ approaches the underlying reflector.

[4]The "zero-lag correlation of two time series" at $\mathbf{x}$ is a fancy way of saying "the dot product of two vectors," where one vector is the discrete time series for the source-modeled field $D(\mathbf{x}, t)$ and the other vector contains the back-propagated field $U(\mathbf{x}, t)$ at the spatial position $\mathbf{x}$.

```
%%%%%%%%%%%%%%%%%%%%%%%%%%%%%%%%%%%%%%%%%%%%%%%%%%%%%%%%%%%%%%%%%%%%%%%%%%%%
% Reverse time migration of single shot gather CSG(1:NX,1:it)
% The finite-difference code is run backward in time for point
% sources at the surface locations of the geophones; this emulates
% acausal Green's functions. The GF's source wavelets are the recorded
% traces recorded at these surface geophones.
% (NX,NZ,NT)          - input- (Horizontal,Vertical) gridpt dim. of
%                              velocity model and # Time Steps
% FR                  - input- Peak frequency of Ricker wavelet
% BVEL(NX,NZ)         - input- NXxNZ matrix of background velocity model
% c(NX,NZ)            - input- NXxNZ matrix of actual earth velocity model
% (dx,dt)             - input- (space, time) sample intervals
% (XS,ZS)             - input- (x,z) coordinates of line source
% RICKER(NT)          - input- NTx1 vector of source time histories
% IH(NX,NZ)           - input- NXxNZ preconditioner matrix of approx. inverse
%                              Hessian
% (p2,p1,p0)          -calcul- (future,present,past) NXxNZ matrices of
%                              Pressure
% slow(NX,NZ)         -output- Migration Image.
%%%%%%%%%%%%%%%%%%%%%%%%%%%%%%%%%%%%%%%%%%%%%%%%%%%%%%%%%%%%%%%%%%%%%%%%%%%%
clear all; %SET MODEL PARAMETERS AND COMPUTE SOURCE TIME HISTORY
[NX,NZ,NSP,NT,FR,niter,BVEL,cmax,cmin,dx,dt,t,RICKER,REALDATA,c]=indata;
RICKER=[diff(RICKER) 0];xs=NX/2; zs=2;
figure(1);[REALDATA]=...
    CSG(dx,dt,xs,zs,NX,NZ,FR,NT,RICKER,c);% COMPUTE REFL+DIRECT WAVE DATA
[SYNDATA,BOUNDARYDATA,XS,ZS,p0,p1]=...% COMPUTE DIRECT WAVE DATA
    synforw(xs,zs,RICKER,BVEL,NX,NZ,NT,FR,dt,dx);
RES=(SYNDATA-REALDATA); % SUBTRACT DIRECT WAVES FROM REFL+DIRECT-->REFL
cns=(dt/dx*BVEL).^2; r0=p0*0;r1=r0;r2=r0;
slow=zeros(NX,NZ); [NSP,i]=size(BOUNDARYDATA);
 for it=NT-1:-1:2 %BACKWARD TIME STEP

   for ns=1:NSP; % Set Direct wavefield as source wavelets @ boundaries
     p1(XS(ns),ZS(ns))=BOUNDARYDATA(ns,it);
   end;
   p2 = 2*p1 - p0 +  cns.*del2(p1);% Backproject Direct Waves by FD Approx.
   p2(:,1)=0;p2(1,:)=0;
   p2(:,NZ)=0;p2(NX,:)=0;
   p0=p1;p1=p2;

   r2 = 2*r1 - r0 + cns.*del2(r1);% Backproject Recorded REFL by FD Approx.
   r2(:,1)=0;r2(1,:)=0; r2(:,NZ)=0;r2(NX,:)=0;
   r2(:,2)= r2(:,2)+RES(:,it);
   r0=r1;r1=r2;
   slow = r2.*p2 + slow;% Update migration image after each time step
   plot0
 end;
 IH=1;mig=slow.*IH;  % Apply preconditioner inverse Hessian
 mig=del2(slow);% Apply Laplacian
```

shot gather defined in the MATLAB function *CSG( )*. Appendix 11A provides the support functions.

For simplicity, no absorbing boundary conditions have been included in the above code, but if they are included, then any first-order derivatives in time must take into account the sign change from backward differencing in time.[5]

---

[5]It is too costly to store and retrieve the multidimensional matrix *FORW*([1 : *nx*], [1 : *nz*], [1 : *nt*]); see Exercise 2 for a parsimonious strategy for computing this forward field.

11.3 Numerical examples of RTM

The main benefit of RTM compared to conventional one-way, wave-equation migration (OWEM) or Kirchhoff migration (KM) methods is that all of the arrivals, including multiples and turning waves, are accounted for by the finite-difference solution to the wave equation. If the migration velocity model is accurate, then reflection events get relocated back to their places of origin along reflecting interfaces. This is illustrated by the synthetic data example in Figure 11.3, where seismic reflections are migrated by the KM and RTM methods. Because the standard KM

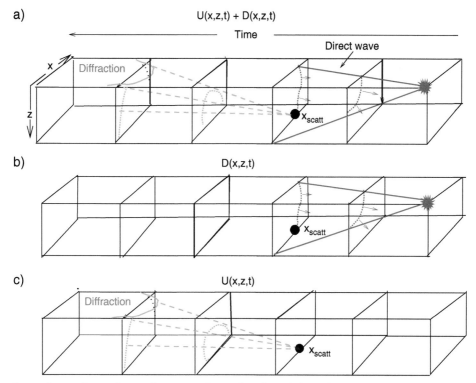

a) $U(x,z,t) + D(x,z,t)$

Figure 11.2. Snapshots of wavefronts for a point source located at the origin and a scatterer at $\mathbf{x}_{\text{scatt}}$. The snapshots depict (a) the total wavefield, (b) forward-propagated wavefield $D(\mathbf{x}, t)$, and (c) the back-propagated scattered field $U(\mathbf{x}, t)$. According to equation 11.11, the migration image is obtained by temporally summing the product of the green fields $U(\mathbf{x}, t)$ in (c) and the red fields $D(\mathbf{x}, t)$ in (b), where the only nonzero product is at $\mathbf{x}_{\text{scatt}}$.

method only migrates primary reflections, then "prismatic" multiple reflections (see Figure 11.3) are ignored. However, these prismatic events might help illuminate the "root" of the salt tooth as seen in the RTM image in Figure 11.3b.[6] A comparison of KM, OWEM, and RTM applied to field data is shown in Figure 11.4, where the sides of the salt flank are imaged best by RTM.

It is often the case that the OWEM and KM methods produce migration images with less noise than RTM images. This is partly because the $U(\mathbf{x}, t)$ and $D(\mathbf{x}, t)$ wavefields extrapolated by OWEM methods are purely upward and downward extrapolated waves, respectively, which means that the reflections are smeared only along the appropriate migration ellipses in, e.g., Figure 10.4. This is not the case with RTM because the finite-difference solutions to the wave equation generate both upgoing and downgoing waves in the extrapolation process, which then will yield nonzero correlations along the upgoing or downgoing raypaths. This will appear as coherent artifacts in the RTM image, a subject discussed in Chapter 13. These

artifacts can be reduced by applying one-way filters to the wavefields prior to migration (see Chapter 13).

A source of unwanted correlations is the migration of the strong diving wave recorded in long-offset marine data. The back propagation of this diving wave will

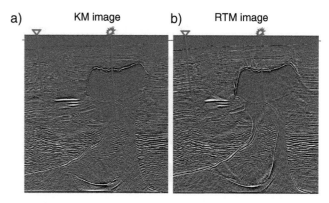

a)   KM image   b)   RTM image

Figure 11.3. Images obtained by (a) KM and (b) RTM methods applied to synthetic acoustic data (images courtesy of Yu Zhang of CGGVeritas). Kirchhoff migration does not image the inner flanks of the salt body clearly because, unlike RTM, it does not take into account prism-like reflections.

---

[6]The geometry of the horizontal interface must be known accurately, otherwise the finite-difference prediction of the prismatic multiple will be inaccurate, leading to a blurred image.

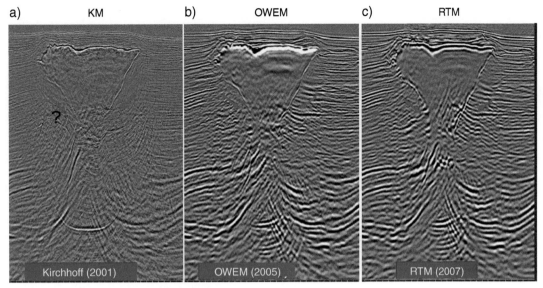

Figure 11.4. Images obtained by (a) KM, (b) OWEM, and (c) RTM methods applied to marine data. Images courtesy of CGGVeritas.

show strong correlations with the forward-propagated diving wave everywhere along the wavepath (Luo, 1992; Woodward, 1992), not just along the bottom part of the diving ray. This results in low-wavenumber migration artifacts away from the reflecting interfaces, as illustrated in Figure 11.5b.

11.4 Practical implementation of RTM

Some procedures for reducing artifacts in RTM images include direct-wave muting, illumination compensation (i.e., preconditioning), smoothing of the velocity model, tapering of data at the edges of the recording aperture, upgoing and downgoing wavefield separation, and filtering of the image. Further details are in Fletcher et al. (2005) and Chapter 15.

1. Preconditioning. Solving an ill-posed problem often is characterized by slow convergence with a gradient

optimization method. Therefore, a preconditioning term that approximates the inverse to the forward-modeling operator should be used with RTM, to boost up weak migration amplitudes at depth, for instance.

A preconditioning term can be obtained using the compact notation of equation 10.27 and equations 10.44 and 10.45 to get

$$
\mathbf{m}^{\text{mig}} = [\mathbf{L}^{\dagger}\mathbf{L}]\mathbf{m} \rightarrow m(\mathbf{x})^{\text{mig}} = 4\omega^4 |W(\omega)|^2
$$

$$
\times \int_{V_o} G(\mathbf{x}|\mathbf{s})^* G(\mathbf{x}'|\mathbf{s})
$$

$$
\times \left[\int_{S_g} G(\mathbf{x}|\mathbf{g})^* G(\mathbf{x}'|\mathbf{g}) dx_g^2 \right] m(\mathbf{x}') dx'^3,
$$

$$
= \int_{V_o} \Gamma(\mathbf{x}|\mathbf{x}') m(\mathbf{x}') dx'^3, \qquad (11.13)
$$

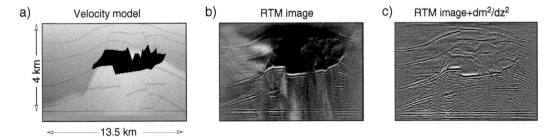

Figure 11.5. (a) Velocity model. Images after (b) RTM and (c) RTM followed by a second derivative in the depth coordinate. Applying a Laplacian to the RTM image did not significantly improve the image compared to (c). However, images with steeply dipping reflectors might be filtered more suitably by the Laplacian because it is not biased in the depth direction. Images courtesy of Wei Dai.

in which

$$[\mathbf{L}^\dagger \mathbf{L}]_{ii'} = \Gamma(\mathbf{x}_i | \mathbf{x}_{i'}) = 4\omega^4 |W(\omega)|^2 G(\mathbf{x}_i | \mathbf{s})^* G(\mathbf{x}_{i'} | \mathbf{s})$$

$$\times \left[\int_{S_g} G(\mathbf{x}_i | \mathbf{g})^* G(\mathbf{x}_{i'} | \mathbf{g}) dx_g^2 \right]. \quad (11.14)$$

Assuming a diagonally dominant Hessian for a discretized slowness model, the elements of the inverse matrix can be approximated by

$$[\mathbf{L}^\dagger \mathbf{L}]_{ij}^{-1} \approx \frac{\delta_{ij}}{[\mathbf{L}^\dagger \mathbf{L}]_{ii}},$$

in which

$$[\mathbf{L}^\dagger \mathbf{L}]_{ii} = 4\omega^4 |W(\omega)|^2 |G(\mathbf{x}_i | \mathbf{s})|^2 \int_{S_g} |G(\mathbf{x}_i | \mathbf{g})|^2 dx_g^2.$$

$$(11.15)$$

For a homogeneous medium, this last expression becomes

$$[\mathbf{L}^\dagger \mathbf{L}]_{ii} = \omega^4 |W(\omega)|^2 \frac{1}{64\pi^4 |\mathbf{x}_i - \mathbf{s}|^2} \int_{S_g} \frac{1}{|\mathbf{x}_i - \mathbf{g}|^2} dx_g^2.$$

$$(11.16)$$

This equation says that the ith diagonal component of the Hessian matrix is computed by taking the integration of the squared amplitudes of the recorded wavefields that visit the ith slowness cell.

The illumination function $I(\mathbf{x}_i) = 1/[\mathbf{L}^\dagger \mathbf{L}]_{ii}$ in equation 11.12 corrects for the amplitude weakening of events at $\mathbf{x}_i$ arising from geometric spreading for a source at $\mathbf{s}$. If source deconvolution is used, it can also whiten the source wavelet and partly compensate for amplitude loss from defocusing by rocks with strong velocity contrasts, such as salt bodies.

For a heterogeneous medium, a ray-tracing method (Beydoun and Mendes, 1989) can be used to compute the Green's functions in equation 11.15, or a finite-difference solution to the wave equation (Rickett, 2003; Kaelin and Guitton, 2006) is used. This latter approach can be expensive, but there are alternative approximations to the inverse of the Hessian:

a. To estimate the illumination compensation $I(\mathbf{x}_i) = 1/[\mathbf{L}^\dagger \mathbf{L}]_{ii}$ term in equation 11.15, use a finite-difference method to compute $W(\omega)G(\mathbf{x}_i | \mathbf{g})$ for a source at $\mathbf{g}$ and $W(\omega)G(\mathbf{x}_i | \mathbf{s})$ for a source at $\mathbf{s}$. Then, compute the intensities $|W(\omega)| |G(\mathbf{x}_i | \mathbf{s})|^2$ and $|W(\omega)| |G(\mathbf{x}_i | \mathbf{g})|^2$. If a space-time method is used, this means squaring and summing the amplitudes of $w(t) \star g(\mathbf{x}_i, t | \mathbf{s}, 0)$ and $w(t) \star g(\mathbf{x}_i, t | \mathbf{g}, 0)$ over time.

b. Approximate $I(\mathbf{x}_i) = [\mathbf{L}^\dagger \mathbf{L}]_{ii}^{-1}$ by computing the common-shot gather $W(\omega)G(\mathbf{x}_i | \mathbf{s})$ for a single source and a multitude of frequencies, and associating the diagonal of the Hessian to the intensity of the resulting field

$$[\mathbf{L}^\dagger \mathbf{L}]_{ii} \approx \int \omega^2 |W(\omega)|^2 |G(\mathbf{x}_i | \mathbf{s})|^2 d\omega, \quad (11.17)$$

at $\mathbf{x}_i$ in the subsurface.

Figure 11.6 illustrates the result of inserting equation 11.17 into $I(\mathbf{x}_i) = 1/[\mathbf{L}^\dagger \mathbf{L}]_{ii}$ and applying it to an RTM image for a single shot gather. Plessix and Mulder (2004) suggest alternative approximations, and Ge Zhan (personal communication, 2014) prefers the method (adopted from Kaelin and Guitton, 2006) of backprojecting the recorded data into the subsurface to get $U(\mathbf{x}_i, t)$, computing the downgoing wavefield from a single source to get $D(\mathbf{x}_i, t)$, and then computing $\int |\ddot{D}(\mathbf{x}_i, t)|^2 |\ddot{U}(\mathbf{x}_i, t)|^2 dt$ as an approximation for $[\mathbf{L}^\dagger \mathbf{L}]_{ii}$.

c. The Hessian inverse can be approximated by the migration deconvolution approach of Hu et al. (2001) and Yu et al. (2006). This approximation (see Chapter 18) costs less than one migration for each shot gather, incorporates off-diagonal terms in the Hessian, and automatically deconvolves the estimated source wavelet.

2. Velocity-model smoothing. A smooth velocity model should be used for RTM, otherwise reflections from impedance discontinuities will be generated and create artifacts in the migration image. As shown in Figure 11.7d, too much smoothing blurs the reflection interfaces, and too little retains the low-wavenumber "rabbit ear" artifacts associated with the RTM operator. As will be discussed in Chapters 12 and 13, smooth velocity models subdue the low-wavenumber artifacts associated with the rabbit ears and emphasize the high-wavenumber migration smile in the RTM kernels.

One possible compromise is to apply a high-pass filter, such as a Laplacian, to the migration image. A Laplacian filter might be a good choice because the migration image in equation 11.10 is a sum of weighted Green's functions, which are solutions to the Helmholtz equation. Applying the Laplacian to the migration image then will convert the Green's function in the integrand to weighted Green's functions, in which the weight is proportional to k^2, a seemingly benign high-pass filter (see Exercise 7). Indeed, applying a Laplacian to the migration images in Figure 11.7 gives the more acceptable results in Figure 11.8. Sometimes a simple derivative in the depth direction in the migration image will be sufficient, but a Laplacian filter or second-order vertical derivative filter can

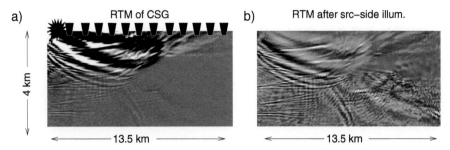

Figure 11.6. RTM image of a shot gather (a) before and (b) after source-side illumination compensation. Images courtesy of Wei Dai.

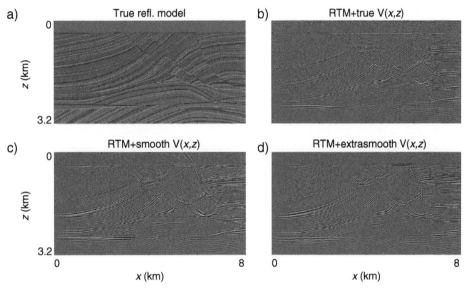

Figure 11.7. The (a) true reflectivity model and the RTM images computed with a migration velocity equal to the (b) true velocity model, (c) smoothed velocity model, and (d) supersmoothed velocity model. Too much smoothing blurs the reflectors, too little smoothing promotes the low-wavenumber artifacts seen in (b). Images courtesy of Han Yu.

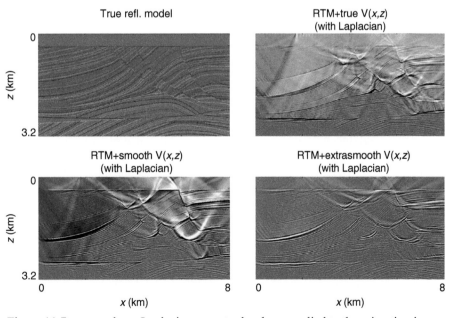

Figure 11.8. Same as Figure 11.7, except that a Laplacian operator has been applied to the migration images. See MATLAB codes under the topic RTM in the Computational Toolkit. Images courtesy of Han Yu.

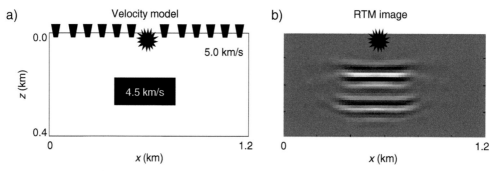

Figure 11.9. (a) Velocity model and (b) RTM image obtained from a single shot gather using the code in section 11.2.2 and Appendix 11A.

be used (see Figure 11.5c). An alternative strategy is to detect dips along the interfaces numerically and apply directional derivatives perpendicular to the interface boundary to eliminate long-wavelength interbed artifacts (Chen et al., 2013).

3. Taper traces. Taper traces in the shot gather so that the far-offset trace amplitudes are reduced smoothly to zero by a cosine taper starting about one wavelength from the last trace.

4. Muting. Mute the direct arrivals and the early arrival diving waves. If they are not muted prior to migration, then there will be strong low-wavenumber artifacts along the associated wavepaths. For example, see the low-wavenumber artifacts in the salt body of Figure 11.5 and the cigar-shaped noise in Figure 11.6. One strategy is to model the direct waves in a smooth velocity model and adaptively subtract them from the data.

11.5 Summary

The iterative equations of seismic imaging are derived, and the special cases are RTM, LSM, and FWI. The RTM formula is the misfit gradient after the first iteration, and LSM is a series of prestack migrations in which only the reflectivity distribution is updated at each iteration. Full-waveform inversion updates both the high-wavenumber reflectivity and the smooth slowness distributions after each iteration.

The standard interpretation of RTM is that the migration image at **x** is formed by zero-lag correlation between the forward-propagated source field and the back-propagated scattered field at **x**. The advantage of RTM is that, unlike OWEM and KM methods, RTM accounts for all scattered events in the data if the migration velocity model is sufficiently accurate. This can illuminate salt flanks normally invisible to KM or OWEM methods, and it can lead to strong focusing beneath bodies with large velocity contrasts, such as salt lenses. Another potential advantage is

that accurate imaging of multiples will lead to higher spatial resolution, which only can be achieved if the velocity model is accurate enough.

Reverse time migration does have some limitations. For wideband 3D data greater than 20 Hz, it can be significantly more computationally expensive than the OWEM and KM methods, and its migration image can be more sensitive to errors in the velocity model. Another liability is that there is more noise in the RTM image because the back-propagated reflections correlate with the source field away from reflector boundaries. This correlation noise can be useful for waveform inversion but not for migration images. Filtering methods to alleviate this problem are discussed, and a more detailed analysis is given in Chapters 12 and 13.

11.6 Exercises

1. Run the MATLAB RTM code in section 11.2.2 and Appendix 11A to get the results shown in Figure 11.9. Answer the following questions.

   - Why don't the sides of the rectangular scatterer get imaged? Why would increasing the aperture width mitigate this problem?
   - As the time stepping evolves backward from late time step = 300 to early time step = 1, notice that the bottom part of the rectangular scatterer gets imaged at time step = 180 while the shallow part gets imaged at time step = 120. Explain.
   - Adjust the code so the sides of the scatterer get imaged by including more shot gathers, where the shots are to the left and right of scatterer. Explain why this strategy is successful.
   - Why is it important to eliminate the direct wave from the data prior to RTM? Illustrate your answer by adjusting the code so the direct wave is not eliminated from the input data, and compute the RTM image.
   - Write a code to compensate for geometric spreading: call this preconditioning function I(x, z) and apply it to the image. Remember, the 2D finite-difference

Causal Green's function

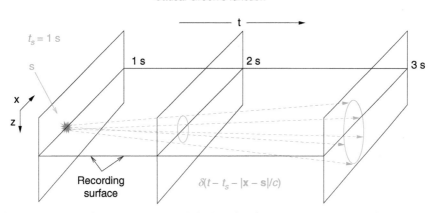

Figure 11.10. Plot of the support (dashed green rays and circles) for the causal Green's function $\delta(t - t_s - |\mathbf{x} - \mathbf{s}|/c)$, where geometric spreading is ignored harmlessly. Here, a single impulse at $t_s = 1$ sec is excited at the point $\mathbf{s}$ on the recording surface. The support is only nonzero along the cone with its tip at the source position (green star). If the time history of the impulse source is described by the hyperbola in Figure 11.11, then the resulting fields are found by placing the light cones at each impulse along the hyperbola and superimposing the resulting cones.

(FD) solution is for a 2D line source so the geometric spreading is inversely proportional to the square root of distance.

- Apply a zero-lag deconvolution imaging condition (DIC) instead of the zero-lag correlation imaging condition (CIC). What are the benefits and possible problems of DIC compared to the CIC.

- Comment about the benefits and liabilities of the Laplacian filter applied to the data. Add noise and migrate with and without a Laplacian filter applied to the image. There is a rule of thumb in geophysics: after application of a whitening filter, always follow up with a high-cut filter. Does this rule apply to your noisy RTM image after application of the Laplacian filter?

- There are other imaging conditions for RTM as described by Chattopadhyay and McMechan (2008). Implement some of them with the MATLAB code in section 11.2.2. Comment about their relative merits and liabilities.

2. Write a parsimonious MATLAB code to compute sequentially the forward field $FORW(x, z, t)$ at decreasing time steps starting from the final conditions; the parsimony should be for minimizing storage of arrays. It is too costly to store and retrieve the multidimensional matrix $FORW([1 : nx], [1 : nz], [1 : nt])$; instead, a finite-difference simulation is used to compute the forward field all along the exterior spatial boundaries of the medium. These boundary values are saved for all time steps and the last two $x - z$ panels of pressure also are saved. With these saved traces, the finite-difference program can be run backwards in time, starting at the second-to-last time step, to recreate sequentially the forward field $FORW([1 : nx], [1 : nz], t)$ everywhere in

space and at decreasing time t. Hint: this code already is implemented in the MATLAB code in section 11.2.2.

3. Figure 11.10 illustrates the support of a causal Green's function $\delta(t - t_s - |\mathbf{x} - \mathbf{s}|/c)$ for an impulsive source excited at time $t_s = 1$ sec and located at $\mathbf{s}$; here, the geometrical spreading factor is ignored harmlessly. Interrogating the resulting wavefield at the listening time $t = 3$ sec shows the large circle at $t = 3$ sec. Sketch the wavefield at listening time $t = 3$ sec for an impulse at $\mathbf{s}$ and an excitation time $t_s = 2$ sec. Sketch the acausal wavefront for $\delta(t - t_s + |\mathbf{x} - \mathbf{s}|/c)$ for $t_s = 2$ sec.

4. Figure 11.11 illustrates the upgoing scattered field $U(\mathbf{x}, t) = \sum_s d(\mathbf{s}, -t)\delta(t - t_s - |\mathbf{x} - \mathbf{s}|/c)$, where the factor for geometric spreading is ignored. Similar to this drawing, sketch the wavefront diagrams corresponding to $\sum_s d(\mathbf{s}, t)\delta(t - t_s - |\mathbf{x} - \mathbf{s}|/c)$, in which the data hyperbola $d(\mathbf{s}, t)$ is reversed in time compared to $d(\mathbf{s}, -t)$. Is the downgoing wave a collapsing or expanding wavefront. Explain why this is the effect that a free surface has on an upgoing wave.

5. Similar to Figure 11.11, draw the diagram of wavefronts that describe $U(\mathbf{x}, t) = \sum_s d(\mathbf{s}, t)\delta(t - t_s + |\mathbf{x} - \mathbf{s}|/c)$. Does this emulate collapsing or expanding wavefronts? Do the tips of the light cones point toward increasing time or decreasing time? Why?

6. If attenuation is modeled with the asymptotic Green's function $G(\mathbf{x}|\mathbf{x}') = e^{i\omega\tau_{xx'} - \omega\tau_{xx'}/Q} A(\mathbf{x}, \mathbf{x}')$, derive the associated formula for illumination compensation. In light of the fact that the complex conjugate $G(\mathbf{x}|\mathbf{x}')^* = e^{-i\omega\tau_{xx'} - \omega\tau_{xx'}/Q} A(\mathbf{x}, \mathbf{x}')$ does not compensate for geometric spreading, explain the necessity for illumination compensation. Here, $A(\mathbf{x}|\mathbf{x}')$ is the term that accounts for geometric spreading and Q accounts for attenuation in rocks.

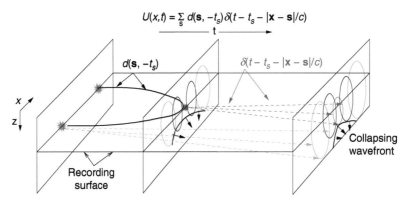

Figure 11.11. Collapsing wavefronts (solid black curves) obtained by multiplying the causal Green's function $\delta(t - t_s - |\mathbf{x} - \mathbf{s}|/c)$ by the time reversed traces $d(\mathbf{s}, -t)$ and summing over the trace positions $\mathbf{s}$ on the recording surface. The recorded arrivals trace out a hyperbolic curve in $x - t$ space, and they are associated with a buried scatterer at the focus point of the collapsing wavefronts.

7. Show that the Laplacian applied to the migration image $m(\mathbf{x})^{\text{mig}}$ is

$$\nabla^2 m(\mathbf{x})^{\text{mig}} = \omega^2 \int d(\mathbf{g}|\mathbf{s})^*[G(\mathbf{x}|\mathbf{g})\nabla^2 G(\mathbf{x}|\mathbf{s})$$

$$+ G(\mathbf{x}|\mathbf{s})\nabla^2 G(\mathbf{x}|\mathbf{g})]dx_g dx_s,$$

$$+ 2\omega^2 \int d(\mathbf{g}|\mathbf{s})^*\nabla G(\mathbf{x}|\mathbf{g}) \cdot \nabla G(\mathbf{x}|\mathbf{s})dx_g dx_s,$$

$$= 2\omega^2 \int d(\mathbf{g}|\mathbf{s})^*[-k(\mathbf{x})^2 G(\mathbf{x}|\mathbf{g})G(\mathbf{x}|\mathbf{s})$$

$$+ \nabla G(\mathbf{x}|\mathbf{g}) \cdot \nabla G(\mathbf{x}|\mathbf{s})]dx_g dx_s,$$

$$(11.18)$$

where $k(\mathbf{x}) = \frac{\omega}{c(\mathbf{x})}$. Now, show that the farfield gradient of the upgoing reflection $G(\mathbf{x}|\mathbf{s})^{\text{refl}} = rA(\mathbf{s}, \mathbf{x})^{\text{refl}}e^{i\omega\tau_{xs}^{\text{refl}}}$ is $i\mathbf{k}(\mathbf{x}, \mathbf{s})G(\mathbf{x}|\mathbf{s})^{\text{refl}}$, where r is the reflection coefficient, $A(\mathbf{s}, \mathbf{x})^{\text{refl}}$ is the geometric-spreading factor, τ_{xs}^{refl} is the specular traveltime of the upgoing reflection for a source at $\mathbf{s}$ and receiver at $\mathbf{x}$, and $\mathbf{k}(\mathbf{x}, \mathbf{s}) = \omega\nabla\tau_{xs}^{\text{refl}}$ is the wavenumber vector of the upgoing reflection.

Also show that the gradient of the downgoing direct wave $G(\mathbf{x}|\mathbf{g})^{\text{dir}} = A(\mathbf{g}, \mathbf{x})^{\text{dir}}e^{i\omega\tau_{xg}^{\text{dir}}}$ for a source at $\mathbf{g}$ is $i\mathbf{k}(\mathbf{x}, \mathbf{g})G(\mathbf{x}|\mathbf{g})^{\text{dir}}$, in which $\mathbf{k}(\mathbf{x}, \mathbf{g}) = \omega\nabla\tau_{xg}^{\text{dir}}$. Set $G(\mathbf{x}|\mathbf{g}) \to G(\mathbf{x}|\mathbf{g})^{\text{dir}}$ and $G(\mathbf{x}|\mathbf{s}) \to G(\mathbf{x}|\mathbf{s})^{\text{refl}}$. Show that the migration image is zero for $\mathbf{x}$ along the upgoing reflection raypath, which eliminates the low-wavenumber artifacts (see Chapter 12) in the migration image. Also show that the migration image $m(\mathbf{x})^{\text{mig}} \neq 0$ when $\mathbf{x}$ is at the reflector position with $G(\mathbf{x}|\mathbf{g}) \to G(\mathbf{x}|\mathbf{g})^{\text{dir}}$ and $G(\mathbf{x}|\mathbf{s}) \to G(\mathbf{x}|\mathbf{s})^{\text{dir}}$.

11.7 Computational labs

1. Carry out the labs in the Computational Toolkit under the topic RTM.

Appendix 11A: MATLAB RTM code

The MATLAB code for producing Figure 11.9 is in section 11.2.2, and the associated function calls are below.

```
%%%%%%%%%%%%%%%%%%%%%%%%%%%%%%%%%%%%%%%%%%%%%%%%%%%%%%%%%%%%%%%%%%%%%%%%%%%%%%%%%%%%
% "CSG.m" uses 2-2 FD algorithm to compute pressure field for a source at (xs,zs) and geophones
% at one node beneath free surface. In fact, free surface is assumed along all 4 sides
% of model, but ABCs can be placed on 3 sides. The output is dumped into REALDATA and is
% considered as the observed data to be used in waveform inversion.
%
% (NX,NZ,NT)    - input- (Horizontal,Vertical) gridpoint dimension of velocity model and # Time Steps
% FR            - input- Peak frequency of Ricker wavelet
% (dx,dt)       - input- (space, time) sample intervals
% (xs,zs)       - input- (x,z) coordinates of line source
% RICKER(NT)    - input-  NT vector of source time histories
% c(NX,NZ)      -calcul- NXxNZ matrix of velocity model
```

```
% (p2,p1,p0)      -calcul- (future,present,past) NXxNZ matrices of modeled pressure field
% REALDATA(NX,NT)-output- CSG pressure seismograms at 1 node beneath surface z=0;
%                         To be used as input into invert.m code
%%%%%%%%%%%%%%%%%%%%%%%%%%%%%%%%%%%%%%%%%%%%%%%%%%%%%%%%%%%%%%%%%%%%%%%%%%%%%%
function [REALDATA]=CSG(dx,dt,xs,zs,NX,NZ,FR,NT,RICKER,c)
%
% BUILD ACTUAL VELOCITY MODEL
%
cns=(dt/dx*c).^2;
p0=zeros(NX,NZ);p1=p0;p2=p0;bc=zeros(NX,1);REALDATA=zeros(NX,NT);
%
% COMPUTE REAL DATA CSG for GEOPHONES AT z=2.
%
for it=1:1:NT
   p2 = 2*p1 - p0 +  cns.*del2(p1);
   p2(xs,zs)=p2(xs,zs)+RICKER(it);
       if it==round(it/30)*30;imagesc([1:NX]*dx,[1:NZ]*dx,p2');
 plot1(NX,NT,dx,dt,p2,['OBSERVED PRESSURE SNAPSHOT  T= ',num2str(dt*it),' sec'],'Offset
 (ft)','Depth (ft)');
       end;
   REALDATA(:,it)=p2(:,2);
   p2(1:NX,1)=bc(1:NX);
   p0=p1;p1=p2;
end;


%%%%%%%%%%%%%%%%%%%%%%%%%%%%%%%%%%%%%%%%%%%%%%%%%%%%%%%%%%%%%%%%%%%%%%%%%%%%%%%%
% "synforw.m" uses 2-2 FD algorithm to compute pressure field for a source at (xs,zs) and geophones
% at one node beneath free surface. In fact, free surface is assumed along all 4 sides
% of model, but ABCs can be placed on 3 sides. The CSG output is dumped into SYNDATA and is
% considered as the synthetic data to be used in waveform inversion. The output
% BOUNDARYDATA is the boundary values at 1 node from model boundary.
%

% (NX,NZ,NT)           - input- (Horizontal,Vertical) gridpoint dimension of velocity
model and # Time Steps
% FR                   - input- Peak frequency of Ricker wavelet
% BVEL                 - input- NXxNZ matrix of background velocity model
% (dx,dt)              - input- (space, time) sample intervals
% (XS,ZS)              - input- (x,z) coordinates of line source
% RICKER(NT)           - input- NT vector of source time histories
% (p2,p1,p0)           -calcul- (future,present,past) NXxNZ matrices of modeled pressure field
% SYNDATA(NX,NT)       -output- CSG pressure seismograms at 1 node beneath surface z=0;
%                      to be used as input into invert.m code
% BOUNDARYDATA(NX,NT)-output- CSG pressure seismograms at 1 node from boundary for all 4
sides.
% (p0,p1)              -output- Old and present pressure panels at time NT.


%%%%%%%%%%%%%%%%%%%%%%%%%%%%%%%%%%%%%%%%%%%%%%%%%%%%%%%%%%%%%%%%%%%%%%%%%%%%%%

function
[SYNDATA,BOUNDARYDATA,XS,ZS,p0,p1]=synforw(xs,zs,RICKER,BVEL,NX,NZ,NT,FR,dt,dx)
c=BVEL;
SYNDATA=zeros(NX,NT); BSEISMO=zeros(NX,NT); LSEISMO=zeros(NZ,NT); RSEISMO=zeros(NZ,NT);
p0=zeros(NX,NZ);p1=p0;p2=p0;bc=zeros(NX,1);
cns=(dt/dx*c).^2;

for it=1:1:NT
   p2 = 2*p1 - p0 +  cns.*del2(p1);
   p2(xs,zs)=p2(xs,zs)+RICKER(it);
   if it==round(it/30)*30;
   plot1(NX,NZ,dx,dx,p2,'Predicted Pressure Snapshot','Offset (ft)','Depth (ft)');
   end;

   SYNDATA(:,it)=p2(:,2); BSEISMO(:,it)=p2(:,NZ-1);
   LSEISMO(:,it)=p2(2,:)'; RESINS(:,it)=p2(NX-1,:)';
   p2(1:NX,1)=bc(1:NX);
   p0=p1;p1=p2;
end;
p1=p0;p0=p2;
```

```
imagesc(SYNDATA');
plot1(NX,NZ,dx,dt,SYNDATA,'Synthetic Pressure Snapshot','Offset (ft)','Time (s)');
BOUNDARYDATA=[SYNDATA(2:NX-1,:);RESINS(3:NZ-2,:);BSEISMO(2:NX-1,:);LSEISMO(3:NZ-2,:)];
XS=[2:(NX-1) ones(1,NZ-4)*(NX-1) [2:(NX-1)] ones(1,NZ-4)*2];
ZS=[ ones(1,NX-2)*2 [3:NZ-2] ones(1,NX-2)*(NZ-1) [3:NZ-2]];


% Subroutine plot0.m
if it==round(it/10)*10;figure(3);colorman('gray');
     subplot(211);imagesc([1:NX]*dx,[1:NZ]*dx,c');label('Z (ft)');
     hold on;plot(dx*xs,dx*zs,'*');hold off
     title('Velocity Model');
     axis([600 1200 0 400]);
     text(800,200,'4500 ft/s','color','w');text(800,350,'5000 ft/s');
     subplot(212);imagesc([1:NX]*dx,[1:NZ]*dx,slow');
     axis([600 1200 0 400]);pause(.1);
     title(['Migration Image at Time Step ',num2str(it)]);label('X (ft)');label('Z
     (ft)');pause(1);
end
-------------------------------------------------------------------------------
function plot1(NX,NZ,dx,dt,c,tit,titi,titi)
colorman('jet');imagesc([1:NX]*dx,[1:NZ]*dx,c');
title([num2str(tit)]);label([num2str(titi)]);label([num2str(titi)]);pause(1);
-------------------------------------------------------------------------------


function [NX,NZ,NSP,NT,FR,niter,BVEL,cmax,cmin,dx,dt,t,RICKER,REALDATA,c]=indata
NX=200;NZ=100;NSP=1;NT=350;FR=20;niter=12;
BVEL=ones(NX,NZ)*5000; cmax=6500;cmin=3500;
dx=.05*cmin/FR;dt=.02/FR;
if dt >= 1.7*dx/cmax;dt=1.6*dx/cmax;end;
t=[0:1:NT-1]*dt-0.95/FR;RICKER=zeros(length(t));
RICKER= (1-t .*t * FR^2 *pi^2  ) .*exp(- t.^2 * pi^2 * FR^2 ) ;
RICKER=[diff(RICKER) 0]; REALDATA=zeros(NX,NT);
c=ones(NX,NZ)*5000;
for j=NX/2-10:NX/2+10;for i=NZ/5:NZ/5+10;c(j,i)=4500.;end;end;
colorman('hot');imagesc([1:NX]*dx,[1:NZ]*dx,c');
title('Actual Velocity Model');colorbar;label('Offset (ft)');label('Depth
(ft)');pause(1);
```

Chapter 12: Wavepaths

The high-frequency approximation of ray tracing assumes that seismic energy propagates from point A to point B exclusively along a skinny ray, sometimes referred to as the Fermat ray. In contrast, wave-equation tomography assumes that the energy is mostly transported along a "fat" ray (Harlan, 1990), in which the slowness model within the fat ray can influence the traveltime of the first arrival at position B. Woodward (1989, 1992) refers to this fat ray as a wavepath, which is similar to the Fresnel volume discussed by Kravtsov and Orlov (1980). The transmitted fat ray in a homogeneous medium is centered about the Fermat ray with a maximum width proportional to $\sqrt{L\lambda}$, in which L is the distance between A and B, and λ is the wavelength. This thickness is used to deduce the resolution limits of traveltime tomograms (Williamson, 1991; Williamson and Worthington, 1993; Schuster, 1996), migration images (Beylkin, 1984; Beylkin et al., 1985; Schuster, 1996), and wave-equation traveltime tomograms (Woodward, 1989 and 1992; Sheng and Schuster, 2003; Dahlen, 2004).

In this chapter, we will derive the formulas for the wavepaths associated with finite-frequency traveltime tomography and migration. The wavepath image is computed by migrating the window-weighted trace associated with a point source, where the window is centered about the arrival of interest. Examples of wavepaths are shown for both reflections and transmitted arrivals.

12.1 Traveltime wavepaths

In the high-frequency approximation, the perturbed traveltimes $\delta t(\mathbf{g}, \mathbf{s})$ of first arrivals are related to the perturbations in the slowness model by the linearized traveltime integral

$$\delta t(\mathbf{g}, \mathbf{s}) = \int \mathcal{L}(\mathbf{g}, \mathbf{s}, \mathbf{x}')\delta s(\mathbf{x}')dl', \qquad (12.1)$$

in which $\mathcal{L}$ is the raypath function (Woodward, 1992) that has support only along the skinny raypath. If the perturbation of the slowness model is only at the point $\mathbf{x}$ such that $\delta s(\mathbf{x}') = \delta(\mathbf{x}' - \mathbf{x})\delta s(\mathbf{x})$, then the traveltime Fréchet derivative becomes

$$\frac{\delta t(\mathbf{g}, \mathbf{s})}{\delta s(\mathbf{x})} = \mathcal{L}(\mathbf{g}, \mathbf{s}, \mathbf{x}). \qquad (12.2)$$

Under the high-frequency approximation and a pixelated medium, this equation (see equation 5.6) can be approximated by

$$\frac{\delta t(\mathbf{g}, \mathbf{s})}{\delta s(\mathbf{x})} = dl, \qquad (12.3)$$

where dl is the length of the raypath segment in the discretized cell centered at $\mathbf{x}$. If the Fermat ray does not pass through the cell centered at $\mathbf{x}$, then the Fréchet derivative is zero at $\mathbf{x}$.

Woodward (1989, 1992) avoids the high-frequency approximation of the raypath function $\mathcal{L} = \delta t/\delta s$ by deriving the Fréchet derivative under the Rytov approximation in the space-frequency domain. She denotes the resulting $\mathcal{L}$ as the wavepath function in the frequency domain. In contrast, Luo and Schuster (1991a) derive a wavepath function in the space-time domain with wave-equation traveltime inversion in which

$$\frac{\delta \tau(\mathbf{g}, \mathbf{s})}{\delta s(\mathbf{x})} = \frac{-2s(\mathbf{x})}{E} \int dt \overbrace{\dot{g}(\mathbf{x}, t | \mathbf{g}, 0) \star \dot{p}(\mathbf{x}, t | \mathbf{s}, 0)}^{\text{migration kernel}}$$
$$\cdot \dot{p}(\mathbf{g}, t + \Delta \tau_{gs} | \mathbf{s}, 0)^{\text{obs}}. \qquad (12.4)$$

Here, $\dot{g}(\mathbf{x}, t | \mathbf{g}, 0) \star \dot{p}(\mathbf{x}, t | \mathbf{s}, 0)$ is the migration kernel[1] and E is a normalization factor defined in equation 20.42. The above Fréchet derivative and the Rytov wavepath in Woodward (1992) are used for inverting traveltime data and overcome the high-frequency limitation in ray-based tomography (Zhou et al., 1995 and 1997). It also is used by earthquake seismologists (Marquering et al., 1999; Dahlen et al., 2002; Dahlen, 2004; Montelli et al., 2004; van der Hilst and de Hoop, 2006; Xu and Xie, 2009) for finite-frequency traveltime tomography and evaluating the resolution limits in whole-earth tomograms.

---

[1] Also denoted as the migration Green's function in Schuster and Hu (2000).

The physical meaning of equation 12.4 is obtained by examining the special case of a trace recorded in a homogeneous medium and a point source with a band-limited Ricker wavelet denoted by $w(t)$. Defining $\dot{g}(\mathbf{x}, t|\mathbf{g}, 0) = \frac{\delta(t - \tau_{xg})}{4\pi |\mathbf{x} - \mathbf{g}|}$ and $\dot{p}(\mathbf{x}, t|\mathbf{s}, 0) = \frac{\dot{w}(t - \tau_{xs})}{|\mathbf{x} - \mathbf{s}|}$, the convolution term in equation 12.4 becomes

$$\dot{g}(\mathbf{x}, t|\mathbf{g}, 0) \star \dot{p}(\mathbf{x}, t|\mathbf{s}, 0) = \frac{\ddot{w}(t - \tau_{xg} - \tau_{xs})}{4\pi |\mathbf{x} - \mathbf{g}||\mathbf{x} - \mathbf{s}|}. \qquad (12.5)$$

Defining $\dot{p}(\mathbf{g}, t|\mathbf{s}, 0)^{\text{obs}} = \frac{\dot{w}(t - \tau_{gs})}{|\mathbf{s} - \mathbf{g}|}$, inserting equation 12.5 into equation 12.4, and setting the observed first-arrival time residual $\Delta \tau_{gs} = 0$ yields

$$\frac{\delta \tau(\mathbf{g}, \mathbf{s})}{\delta s(\mathbf{x})} = \frac{-s(\mathbf{x})}{2\pi E |\mathbf{x} - \mathbf{g}||\mathbf{x} - \mathbf{s}||\mathbf{s} - \mathbf{g}|}$$
$$\times \int dt' \, \ddot{w}(t' - \tau_{xg} - \tau_{xs}) \dot{w}(t' - \tau_{sg}), \qquad (12.6)$$

in which the change in variable $t = t' - \tau_{sg}$ gives

$$\frac{\delta \tau(\mathbf{g}, \mathbf{s})}{\delta s(\mathbf{x})} = \frac{-s(\mathbf{x})}{2\pi E |\mathbf{x} - \mathbf{g}||\mathbf{x} - \mathbf{s}||\mathbf{s} - \mathbf{g}|}$$
$$\times \int dt \, \ddot{w}(t + \tau_{sg} - \tau_{xg} - \tau_{xs}) \dot{w}(t). \qquad (12.7)$$

Using the identity $\frac{\partial w(t + \tilde{\tau})}{\partial t} = \frac{\partial w(t + \tilde{\tau})}{\partial \tilde{\tau}}$, equation 12.7 becomes

$$\frac{\delta \tau(\mathbf{g}, \mathbf{s})}{\delta s(\mathbf{x})} = \frac{-s(\mathbf{x})}{2\pi E |\mathbf{x} - \mathbf{g}||\mathbf{x} - \mathbf{s}||\mathbf{s} - \mathbf{g}|} \frac{\partial}{\partial \tilde{\tau}}$$
$$\times \int dt \dot{w}(t + \tilde{\tau}) \dot{w}(t) = \dot{\Phi}(\tilde{\tau}), \qquad (12.8)$$

in which $\tilde{\tau} = \tau_{sg} - \tau_{xg} - \tau_{xs}$ and $\Phi(t)$ is the symmetric autocorrelation of $\dot{w}(t)$ scaled by $\frac{s(\mathbf{x})}{2\pi E |\mathbf{x} - \mathbf{g}||\mathbf{x} - \mathbf{s}||\mathbf{s} - \mathbf{g}|}$. The above equation says that the wavepath function $\mathcal{L} = \delta \tau / \delta s$ vanishes[2] along the Fermat raypath that connects the source and geophone. The importance of this "zero value" feature in wavepath tomography has stirred some discussion (van der Hilst and de Hoop, 2006), but the main significance of equation 12.8 is that it defines the slownesss regions along the wavepath that significantly influence the traveltime of a bandlimited event recorded at $\mathbf{g}$.

Wavepath → raypath

For an extremely wideband source wavelet, the bandlimited wavepath reduces to a skinny raypath by replacing

---

[2]Recall that the time derivative of a symmetric smooth function vanishes at time zero; therefore $\dot{\Phi}(\tilde{\tau})|_{\tilde{\tau}=0} = 0$ along the Fermat raypath defined by values of $\mathbf{x}$ that satisfy $\tilde{\tau} = \tau_{gs} - \tau_{gx} - \tau_{xs} = 0$.

$w(t + \tilde{\tau}) \to \delta(t + \tilde{\tau})$ in equation 12.8:

$$\frac{\delta \tau(\mathbf{g}, \mathbf{s})}{\delta s(\mathbf{x})} = \frac{-s(\mathbf{x})}{2\pi E |\mathbf{x} - \mathbf{g}||\mathbf{x} - \mathbf{s}||\mathbf{s} - \mathbf{g}|} \frac{\partial}{\partial \tilde{\tau}} \int dt \, \dot{\delta}(t + \tilde{\tau}) \dot{\delta}(t), \qquad (12.9)$$

so that $\frac{\delta \tau(\mathbf{g}, \mathbf{s})}{\delta s(\mathbf{x})}$ is only nonzero when the interrogation point $\mathbf{x}$ is just next to either side of the straight raypath shown in Figure 12.1a. In contrast, a bandlimited source wavelet such as a Gaussian wavelet with temporal width T_o says that the significant nonzero portion of $\frac{\delta \tau(\mathbf{g}, \mathbf{s})}{\delta s(\mathbf{x})}$ is found for values of $\mathbf{x}$ that satisfy

$$|\tau_{sg} - \tau_{xg} - \tau_{xs}| \leq T_o/2, \qquad (12.10)$$

the region that defines the first Fresnel zone associated with the source and receiver positions. As illustrated in Figure 12.1a, the first Fresnel zone of a transmitted wavepath in a homogeneous medium is defined by the ellipse with foci at the source and receiver positions and $\mathbf{x}$ satisfying equation 12.10. Hence, slowness variations with finite area along the length and width of the wavepath can account for the traveltime residual for a transmission arrival originating from a point source at $\mathbf{s}$ and recorded at $\mathbf{g}$. *Because the wavepath width is much shorter than the length of the wavepath for large enough L, we conclude that the slowness resolution of wavepath traveltime tomography is best along directions perpendicular to the ray and is worst parallel to the ray.* This statement is consistent with the projection slice theorem described by equation 6.36.

Figure 12.1c plots a wavepath function for a trace excited by a point source and recorded in the layered velocity model of Figure 12.1b. For strong low-velocity layers, a shooting ray-trace method might not be able to compute a ray into a shadow zone of the receivers, or the first-arrival ray might be associated with negligible energy as denoted by the A event in Figure 12.1d. In contrast, the yellow-red wavepath in Figure 12.1c (Luo, 1991) delineates the parts of the model that fall within the first Fresnel zone of early arrivals with significant amplitude. These are the slowness regions that should be adjusted to explain discrepancies in the traveltime data.

12.1.1 Computing traveltime wavepaths

Following Luo (1991), the wavepath $\mathcal{L}(\mathbf{g}, \mathbf{s}, \mathbf{x})$ can be computed by a reverse time migration of a single trace windowed about a selected arrival. The following describes Luo's workflow for computing a traveltime wavepath.

1. Specify the positions of the geophone $\mathbf{g}$ and the point source $\mathbf{s}$. Forward model the source field to get $p(\mathbf{x}, t|\mathbf{s}, 0)$ for a point source at $\mathbf{s}$ and receiver at $\mathbf{x}$.

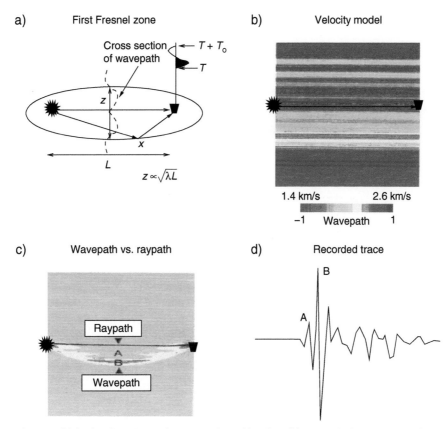

Figure 12.1. (a) Several rays within the first Fresnel zone enclosed by the ellipse such that energy arrives within $T_0/2$ of the first arrival at the receiver. In this case, the maximum width z of this first Fresnel zone is proportional to $\sqrt{\lambda L}$, in which L is the distance between the source and receiver. The dashed curve corresponds approximately to the amplitude weighting in equation 12.8. Panel (b) is the velocity model, (c) is the wavepath and (d) is the associated trace. Note the first arrival at A in the trace and on the wavepath is weak, although the later arrival at B is much stronger. Figures modified from Luo (1991).

Also model the field $g(\mathbf{x}, t|\mathbf{g}, 0)$ for a point source at $\mathbf{g}$ with a wideband source wavelet. If only synthetic data are available, the observed trace $p(\mathbf{g}, t|\mathbf{s}, 0)^{\text{obs}}$ is calculated for a point source at $\mathbf{s}$ and a receiver at $\mathbf{g}$. The synthetics usually are computed by a finite-difference solution to the acoustic wave equation for a bandlimited point source. The arrivals of interest in this trace are windowed prior to migration.

2. Convolve $\dot{p}(\mathbf{x}, t|\mathbf{s}, 0)$ with $\dot{g}(\mathbf{x}, t|\mathbf{g}, 0)$ to get the migration kernel $\mathcal{G}(\mathbf{g}, \mathbf{s}, \mathbf{x}, t) = \dot{p}(\mathbf{x}, t|\mathbf{s}, 0) \star \dot{g}(\mathbf{x}, t|\mathbf{g}, 0)$.

3. Apply the imaging condition

$$\mathcal{L}(\mathbf{g}, \mathbf{s}, \mathbf{x}) \propto \int dt \mathcal{G}(\mathbf{g}, \mathbf{s}, \mathbf{x}, t) p(\mathbf{g}, t|\mathbf{s}, 0)^{\text{obs}}, \quad (12.11)$$

to get the wavepath function (see Figure 12.1c) at $\mathbf{x}$ for a fixed $\mathbf{g}$ and $\mathbf{s}$. As shown in Chapter 11, this imaging equation is similar to that for standard RTM. This means that applying RTM to a single trace (with a windowed first arrival) will give the same wavepath image defined by equation 12.11. This procedure is

also the inspiration for generalized diffraction migration in Chapter 13, in which the migration image is computed by a temporal inner product between the migration Green's function $\mathcal{G}(\mathbf{g}, \mathbf{s}, \mathbf{x}, t)$ and the recorded data $p(\mathbf{g}, t|\mathbf{s}, 0)^{\text{obs}}$.

12.2 Pressure wavepaths

It is also important to analyze the resolution properties of images computed by RTM, least-squares migration, or waveform inversion. This can be done by using the Fréchet derivative $\delta P/\delta s$ of the pressure field, similar to that for the traveltime wavepath function $\delta \tau/\delta s$. The Fréchet derivative of the pressure field can be derived by taking the inverse Fourier transform of equation 10.23 to give

$$\frac{\delta p(\mathbf{g}, t|\mathbf{s}, 0)}{\delta s(\mathbf{x})} = -2s(\mathbf{x})g(\mathbf{g}, t|\mathbf{x}, 0) \star \ddot{w}(t) \star g(\mathbf{x}, t|\mathbf{s}, 0).$$

$$(12.12)$$

To relate this to $\delta \tau/\delta s$, take the case of a transmission arrival such that $g(\mathbf{x}', t|\mathbf{x}, 0) = \frac{\delta(t - \tau_{\mathbf{x}\mathbf{x}'})}{4\pi|\mathbf{x} - \mathbf{x}'|}$ so that equation 12.12 becomes

$$\frac{\delta p(\mathbf{g}, t|\mathbf{s}, 0)}{\delta s(\mathbf{x})} = \frac{-s(\mathbf{x})}{8\pi^2 |\mathbf{x} - \mathbf{g}||\mathbf{x} - \mathbf{s}|} \frac{\partial^2 w(t - \tau_{xg} - \tau_{xs})}{\partial t^2}.$$

(12.13)

Unlike the traveltime Fréchet derivative in equation 12.4, the value of the pressure Fréchet derivative $\delta p(\mathbf{g}, t|\mathbf{s}, 0)/\delta s(x)$ is nonzero along the central ray when $t = \tau_{sg}$ for a symmetrical source wavelet. However, the argument $\tau_{sg} - \tau_{xg} - \tau_{xs}$ in equation 12.4 is similar to that in equation 12.13 for $t \to \tau_{sg}$, so their Fresnel zones overlap one another. Hence, the resolution properties of the Fréchet derivative for either traveltime data or waveform data are somewhat similar for the same transmission event. For example, wavepaths become fatter with decreasing frequency and the width of the first Fresnel zone is proportional to $\sqrt{L\lambda}$. We also conclude that the best transmission resolution is perpendicular to the raypath, and the worst resolution is along the raypath. For example, sliding a slowness anomaly along the transmission raypath will hardly affect the traveltime of the transmission arrival.

12.2.1 Computing pressure wavepaths

Equation 12.12 suggests that the pressure wavepath can be constructed by first computing the trace $\dot{g}(\mathbf{x}, t|\mathbf{g}, 0)$ recorded at $\mathbf{x}$ for a source at $\mathbf{g}$ and the trace $w(t) \star \dot{g}(\mathbf{x}, t|\mathbf{s}, 0)$ at $\mathbf{x}$ for a source at $\mathbf{s}$, then convolving them with each other at each image point $\mathbf{x}$ to get $\frac{\delta p(\mathbf{g}, t|\mathbf{s}, 0)}{\delta s(\mathbf{x})}$. Assessing resolution from a function $\frac{\delta p(\mathbf{g}, t|\mathbf{s}, 0)}{\delta s(\mathbf{x})}$ of both spatial and temporal variables is tedious, so an alternative is to eliminate the time variable by computing the waveform misfit gradient in Chapter 11:

$$\gamma(\mathbf{x}) \propto \int \frac{\delta p(\mathbf{g}, t|\mathbf{s}, 0)}{\delta s(\mathbf{x})} p(\mathbf{g}, t|\mathbf{s}, 0)^{\mathrm{obs}} dt,$$

$$= -2s(\mathbf{x}) \int [\dot{g}(\mathbf{g}, t|\mathbf{x}, 0) \star w(t)$$

$$\star \dot{g}(\mathbf{x}, t|\mathbf{s}, 0)] p(\mathbf{g}, t|\mathbf{s}, 0)^{\mathrm{obs}} dt. \quad (12.14)$$

This gradient can be computed in the same manner as the traveltime Fréchet derivative, either by computing the migration kernel $\mathcal{G}(\mathbf{g}, \mathbf{s}, \mathbf{x}, t) = \dot{g}(\mathbf{g}, t|\mathbf{x}, 0) \star w(t) \star \dot{g}(\mathbf{x}, t|\mathbf{s}, 0)$ and carrying out the integration in equation 12.14, or by RTM of a single trace at $\mathbf{g}$ excited by a source at $\mathbf{s}$. See Figure 21.10 for examples of reflection and diving wavepaths. If this trace is windowed about the first arrival, then the traveltime and pressure wavepaths have similar support in model space.

As an example, the point-source response of the vertical reflector model in Figure 12.2 is computed by a finite-difference method. The trace at $\mathbf{g}$ for a source at $\mathbf{s}$ then is migrated by RTM to get the migration image. Computing the transmission wavepath gives a smiling cigar-shaped region that connects the source with the receiver. In contrast, the reflection wavepaths are centered about the specular rays that reflect from the vertical reflector. As the wavepaths length L gets longer, they thicken as $\propto \sqrt{L\lambda}$ (Williamson, 1991; Williamson and Worthington, 1993) and the deep reflection wavepath has less resolution than the shallow transmission wavepath.

A peculiar wavepath is the vertically oriented curve on the left side of Figure 12.2b, which is the thick migration ellipse associated with reflection migration. As discussed in Chapters 13 and 14, this is the only type of wavepath that should be used for RTM. In contrast, the thicker reflection and transmission wavepaths also should be used for directly updating the velocity model in waveform inversion. In waveform inversion, the ellipse feature is used mainly to locate the reflector positions for accurate modeling of reflections.

12.3 Summary

The Fréchet derivative, also known as the wavepath function $\mathcal{L}(\ )$, is defined for both traveltime tomography as $\delta t(\mathbf{g}, \mathbf{s})/\delta s(\mathbf{x})$ and for pressure fields as $\delta p(\mathbf{g}, t|\mathbf{s}, 0)/\delta s(\mathbf{x})$. They enjoy the following properties.

- The traveltime wavepath is the plot, in model space coordinates, of the Jacobian $\delta \tau(\mathbf{g}|\mathbf{s})/\delta s(\mathbf{x})$ and defines how

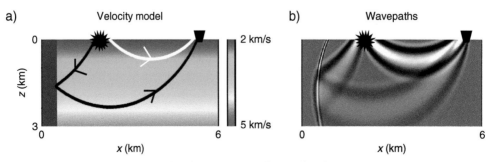

Figure 12.2. (a) Vertical reflector model along with the direct and black reflection raypaths. (b) Reflection and transmission wavepaths obtained by reverse time migration of a trace recorded at the geophone (quadrilateral) and excited by a bandlimited source (star). Figures courtesy of Ge Zhan.

much the slowness perturbation at **x** influences the trace at **g** excited by a source at **s**. The first Fresnel zone region in a wavepath is the most important part of the model that explains the windowed arrival of interest. The pressure Fréchet derivative $\delta p(\mathbf{g}, t|\mathbf{s}, 0)/\delta s(\mathbf{x})$ is similar, except it defines the sensitivity of the pressure field trace with respect to slowness perturbations at **x** at a specified recording time t.

- The pressure Fréchet derivative is a 4D function, so it is more practical to eliminate the time variable by computing the misfit gradient of a single trace. This is equivalent to RTM of a single trace, which is similar to the procedure for computing a traveltime Fréchet derivative. It is sometimes a useful diagnostic tool to display the pressure Fréchet derivative as a movie to reveal which parts of the model influence an event of interest.

- The maximum width of the transmission wavepath in a homogeneous medium is proportional to $\sqrt{L\lambda}$, so longer wavepaths have less slowness resolution than shorter wavepaths. The best slowness resolution is perpendicular to the central portion of the wavepath.

- The angular diversity of wavepaths that intersect a slowness cell provides resolution associated with an ensemble of wavepaths. For migration, wavepaths can be used to

estimate the resolution capabilities of migration imaging for specified acquisition geometries. See Chapter 14 for details.

12.4 Exercises

1. Use a finite-difference solution of the wave equation to compute a wavepath that honors equation 12.9. Employ a homogeneous model with several point scatterers embedded at different depth. Comment on the resolution properties of traveltime tomography as a function of scatterer depth.

2. Show that the maximum width of the first Fresnel zone in a homogeneous medium is proportional to $\sqrt{L\lambda}$, in which L is the distance between the source and receiver and λ is the wavelength.

3. The width of the vertically oriented elliptical wavepath in Figure 12.2b is proportional to λ, as illustrated by the prestack migration ellipse in Figure 10.4. For deep reflectors, the cigar-shaped reflector wavepaths are much thicker with low resolution than the migration ellipses with high resolution. Hence, there seems to be a resolution gap at intermediate resolution. Is this gap related to that discussed in Jannane et al. (1989)?

Chapter 13: Generalized Diffraction-stack Migration and Filtering of Coherent Noise*

A standard reverse time migration (RTM) image is obtained by computing the zero-lag correlation of the back-projected data with the source wavefield. The forward-modeling and back-projection operations usually are computed by a finite-difference solution to the two-way wave equation. For back projection, each recorded trace acts as a source-time history (in reverse time) of a virtual point source at the geophone location. This is a simple and easily understood migration method that most often is preferred for imaging beneath complex geology such as salt bodies. Chapter 13 highlights a recent development in diffraction migration – a reformulated approach to reverse-time migration. Here, you will find a reprint of "Generalized diffraction-stack migration and filtering of coherent noise," by Ge Zhan, Wei Dai, Min Zhou, Yi Luo, and myself, originally published in Geophysical Prospecting. This 2014 paper describes a new approach to image migration, from the original team who developed the method. I add footnotes and a set of exercises following the reprinted piece, but the paper stands alone and deserves to be reprinted in its entirety. Special thanks to my coauthors and to *Geophysical Prospecting* for their kind permission to reprint this work.

Abstract

We reformulate the equation of reverse-time migration so that it can be interpreted as summing data along a series of hyperbola-like curves, each one representing a different type of event such as a reflection or multiple. This is a generalization of the familiar diffraction-stack migration algorithm where the migration image at a point is computed by the sum of trace amplitudes along an appropriate hyperbola-like curve. Instead of summing along the curve associated with the primary reflection, the sum is over all scattering events and so this method is named generalized diffraction-stack migration. This formulation leads to filters that can be applied to the generalized diffraction-stack migration operator to mitigate coherent migration artefacts due to, e.g., crosstalk and aliasing. Results with both synthetic and field data show that generalized diffraction-stack migration images have fewer artefacts than those computed by the standard reverse-time migration algorithm. The main drawback is that generalized diffraction-stack migration is much more memory intensive and I/O limited than the standard reverse-time migration method.

Keywords: Reverse-time migration (RTM) artefacts, Migration operator filtering, Reverse-time migration (RTM) antialiasing.

13.1 Introduction

The two end members of migration algorithms are diffraction stack migration (French 1974) and reverse-time migration (McMechan 1983; Whitmore 1983). The former is computationally inexpensive, easily adaptable to different filtering strategies but subject to the high-frequency approximation of ray tracing. Consequently, it has difficulty in complex velocity models, which precludes the accurate use of ray tracing and the modelling of multiply-scattered arrivals. To overcome this limitation, reverse-time migration uses finite-difference solutions to the wave equation to accurately propagate seismic energy through complex models. But the price paid is a computationally expensive algorithm that appears resistant to efficiency improvements or filtering strategies such as obliquity and intrinsic anti-aliasing filters that suppress migration noise.

An example of a migration artefact is the strong amplitude, low-frequency noise often seen on reverse-time migration (RTM) images where a high-velocity gradient exists. Such crosstalk artefacts are usually produced by the unwanted cross-correlation of head waves, diving waves and back-scattered waves at the imaging step (Yoon et al. 2004), which severely contaminate the migration image. Various remedies have been proposed to suppress such migration artefacts such as smoothing the velocity model

*Reprinted with permission from EAGE from Zhan, G., W. Dai, M. Zhou, Y. Luo, and G. T. Schuster, 2014, Generalized diffraction-stack migration and filtering of coherent noise: Geophysical Prospecting, **62**, no. 3, 427–442. doi: 10.1111/1365-2478.12086.

before migration to reduce reflections (Loewenthal, Stoffa and Faria 1987) or low-cut filtering (Mulder and Plessix 2003) the migration image to reduce artefacts. Fletcher et al. (2005) attenuated reflections at boundaries by introducing a directional damping term to the non-reflection wave equation, while Guitton et al. (2007) reduced artefacts by using a least-squares filter. A physics based migration filter is the Poynting vector (Yoon and Marfurt 2006) to improve the cross-correlation based imaging condition. Recently, Liu et al. (2007, 2011) decomposed the full wavefield of back propagated data into its one-way components and applied the imaging condition to the appropriate parts. A similar procedure was used by Fei et al. (2010) where dip filtering was applied to vertical and horizontal slabs of back-propagated data.

A difficulty with the above approaches is that the precise filtering of back-projected data cannot distinguish data noise from operator noise. As an example, Kirchhoff migration images can have aliasing artefacts caused by undersampling both the data and the migration operator (Claerbout 1992). In this case, the data are filtered separately from the migration operator to avoid loss of data information by aggressive data filtering. In contrast, the filtered RTM approach of Liu et al. (2007, 2011) and Fei et al. (2010) extrapolates the data into the medium and the resulting wavefields are dip filtered at each time step. The back-projected data are intertwined with the RTM operator and so the dip filter simultaneously attacks both data and extrapolator noise. If the noise regime of the operator overlaps the signal of the data, then important data information can be needlessly lost. It is more desirable that the operator is filtered separately from the data.

We now propose a general dip filtering of the reverse-time extrapolation operator that is separate from the data filtering. The operator filtering can be performed using the generalized diffraction-stack migration (GDM) method proposed by Schuster (2002), which is mathematically equivalent to RTM but its implementation is different. Ehinger et al. (1996) described a related, but not identical, method for performing prestack depth migration by computing Green's functions at the surface with a wavefield extrapolation method and then using them in a frequency-dependent Kirchhoff migration. Unlike RTM that intertwines the extrapolation operator with the data at all depth levels, GDM separately computes the complete migration operator[1] and then applies it to the recorded data in the form of a dot product to obtain the migration image. Unlike a Kirchhoff migration (KM) operator which plots as a single hyperbola-like curve in the shot gather for a specified image point, all events are included in the generalized migration operator such as direct waves, multiples, reflections

and diffractions. Similar to an anti-alias filter (Lumley, Claerbout and Bevc 1994) or a dip filter for the KM operator, a filter can be applied to the GDM operator. Other implementations of GDM include wave equation wavefront migration (Zhou and Schuster 2002) which only includes the early arrivals in the migration operator, target-oriented redatuming and migration using the GDM idea (Dong et al. 2009) and GDM with imaging of multiples (Zhan, Luo and Schuster 2010).

This paper is divided into four parts: an introduction, a theory section that describes how reverse-time migration can be reformulated as GDM and an application section that applies filters to GDM for both synthetic data and a field data example. The filtering examples are similar to those in Liu et al. (2007, 2011) and Fei et al. (2010), except we only apply the filter to the migration operator to avoid excessive filtering of both data and operator. The final section is a summary of our work.

13.2 Theory of Generalized Diffraction Migration

We first derive the equation for generalized diffraction-stack migration and then show how it can be interpreted as a dot product of the migration kernel and the data. Similar to Kirchhoff migration, the GDM implementation allows for the straightforward design of migration operator filters.

For weak scattering, the scattered data $\tilde{d}(\mathbf{r}|\mathbf{s})$ in the frequency domain or $d(\mathbf{r}, t|\mathbf{s}, 0)$ in the time domain can be migrated (Stolt and Benson 1987; Claerbout 1992) using the Born formula:

$$
\begin{aligned}
m_{mig}(\mathbf{x}, \mathbf{s}) &= \iint_B -\omega^2 G^*(\mathbf{x}|\mathbf{s})[G^*(\mathbf{x}|\mathbf{r})\tilde{d}(\mathbf{r}|\mathbf{s})]d\mathbf{r}d\omega, \\
&= \iint_B g(\mathbf{x}, t|\mathbf{s}, 0)[g(\mathbf{x}, -t|\mathbf{r}, 0) \star \ddot{d}(\mathbf{r}, t|\mathbf{s}, 0)]d\mathbf{r}dt,
\end{aligned}
$$

(1)

where ω is the angular frequency, the frequency integration is over the bandwidth of the source and $G(\mathbf{x}|\mathbf{x}')$ ($\mathbf{x}'$ may be at $\mathbf{s}$ or $\mathbf{r}$) represents the space-frequency Green's function for the Helmholtz equation with a source at $\mathbf{x}'$ and a receiver at $\mathbf{x}$. The symbol $\star$ stands for convolution and $g(\mathbf{x}, t|\mathbf{x}', 0)$ is the corresponding Green's function in the space-time domain. The term $d(\mathbf{r}, t|\mathbf{s}, 0)$ represents the band-limited data in the time domain for a source at $\mathbf{s}$ and a receiver at $\mathbf{r}$. Here we assumed a wideband source spectrum $W(\omega) = 1$ in the Born modelling, the time integration is over the duration time of the trace and the $d\mathbf{r}$ integration is over the receiver coordinate $\mathbf{r} \in B$ associated with receivers on a horizontal surface denoted by B.

The double dot symbol represents the trace differentiated twice in time and $g(\mathbf{x}, -t|\mathbf{r}, 0) \star \ddot{d}(\mathbf{r}, t|\mathbf{s}, 0)$ represents

---

[1]The $\mathcal{G}(\mathbf{s}, \mathbf{g}, \mathbf{x}, t)$ function also is denoted as the migration Green's function by Schuster and Hu (2000).

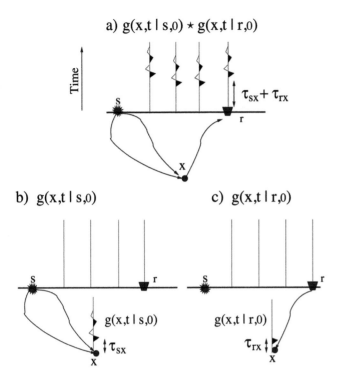

a) $g(x,t \mid s,0) \star g(x,t \mid r,0)$

b) $g(x,t \mid s,0)$

c) $g(x,t \mid r,0)$

Figure 1 a) Migration kernel $\mathcal{G}(\mathbf{r}, \mathbf{s}, \mathbf{x}, t) = g(\mathbf{x}, t|\mathbf{s}, 0) \star g(\mathbf{x}, t|\mathbf{r}, 0)$ for a fixed image point at $\mathbf{x}$ decomposed into the two modelling kernels: b) one $g(\mathbf{x}, t|\mathbf{s}, 0)$ for a source at $\mathbf{s}$ and c) the other $g(\mathbf{x}, t|\mathbf{r}, 0)$ for a source at $\mathbf{r}$. Convolving the trace in b) with the trace in c) gives the far-right trace shown in a). The other traces in a) represent the migration kernels at other receiver positions.

convolution of the time-reversed Green's function traces with the time-differentiated trace recorded at $\mathbf{r}$. This operation back-propagates the trace energy at $\mathbf{r}$ to the subsurface point at $\mathbf{x}$. In contrast, the Green's function $g(\mathbf{x}, t|\mathbf{s}, 0)$ forward propagates the energy at the source point $\mathbf{s}$ to the subsurface point $\mathbf{x}$, and the migration image at $\mathbf{x}$ is formed by taking the zero-lag temporal correlation of $g(\mathbf{x}, t|\mathbf{s}, 0)$ with the back-propagated trace at $\mathbf{x}$. Traditional reverse-time migration simulates back-propagation by a finite-difference solution to the acoustic wave equation, where the point sources are at the traces located on the surface and the traces act as the time histories for back-propagating seismic wavefields recorded at the receiver locations (McMechan 1983).

A different implementation of reverse-time migration can be obtained by left shifting the square brackets in equation (1) to obtain (Schuster 2002):

$$m_{mig}(\mathbf{x}, \mathbf{s}) = \iint_B -\omega^2 [G(\mathbf{x}|\mathbf{s})G(\mathbf{x}|\mathbf{r})]^* \tilde{d}(\mathbf{r}|\mathbf{s}) dr d\omega,$$

$$= \iint_B \overbrace{[g(\mathbf{x}, t|\mathbf{s}, 0) \star g(\mathbf{x}, t|\mathbf{r}, 0)]}^{GDM\ kernel} \ddot{d}(\mathbf{r}, t|\mathbf{s}, 0) dr dt. \quad (2)$$

Here, the data term absorbs the 2π constant associated with the inverse Fourier transform. The bracketed term:

$$\mathcal{G}(\mathbf{r}, \mathbf{s}, \mathbf{x}, t) = g(\mathbf{x}, t|\mathbf{s}, 0) \star g(\mathbf{x}, t|\mathbf{r}, 0), \quad (3)$$

is the migration kernel that refocuses reflection energy recorded at $\mathbf{r}$ (for a source at $\mathbf{s}$) back to the scatterer at $\mathbf{x}$. As illustrated, $\mathcal{G}(\mathbf{r}, \mathbf{s}, \mathbf{x}, t)$ in Fig. 1(a) is obtained by computing the Green's function $g(\mathbf{x}, t|\mathbf{x}', 0)$ for a receiver at $\mathbf{x}$ and sources at $\mathbf{x}' \in B$ and convolving $g(\mathbf{x}, t|\mathbf{s}, 0)$ in Fig. 1(b) with $g(\mathbf{x}, t|\mathbf{r}, 0)$ in Fig. 1(c).

Equation (2) says that the migration image at $\mathbf{x}$ is computed by taking the dot product in space and time between the time-differentiated shot gather $\ddot{d}(\mathbf{r}, t|\mathbf{s}, 0)$ and the migration kernel $\mathcal{G}(\mathbf{r}, \mathbf{s}, \mathbf{x}, t)$ in Fig. 1(a). This is similar to the interpretation of KM, except only primary events are accounted for in standard KM, while GDM takes into account both primaries and multiples (see Appendix A).

13.3 Directional Filtering the Generalized Diffraction-Stack Migration Kernel

We will now illustrate dip filtering of the GDM kernel for two simple examples: the horizontal reflector model in Fig. 2(a) and the vertical reflector model in Fig. 2(c), each of which has a background velocity that increases with depth. The single trace migration responses are respectively shown in Fig. 2(b,d), which can be decomposed into separate components with the following analysis.

13.3.1 Horizontal reflector model

The Green's function for the horizontal reflector model can be decomposed into downgoing transmitted $D^t(\mathbf{x}|\mathbf{s})$ and upgoing reflected $U^r(\mathbf{x}|\mathbf{s})$ wave components in the first layer as illustrated in Fig. 3:

$$G(\mathbf{x}|\mathbf{s}) = D^t(\mathbf{x}|\mathbf{s}) + \mathcal{R}U^r(\mathbf{x}|\mathbf{s});$$
$$G(\mathbf{x}|\mathbf{r}) = D^t(\mathbf{x}|\mathbf{r}) + \mathcal{R}U^r(\mathbf{x}|\mathbf{r}), \quad (4)$$

where $\mathbf{x}$ is the trial image point anywhere along the specular portion of the reflection ray, $\mathcal{R}$ is the reflection coefficient normalized to the downgoing source field, and the superscripts t and r are associated with transmission and reflection, respectively.

The dominant components of the migration image $m_{mig}(\mathbf{x}, \mathbf{s})$ described by equation (2) will be along the raypaths where the phase of $G^*(\mathbf{x}|\mathbf{s})G^*(\mathbf{x}|\mathbf{r})$ cancels for events

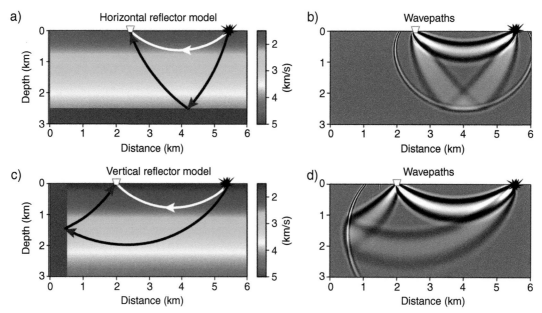

Figure 2 a) Horizontal and c) vertical reflector models along with their associated wavepaths (Woodward 1992) to the right; the wavepaths in b) take the shapes of a cigar, rabbit ears and an elliptical smile. The wavepaths were computed by migrating a single trace excited by a wideband point source (star) and recorded at the receiver (quadrilateral).

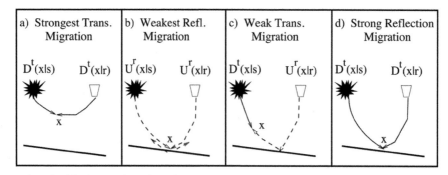

Figure 3 Raypaths associated with the products in $[D^t(\mathbf{x}|\mathbf{r}) + U^r(\mathbf{x}|\mathbf{r})][D^t(\mathbf{x}|\mathbf{s}) + U^r(\mathbf{x}|\mathbf{s})]$. The phase of these products at certain trial image points $\mathbf{x}$ will annihilate the phase in the data for either $\tilde{d}^t(\mathbf{r}|\mathbf{s})$ or $\tilde{d}^r(\mathbf{r}|\mathbf{s})$ but not both. The diving ray in a) can lead to strong artefacts in the RTM image.

in the data $\tilde{d}(\mathbf{r}|\mathbf{s}) = \tilde{d}^t(\mathbf{r}|\mathbf{s}) + \mathcal{R}\tilde{d}^r(\mathbf{r}|\mathbf{s})$, i.e., inserting equation (4) into equation (2) gives:

$$m_{mig}(\mathbf{x}, \mathbf{s}) = -\iint_B d\omega d\mathbf{r}\, \omega^2 [\tilde{d}^t(\mathbf{r}|\mathbf{s}) + \mathcal{R}\tilde{d}^r(\mathbf{r}|\mathbf{s})][D^t(\mathbf{x}|\mathbf{r})$$

$$+ \mathcal{R}U^r(\mathbf{x}|\mathbf{r})]^*[D^t(\mathbf{x}|\mathbf{s}) + \mathcal{R}U^r(\mathbf{x}|\mathbf{s})]^*,$$

$$\approx -\iint_B d\omega d\mathbf{r}\, \omega^2 [$$

$$\overbrace{D^t(\mathbf{x}|\mathbf{r})^* D^t(\mathbf{x}|\mathbf{s})^* \tilde{d}^t(\mathbf{r}|\mathbf{s})}^{strongest\ trans.\ mig.} \quad x \in direct\ raypath$$

$$\overbrace{+ \mathcal{R}^3 U^r(\mathbf{x}|\mathbf{r})^* U^r(\mathbf{x}|\mathbf{s})^* \tilde{d}^r(\mathbf{r}|\mathbf{s})}^{weakest\ refl.mig.}$$

$$\mathbf{x} \in specular\ refl.\ point$$

$$\overbrace{+ \mathcal{R}^2 U^r(\mathbf{x}|\mathbf{r})^* D^t(\mathbf{x}|\mathbf{s})^* \tilde{d}^r(\mathbf{r}|\mathbf{s})}^{weak\ sou\text{–}side\ trans.\ mig.}$$

$$\mathbf{x} \in sou - side\ interbed\ raypath$$

$$\overbrace{+ \mathcal{R}^2 D^t(\mathbf{x}|\mathbf{r})^* U^r(\mathbf{x}|\mathbf{s})^* \tilde{d}^r(\mathbf{r}|\mathbf{s})}^{weak\ rec\text{–}side\ trans.\ mig.}$$

$$\mathbf{x} \in rec - side\ interbed\ raypath$$

$$\overbrace{+ \mathcal{R}D^t(\mathbf{x}|\mathbf{r})^* D^t(\mathbf{x}|\mathbf{s})^* d^r(\mathbf{r}|\mathbf{s})]}^{strong\ refl.\ mig.}$$

$$\mathbf{x} \in specular\ refl.\ pt. + ellipe, \quad (5)$$

where unimportant terms are ignored and $\mathbf{x}$ is the trial image point where the phase of the migration kernel is equal and opposite to that of the reflection data.

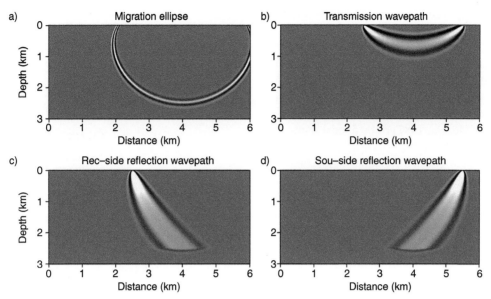

Figure 4 Wavepaths in Fig. 2(b) separated by dip filtering the migration kernel $G(\mathbf{x}|\mathbf{s})G(\mathbf{x}|\mathbf{r})$ associated with the horizontal reflector model in Fig. 2(a) (see the kernels in equation (5)).

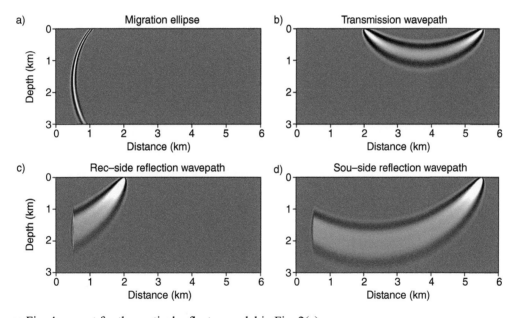

Figure 5 Same as Fig. 4, except for the vertical reflector model in Fig. 2(c).

The amplitude of the transmitted arrival $\tilde{d}^t(\mathbf{r}|\mathbf{s})$ is $O(1)$, so the strongest part of the migration image $D^t(\mathbf{x}|\mathbf{r})^*D^t(\mathbf{x}|\mathbf{s})^*\tilde{d}^t(\mathbf{r}|\mathbf{s})$ is for $\mathbf{x}$ to be along the direct ray shown in Fig. 3(a), which coincides with the central part of the transmission wavepath in Fig. 2(b). The weakest contribution in the above approximation is $\mathcal{R}^3 U^r(\mathbf{x}|\mathbf{r})^*U^r(\mathbf{x}|\mathbf{s})^*\tilde{d}^r(\mathbf{r}|\mathbf{s})$ with strength $O(\mathcal{R}^3)$, and contributes at the specular reflection point shown in Fig. 3(b). The undesirable components of the migration image are along the interbed raypaths with strength $O(\mathcal{R}^2)$ shown in Fig. 3(c), which coincide with the central portions of

the rabbit ear wavepaths in Fig. 2(b). These undesirable components[2] for migration are, however, desirable for full-waveform inversion (Mora 1989). Finally, the most desirable component of the migration image is the Kirchhoff-like image $\mathcal{R}D^t(\mathbf{x}|\mathbf{r})^*D^t(\mathbf{x}|\mathbf{s})^*d^r(\mathbf{r}|\mathbf{s})$ with strength $O(\mathcal{R})$. It contributes not only to the image at the specular reflection point in Fig. 3(d), but also to the thick ellipse in Fig. 2(b).

---

[2]However, these undesirable contributions are desirable for full waveform inversion because they contribute to the long-wavelength velocity updates within the rabbit ears in Figure 2b (Mora, 1989; Zhou et al., 1997).

For reflection migration, only the Kirchhoff-like term should be used and images from all other terms should be filtered out. This goal can be accomplished by dip filtering the Green's functions[3] to separate upgoing and downgoing waves, and so only the Kirchhoff-like kernel $D^t(\mathbf{x}|\mathbf{r})^* D^t(\mathbf{x}|\mathbf{s})^*$ should be used for GDM. Dip filtering can be performed in the frequency-wavenumber (F-K) domain (Hu and McMechan 1987) or by a local slant-stack algorithm (Yilmaz 2001).

As an example, the Green's functions associated with the GDM image in Fig. 2(b) can be filtered to give the separate components in Fig. 4. Here, the desirable image is the ellipse in Fig. 4(a) (the last term in equation (5)), and the undesirable parts are the smile in Fig. 4(b) (the 1st term in equation (5)) and the rabbit ears in Fig. 4(c,d) (the 3rd and 4th terms in equation (5)).

Applying a dip filter to the migration kernels separates the migration image into the different portions shown in Fig. 4(a–d). Since we are only interested in imaging the reflector boundary, then only the migration kernel associated with the ellipse should be kept.

13.3.2 Vertical reflector model

If the reflector is vertically oriented and the source and receiver are to the right of the reflector, then a dip filter can be used to separate leftgoing and rightgoing terms. Migrating a single trace associated with the vertical reflector model in Fig. 2(c) gives the migration image in Fig. 2(d). Only the ellipse-like feature is desired, which can be isolated by replacing the upgoing reflection Green's function $U^r(\mathbf{x}|\mathbf{s})$ by the rightgoing one $R^r(\mathbf{x}|\mathbf{s})$ in equation (5) to give:

$$m_{mig}(x,s) = -\iint_B d\omega d\mathbf{r}\, \omega^2 [\tilde{d}^t(\mathbf{r}|\mathbf{s}) + \tilde{d}^r(\mathbf{r}|\mathbf{s})][D^t(\mathbf{x}|\mathbf{r})$$
$$+ R^r(\mathbf{x}|\mathbf{r})]^* [D^t(\mathbf{x}|\mathbf{s}) + R^r(\mathbf{x}|\mathbf{s})]^*,$$
$$\approx -\iint_B d\omega d\mathbf{r}\, \omega^2 [$$

$$\overbrace{D^t(\mathbf{x}|\mathbf{r})^* D^t(\mathbf{x}|\mathbf{s})^* \tilde{d}^t(\mathbf{r}|\mathbf{s})}^{\text{strongest trans. mig.}}$$

$$\mathbf{x} \in \text{direct raypath}$$

$$+ \overbrace{\mathcal{R}^3 R^r(\mathbf{x}|\mathbf{r})^* R^r(\mathbf{x}|\mathbf{s})^* \tilde{d}^r(\mathbf{r}|\mathbf{s})}^{\text{weakest refl. mig.}}$$

$$\mathbf{x} \in \text{specular refl. point}$$

$$+ \overbrace{\mathcal{R}^2 R^r(\mathbf{x}|\mathbf{r})^* D^t(\mathbf{x}|\mathbf{s})^* \tilde{d}^r(\mathbf{r}|\mathbf{s})}^{\text{weak sou-side trans. mig.}}$$

$$\mathbf{x} \in sou - side\ interbed\ raypath$$

$$+ \overbrace{\mathcal{R}^2 D^t(\mathbf{x}|\mathbf{r})^* R^r(\mathbf{x}|\mathbf{s})^* \tilde{d}^r(\mathbf{r}|\mathbf{s})}^{\text{weak rec-side trans. mig.}}$$

$$\mathbf{x} \in rec - side\ interbed\ raypath$$

$$+ \overbrace{\mathcal{R} D^t(\mathbf{x}|\mathbf{r})^* D^t(\mathbf{x}|\mathbf{s})^* d^r(\mathbf{r}|\mathbf{s})}^{\text{strong refl. mig.}}]$$

$$\mathbf{x} \in specular\ refl.\ pt. + ellipe. \quad (6)$$

Dip filtering can be used to separate the leftgoing and rightgoing waves in the migration kernel, and the image of the desired Kirchhoff kernel is shown in Fig. 5(a). The dot product of this kernel with the data can be used to obtain the desirable image of the vertical reflector. Fig. 5(b–d) corresponds, respectively, to the 1st, 3rd and 4th terms in equation (6), which are the undesirable parts for migration.

13.4 Anti-Aliasing Filtering the Generalized Diffraction-Stack Migration Kernel

The anti-aliasing condition for the Kirchhoff migration (KM) operator (Gray 1992; Lumley et al. 1994; Abma, Sun and Bernitsas 1999; Biondi 2001; Zhang, Sun and Gray 2003) says that the local slope dt/dx (e.g., computed from the traveltime table) of the associated hyperbola diffraction curve in $x - t$ space should satisfy the Nyquist sampling criterion:

$$\left| \frac{dt}{dx} \right| < \frac{T}{2\Delta x} = \frac{1}{2f\,\Delta x}, \quad (7)$$

where T is the minimum period in the data at frequency f and Δx is the input trace spacing. If this condition is not satisfied for any (x, t) sample in the shot gather, a local portion of the corresponding trace centered at time t is high-cut filtered to $f_{cut} = 1/(2\Delta x)/|dt/dx|$. The Nyquist criterion is then satisfied with respect to the new lower frequency of this sample.

With the GDM algorithm, we can construct an anti-aliasing filter that is similar to the anti-aliasing scheme used for KM. That is, the migration operator is low-pass filtered in data space so that the dominant wavelength in the operator λ^{oper} is greater than two times the trace sampling interval Δx, except it is applied to both primary and multiple reflection events. In addition, instead of applying this filter to the data in the traditional KM operation, we apply the anti-aliasing filter to the GDM operator.

---

[3] Dip filtering can be applied to the space-time traces associated with $G(\mathbf{x}|\mathbf{g})$ in the FK domain or by a local slant-stack algorithm. For example, the ellipse Figure 4a is computed by only convolving a trace with a downgoing direct wave from the geophone, and convolving the result with a trace that has a downgoing direct wave from the source.

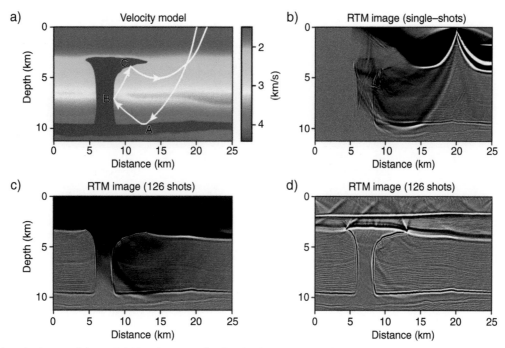

Figure 6 a) Salt velocity model overlaid by the raypath of a single source-receiver pair. b), c) and d) are RTM images of this model. Shallow part of the image is overwhelmed by strong artefacts. A high-pass filter is effective in suppressing these artefacts but large residuals still remain.

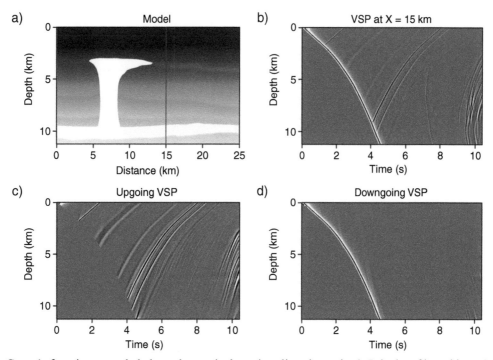

Figure 7 b) The Green's function recorded along the vertical receiver line shown in a). It is then filtered into c) upgoing and d) downgoing components.

The GDM algorithm with anti-aliasing filtering is described as follows.

1. Use a finite-difference solution to the space-time wave equation to compute $g(\mathbf{x}, t|\mathbf{x}', 0)$ for a source at $\mathbf{x}'$ and a receiver at $\mathbf{x}$. Here $\mathbf{x}$ is in the model space and $\mathbf{x}'$ is on the surface and can be at either $\mathbf{s}$ or $\mathbf{r}$.

2. Convolve $g(\mathbf{x}, t|\mathbf{s}, 0)$ with $g(\mathbf{x}, t|\mathbf{r}, 0)$ to get the GDM operator $\mathcal{G}(\mathbf{r}, \mathbf{s}, \mathbf{x}, t) = g(\mathbf{x}, t|\mathbf{s}, 0) \star g(\mathbf{x}, t|\mathbf{r}, 0)$, where $\star$ denotes temporal convolution.

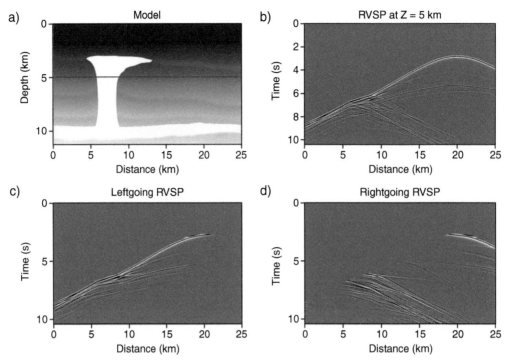

Figure 8 b) The Green's function recorded along the horizontal receiver line shown in a). It is then filtered into c) leftgoing and d) rightgoing components.

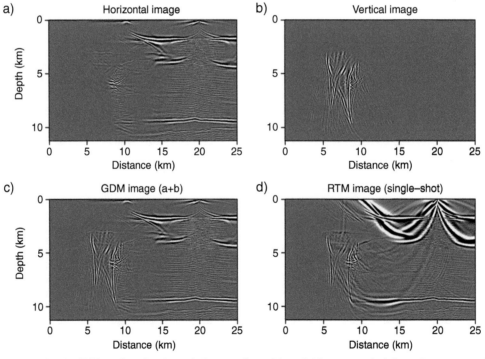

Figure 9 Applying the Kirchhoff-like migration kernels in equations (5) and (6) to recorded data gives, respectively, a) and b). Stacking a) and b) gives c). d) The high-pass-filtered RTM image of the same shot gather.

3. Apply local low-pass filters to every time sample of this kernel so that the anti-aliasing condition (equation (7)) is satisfied. Denote this filtered operator as $\bar{\mathcal{G}}(\mathbf{r}, \mathbf{s}, \mathbf{x}, t)$.

4. Take dot-products (see equation (2)) of the filtered migration kernel $\bar{\mathcal{G}}(\mathbf{r}, \mathbf{s}, \mathbf{x}, t)$ with the recorded data $d(\mathbf{r}, t|\mathbf{s}, 0)$ to get the prestack migration image $m_{mig}(\mathbf{x}, \mathbf{s})$ for a source at $\mathbf{s}$. The resulting image will be free of aliasing artefacts.

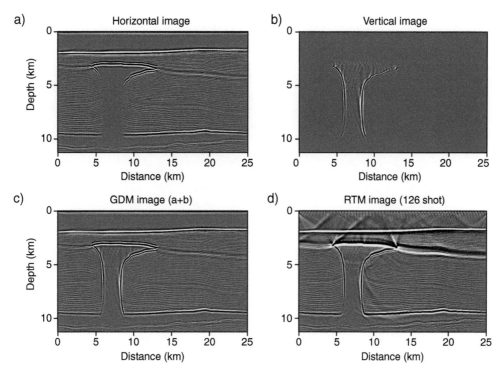

Figure 10 Same as Fig. 9, except that all 126 shot gathers are used to construct the stacked image.

13.5 Numerical Examples

13.5.1 Directional filtering results

Realistic synthetic data are used to illustrate the benefits of GDM with directional filtering to reduce noise in the migration image for imaging the salt-flank model in Fig. 6. The white lines in Fig. 6(a) depict the raypath for a third-order reflection that can significantly contribute to the migration image. Imaging of reflection points at A and C demands the filtering of upgoing and downgoing components for the Kirchhoff-like migration kernel in equation (5). In contrast, the migration image at point B requires the filtering of leftgoing and rightgoing events for the last GDM kernel in equation (6).

To filter such events, the Green's function for the migration kernel is computed by a finite-difference solution to the wave equation and Figs. 7 and 8 show the shot gathers recorded along vertical (Fig. 7b) and horizontal (Fig. 8b) receiver lines; here the shot is at the surface. These shot gathers are easily dip filtered into their corresponding one-way components in the F-K domain, either upgoing (Fig. 7c) and downgoing (Fig. 7d) waves for the vertical receiver line, or leftgoing (Fig. 8c) and rightgoing (Fig. 8d) waves for the horizontal receiver line. The Kirchhoff-like kernels in either equation (5) or equation (6) can then be used to get the, respectively, artefact-free RTM images of a single recorded shot gather in Figures 9(a,b). The artefacts are successfully eliminated

in Fig. 9(c) and the image quality is noticeably improved compared to Fig. 9(d). Figure 10 shows a stacked GDM image of 126 shot gathers with the shot at different surface locations.

We next test the filtered GDM on a marine seismic data set recorded in the Gulf of Mexico. This data set is known as the Mississippi Canyon line and was released by Westerngeco as a benchmark test for the 1997 SEG workshop on multiple attenuation (Dragoset 1999). Fig. 11(a) shows the migration velocity model, where a shallow salt body with a high velocity (around 4.7 km/s) is embedded in a background sediment model with a smoothly varying velocity distribution. The water bottom is at a depth of about 1.5 km.

Fig. 11(b) displays a raw RTM image migrated with the velocity model shown in Fig. 11(a). Due to the strong velocity contrast in the model, especially around the top of the salt, strong amplitude, low-frequency artefacts are present in the image, which are undesired and obscure the image of sediment layers above the salt. A high-pass filter is applied to the RTM image to reduce these artefacts and the result is shown in Fig. 12(a). As we can see, this simple filtering is effective in reducing the artefacts but large residuals still remain. To compute an image with less migration noise, we apply the filtered GDM algorithm associated with equation (5) and only take the last term in equation (5) to obtain the clean image shown in Fig. 12(b). The artefacts are successfully eliminated in Fig. 12(b) and as a result, the geology of the shallow

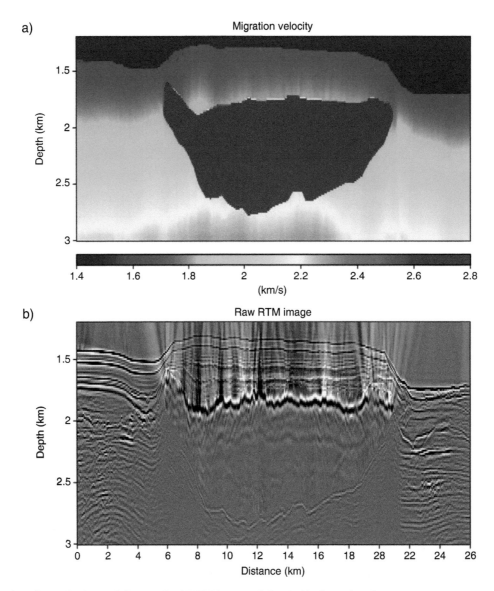

Figure 11 The migration velocity and the standard RTM image of the Gulf of Mexico data set.

sediments is much easier to interpret compared to that in Fig. 11(b).

If the events are too complex to separate with a simple F-K filtering method, then more complicated separation schemes can be used such as least-squares migration filtering (Nemeth, Wu and Schuster 1999) or moveout based dip filtering in either the semblance (Thorson and Claerbout 1985) or the τ-p (Yilmaz 2001) domains. We can also utilize the fact that the finite-difference solution of the first-order wave equations computes both the displacement and particle velocity components at any point in the grid. This means that analytical formulas (Claerbout 1976; Yilmaz 2001) can be employed to separate waves propagating from different directions; inputting both particle velocities and displacements also provides better separation capabilities for least-squares migration filtering.

13.5.2 Anti-aliasing filtering results

Synthetic tests associated with a fan model (Fig. 13a) are presented to demonstrate the effectiveness of the proposed GDM anti-aliasing filter. The velocity model shown in Fig. 13(a) has a homogeneous background velocity of 2.0 km/s perturbed by a series of dipping events and deep scatterers with a higher velocity of 2.5 km/s. Figure 13(b) displays a typical shot gather for this model calculated by a finite-difference solution to the acoustic wave equation. Fifty-one shot gathers are computed with the shot interval of 160 m and the first shot is fired at $X = 2$ km. A fixed spread is used and 301 traces are recorded along the surface with a trace interval of 40 m. The peak frequency of the Ricker wavelet is 15 Hz and the record length is 6 s. Both reflections and diffractions can be clearly seen in the shot gather.

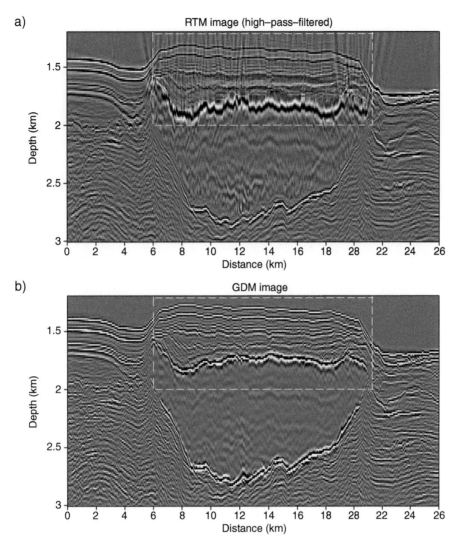

Figure 12 The GDM image in comparison with the filtered RTM image. The white dashed box highlights the differences of the two images.

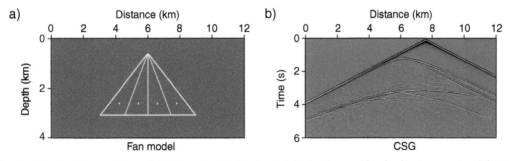

Figure 13 a) Synthetic velocity model used in the anti-aliasing tests. The background velocity (grey colour) is 2.0 km/s and the perturbed velocity (white colour) is 2.5 km/s. b) A typical common-shot gather (CSG) at $X = 7.6$ km.

Before computing the GDM image, we first apply KM to this synthetic data set to illustrate the migration aliasing problem for this model. Figure 14(a) shows a shot gather with the surface shot at $X = 7.6$ km, where the direct waves are removed. Figure 14(b) depicts the KM operator, which is a hyperbola-like curve for a fixed trial image point at **x** (located at $X = 6$ km and $Z = 3$ km). The KM operation for a trial image point **x** can be viewed as summing energy along this hyperbola. Figure 14(c,d) is the corresponding stacked KM images for 51 shot gathers with and without applying an anti-aliasing filter. Aliasing artefacts are visible in Fig. 14(c) and are then suppressed

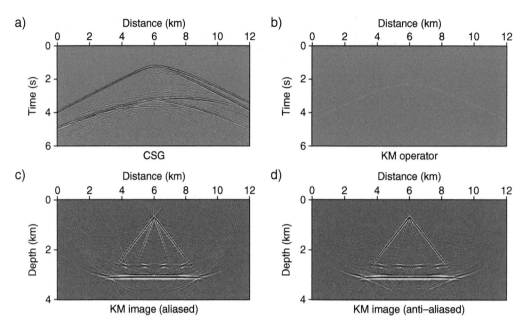

Figure 14 Anti-aliasing examples in Kirchhoff migration.

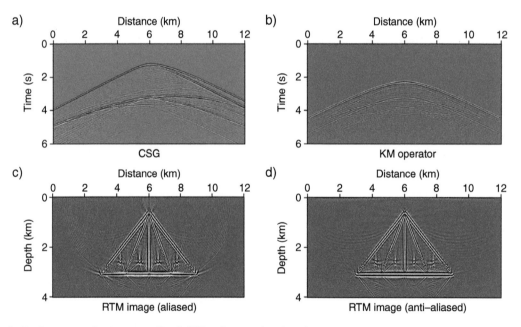

Figure 15 Anti-aliasing examples in generalized diffraction-stack migration.

with a KM anti-aliasing filter proposed by Lumley et al. (1994).

The GDM anti-aliasing filter described in the theory part is now applied to the same synthetic data. Fig. 15(b) presents the GDM operator of the same trial image point at **x** for the same shot gather as shown in Fig. 14(b). Unlike the hyperbola traveltime curve for the KM operator, the GDM operator contains both primary and multiples along with amplitude and phase information. Fig. 15(c) shows

the stacked GDM image of this model. Aliasing artefacts seen in the standard GDM image are similar to those in Fig. 14(c). The GDM anti-aliasing filter is then constructed using the proposed approach and applied to the GDM operator to eliminate the offending high-frequency components. Fig. 15(d) displays the GDM image with the anti-aliasing filter applied. Compared to Fig. 15(c), the aliasing artefacts are significantly attenuated by applying this filter.

13.6 Conclusions

We have shown that reverse-time migration (RTM) is equivalent to generalized diffraction-stack migration (GDM), where the generalized migration image at a point **x** is obtained by taking the space-time dot product of the appropriate migration operator with the data. GDM is a generalization of simple diffraction-stack migration, which sums the data over the hyperbola-like curve associated with the primary reflections. Instead of using asymptotic Green's functions computed by ray tracing, we use finite-difference solutions to the wave equation to get the migration kernels. These kernels do not require a high-frequency approximation and automatically take into account diving waves, primaries and multiples. The advantage of GDM over RTM is that moveout-based noise can be precisely filtered from the migration kernel, which can lead to precise suppression of migration artefacts and no unintentional filtering of data. In contrast, the standard RTM approach can only filter back-propagated data, which is an inseparable mixture of both the migration kernel and data contributions. We demonstrated the effective reduction of migration noise by dip filtering the decomposed migration kernel for both synthetic and field data. We also successfully demonstrated the use of applying an anti-aliasing operator to the GDM kernel.

A significant challenge in implementing GDM is the demanding memory and computation expenses of the migration operators. This issue is addressed in Appendix B. Nevertheless, GDM should be restricted for now to smaller data sets but with wavelet compression it can be practical for target-oriented migration and iterative least-squares GDM.

13.7 Acknowledgements

We thank the Supercomputing Laboratory at the King Abdullah University of Science and Technology (KAUST) in Thuwal, Saudi Arabia for the computer cycles provided to this project. We appreciate the reviews by the associate editor Ian Jones and the anonymous reviewers, who made a number of helpful suggestions that improved the quality of our manuscript. We would also like to thank WesternGeco for providing the field data. We acknowledge the support of the Center of Subsurface Imaging and Fluid Modelling (CSIM) sponsors (http://csim.kaust.edu.sa/).

References

Abma R., Sun J. and Bernitsas N. 1999. Antialiasing methods in Kirchhoff migration. *Geophysics* **64**, 1783–1792.

Biondi B. 2001. Kirchhoff imaging beyond aliasing: *Geophysics*, **66**, 654–666.

Claerbout J. 1976. *Fundamentals of Geophysical Data Processing.* Blackwell Science Ltd.

Claerbout J. 1992. *Earth Soundings Analysis: Processing Versus Inversion.* Blackwell Science Ltd.

Dong S., Luo Y., Xiao X., Chávez-Pérez S. and Schuster G.T. 2009. Fast 3D target-oriented reverse-time datuming. *Geophysics* **74**, WCA141–WCA151.

Dragoset B. 1999. A practical approach to surface multiple attenuation. *The Leading Edge* **18**, 104–108.

Ehinger A., Lailly P. and Marfurt K. 1996. Green's function implementation of common-offset, wave-equation migration. *Geophysics* **61**, 1813–1821.

Fei T.W., Luo Y., Aramco S. and Schuster G.T. 2010. De-blending reverse-time migration. *SEG Technical Program Expanded Abstracts* **29**, 3130–3134.

Fletcher R.F., Fowler P., Kitchenside P. and Albertin U. 2005. Suppressing artefacts in prestack reverse time migration. *SEG Technical Program Expanded Abstracts* **24**, 2049–2051.

French W.S. 1974. Two-dimensional and three-dimensional migration of model-experiment reflection profiles. *Geophysics* **39**, 265–277.

Gray S.H. 1992. Frequency-selective design of the Kirchhoff migration operator. *Geophysical Prospecting* **40**, 565–571.

Guitton A., Kaelin B. and Biondi B. 2007. Least-squares attenuation of reverse-time-migration artefacts. *Geophysics* **72**, S19–S23.

Hu L. and McMechan G. 1987. Wavefield transformations of vertical seismic profiles. *Geophysics* **52**, 307–321.

Liu W. and Wang Y. 2008. Target-oriented reverse time migration for two-way prestack depth imaging. *SEG Technical Program Expanded Abstracts* **27**, 2326–2330.

Liu F., Zhang G., Morton S.A. and Leveille J.P. 2007. Reverse-time migration using one-way wavefield imaging condition. *SEG Technical Program Expanded Abstracts* **26**, 2170–2174.

Liu F., Zhang G., Morton S.A. and Leveille J.P. 2011. An effective imaging condition for reverse-time migration using wavefield decomposition. *Geophysics* **76**, S29–S39.

Loewenthal D., Stoffa P.L. and Faria E.L. 1987. Suppressing the unwanted reflections of the full wave equation. *Geophysics* **52**, 1007–1012.

Lumley D.E., Claerbout J.F. and Bevc D. 1994. Anti-aliased Kirchhoff 3-D migration. *SEG Technical Program Expanded Abstracts* **13**, 1282–1285.

Luo Y. and Schuster G.T. 1992. Wave packet transform and data compression. *SEG Technical Program Expanded Abstracts* **11**, 1187–1190.

McMechan G.A. 1983. Migration by extrapolation of time-dependent boundary values. *Geophysical Prospecting* **31**, 413–420.

Mora P. 1989. Inversion = migration + tomography. *Geophysics* **54**, 1575–1586.

Mulder W.A. and Plessix R.-E. 2003. One-way and two-way wave-equation migration. *SEG Technical Program Expanded Abstracts* **22**, 881–884.

Nemeth T., Wu C. and Schuster G. 1999. Least-squares migration of incomplete reflection data. *Geophysics* **64**, 208–221.

Schuster G.T. 2002. Reverse-time migration = generalized diffraction stack migration. *SEG Technical Program Expanded Abstracts* **21**, 1280–1283.

Stolt R.H. and Benson A.K. 1987. Seismic migration: Theory and practice, vol. 5 of the handbook of geophysical exploration.

The Journal of the Acoustical Society of America **81**, 1651–1652.

Thorson J. and Claerbout J. 1985. Velocity-stack and slant-stack stochastic inversion. *Geophysics* **50**, 2727–2741.

Whitmore N.D. 1983. Iterative depth migration by backward time propagation. *SEG Technical Program Expanded Abstracts* **2**, 382–385.

Yilmaz Ö. 2001. Seismic data analysis: Processing, inversion, and interpretation of seismic Data. *Society of Exploration Geophysicists.*

Yoon K. and Marfurt K.J. 2006. Reverse time migration using the Poynting vector. *Exploration Geophysics* **37**, 102–107.

Yoon K., Marfurt K.J. and Starr W. 2004. Challenges in reverse-time migration. *SEG Technical Program Expanded Abstracts* **23**, 1057–1060.

Zhan G., Luo Y. and Schuster G.T. 2010. Modified form of reverse time migration tuned to multiple. 72nd Annual Conference and Exhibition, EAGE, Extended Abstracts, P594.

Zhan G. and Schuster G.T. 2010. Skeletonized least squares wave equation migration. *SEG Technical Program Expanded Abstracts* **29**, 3380–3384.

Zhang Y., Sun J.C. and Gray S.H. 2003. Aliasing in wavefield extrapolation prestack migration. *Geophysics* **68**, 629–633.

Zhou M. and Schuster G.T. 2002. Wave-equation wavefront migration. *SEG Technical Program Expanded Abstracts* **21**, 1292–1295.

Appendix A
Migration as a Pattern Matching Operation

The similarity between two demeaned digital photos (each assumed to be a 100×100 pixelated image in the *x–y* plane) can be quantified by representing each photo by a $10,000 \times 1$ vector and taking their dot product. If the photos are very similar then the dot product will yield a sum of mostly positive numbers to give a very high correlation coefficient. Conversely, the dot product between dissimilar photos will yield a sum of both positive and negative numbers to give a small correlation coefficient. Taking dot products of photos is a common pattern matching operation.

Summing the data over migration hyperbola in *x-t* space can also be thought of as a pattern matching operation. Fig. A1(a) depicts the primary migration curves in $x - t$ space as pink and green curves, where each coloured curve is associated with a different trial image point with the same colour. Summing the data over a weighted curve is equivalent to a 2D dot product between the migration operator image and the data image. If the trial image point is near the actual scatterer, then the, e.g., pink, migration operator in Fig. A1(a) matches the data very well. Hence, the migration image at that trial image point has a high value. At other trial image points, the pattern of the migration operator correlates poorly with the data so the correlation is small to give a small value in the migration image.

Migration operator for multiple arrivals

In theory, migrating many types of events with different arrival angles to their common reflector point leads to a better resolution at that point and a cleaner migration image. This is similar to looking at a diamond from different view angles, each new view angle revealing a new facet of the gem. To achieve this extra resolution with seismic images, one can tune a diffraction migration operator to migrate both primary reflections and scattered multiples.[4] A representative primary+multiple migration operator is illustrated in Fig. A1(b), where, for a trial image point, the summation of energy is along the hyperbolic curves (e.g., the solid and dashed pink curves or the solid and dashed green curves) that represent the traveltimes for both primaries and multiples. For the correct trial image point at the black star, a huge amount of seismic energy gets placed at the scatterer's location by primary+multiple migration compared to that for primary migration.

From a pattern matching point of view, the complicated pattern of the primary+multiple migration operator correlates well with data only if the trial image point is in a small neighbourhood of the actual scatterer point; thus, the image resolution is very good. Compare this to matching the simple primary migration operator to the data in Fig. A1(a); there is a relatively large neighbourhood around the actual scatterer that gives a good match between the operator's pattern and the actual data. This means that a primary migration image will have a worse resolution compared to the primary+multiple migration image.

The disadvantage of primary+multiple migration is that its migration image is especially sensitive to errors in the migration velocity model. Small migration velocity errors tend to give a noisier image compared to the primary migration image.

Appendix B
Computation and Compression of the Migration Kernel

The most significant drawback of GDM relative to RTM is the extra expense in storing and computing the

---

[4] A multiple migration algorithm can be constructed by ray tracing the traveltimes for *both primaries and multiples and including the extra summations in the diffraction-stack migration formula.* An alternative method is by using a finite-difference method to solve the wave equation to get the appropriate Green's functions.

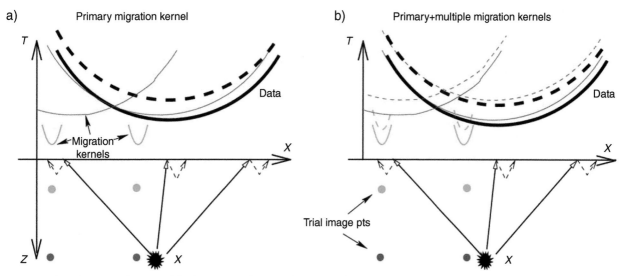

Figure A1 Migration kernels plotted in data space for a) primary and b) primary+multiple events associated with the shallow (green) and deep (pink) trial image points. The best match between the data (black hyperbolas) and migration curves (pink and green) is when the trial image point is near the location of the actual scatterer. Unlike the primary migration kernel, the dot product in $x - t$ space between the predicted multiple moveout curves (solid and dashed coloured lines) and the actual moveout of the data (black hyperbolas) is negligible unless the trial image point is very close to the actual scatterer location (star). Hence, the multiple migration image has much higher spatial resolution than the primary migration image.

migration kernels. This problem can be partly, not fully, remedied in the following ways.

Computation of the migration kernel

The migration kernel in equation (3) can be computed in one of two ways.

1. Place a source point on the surface at **s** and solve for the field everywhere in the model by a finite-difference method to get the Green's function $g(\mathbf{x}, t|\mathbf{s}, 0)$. Reciprocity says that $g(\mathbf{s}, t|\mathbf{x}, 0) = g(\mathbf{x}, t|\mathbf{s}, 0)$, and if we replace $\mathbf{s} \to \mathbf{r}$ then this gives $g(\mathbf{r}, t|\mathbf{x}, 0)$. Thus, $g(\mathbf{x}, t|\mathbf{r}, 0)$ can be convolved with $g(\mathbf{x}, t|\mathbf{s}, 0)$ to give the migration kernel $\mathcal{G}(\mathbf{r}, \mathbf{s}, \mathbf{x}, t)$ in equation (3) with the receiver at **r** and the source at **s** for all subsurface points **x**.

2. Alternatively, a point source can be placed at depth **x** and the field can be solved everywhere to get $g(\mathbf{r}, t|\mathbf{x}, 0)$. This can be cost effective for target-oriented migration (or waveform inversion), so that we only need the Green's functions for point sources along the boundary of the target (Dong et al. 2009). Reciprocity says that $g(\mathbf{r}, t|\mathbf{x}, 0) = g(\mathbf{x}, t|\mathbf{r}, 0)$, and letting $\mathbf{r} \to \mathbf{s}$ yields $g(\mathbf{x}, t|\mathbf{s}, 0)$. The migration kernel at **x** can now be computed by equation (3). This is the method (Liu and Wang 2011; Dong et al. 2009) for target-oriented migration.

Zhou and Schuster (2002) demonstrated how to efficiently compute these migration operators by finite differencing along the leading portion of the wavefront.

Compression of the migration kernel

A wavelet transform with compression (Zhan and Schuster 2010) can be used to reduce storage costs associated with the GDM kernel, as follows.

1. Compute the source-side $g(\mathbf{x}, t|\mathbf{s}, 0)$ and the receiver-side $g(\mathbf{x}, t|\mathbf{r}, 0)$ band-limited Green's functions by a numerical solution to the wave equation.

2. A wavelet transform (Luo and Schuster 1992) is applied to the Green's function $g(\mathbf{x}, t|\mathbf{s}, 0)$ and $g(\mathbf{x}, t|\mathbf{r}, 0)$ to get $\mathcal{W}[g(\mathbf{x}, t|\mathbf{s}, 0)]$ and $\mathcal{W}[g(\mathbf{x}, t|\mathbf{r}, 0)]$, respectively. Here, $\mathcal{W}[]$ represents the wavelet transform with up to an order-of-magnitude reduction in storage requirements. Then, mute all wavelet coefficients below a given threshold in the wavelet domain and only store the significant coefficients to get the compressed Green's functions $\mathcal{W}[\tilde{g}(\mathbf{x}, t|\mathbf{r}, 0)]$ and $\mathcal{W}[\tilde{g}(\mathbf{x}, t|\mathbf{r}, 0)]$. Save these compressed Green's functions on a disk.

3. After reading these compressed Green's functions from the disk, an inverse wavelet transform is performed to reconstruct the Green's functions $\tilde{g}(\mathbf{x}, t|\mathbf{s}, 0)$ and $\tilde{g}(\mathbf{x}, t|\mathbf{r}, 0)$ by inverse transforming $\mathcal{W}[\tilde{g}(\mathbf{x}, t|\mathbf{s}, 0)]$ and $\mathcal{W}[\tilde{g}(\mathbf{x}, t|\mathbf{r}, 0)]$. This is followed by a convolution step using a fast Fourier transform to get the compressed migration kernel $\bar{\mathcal{G}}(\mathbf{r}, \mathbf{s}, \mathbf{x}, t)$ in equation (3):

$$\tilde{\mathcal{G}}(\mathbf{r}, \mathbf{s}, \mathbf{x}, t) = \tilde{g}(\mathbf{x}, t|\mathbf{s}, 0) \star \tilde{g}(\mathbf{x}, t|\mathbf{r}, 0), \qquad \text{(B1)}$$

where $\tilde{g}(\mathbf{x}, t|\mathbf{x}', 0) = \mathcal{W}^{-1}[\tilde{g}(\mathbf{x}, t|\mathbf{s}, 0)](\mathbf{x}' = \mathbf{s} \text{ or } \mathbf{r})$. Here, the tilde denotes the function after lossy compression and decompression and $\star$ stands for convolution.

4. The compressed migration operator $\bar{\mathcal{G}}(\mathbf{r}, \mathbf{s}, \mathbf{x}, t)$ is a Kirchhoff-like kernel that describes, for a single shot gather, pseudo-hyperbolas of multi-arrivals in r-t coordinates. The reflection energy in a recorded shot gather $d(\mathbf{r}, t|\mathbf{s}, 0)$ is then summed along such pseudo-hyperbolas to give the migration image:

$$m_{mig}(x) = \sum_s \sum_r \sum_t \tilde{\mathcal{G}}(\mathbf{r}, \mathbf{s}, \mathbf{x}, t) d(\mathbf{r}, t|\mathbf{s}, 0). \quad \text{(B2)}$$

This summation is equivalent to a dot product between the recorded shot gathers and the compressed GDM kernels and has the advantage over Kirchhoff migration in that there is no high-frequency approximation and multi-arrivals are included in the imaging.

Exercises

1. Compute the rabbit ear wavepaths for a simple dipping layered model. Compute the Green's functions by solving the two-way wave equation.

2. Same as previous exercise, except generate the rabbit ear Green's functions by ray tracing.

3. The ellipse migration kernel is sometimes generated by computing the Green's functions for a smooth velocity model. Explain why this Green's function will not generate a migration kernel with rabbit ear wavepaths.

4. Show how one can generate rabbit ear wavepaths for specified reflector boundaries from Green's functions computed for a smooth velocity model.

Chapter 14: Resolution Limits for Wave Equation Imaging*

In 2014, I coauthored the following reprinted paper with Yunsong Huang on deriving resolution limits for imaging wave equations, based on our work together at King Abdullah University of Science and Technology (KAUST), in Thuwal, Saudi Arabia.

As noted in the opening paragraphs, "To optimize the use of wave equation imaging one must understand its limits of spatial resolution. Without this understanding, models can be over parameterized and lead to solutions that honor the data but violate the wavelength-based resolution limits of wave propagation. Such models should be avoided in our attempts to understand the earth."

"Resolution limits for wave equation imaging," published in the *Journal of Applied Geophysics*, builds on developments over the past 30 years in mathematically defining resolution limits. It begins by showing how wavepaths can estimate resolution for traveltime tomography and migration. Spatial resolution is defined intuitively as the minimum width and height of the intersection of Fresnel zones at the trial image point. Then, that definition is proved by deriving the resolution limits for each variety of wavepath, showing their relationship to the acquisition geometry. This work gives a comprehensive asymptotic analysis of the model resolution function for least-squares migration, with resulting formulae that allow the geoscientist to optimize resolution characteristics in full-waveform inversion, least-squares migration, and reverse time migration.

Abstract

Formulas are derived for the resolution limits of migration-data kernels associated with diving waves, primary reflections, diffractions, and multiple reflections. They are applicable to images formed by reverse time migration (RTM), least squares migration (LSM), and full waveform inversion (FWI), and suggest a multiscale approach to iterative FWI based on multiscale physics. That is, at the early stages of the inversion, events that only generate low-wavenumber resolution should be emphasized relative to the high-wavenumber resolution events. As the iterations proceed, the higher-resolution events should be emphasized. The formulas also suggest that inverting multiples can provide some low- and intermediate-wavenumber components of the velocity model not available in the primaries. Finally, diffractions can provide twice or better the resolution than specular reflections for comparable depths of the reflector and diffractor. The width of the diffraction-transmission wavepath is approximately λ at the diffractor location for the diffraction-transmission wavepath.

14.1 Introduction

FWI (Lailly, 1984; Tarantola, 1984, 2005), RTM (Baysal et al., 1983; McMechan, 1983; Whitmore, 1983), LSM (Nemeth et al., 1999; Duquet et al., 2000; Tang, 2009; Dai et al., 2012) and wave-equation traveltime inversion (Woodward, 1989, 1992; Luo, 1991; Luo and Schuster, 1991; De Hoop and van Der Hilst, 2005) are important tools for imaging seismic data at the engineering (Buddensiek et al., 2008), exploration (Mora, 1988, 1989; Pica et al., 1990; Pratt and Goulty, 1991; Zhou et al., 1995; Shin and Cha, 2008; Krebs et al., 2009; Virieux and Operto, 2009) and earthquake (Tong et al., 1998; Marquering et al., 1999; De Hoop and van Der Hilst, 2005; Van Der Hilst and Maarten, 2005; Fichtner et al., 2009; Tape et al., 2009; Fichtner, 2011; Fichtner and Trampert, 2011a,b) scales. In all of the above methods, the wave equation is inverted to estimate the model that minimizes, in some sense, the difference between the predicted and observed data. The main value of these wave equation-based imaging methods is that they overcome the high-frequency assumption of

*Reprinted with permission from Elsevier from Huang, Yunsong and G. T. Schuster, 2014, Resolution limits for wave equation imaging: Journal of Applied Geophysics, **107**, 137–148. doi: 10.1016/j.jappgeo.2014.05.018.

ray-based methods and use many, if not all, of the arrivals to reconstruct a finely detailed earth model. The hope is to find models with spatial resolution of one-half wavelength, and perhaps even better if evanescent energy can be exploited (de Fornel, 2001; Fink, 2008; Schuster et al., 2012). The main limitations of wave equation imaging are computational cost and extensive preprocessing of the data, compared to the ray-based methods.

To optimize the use of wave equation imaging one must understand its limits of spatial resolution. Without this understanding, models can be over parameterized and lead to solutions that honor the data but violate the wavelength-based resolution limits of wave propagation. Such models should be avoided in our attempts to understand the earth.

In the last 30 years, there has been much progress in mathematically defining the resolution limits of seismic images. The two most important categories of seismic imaging and their resolution limits are for traveltime tomography and reflection imaging.

14.1.1 Resolution limits for traveltime tomography

In raypath traveltime tomography, the velocity is updated only along the raypath that connects the source at s with the receiver at g, whereas in finite-frequency travel time tomography, velocity updates can be confined to the first Fresnel zone for the specified source-receiver pair (Harlan, 1990). He states, "band-limited waves can follow paths that are not Fermat raypaths and still cover the distance between two points in almost the same time. All arriving waves that are delayed by less than half a wavelength will add constructively to the first arrival."

As an example, the raypaths and Fresnel zones for reflection and transmission arrivals are illustrated in Fig. 1. A point x is in the Fresnel zone (FZ) if and only if it satisfies the following condition (Kravtsov and Orlov, 1990; Cerveny and Soares, 1992):

$$|\tau_{sx} + \tau_{xg} - \tau_{sg}| \leq T/2, \qquad (1)$$

where, T is the dominant period of the source wavelet, τ_{sx} is the traveltime for a particular type of wave to propagate from s to the trial image point at x, and τ_{sg} is the traveltime to propagate from s to the specified geophone at g.

In a homogeneous medium, the maximum width of the first Fresnel zone can be shown (Williamson, 1991) to be proportional to $\sqrt{\lambda L}$, where L is the source-receiver distance and λ is the dominant wavelength. Thus, widening the distance between the source and receiver lowers the spatial resolution of the traveltime tomogram. More generally, Appendix A derives the formula for the length between any two points on opposite sides of the ellipse, which provides the horizontal resolution limit for any orientation of the ellipse. In addition, Appendix A derives the formula for horizontal resolution in multilayered, rather than homogeneous, media.

The effective spatial resolution limits Δx and Δz of traveltime tomograms can be estimated (Schuster, 1996) as the minimum width and height of the *intersection* of first Fresnel zones at the trial image point. This can be

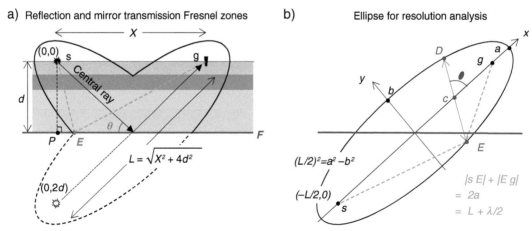

Fig. 1. a) First Fresnel zones for the specular reflection and for the transmission arrival excited by the mirror source at $(0,2d)$. In the latter case, the velocity model below the reflector (the thick horizontal line denoted by F) has been extended to be the mirror-reflection of the velocity model above the reflector. Colored layers denote the possibility that the velocity model is multilayered, instead of homogeneous. In this case, although the Fresnel zone is not an ellipse, the horizontal resolution can be computed approximately involving the RMS velocity v_{RMS} (see Appendix A). b) An ellipse intersected by a line segment DE, where its length $\overline{DE} = \frac{2ab\sqrt{b^2\cos^2\theta + (a^2 - c^2)\sin^2\theta}}{b^2\cos^2\theta + a^2\sin^2\theta}$ defines the resolution limit (see Appendix A).

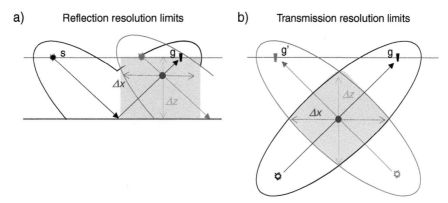

Fig. 2. Same as Fig. 1 except there is an additional source–receiver pair. The minimum width and height of the shaded intersection zone define, respectively, the effective horizontal Δx and vertical Δz resolution limits of the traveltime tomogram at ●.

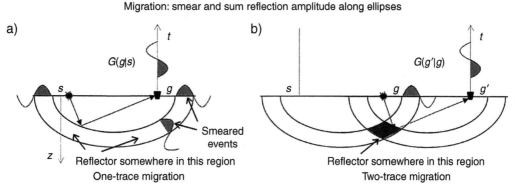

Fig. 3. Migration is the smearing and summation of trace amplitudes along the appropriate fat ellipses in (x, z) for each source–receiver pair **s**–**g** (Claerbout, 1992). Migration of two traces in b) has better spatial resolution than migrating just one trace in a), and the minimum thickness of each fat ellipse is 0.5λ, where T is the dominant period of the source wavelet.

seen by assuming the L_2 traveltime misfit $J = \sum_i J_i$, where J_i denotes the traveltime misfit owing to the ith source–receiver pair, and assuming model consistency, i.e., there exists a velocity model that can explain all observed traveltimes. If a part of the trial model lies farthest from the Fresnel zone prescribed by the ith source–receiver pair, then J_i will dominate and steepest descent updates will propel this trial model point towards the center of this Fresnel zone. The rule that the traveltime error is less than $T/2$ for all source–receiver pairs defines an intersection of all the individual Fresnel zones. As an example, Fig. 2 illustrates the intersection zone for both a) reflection and b) transmission rays. At any point on the central raypath, the narrowest width is along the line perpendicular to this ray, which also defines the direction of best resolution. Thus, *a horizontal ray gives the best vertical resolution while a vertically oriented ray provides the best horizontal resolution for transmission tomography,* where the velocity is updated by smearing residuals along the first FZ (also referred to as a wavepath). As will be shown in the next section, this rule of thumb is also true for transmission wavepaths in FWI tomograms, except the *waveform residual* is smeared along the associated wavepath.

14.1.2 Resolution limits for reflection imaging

A seismic migration image is formed by taking the reflection energy arriving at time $\tau_{sx} + \tau_{xg}$ and smearing (Claerbout, 1992) it along the appropriate ellipse in the model-space coordinates x (see Fig. 3a). For several traces, the migration image in Fig. 3b is formed by smearing[1] and summing the reflection energy along the appropriate ellipses in the model space. It is obvious that the *narrowest horizontal slice of the fat ellipse is for a trial image point at the far left and far right of the ellipse to give the best horizontal resolution in the reflection migration image. We also see that the narrowest vertical slice is directly beneath the midpoint of the source–receiver pair to give the best vertical resolution.* For post-stack data, these resolution limits are given on the right side of Fig. 4e, which say that the far-offset (near-offset) trace from a trial image point gives the best horizontal (vertical) resolution.

---

[1] The seismic amplitude is smeared over the thick ellipse shown in Fig. 3a, where the period T of the trace's source wavelet determines the thickness of the fat ellipse in (x, z) space; Fig. 3b illustrates that the minimum thickness of the fat ellipse as 0.5λ.

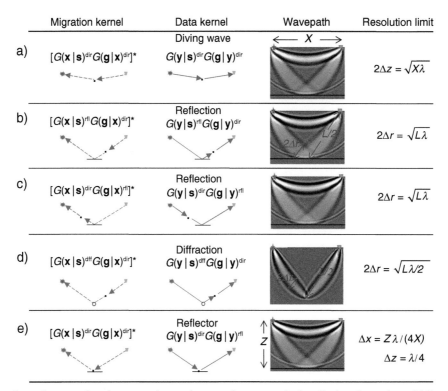

Migration kernel	Data kernel	Wavepath	Resolution limit

a) $[G(\mathbf{x}\,|\,\mathbf{s})^{\mathrm{dir}}G(\mathbf{g}\,|\,\mathbf{x})^{\mathrm{dir}}]^*$ — Diving wave $G(\mathbf{y}\,|\,\mathbf{s})^{\mathrm{dir}}G(\mathbf{g}\,|\,\mathbf{y})^{\mathrm{dir}}$ — $2\Delta z = \sqrt{X\lambda}$

b) $[G(\mathbf{x}\,|\,\mathbf{s})^{\mathrm{rfl}}G(\mathbf{g}\,|\,\mathbf{x})^{\mathrm{dir}}]^*$ — Reflection $G(\mathbf{y}\,|\,\mathbf{s})^{\mathrm{rfl}}G(\mathbf{g}\,|\,\mathbf{y})^{\mathrm{dir}}$ — $2\Delta r = \sqrt{L\lambda}$

c) $[G(\mathbf{x}\,|\,\mathbf{s})^{\mathrm{dir}}G(\mathbf{g}\,|\,\mathbf{x})^{\mathrm{rfl}}]^*$ — Reflection $G(\mathbf{y}\,|\,\mathbf{s})^{\mathrm{dir}}G(\mathbf{g}\,|\,\mathbf{y})^{\mathrm{rfl}}$ — $2\Delta r = \sqrt{L\lambda}$

d) $[G(\mathbf{x}\,|\,\mathbf{s})^{\mathrm{dff}}G(\mathbf{g}\,|\,\mathbf{x})^{\mathrm{dir}}]^*$ — Diffraction $G(\mathbf{y}\,|\,\mathbf{s})^{\mathrm{dff}}G(\mathbf{g}\,|\,\mathbf{y})^{\mathrm{dir}}$ — $2\Delta r = \sqrt{L\lambda/2}$

e) $[G(\mathbf{x}\,|\,\mathbf{s})^{\mathrm{dir}}G(\mathbf{g}\,|\,\mathbf{x})^{\mathrm{dir}}]^*$ — Reflector $G(\mathbf{y}\,|\,\mathbf{s})^{\mathrm{dir}}G(\mathbf{g}\,|\,\mathbf{y})^{\mathrm{rfl}}$ — $\Delta x = Z\lambda/(4X)$, $\Delta z = \lambda/4$

Fig. 4. Migration-data kernels, associated wavepaths, and approximate resolution limits along the middle of the wavepaths for (a–d). Here, the dashed lines in the first column represent the raypaths associated with the conjugated kernels; the solid lines with arrows in the second column represent the raypaths associated with the data kernels; the trial image points x and y are represented by ●; the diffractor in (d) is denoted by a small red circle; and the resolution limit perpendicular to the wavepath is denoted by $2\Delta r$. The resolution limits for reflection migration in (e) are for post-stack data, where X corresponds to aperture width, and Δx and Δz correspond to the skinniest width and thickness of the fat migration ellipse.

The resolution limits for migration (Berkhout, 1984; Safar, 1985; Vermeer, 1997; Chen and Schuster, 1999) are equivalent to those for linearized inversion in a homogeneous (Devaney, 1984; Wu and Toksoz, 1987) and an inhomogeneous medium (Beylkin, 1985) with smooth velocity variations. The key idea is that the model wavenumber vector $\mathbf{k}$ can be equated to the sum of the source–scatterer and geophone–scatterer wavenumbers $\mathbf{k} = \mathbf{k}_{sr_o} + \mathbf{k}_{gr_o}$ shown in Fig. 5. If $\mathcal{D}$ defines the range of wavenumbers available from the source–receiver positions, then the horizontal Δx and vertical Δz spatial resolution limits of the migration image are defined as

$$\Delta x = \min_{\mathcal{D}}\left[\frac{2\pi}{k_x}\right] = \min_{\mathcal{D}}\left[\frac{2\pi}{k_{sx_o}+k_{gx_o}}\right],$$

$$\Delta z = \min_{\mathcal{D}}\left[\frac{2\pi}{k_z}\right] = \min_{\mathcal{D}}\left[\frac{2\pi}{k_{sz_o}+k_{gz_o}}\right]. \quad (2)$$

In the far-field approximation, these limits are given in Fig. 4e for post-stack migration.

The above resolution analysis has been developed for migration and traveltime tomography. Until now, there has not been a comprehensive treatment of the resolution limits associated with LSM. We now present such an analysis

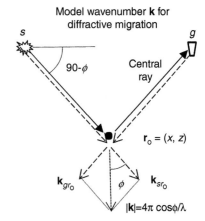

Fig. 5. Scatterer at $\mathbf{r}_o = (x,z)$ where the sum of the dashed source–scatterer $\mathbf{k}_{sr_o}$ and geophone–scatterer wavenumbers $\mathbf{k}_{gr_o}$ is equal to the recoverable model wavenumber $\mathbf{k}$. Solid rays define the central raypath.

by applying an asymptotic analysis to the model resolution function for LSM. The resulting resolution formulas can be used to better understand and optimize the resolution characteristics of FWI, LSM, and RTM.

This paper is divided into three parts. The introduction heuristically explains how wavepaths are used to estimate resolution for both traveltime tomography and migration. This leads to an intuitive description of spatial resolution as the minimum width and height of the intersection of Fresnel zones at the trial image point. The next part validates this heuristic definition by rigorously deriving the resolution limits for each type of wavepath, and explains their relationship to the acquisition geometry. Finally, a discussion and summary are given.

14.2 Born forward and adjoint modeling

The model resolution function $\mathbf{L}^{\dagger}\mathbf{L}$ is a product of forward $\mathbf{L}$ and adjoint $\mathbf{L}^{\dagger}$ modeling operators under the Born approximation (Stolt and Benson, 1986). We now define the equations for these modeling operators.

14.2.1 Born forward modeling

The trace $d(\mathbf{g}|\mathbf{s})$ excited by a harmonic point source at $\mathbf{s}$ and recorded by a geophone at $\mathbf{g}$ is given by the Born modeling equation:

$$\delta d(\mathbf{g}|\mathbf{s}) = \omega^2 \int_{\Omega} G(\mathbf{g}|\mathbf{x})\delta m(\mathbf{x}) G(\mathbf{x}|\mathbf{s}) dx^2 \rightarrow \delta \mathbf{d} = \mathbf{L}\delta\mathbf{m}, \tag{3}$$

where $G(\mathbf{g}|\mathbf{x})$ is the Helmholtz Green's function for the background velocity model, the model function perturbed from the background model is given by $\delta m(\mathbf{x}) = 2\delta s(\mathbf{x})s(\mathbf{x}) \rightarrow \delta\mathbf{m}$, $s(\mathbf{x})$ is the background slowness model, $\delta s(\mathbf{x})$ is the perturbation of the slowness field, and ω is the angular frequency. For notational economy, this equation can be represented in operator notation by $\delta \mathbf{d} = \mathbf{L}\delta\mathbf{m}$, where $\delta \mathbf{d}$ represents the scattered seismic field $\delta d(\mathbf{g}|\mathbf{s})$ under the weak scattering approximation, $\mathbf{L}$ represents the integral operator, and Ω defines the integration points in the model region.

The integration in Eq. (3) is over the entire model space, but if the trace is windowed about a specific event then the integration can be approximated by that over the event's first Fresnel zone associated with the specific source–receiver pair. For example, if the trace only contains the transmitted arrival, then $\Omega = \Omega_{trans}$ defines the points in the yellow colored wavepath in Fig. 4a of the diving wave's first Fresnel zone; only velocity perturbations in this zone will significantly affect the character of the diving wave arrival in the trace.

14.2.2 Born adjoint modeling

Eq. (3) can be inverted by the iterative steepest descent formula

$$\delta m(\mathbf{x})^{k+1} = \delta m(\mathbf{x})^k - \alpha \delta m(\mathbf{x})^{mig}, \tag{4}$$

where the misfit gradient $\delta m(\mathbf{x})^{mig}$ is given by the Born adjoint modeling equation

$$\delta m(\mathbf{x})^{mig} = \omega^2 \int_D [G(\mathbf{g}|\mathbf{x})G(\mathbf{x}|\mathbf{s})]^{\star}\delta d(\mathbf{g}|\mathbf{s})dx_g dx_s$$
$$\rightarrow \delta \mathbf{m}^{mig} = \mathbf{L}^{\dagger}\delta\mathbf{d}, \tag{5}$$

and the integration of points in D is over the range of the horizontal source and receiver coordinates along the horizontal recording line at $z = 0$. Here, $\delta d(\mathbf{g}|\mathbf{s}) = d(\mathbf{g}|\mathbf{s}) - d(\mathbf{g}|\mathbf{s})^{obs}$, $\mathbf{L}^{\dagger}$ represents the adjoint of the modeling operator $\mathbf{L}$, the step length is denoted by α, $d(\mathbf{g}|\mathbf{s})$ is the trace predicted from the estimated slowness model, and the observed trace is represented by $d(\mathbf{g}|\mathbf{s})^{obs}$. The misfit gradient symbol $\delta m(\mathbf{x})^{mig}$ is superscripted by mig because it also represents the migration of the residual. In fact, the first iteration $k = 0$ of Eq. (5) represents the reverse time migration of the scattered data recorded at the surface.

If the windowed event is the reflection, Eq. (5) says that the velocity model is updated by smearing the residual[2] along the yellow colored rabbit ears[3] in Fig. 4b–c and the yellow ellipse in Fig. 4e. Smearing residuals along the rabbit ears (ellipse) with the b–c (e) migration kernel updates the low-wavenumber (high-wavenumber) portion of the velocity model (Mora, 1989; Zhou et al., 1995; Liu et al., 2011). The spatial resolution limits Δx and Δz associated with any point along the central rays are determined by the, respectively, horizontal and vertical widths of the first Fresnel zone.

14.3 Model resolution function and FWI resolution limits

In the Introduction, the model resolution limits were defined for traveltime transmission tomography and reflection migration, where λ is considered as the dominant wavelength. For a band-limited source wavelet, the dominant wavelength is typically associated with the peak frequency. Now the model resolution limits will be derived for FWI by applying asymptotic analysis to the model resolution function that relates the model $\delta\mathbf{m}$ to the reconstructed image $\delta\mathbf{m}^{mig}$. Note in passing that in practice, FWI is typically carried out in multiscale (Bunks et al., 1995; Sirgue and Pratt, 2004) such that at a given stage, FWI only concerns the source wavelet filtered into a narrowband. In this case,

---

[2]The residual can be either the traveltime residual or the waveform residual.

[3]There are two steps for creating an upgoing reflection wavepath: first, generate the migration image and use the reflectors as exploding sources that explode at the traveltime from the source to the reflector. Then, fire off these exploding reflectors to get the upgoing reflection fields $U(\mathbf{x}, t)$. The upgoing rabbit ear wavepath is computed by taking the zero-lag correlation between $U(\mathbf{x}, t)$ and the backpropagated data $B(\mathbf{x}, t)$.

the pertinent λ still belongs to the peak frequency of the narrowband source. In contrast, LSM is carried out with the original band-limited source wavelet. Because the inversion process of LSM tends to deconvolve the source wavelet, the resolution limits are defined asymptotically by the λ associated with the upper cutoff frequency of the source wavelet.

14.3.1 Model resolution equation: $m^{mig} = L^{\dagger}Lm$

The forward and adjoint modeling equations can be combined to give the equation for model resolution, i.e., plugging Eq. (3) into Eq. (5) gives

$$\delta m(\mathbf{x})^{mig} = \omega^4 \int_D \overbrace{[G(\mathbf{g}|\mathbf{x})G(\mathbf{x}|\mathbf{s})]^*}^{\text{migration kernel}}$$
$$\times \int_\Omega \overbrace{G(\mathbf{g}|\mathbf{y})G(\mathbf{y}|\mathbf{s})}^{\text{data kernel}} \delta m(\mathbf{y}) dy^2 dx_g dx_s, \quad (6)$$

or in more compact notation

$$\delta \mathbf{m}^{mig} = \mathbf{L}^{\dagger}\mathbf{L}\delta \mathbf{m}. \quad (7)$$

The kernel for the operator $\mathbf{L}^{\dagger}\mathbf{L}$ is related to the model resolution matrix (Menke, 1989) and is interpreted as the point spread function (Schuster and Hu, 2000) similar to that used in optics, except here, if $\delta m(\mathbf{y}) = \delta(\mathbf{y} - \mathbf{r}_o)$, it is the migration response to a point slowness perturbation in the model at $\mathbf{r}_o$. The ideal response to a point slowness anomaly is the same point with perfect resolution.

For a two-layer medium, the above Green's function can be decomposed into its direct and reflection components:

$$G(\mathbf{g}|\mathbf{x}) = G(\mathbf{g}|\mathbf{x})^{dir} + G(\mathbf{g}|\mathbf{x})^{rfl},$$
$$G(\mathbf{s}|\mathbf{x}) = G(\mathbf{s}|\mathbf{x})^{dir} + G(\mathbf{s}|\mathbf{x})^{rfl}, \quad (8)$$

where $G(\mathbf{g}|\mathbf{x})^{dir}$ and $G(\mathbf{g}|\mathbf{x})^{rfl}$ are, respectively, the Green's function for the direct wave and upgoing reflection in the upper layer. Inserting Eq. (8) into the migration kernel in Eq. (6) results in the five migration kernels shown in Fig. 4, each of which is used to smear residuals along one of the five yellow colored wavepaths (Liu et al., 2011; Zhan et al., 2014).

14.3.1.1 Reflection migration

Reflection migration smears residuals along the yellow colored ellipse in Fig. 4e for a specified source and receiver pair. When two traces are migrated, Fig. 3b suggests that the minimum width and height of the intersecting fat ellipses define the resolution limits of reflection migration.

The formulas for migration resolution limits were more rigorously derived (Beylkin, 1985) by applying the migration kernel to traces that only contain the diffraction arrival from a single diffractor. For a localized scatterer[4] in a background medium with smooth velocity variations, Eq. (6) asymptotically becomes the Fourier integral over the model wavenumbers k_x and k_z:

$$\delta m(\mathbf{x})^{mig} = \alpha \int_{\mathcal{D}} e^{-i\mathbf{k}\cdot\mathbf{x}} \delta M(\mathbf{k}) J^{-1} dk_x dk_z, \quad (9)$$

where α is related to geometrical spreading, J is the Jacobian, which is derived in Appendix C, and the range of model wavenumbers $\mathcal{D}$ in the integral depends on the range of source–receiver pairs. In fact, the model wavenumber vector $\mathbf{k}$ can be equated to the sum of the source–scatterer and geophone–scatterer wavenumbers $\mathbf{k} = \mathbf{k}_{gr_o} + \mathbf{k}_{sr_o}$ shown in Fig. 5. We will now show how Eqs. (6) and (9) can be used to estimate the resolution limits of the other wavepaths in Fig. 4a–d.

14.3.1.2 Diving wave transmission

Migration of the diving wave residual along the yellow transmission wavepath in Fig. 4a provides the low-wavenumber velocity update for waveform inversion (Mora, 1989; Zhou et al., 1995), or wave equation traveltime inversion (Woodward, 1989, 1992; Luo and Schuster, 1991) if the trace residual is replaced by the recorded trace weighted by the traveltime residual. The boundary of the first Fresnel zone wavepath[5] is defined by values of $\mathbf{x}$ for the delayed diving wave time $\tau_{sg}^{dive} + T/2 = \tau_{sx} + \tau_{xg}$, where τ_{sg}^{dive} is the diving wave traveltime at the geophone location $\mathbf{g}$. As illustrated in Fig. 2b, the minimum width and height of the intersecting fat ellipses define the effective resolution limits of transmission tomography (Williamson, 1991) or transmission migration (Sheley and Schuster, 2003).

More rigorously, Appendix B shows that the model resolution Eq. (6) for diving waves can be transformed into the Fourier integral

$$\delta m(\mathbf{x})^{mig} = \alpha \int_{\mathcal{D}_{\tau_o}} e^{-i\mathbf{k}\cdot\mathbf{x}} \delta M(\mathbf{k}) J^{-1} dk_x dk_z, \quad (10)$$

where α is a term related to geometrical spreading and $\mathcal{D}_{r_o}$ defines the range of source–geophone pairs whose first Fresnel zone wavepaths visit the scatterer localized at $\mathbf{r}_o$. The formulas for resolution limits are the same as in Eq. (2), except $\mathcal{D}$ is replaced by $\mathcal{D}_{r_o}$.

The range of allowable source–geophone pairs (see Sheng and Schuster, 2003) in $\mathcal{D}_{r_o}$ is illustrated in Fig. 6b,

---

[4]We will assume a 2D model where the "point" source and scatterer are equivalent to a line source and a line scatterer, with no field variations along the y-axis.

[5]Dahlen (2004) refers to the shape of a diving wavepath as a banana.

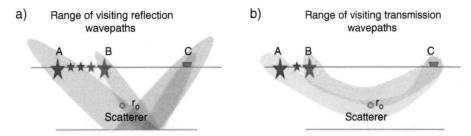

Fig. 6. Range of sources ($\star$) that generate a) reflection and b) transmission wavepaths that visit the scatterer ($\circ$). Here, the wavepath is approximated by the first Fresnel zone for the specified source and geophone pair.

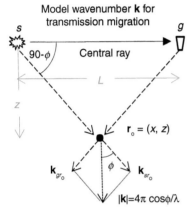

Fig. 7. Transmission ray and scatterer at $\mathbf{r}_o = (x, z)$ where $x = L/2$ for a homogeneous medium. We assume $L \gg z$ and z is equal to the half-width $z \approx \sqrt{\lambda L/4}$ of the 1st Fresnel zone in a homogeneous medium. In this case, $\cos\phi \approx z/\sqrt{L^2/4 + z^2} \approx 2z/L$; inserting the half-width formula gives $\cos\phi \approx \sqrt{\lambda/L}$ so $k_z = 4\pi \cos\phi/\lambda = 4\pi/\sqrt{L\lambda}$.

where only the sources between the blue and red stars will contribute to the slowness update around the scatterer point at $\mathbf{r}_o$. This differs from the Fourier integral in Eq. (9) for diffraction imaging where *all* source–geophone pairs contribute to the integration domain in $\mathcal{D}$ for a recorded diffraction. Hence, the resolution limits for migrating transmission residuals with the kernel $[G(\mathbf{g}|\mathbf{x})^{dir}G(\mathbf{x}|\mathbf{s})^{dir}]^*$ should be worse than migrating diffraction residuals with the same kernel.

The precise connection between intersecting wavepaths in Fig. 2b, the range of available wavenumbers, and resolution limits in Eq. (2) can be made by assuming a homogeneous medium. In this case, Fig. 7 shows that the half-width Δz of the first Fresnel zone at the point midway between the source and geophone is equal to

$$\Delta z = \sqrt{L\lambda/4}, \qquad (11)$$

where L is the distance between the source and geophone, which is equal to that given by Eq. (2). It also shows that Δz is inversely proportional to the sum of the source–scatterer and geophone–scatterer wavenumbers, implying that min

$1/k_z$ is equivalent to finding the width of the wavepath intersections in Fig. 2b.

For a single source–geophone pair, the *best direction of transmission spatial resolution for a slowness anomaly midway between the source and geophone is perpendicular to the central ray*. This means that a slowness anomaly moved perpendicular to the ray from the central ray would lead to the most noticeable change in the transmission arrival. The *worst direction of spatial resolution is along the ray itself* because the slowness anomaly can be slid along it without changing the traveltime; moreover, the model wavenumber $\mathbf{k} = \mathbf{k}_{sx} + \mathbf{k}_{xg}$ is zero all along the transmission central ray for a homogeneous medium.

14.3.1.3 Reflection–transmission

Migrating the reflection arrival with any of the kernels in the first column of Fig. 4b–c leads to the low-wavenumber velocity update along the rabbit-ear wavepaths in Fig. 4b–c or Fig. 1a.

The corresponding resolution formula for the rightmost rabbit-ear wavepath is

$$\delta m(\mathbf{x})^{mig} = \omega^4 \int_{D_{r_o}} \left[G(\mathbf{g}|\mathbf{x})^{dir} G(\mathbf{x}|\mathbf{s})^{refl} \right]^*$$
$$\times \int_{\Omega_{gs}} G(\mathbf{g}|\mathbf{y})^{dir} G(\mathbf{s}|\mathbf{y})^{refl} \delta m(\mathbf{y}) dy^2 dx_g dx_s, \qquad (12)$$

and, as before, can be analyzed for the resolution limits. However, now the asymptotic Green's functions for the transmitted arrival $G(\mathbf{g}|\mathbf{x})^{dir}$ and the reflection field

$$G(\mathbf{x}|\mathbf{s})^{refl} = A_{sx}^{refl} e^{-i\omega\tau_{sx}^{refl}}, \qquad (13)$$

are plugged into Eq. (12) to give the resolution limits for updating the velocity by smearing the reflection residual along the rabbit ears. Here, A_{sx}^{refl} accounts for amplitude and phase effects from geometrical spreading and the reflection coefficient; τ_{sx}^{refl} is the time it takes reflection energy to propagate from the source at s to the listener at $\mathbf{x} = \mathbf{r}_o$ along the specular dashed raypath in Fig. 1a.

a)   Diffraction resolution: $\Delta r = \sqrt{\lambda L/8}$ b)   Reflection resolution: $\Delta r = \sqrt{\lambda L/4}$

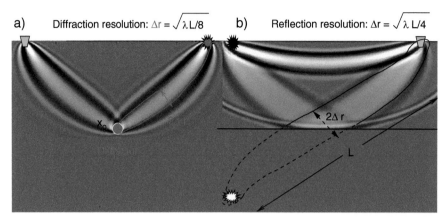

Fig. 8. Wavepaths for migrating a) diffraction (red ellipse) and b) specular reflection (black ellipse) events along their transmission wavepaths. The diffraction resolution limit $2\Delta r$ perpendicular to the widest part of the diffraction wavepath is $1/\sqrt{2}$ of that for the specular reflection. Dashed wavepath in b) is the mirror image of the source-side wavepath, with the mirror source denoted by the white star. These wavepaths were obtained by first generating acoustic data for a) a diffractor model and b) a two-layer reflector model. Windowing about the scattered arrivals, the diffraction and reflection traces were then migrated, respectively, with the kernels $[G(\mathbf{g}|\mathbf{x})^{diff} G(\mathbf{x}|\mathbf{s})^{dir}]^*$ and $[G(\mathbf{g}|\mathbf{x})^{dir} G(\mathbf{x}|\mathbf{s})^{dir}]^*$.

Estimating the resolution limits for the rabbit-ear wavepaths will result in model resolution formulas similar to that given in Fig. 4a for transmission imaging. This can be understood without going through the detailed algebra by recognizing that the upgoing reflection wavepath (rightmost rabbit ear in Fig. 1a) is identical to the transmission wavepath in Fig. 1b above the interface. This is denoted as a mirror transmission wavepath because it coincides with the first Fresnel zone for a source at the mirror position $(0, 2d)$ in a homogeneous velocity. Thus, the reflection traveltime in a) is identical to the transmission traveltime in b) for any receiver at $\mathbf{r}_o$. This means that the resolution limits defined by Eq. (2) are applicable to the transmission wavepaths in Fig. 1b and the reflection wavepaths in Fig. 1a. However, the range of available wavenumbers for the traces recorded at $\mathbf{g}$ is determined by the limited range of sources in Fig. 6a that allow for the intersection of their first Fresnel zones with the scatterer. For example, the resolution limit $2\Delta r$ perpendicular to the ray at the midpoint should be equal to $2\Delta r = \sqrt{\lambda L}$ in Fig. 1a, except the total length of the reflection ray is $L = \sqrt{X^2 + 4d^2}$.

14.3.1.4 Diffraction–transmission

How do the resolution characteristics of the diffraction–transmission wavepaths in Fig. 4d compare to those for the reflection–transmission wavepaths in Fig. 4b–c? Fig. 8 suggests that the diffraction resolution limit will be significantly better because the diffraction propagation distance is effectively halved, leading to a narrower wavepath. This means that, if the waveform residuals are used to update the velocity, then the diffraction updates will have significantly better resolution than the reflection updates.

The resolution limits for diffraction–transmission migration can be quantified according to Eq. (11), to obtain the maximum resolution limits perpendicular to the diffraction and reflection central rays: $2\Delta r^{diff} \approx \sqrt{\lambda L/2}$ and $2\Delta r^{refl} \approx \sqrt{\lambda L}$. In this case, $L/2$ is the effective length of the central ray between the geophone and the scatterer in Fig. 8a. These limits can be rigorously derived by defining the diffraction Green's function $G(\mathbf{x}|\mathbf{s})^{diff}$ as

$$G(x|s)^{diff} = A^{diff}_{sx_ox} e^{-i\omega(\tau_{sx_o} + \tau_{x_ox})}, \qquad (14)$$

where the diffractor is located at $\mathbf{x}_o$, the trial image point is at $\mathbf{x}$, and $A^{diff}_{sx_ox}$ accounts for the effects of geometrical spreading, reflection amplitude, and phase changes due to scattering. Replacing the migration kernel in Eq. (6) by $[G(\mathbf{g}|\mathbf{x})^{diff} G(\mathbf{x}|\mathbf{s})^{dir}]^*$ and the data kernel by $[G(\mathbf{g}|\mathbf{y})^{diff} G(\mathbf{y}|\mathbf{s})^{dir}]$, and using the explicit expression for the Green's functions yields the model resolution function for diffraction imaging:

$$\delta m(\mathbf{x})^{mig} = \omega^4 \int_D \left[A^{diff}_{sx_ox} A_{gx} \right]^*$$
$$\times \int_\Omega A^{diff}_{sx_oy} A_{gy} e^{i\omega(\tau_{gx} - \tau_{gy} + \tau_{x_ox} - \tau_{x_oy})} dy^2 dx_g dx_s. \quad (15)$$

The salient difference between this formula and the one for reflections in Eq. (B.4) is that τ_{x_ox} and τ_{x_oy} replace τ_{sx} and τ_{sy}. This says that the diffraction wavepath is generated by a "virtual" source at the diffractor $\mathbf{x}_o$ rather than at the actual source location $\mathbf{s}$. Hence, the diffraction wavepath should be thinner than the specular reflection wavepath in Fig. 8. In addition, every source–geophone pair has a diffraction wavepath that intersects the diffractor. This means that, similar to diffraction migration, many more diffraction wavenumbers will be available for velocity updates compared to specular reflection–transmission wavepaths.

14.3.2 Wavelength imaging at the diffractor

Figs. 4d and 8a illustrate that the width of the diffraction–transmission wavepath is proportional to λ at the diffractor location. This can be mathematically proven by locating the point **E** on the Fig. 1b ellipse so that the line through it and the focus at **g** is perpendicular to the elliptical axis. The distance between **E** and **g** is denoted as $\overline{Eg}$. In the far-field approximation, $L \gg \overline{Eg} = z_o$ so we can approximate the ellipse formula for the first Fresnel zone centering about **g** as

$$\lambda/2 = \sqrt{z_o^2 + L^2} + z_o - L \approx z_o. \qquad (16)$$

This suggests that the resolution limit of the updated velocity model is about λ near the scatterer, which is much finer than the resolution limit of $\sqrt{L\lambda/4}$ along the middle of the Fig. 8a wavepath. This unexpectedly high-resolution limit near the reflector boundaries can be observed in wave equation reflection traveltime (Zhang et al., 2012) and tomograms of MVA.

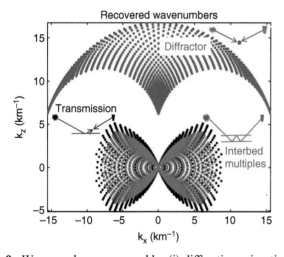

Recovered wavenumbers

Fig. 9. Wavenumbers recovered by (i) diffraction migration (denoted by blue dots) have larger magnitudes than those (denoted by black dots) recovered by (ii) specular transmission migration. Wavenumbers recovered by (iii) interbed 1st-order multiples are denoted by red dots. The red wavenumbers form a denser distribution at the low wavenumbers around the origin than (i) and (ii). The acquisition geometry is a 5 km long line of geophones and sources on the top interface with the trial image point and shallow reflector at the depth of 1 km; the deeper reflector is at the depth of 1.2 km. [Figure and caption updated from original printing.]

To illustrate the range of wavenumbers estimated from diffraction and transmission migration, Fig. 9 depicts the low wavenumbers (black dots) of the model recovered with transmission migration (see Fig. 7) and the higher wavenumbers (blue dots) recovered by diffraction migration (Fig. 5). Note the large gap between the recovered low- and high-wavenumber spectra, which will be denoted as the missing intermediate wavenumbers. The absence of such intermediate model wavenumbers is a serious challenge for waveform inversion, which will be addressed in the next section.

14.4 Filling in the model spectrum with multiples

The previous sections derived the model resolution equations for diving waves, primaries, and diffractions. What are the resolution benefits for migrating multiples,[6] particularly prism waves or interbed multiples? The short answer is that their associated central rays are longer than those of primaries, so their first Fresnel zones should be wider. This means that they can reconstruct low-wavenumber and intermediate-wavenumber models that can only be inverted with primaries at impractically wide source–geophone offsets or using sources with unrealistic low frequencies.

14.4.1 Lower wavenumber resolution with prism waves and free-surface multiples

To demonstrate the enhanced wavenumber coverage of multiples, the point-source response of the black vertical reflector in Fig. 10 is computed by a finite-difference method. The trace is windowed about the reflections and then migrated by RTM to get the prism wavepath image (Dai and Schuster, 2013). As the length L of the prism ray gets longer, the wavepath becomes thicker by $\sqrt{\lambda L}$. In this way, the deep prism-reflection wavepath provides lower wavenumber information about the model compared to primaries. Such low wavenumbers are at the top of the FWI wish list for providing a good starting model for subsalt imaging.

Another example is shown in Fig. 11. Here, the prism-wave reflection in b) achieves the same low-wavenumber resolution as the 1st-order free-surface multiple in a), but only requires about 1/2 the source–geophone offset of a). The deeper the reflector for the free-surface multiple is, the thicker is the wavepath and the lower is the wavenumber in the estimated model.

---

[6]Excluding certain multiples such as ghosts that may impair image resolution.

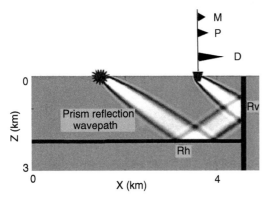

Fig. 10. Prism wavepath due to a horizontal and a vertical reflector (Rh and Rv, respectively) and a trace computed by a finite-difference solution to the wave equation. D denotes the direct arrival; P denotes the primary reflection from Rh; and M denotes the two-fold reflection from Rh and Rv. RTM was applied to the windowed events (P and M in the rectangle) to produce this wavepath. [Figure updated from original printing.]

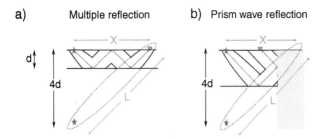

Fig. 11. Wavepaths for a) the 1st-order free-surface multiple and b) the prism-wave reflection from the yellow block. Note, the source–geophone offset for b) is about 1/2 that for a), and the dashed ellipse is the wavepath for the mirror source at the bottom left.

14.4.2 Intermediate-wavenumber resolution with interbed multiples

Figure 9 illustrates that transmission tomography (smearing residuals along rabbit ears) fills in the low-wavenumber part of the spectrum, while reflection migration (smearing residuals along ellipse) fills in the high wavenumbers. Now we show that interbed multiples can fill in some of the low and intermediate wavenumbers denoted by the red dots.

Figure 12a depicts the interbed multiple rays for a thin-bed model with a diffractor at the lower interface. Each order of the multiple will be associated with a different mirror ray, where the depth of the mirror scatterer deepens with the order of the multiple. Therefore, the raypath lengthens with order of multiple, and the wavepath thickens as well. We conclude that the mirror wavepath that intersects

the thin bed[7] thickens progressively with the order of the multiple, and so should fill in some of the "intermediate wavenumber" gap (Jannane et al., 1989) illustrated by the red dots in Fig. 9.

The above analysis can be quantified as in the previous sections by analyzing the model resolution function. In this case, the forward modeling kernel $G(\mathbf{g}|\mathbf{x})G(\mathbf{x}|\mathbf{s})$ is replaced by one that generates an internal multiple rather than a direct wave or primary reflection.[8] The phase term in the Green's function will be replaced by a summation of times corresponding to each leg of the raypaths seen in Fig. 12a. The migration kernel is also modified by terms that will image the internal multiple to one of its bounce points in the thin layer.

14.5 Discussion and summary

Formulas are derived for the resolution limits of the migration-data kernels in Fig. 4, as well as those for multiple reflections. They are applicable to images formed by RTM, LSM, and FWI. Their salient implications are the following.

1. Low- and intermediate-wavenumber information about the velocity distribution is estimated primarily by transmission migration of primaries and multiples. The intermediate wavenumbers can be supplied by interbed multiples, while the lower wavenumbers are contained in deep primaries and free-surface related multiples. Inverting multiples can be an opportunity for estimating subsurface velocity information not available in the primary reflections.

2. Inverting diffractions can provide twice or more the resolution compared to imaging primaries. Smearing residuals along the transmission wavepath can achieve a resolution of λ near the diffractor. On the other hand, diffraction energy can be more than an order-of-magnitude weaker than primary energy, so the diffraction data will be noisier.

3. Diving waves that bottom out at a certain depth will have a better vertical resolution than horizontal resolution. Therefore, it is also important to invert deep reflections to increase both the vertical and horizontal resolution. Since reflections can be an order-of-magnitude weaker than diving waves, it is recommended that diving waves be filtered from the data after a sufficient number of iterations. This might constitute an iterative multi-physics approach to FWI, where inverting

---

[7]The sampling interval between wavenumbers associated with each order of multiple becomes smaller with thinner beds.

[8]This kernel corresponds to just one of the terms in the Neumann series expansion of the Lippmann–Schwinger equation (Stolt and Benson, 1986).

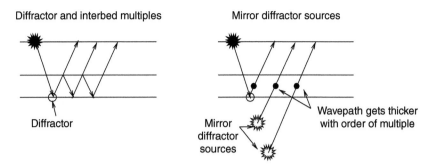

Fig. 12. a) Ray diagram for interbed multiples generated by a diffractor in a thin layer and b) the associated mirror sources diagram. As the order of the interbed multiple increases, so does the thickness of its transmission wavepaths at the filled circles •.

a different type of wavefield should be emphasized at different depths and iteration numbers.

4. The transmission migration kernels in Fig. 4a–d are of the same type as their data kernels. This leads to velocity updates along the transmission wavepaths. In contrast, the traditional migration kernel $[G(\mathbf{g}|\mathbf{x})^{dir}G(\mathbf{x}|\mathbf{s})^{dir}]^*$ in Fig. 4e is a product of two Green's functions for direct waves, while the data kernel is a product of a reflection and a direct-wave Green's function. This mismatch in the type of kernel does not lead to the traditional wavepath where seismic energy propagates, but gives the migration ellipse, which is the zone where reflection energy could have originated, i.e., the interface.

The limitation of this study is that it does not take into account the non-linear effects of resonant or evanescent energy (Fleming, 2008) in determining resolution. Utilizing resonant or evanescent energy with FWI could provide, in theory, resolution much better than λ. It is expected that multiple scattering arrivals between neighboring subwavelength scatterers might provide the extra resolution needed, but not accounted for in this current study.

Acknowledgment

Research reported in this publication was supported by King Abdullah University of Science and Technology (KAUST).

Appendix A.
Resolution properties of Fresnel volume in constant and layered media

We first analyze the resolution of the ellipse depicted in Fig. 1b, and then relate the parameters of this ellipse to an ellipsoid and to those defining a wavepath. Lastly, we examine the case of multilayered media.

The spatial resolution limit near the point c in Fig. 1b is related to the reciprocal of the segment length $\overline{DE}$. This length can be determined by noting that the end points D and E satisfy both the equations of the ellipse and the line, written as

$$\frac{x^2}{a^2} + \frac{y^2}{b^2} = 1, \tag{A.1}$$

$$y = \tan\theta(x - c), \tag{A.2}$$

where a and b are the major and minor radii of the ellipse, respectively, and θ is the angle DE makes with the axis of the ellipse. Eqs. (A.1) and (A.2) can be reduced to a quadratic equation of one variable y, yielding two roots y_D and y_E. The distance $\overline{DE}$ is then obtained as

$$\overline{DE} = \frac{|y_D - y_E|}{|\sin\theta|},$$

$$= \frac{2ab\sqrt{b^2\cos^2\theta + (a^2 - c^2)\sin^2\theta}}{b^2\cos^2\theta + a^2\sin^2\theta}. \tag{A.3}$$

Two special cases of c and θ are immediately verified. We have $\overline{DE} = 2a$ when $\theta = 0$, and $\overline{DE} = 2b$ when $c = 0$ and $\theta = \pi/2$, i.e., the lengths of the major and the minor axes of the ellipse, respectively.

In a homogeneous and isotropic medium, the Fresnel volume is a prolate spheroid, which is an ellipsoid that is rotationally symmetric around the major axis sg depicted in Fig. 1b. Therefore, Eq. (A.3) remains invariant with respect to this rotation. For an arbitrary line of intersection passing through the major axis, the steps to calculate the resolution are: (1) to find the intercept c and the angle θ as depicted in Figs. 1b, and (2) to use eq. (A.3) for the resolution calculation.

Next, the parameters a and b of the ellipse are related to those defining the first Fresnel zone, as depicted in Fig. 1a. Let s and g be the two foci of the ellipse, the distance between s and g be L, and E be an arbitrary point on the ellipse. The first Fresnel zone is delimited by points E on the ellipse that satisfy

$$\overline{sE} + \overline{Eg} = L + \frac{\lambda}{2}. \tag{A.4}$$

$$\text{Also,} \quad \overline{sE} + \overline{Eg} = 2a, \tag{A.5}$$

is a property of the ellipse. Another property of the ellipse relates the focal distance to the major and minor radii by

$$L = 2\sqrt{a^2 - b^2}. \tag{A.6}$$

Eqs. (A.4)–(A.6) give us

$$a = \frac{L}{2} + \frac{\lambda}{4}, \tag{A.7}$$

and

$$b = \sqrt{\frac{\lambda L}{4} + \frac{\lambda^2}{16}}. \tag{A.8}$$

In the limit of $L \gg \lambda, b \rightarrow \frac{1}{2}\sqrt{\lambda L}$. From Eqs. (A.7), (A.8), and (A.3), we see that the resolution can be written as $\overline{DE}(L, \lambda, c, \theta)$, a function of wavepath parameters L, λ, and intersection parameters c and θ.

Lastly, in the case of multilayered media, as denoted by the brown lines in Fig. 1a, we rewrite Eq. (A.4) in terms of traveltimes (cf. Eq. (1)) as

$$\tau_{sE} + \tau_{Eg} = \tau_{sg} + T/2. \tag{A.9}$$

Here, the traveltimes can be computed approximately using the RMS velocity for N layers defined by

$$v_{\text{RMS}} = \sqrt{\frac{\sum_i^N v_i^2 \Delta \tau_i}{\sum_i^N \Delta \tau_i}}, \tag{A.10}$$

where $\Delta \tau_i$ is the vertical 1-way time through the ith layer. Note that in Fig. 1a, the v_{RMS} sensed from the source s to the reflector F is equal to that sensed from F to the receiver g. Write the 1-way vertical traveltime to the reflector F at depth d as $\tau(0) = \sum_i^N \Delta \tau_i$, and the traveltime equation for multilayered media is given as

$$\tau(x) \cong \sqrt{\tau(0)^2 + x^2/v_{\text{RMS}}^2}, \tag{A.11}$$

where x is a 1-way offset, e.g., $\overline{PE}$ in Fig. 1a. By introducing an effective depth

$$d_{\text{eff}} = \tau(0)v_{\text{RMS}}, \tag{A.12}$$

we can rewrite Eq. (A11) as

$$\tau(x) \cong \frac{\sqrt{d_{\text{eff}}^2 + x^2}}{v_{\text{RMS}}}. \tag{A.13}$$

This expression, which applies to every τ term in Eq. (A.9), coincides with the case of constant velocity v_{RMS} and reflector depth d_{eff}. Therefore, for the horizontal resolution at the reflector, the previous resolution analysis based on a constant medium can apply to multilayered media, with the transformations

$$\lambda \rightarrow \lambda_{\text{RMS}} = v_{\text{RMS}}/f_0, \tag{A.14}$$

$$d \rightarrow d_{\text{eff}} = v_{\text{RMS}} \sum_i^N \Delta \tau_i, \tag{A.15}$$

where f_0 is the dominant frequency of the source wavelet. Undergoing such transformations, the effective geometry in Fig. 1a will change. Specifically,

$$L_{\text{eff}} \overset{\text{def}}{=} \overline{sg}_{\text{eff}} = \sqrt{X^2 + 4d_{\text{eff}}^2}, \tag{A.16}$$

$$\theta_{\text{eff}} = \arctan(2d_{\text{eff}}/X), \tag{A.17}$$

while c remains as 0 for this reflection geometry. The corresponding a_{eff} and b_{eff} can be computed from Eqs. (A.7) and (A.8). Finally, Eq. (A.3) can be used to compute the horizontal resolution as desired.

Appendix B.
Resolution limits for imaging diving wave residuals

The resolution limits for imaging diving wave residuals are rigorously derived by using the migration kernel in Fig. 4a for the diving wave arrival

$$\delta d(\mathbf{g}|\mathbf{s}) = \omega^4 \int_{\Omega_{gs}} G(\mathbf{g}|\mathbf{y})^{dir} G(\mathbf{y}|\mathbf{s})^{dir} \delta m(\mathbf{y}) dy^2, \tag{B.1}$$

where the integral over the model-space region Ω is approximated by the one over the region Ω_{gs}. Here, Ω_{gs} coincides with the yellow first-Fresnel zone of the diving wave in Fig. 4a for the source–geophone pair denoted by $\mathbf{s}$ and $\mathbf{g}$. This approximation recognizes that only model perturbations within the first Fresnel zone of the diving wave will strongly affect the timing and/or amplitude of the diving wave arrival at $\mathbf{g}$.

Plugging Eq. (B.1) into Eq. (6) gives

$$\delta m(\mathbf{x})^{mig} = \omega^4 \int_{D_{r_0}} \int_{\Omega_{gs}} [G(\mathbf{g}|\mathbf{x})^{dir} G(\mathbf{x}|\mathbf{s})^{dir}]^*$$
$$\times G(\mathbf{g}|\mathbf{y})^{dir} G(\mathbf{y}|\mathbf{s})^{dir} \delta m(\mathbf{y}) dy^2 dx_g dx_s. \tag{B.2}$$

We now assume a localized sub-wavelength perturbation $\delta m(\mathbf{y})$ centered at $\mathbf{r}_o = (x_o, z_o)$ that is non-zero only within a fraction of a wavelength from $\mathbf{r}_o$. In this case, the range of source–geophone pairs in D is restricted to the set D_{r_o} of source–geophone pairs that allow for first-Fresnel diving wavepaths to visit the localized perturbation centered at $\mathbf{r}_o$. These source–geophone pairs are the only ones whose transmitted diving waves[9] will be significantly influenced by the model perturbations centered at $\mathbf{r}_o$. For example, if the image point is at $\mathbf{y}$ and the geophone is at C in Fig. 6b, then D_{r_o} is limited to the sources between A and B.

For a smooth background velocity, we assume the following asymptotic Green's function for the migration and data kernels

$$G(\mathbf{x}|\mathbf{y})^{dir} = A_{xy}e^{-i\omega\tau_{xy}}, \qquad (B.3)$$

so that Eq. (B.2) becomes

$$\delta m(\mathbf{x})^{mig} = \omega^4 \int_{D_{r_o}} \int_{\Omega_{gs}} A_{sx}A_{gx}A_{sy}$$
$$\times A_{gy}e^{i\omega(\tau_{gx}+\tau_{sx}-\tau_{gy}-\tau_{sy})}\delta m(\mathbf{y})dy^2 dx_g dx_s. \quad (B.4)$$

Here, τ_{xy} is the traveltime for the transmitted wave to propagate from $\mathbf{y}$ to $\mathbf{x}$, and A_{xy} is its attendant geometrical spreading term that satisfies the transport equation.

Assuming that the sub-wavelength scatterer represented by $\delta m(\mathbf{y})$ is located within a fraction of a wavelength from the trial-image point at $\mathbf{x}$, then τ_{sy}, τ_{gy}, τ_{sx}, and τ_{gx}, can be expanded about the center point $\mathbf{r}_o$ to give

$$
\begin{aligned}
\tau_{sy} &\approx \tau_{sr_o} + \nabla\tau_{sr_o} \cdot [\mathbf{y} - \mathbf{r}_o], \\
\tau_{gy} &\approx \tau_{gr_o} + \nabla\tau_{gr_o} \cdot [\mathbf{y} - \mathbf{r}_o], \\
\tau_{sx} &\approx \tau_{sr_o} + \nabla\tau_{sr_o} \cdot [\mathbf{x} - \mathbf{r}_o], \\
\tau_{gx} &\approx \tau_{gr_o} + \nabla\tau_{gr_o} \cdot [\mathbf{x} - \mathbf{r}_o].
\end{aligned}
\qquad (B.5)
$$

Inserting these approximations into Eq. (B.4) gives

$$\delta m(\mathbf{x})^{mig} \approx \omega^4 \int_{D_{r_o}} \int_{\Omega_{gs}} A_{sx}A_{gx}A_{sy}A_{gy}e^{-i\omega\left(\nabla\tau_{gr_o}+\nabla\tau_{sr_o}\right)\cdot[\mathbf{y}-\mathbf{x}]}$$
$$\times \delta m(\mathbf{y})dy^2 dx_g dx_s.$$

---

[9]We exclude the case where the scatterer–diving wave interaction produces significant diffractions, so that all source–geophone pairs see significant diffraction energy, not just changes in the diving wave arrival. This would be the case where the scatterer only has a velocity contrast but no impedance contrast.

Under the far-field approximation, the geometric spreading terms can be taken outside the integral to give

$$\delta m(\mathbf{x})^{mig} = \omega^4 \int_{D_{r_o}} A_{sx}A_{gx}A_{sr_o}A_{gr_o}$$
$$\times \int_{\Omega_{gs}} e^{-i\omega\left(\nabla\tau_{gr_o}+\nabla\tau_{sr_o}\right)\cdot[\mathbf{y}-\mathbf{x}]}\delta m(\mathbf{y})dy^2 dx_g dx_s. \quad (B.6)$$

Here, the gradient of the traveltime field $\nabla\tau_{sr_o}$ is parallel to the direct wave's incident angle at $\mathbf{r}_o$, so, according to the dispersion equation, $\omega\nabla\tau_{sr_o} = \mathbf{k}_{sr_o}$ can be identified as the source-to-scatterer point wavenumber vector $\mathbf{k}_{sr_o}$; similarly, the geophone-to-scatterer wavenumber is denoted as $\omega\nabla\tau_{gr_o} = \mathbf{k}_{gr_o}$. This means that, by definition of the Fourier transform with a restricted domain of integration $\delta M(\mathbf{k}) = \int_{\Omega_{gs}} e^{-i\mathbf{k}\cdot\mathbf{y}}\delta m(\mathbf{y})dy^2$, Eq. (B.6) becomes

$$\delta m(\mathbf{x})^{mig} \approx \omega^4 A_{s_o g_o r_o}^4 \int_{D_{r_o}} e^{i\left(\mathbf{k}_{gr_o}+\mathbf{k}_{sr_o}\right)\cdot\mathbf{x}}\delta M(\mathbf{k}_{gr_o}+\mathbf{k}_{sr_o})dx_g dx_s, \quad (B.7)$$

where $A_{s_o g_o r_o}$ approximates the geometrical spreading for the scatterer at $\mathbf{r}_o$ with the range of allowable source–geophone pairs centered around the pairs denoted by $s_o g_o$, the Fourier spectrum of the model is given by $\delta M(\mathbf{k})$, and the model wavenumber components $\mathbf{k} = (k_x, k_z)$ are

$$
\begin{aligned}
k_x &= k_{sx_o} + k_{gx_o} = \omega s(\mathbf{r}_o)\left(\sin\beta_{sr_o} + \sin\beta_{gr_o}\right), \\
k_z &= k_{sz_o} + k_{gz_o} = \omega s(\mathbf{r}_o)\left(\cos\beta_{sr_o} + \cos\beta_{gr_o}\right),
\end{aligned}
\qquad (B.8)
$$

where β_{sr_o} and β_{gr_o} denote the incidence angles of the source and geophone rays, respectively, at the scatterer's location $\mathbf{y} = (x_o, z_o)$. As shown in this appendix, these incidence angles are implicit functions of the source $(x_s, 0)$, geophone $(x_g, 0)$, and scatterer $\mathbf{r}_o = (x_o, z_o)$ coordinates.

The determinant of the Jacobian in Eq. (C.2) (see Appendix C) can be used to map the $dx_g dx_s$ integration in Eq. (B.7) to the $dk_x dk_z$ integration:

$$\delta m(\mathbf{x})^{mig} = \omega^4 A_{s_o g_o r_o}^4 \int_{\mathcal{D}_{r_o}} e^{-i\mathbf{k}\cdot\mathbf{x}}\delta M(\mathbf{k})J^{-1}dk_x dk_z, \quad (B.9)$$

where $\mathcal{D}_{r_o}$ is the set of wavenumbers that Eq. (B.8) maps from the source–geophone pairs in D_{r_o} for the scatterer at $\mathbf{r}_o$, and J is the determinant of the Jacobian matrix in Eq. (C.2).

Appendix C.

Determinant of a Jacobian matrix

The transformation between the data coordinates $(x_g, 0)$, $(x_s, 0)$ and $(k_x, k_z) = \left(k_{sx_o} + k_{gx_o}, k_{sz_o} + k_{gz_o}\right)$ is given by

$$
\begin{pmatrix} dk_x \\ dk_z \end{pmatrix} = \begin{bmatrix} \dfrac{\partial k_x}{dx_g} & \dfrac{\partial k_x}{dx_s} \\[2mm] \dfrac{\partial k_z}{\partial x_g} & \dfrac{\partial k_z}{\partial x_s} \end{bmatrix} \begin{pmatrix} dx_g \\ dx_s \end{pmatrix}, \qquad \text{(C.1)}
$$

where the 2×2 matrix is the Jacobian matrix. The scaled determinant J of the Jacobian matrix is given by

$$
J = \omega^4 \left| \frac{\partial k_x}{dx_g} \frac{\partial k_z}{\partial x_s} - \frac{\partial k_x}{dx_s} \frac{\partial k_z}{\partial x_g} \right|, \qquad \text{(C.2)}
$$

so that $dk_x dk_z = J dx_g dx_s$. In the case of a homogeneous medium with velocity c and a scatterer at $\mathbf{r}_o = (x_o, z_o)$, the model wavenumbers are

$$
\begin{aligned}
k_x &= \frac{\omega(x_o - x_g)}{c\sqrt{(x_o - x_g)^2 + z_o^2}} + \frac{\omega(x_o - x_s)}{c\sqrt{(x_o - x_s)^2 + z_o^2}}, \\[2mm]
k_z &= \frac{\omega z_o}{c\sqrt{(x_o - x_g)^2 + z_o^2}} + \frac{\omega z_o}{c\sqrt{(x_o - x_s)^2 + z_o^2}},
\end{aligned} \qquad \text{(C.3)}
$$

so that the partial derivatives of the wavenumbers can be easily determined. For a heterogeneous medium, the derivatives can be approximated by finite-difference approximations to the first-order derivatives and the wavenumbers can be computed by a ray-tracing method. Under the far-field approximation $z \gg L$, where L is the aperture width of the source–geophone array, so Eq. (C.3) becomes

$$
\begin{aligned}
k_x &\approx \frac{\omega(x_o - x_g)}{c z_o} + \frac{\omega(x_o - x_s)}{c z_o}, \\[2mm]
k_z &\approx \frac{2\omega}{c},
\end{aligned} \qquad \text{(C.4)}
$$

where the horizontal wavenumbers are now linear functions of the data variables x_g and x_s. This means that Eq. (B.7) represents the inverse Fourier transform of the model spectrum.

References

Baysal, E., Kosloff, D.D., Sherwood, J.W.C., 1983. Reverse time migration. Geophysics 48, 1514–1524.

Berkhout, A.J., 1984. Seismic Resolution: A Quantitative Analysis of Resolving Power of Acoustical Echo Techniques. Geophysical Press.

Beylkin, G., 1985. Imaging of discontinuities in the inverse scattering problem by inversion of a causal generalized radon transform. J. Math. Phys. 26, 99–108.

Buddensiek M.L., Sheng, J., Crosby, T., Schuster, G., Bruhn, R., He, R., 2008. Colluvial wedge imaging using traveltime and waveform tomography along the Wasatch Fault near Mapleton, Utah. Geophys. J. Int. 172, 686–697.

Bunks, C., Saleck, F.M., Zaleski, S., Chavent, G., 1995. Multi-scale seismic waveform inversion. Geophysics 60, 1457–1473.

Cerveny, V., Soares, J.E.P., 1992. Fresnel volume ray tracing. Geophysics 57, 902–915.

Chen, J., Schuster, G.T., 1999. Resolution limits of migrated images. Geophysics 64, 1046–1053.

Claerbout, J., 1992. Earth Soundings Analysis: Processing Versus Inversion. Blackwell Scientific Publications, Cambridge, Massachusetts.

Dahlen, F., 2004. Resolution limit of traveltime tomography. Geophys. J. Int. 157, 315–331.

Dai, W., Schuster, G.T., 2013. Reverse time migration of prism waves for salt flank delineation. SEG Technical Program Expanded Abstracts, pp. 3861–3865.

Dai, W., Fowler, P., Schuster, G.T., 2012. Multi-source least-squares reverse time migration. Geophys. Prospect. 60, 681–695.

de Fornel, F., 2001. Evanescent Waves: From Newtonian Optics to Atomic Optics. Springer.

De Hoop, M., van Der Hilst, R.D., 2005. On sensitivity kernels for wave-equation transmission tomography. Geophys. J. Int. 160, 621–633.

Devaney, A., 1984. Geophysical diffraction tomography. IEEE Trans. Geosci. Remote Sens. GE-22, 3–13.

Duquet, B., Marfurt, K.J., Dellinger, J., 2000. Kirchhoff modeling, inversion for reflectivity, and subsurface illumination. Geophysics 65, 1195–1209.

Fichtner, A., 2011. Full Seismic Waveform Modelling and Inversion. Springer.

Fichtner, A., Trampert, J., 2011a. Hessian kernels of seismic data functionals based upon adjoint techniques. Geophys. J. Int. 185, 775–798.

Fichtner, A., Trampert, J., 2011b. Resolution analysis in full waveform inversion. Geophys. J. Int. 187, 1604–1624.

Fichtner, A., Kennett, B.L., Igel, H., Bunge, H.P., 2009. Full seismic waveform tomography for upper-mantle structure in the Australasian region using adjoint methods. Geophys. J. Int. 179, 1703–1725.

Fink, M., 2008. Time-reversal waves and super resolution. Journal of Physics: Conference Series. IOP Publishing, p. 012004. http://dx.doi.org/10.1088/1742-6596/124/1/012004.

Fleming, M., 2008. Far-field super resolution. Ph.D. thesis. Imperial College London.

Harlan, W.S., 1990. Tomographic estimation of shear velocities from shallow cross-well seismic data. SEG Technical Program Expanded Abstracts, pp. 86–89.

Jannane, M., Beydoun, W., Crase, E., Cao, D., Koren, Z., Landa, E., Mendes, M., Pica, A., Noble, M., Roeth, G., et al., 1989. Wavelengths of earth structures that can be resolved from seismic reflection data. Geophysics 54, 906–910.

Kravtsov, Y.A., Orlov, Y.I., 1990. Geometrical Optics of Inhomogeneous Media. Springer-Verlag.

Krebs, J.R., Anderson, J.E., Hinkley, D., Neelamani, R., Lee, S., Baumstein, A., Lacasse, M.D., 2009. Fast full-wavefield seismic inversion using encoded sources. Geophysics 74, WCC177–WCC188. http://dx.doi.org/10.1190/13230502.

Lailly, P., 1984. Migration methods: partial but efficient solutions to the seismic inverse problem. Inverse problems of acoustic and elastic waves 51, pp. 1387–1403.

Liu, F., Zhang, G., Morton, S.A., Leveille, J.P., 2011. An effective imaging condition for reverse-time migration using wavefield decomposition. Geophysics 76, S29–S39.

Luo, Y., 1991. Calculation of wavepaths for band-limited seismic waves. SEG Technical Program Expanded Abstracts, pp. 1509–1512.

Luo, Y., Schuster, G.T., 1991. Wave-equation traveltime inversion. Geophysics 56, 645–653.

Marquering, H., Dahlen, F., Nolet, G., 1999. Three-dimensional sensitivity kernels for finite-frequency traveltimes: the banana-doughnut paradox. Geophys. J. Int. 137, 805–815.

McMechan, G., 1983. Migration by extrapolation of time-dependent boundary values. Geophys. Prospect. 31, 413–420.

Menke, W., 1989. Geophysical Data Analysis: Discrete Inverse Theory. Elsevier.

Mora, P., 1988. Elastic wave-field inversion of reflection and transmission data. Geophysics 53, 750–759.

Mora, P., 1989. Inversion = migration + tomography. Geophysics 54, 1575–1586.

Nemeth, T., Wu, C., Schuster, G., 1999. Least-squares migration of incomplete reflection data. Geophysics 64, 208–221.

Pica, A., Diet, J., Tarantola, A., 1990. Nonlinear inversion of seismic reflection data in a laterally invariant medium. Geophysics 55, 284–292.

Pratt, R.G., Goulty, N.R., 1991. Combining wave-equation imaging with traveltime tomography to form high-resolution images from crosshole data. Geophysics 56, 208–224.

Safar, M.H., 1985. On the lateral resolution achieved by Kirchhoff migration. Geophysics 50, 1091–1099.

Schuster, G.T., 1996. Resolution limits for crosswell migration and traveltime tomography. Geophys. J. Int. 127, 427–440.

Schuster, G.T., Hu, J., 2000. Green's function for migration: continuous recording geometry. Geophysics 65, 167–175. http://dx.doi.org/10.1190/1.1444707.

Schuster, G.T., Hanafy, S., Huang, Y., 2012. Theory and feasibility tests for a seismic scanning tunneling macroscope. Geophys. J. Int. 190, 1593–1606.

Sheley, D., Schuster, G.T., 2003. Reduced-time migration of transmitted Ps waves. Geophysics 68, 1695–1707.

Sheng, J., Schuster, G.T., 2003. Finite-frequency resolution limits of wave path traveltime tomography for smoothly varying velocity models. Geophys. J. Int. 152, 669–676.

Shin, C., Cha, Y.H., 2008. Waveform inversion in the Laplace domain. Geophys. J. Int. 173, 922–931.

Sirgue, L., Pratt, R.G., 2004. Efficient waveform inversion and imaging. A strategy for selecting temporal frequencies. Geophysics 69, 231–248.

Stolt, R.H., Benson, A.K., 1986. Seismic Migration: Theory and Practice. Pergamon Press.

Tang, Y., 2009. Target-oriented wave-equation least-squares migration/inversion with phase-encoded HessianGeophysics 74, WCA95–WCA107. http://dx.doi.org/10.1190/1.3204768.

Tape, C., Liu, Q., Maggi, A., Tromp, J., 2009. Adjoint tomography of the Southern California crust. Science 325, 988–992.

Tarantola, A., 1984. Inversion of seismic reflection data in the acoustic approximation. Geophysics 49, 1259–1266.

Tarantola, A., 2005. Inverse Problem Theory and methods for model parameter estimation. SIAM.

Tong, J., Dahlen, F., Nolet, G., Marquering, H., 1998. Diffraction effects upon finite-frequency travel times: a simple 2-D example. Geophys. Res. Lett. 25, 1983–1986.

Van Der Hilst, R.D., Maarten, V., 2005. Banana-doughnut kernels and mantle tomography. Geophys. J. Int. 163, 956–961.

Vermeer, G.J.O., 1997. Factors affecting spatial resolution. SEG Technical Program Expanded Abstracts, pp. 27–30.

Virieux, J., Operto, S., 2009. An overview of full-waveform inversion in exploration geophysics. Geophysics 74, WCC1.

Whitmore, N., 1983. Iterative depth migration by backward time propagation. SEG Technical Program Expanded Abstracts, pp. 382–385.

Williamson, P.R., 1991. A guide to the limits of resolution imposed by scattering in ray tomography. Geophysics 56, 202–207.

Woodward, M., 1989. Wave equation tomography. Ph.D. thesis. Stanford University.

Woodward, M., 1992. Wave-equation tomography Geophysics 57, 15–26.

Wu, R.S., Toksoz, M.N., 1987. Diffraction tomography and multi-source holography applied to seismic imaging. Geophysics 52, 11–25.

Zhan, G., Dai, W., Zhou, M., Luo, Y., Schuster, G.T., 2014. Generalized diffraction-stack migration and filtering of coherent noise. Geophys. Prospect. http://dx.doi.org/10.1111/1365-2478.12086 (online).

Zhang, S., Schuster, G., Luo, Y., 2012. Angle-domain migration velocity analysis using wave equation reflection traveltime inversion. SEG Technical Program Expanded Abstracts, pp. 1–6.

Zhou, C., Cai, W., Luo, Y., Schuster, G.T., Hassanzadeh, S., 1995. Acoustic wave-equation traveltime and waveform inversion of crosshole seismic data. Geophysics 60, 765–773.

Part V

Least-Squares Migration

Chapter 15: Iterative Least-Squares Migration

Standard migration images can suffer from migration artifacts arising from 1) poor source-receiver sampling, 2) weak amplitudes caused by geometric spreading, 3) attenuation, 4) defocusing, 5) poor resolution from a limited source-receiver aperture, and 6) an oscillatory source wavelet. To partially remedy these problems, least-squares migration (LSM), also known as linearized seismic inversion (Lailly, 1983; Tarantola, 1984a; Cole and Karrenbach, 1992; Nemeth, 1996; Nemeth et al., 1999; Duquet et al., 2000) or migration deconvolution (Hu et al., 2001; Yu et al., 2006), often is proposed to invert seismic data for the reflectivity distribution. If the migration velocity model is sufficiently accurate, then LSM can mitigate many of the above problems and lead to a more resolved migration image – sometimes with twice the spatial resolution. An example is shown in Figure 15.1. However, there are two problems with LSM: the cost can be an order of magnitude more than standard migration and the quality of the LSM image is no better than the standard image for modest velocity errors. I now show how to get the most from least-squares migration by reducing the cost and the sensitivity of LSM to velocity errors.

15.1 Least-squares migration theory

The theory for least-squares migration (LSM) is described in equations 11.1 to 11.5, in which the smooth background does not change with iteration number. Only the slowness perturbation $\delta s(\mathbf{x})$ along reflector interfaces is updated significantly at each iteration to give the migration image. This algorithm is equivalent to linearized waveform inversion (Lailly, 1983; Tarantola 1984a, 1987), and it can be described for a discrete system as iteratively updating the reflectivity vector $\mathbf{m}$ by

$$\mathbf{m}^{(k+1)} = \mathbf{m}^{(k)} - \alpha \mathbf{P}\mathbf{L}^{\dagger}[\mathbf{L}\mathbf{m}^{(k)} - \mathbf{d}]$$
$$- \text{ gradient of regularization term}, \qquad (15.1)$$

in which α is the step length, $\mathbf{P}$ is the preconditioning matrix that approximates the inverse to the Hessian matrix,

$\mathbf{d}$ is the recorded reflection data, and $\mathbf{L}$ represents the linearized forward-modeling operator that uses a smooth background velocity model.[1] If the preconditioner is inadequate, a conjugate gradient or quasi-Newton method is used to update the solution iteratively. In practice, the algorithm often is implemented in the space-time domain using equation 11.10.

15.2 Overdetermined and underdetermined iterative LSM

Following Dai (2012a, 2012b) and Wang et al. (2013), there are two different strategies for applying LSM to S distinct shot gathers.

Inverting an overdetermined system of equations

The first strategy is to apply iterative LSM simultaneously to all of the shot gathers so that only one reflectivity model explains all of the data in the least-squares sense. In this case, the system of equations for all the shot gathers is overdetermined and inconsistent in the presence of noise and velocity errors, so no model can explain all of the data fully. As an example, the reflectivity model can be defined as the vector $\mathbf{m}$ and the ith shot gather as $\mathbf{d}_i$ so that the system of equations for N_p shot gathers is given by

$$\begin{pmatrix} \mathbf{d}_1 \\ \mathbf{d}_2 \\ \vdots \\ \mathbf{d}_{N_p} \end{pmatrix} = \begin{bmatrix} \mathbf{L}_1 \\ \mathbf{L}_2 \\ \vdots \\ \mathbf{L}_{N_p} \end{bmatrix} (\mathbf{m}), \qquad (15.2)$$

---

[1] A smooth velocity model typically is used so as to avoid smearing residuals along the rabbit ear wavepaths discussed in Chapters 12 and 13. The smearing of residuals only should be along the migration ellipses that are tangent to the reflector boundaries.

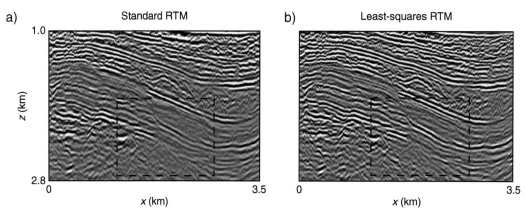

Figure 15.1. (a) RTM and (b) least-squares reverse time migration (LSRTM) images computed from Gulf of Mexico data. The RTM image is computed by migrating and stacking each shot gather, and the LSRTM image maximizes the zero-lag cross correlation between the predicted and the observed traces (Zhang et al., 2013; Dutta et al., 2014; Huang et al., 2014a). There were 515 shot gathers with 480 receivers per shot, with a shot (receiver) interval of 37.5 m (12.5 m). The cable length is 6 km. After Dutta et al. (2014).

in which $\mathbf{L}_i$ is the modeling operator for the ith shot gather. The standard migration operation can be expressed as

$$\mathbf{m}^{\mathrm{mig}} = \begin{bmatrix} \mathbf{L}_1^\dagger & \mathbf{L}_2^\dagger & \cdots & \mathbf{L}_{N_p}^\dagger \end{bmatrix} \begin{pmatrix} \mathbf{d}_1 \\ \mathbf{d}_2 \\ \vdots \\ \mathbf{d}_{N_p} \end{pmatrix} = \sum_{i=1}^{N_p} \mathbf{L}_i^\dagger \mathbf{d}_i, \quad (15.3)$$

where the final migration image is the stack of the individual prestack images.

The least-squares image is the one that minimizes the regularized misfit functional

$$f(\mathbf{m}) = \frac{1}{2} \sum_{i=1}^{N_p} \|\mathbf{L}_i \mathbf{m} - \mathbf{d}_i\|^2 + R, \quad (15.4)$$

in which R is the regularization term, and the optimal $\mathbf{m}$ is the least-squares migration image that best explains the reflection data. Regularization terms or constraints (Sacchi et al., 2006, 2007; Wang and Sacchi, 2007; Dai, 2012a, 2012b; Dai et al., 2013) can be used to account partly for misaligned reflectors because of errors in the migration velocity model.

Inverting an underdetermined system of equations

Iterative LSM is applied separately to each shot gather to get S prestack migration images. Then all S images are stacked together to get the final migration image. The value of this approach is that the stacking of misaligned reflector images arising from velocity errors is delayed until curative measures can be taken, such as applying trim statics to the common image gathers (Huang et al., 2014b).

More precisely, we assume each shot gather $\mathbf{d}_i$ is associated with its own reflectivity model $\mathbf{m}_i$, so an ensemble of prestack images $\widehat{\mathbf{m}}$ can be defined as

$$\widehat{\mathbf{m}} = \begin{pmatrix} \mathbf{m}_1 \\ \mathbf{m}_2 \\ \vdots \\ \mathbf{m}_{N_p} \end{pmatrix}. \quad (15.5)$$

Here, the modeling and migration equations can be expressed as

$$\begin{pmatrix} \mathbf{d}_1 \\ \mathbf{d}_2 \\ \vdots \\ \mathbf{d}_{N_p} \end{pmatrix} = \begin{bmatrix} \mathbf{L}_1 & & & \\ & \mathbf{L}_2 & & \\ & & \ddots & \\ & & & \mathbf{L}_{N_p} \end{bmatrix} \begin{pmatrix} \mathbf{m}_1 \\ \mathbf{m}_2 \\ \vdots \\ \mathbf{m}_{N_p} \end{pmatrix}, \quad (15.6)$$

and

$$\begin{pmatrix} \mathbf{m}_1^{\mathrm{mig}} \\ \mathbf{m}_2^{\mathrm{mig}} \\ \vdots \\ \mathbf{m}_{N_p}^{\mathrm{mig}} \end{pmatrix} = \begin{bmatrix} \mathbf{L}_1^\dagger & & & \\ & \mathbf{L}_2^\dagger & & \\ & & \ddots & \\ & & & \mathbf{L}_{N_p}^\dagger \end{bmatrix} \begin{pmatrix} \mathbf{d}_1 \\ \mathbf{d}_2 \\ \vdots \\ \mathbf{d}_{N_p} \end{pmatrix}. \quad (15.7)$$

The $\widehat{\mathbf{L}}$ forward-modeling operator for all the shot gathers is expressed as

$$\widehat{\mathbf{L}} = \begin{bmatrix} \mathbf{L}_1 & & & \\ & \mathbf{L}_2 & & \\ & & \ddots & \\ & & & \mathbf{L}_{N_p} \end{bmatrix}, \quad (15.8)$$

so that equations 15.6 and 15.7 can be rewritten in compact form

$$\mathbf{d} = \widehat{\mathbf{L}}\mathbf{m}; \quad \widehat{\mathbf{m}}^{\text{mig}} = \widehat{\mathbf{L}}^{\dagger}\mathbf{d}. \tag{15.9}$$

Therefore, the misfit functional with the ensemble of prestack images is defined as

$$f(\widehat{\mathbf{m}}) = \frac{1}{2}\sum_{i=1}^{N_p}\|\mathbf{L}_i\mathbf{m}_i - \mathbf{d}_i\|^2 + R,$$

$$= \frac{1}{2}\|\widehat{\mathbf{L}}\widehat{\mathbf{m}} - \mathbf{d}\|^2 + R. \tag{15.10}$$

The regularization term R (Dai, 2012a, 2012b; Wang et al., 2013) is

$$R = \frac{\gamma}{2}\sum_{i=1}^{N_p-1}\left\|\frac{\mathbf{m}_{i+1}}{\lambda_{i+1}} - \frac{\mathbf{m}_i}{\lambda_i}\right\|^2, \tag{15.11}$$

in which λ_i is the normalization parameter to make the amplitudes of $\mathbf{m}_i$ and $\mathbf{m}_{i+1}$ to be nearly the same magnitude, and γ is the damping coefficient that is chosen by trial-and-error testing. The regularizer function penalizes any differences between migration images computed with slightly different positions of the shots. If the data are transformed into plane-wave gathers (Stork and Kapoor, 2004; Etgen, 2005; Zhang et al., 2005) instead of shot gathers, then this is denoted (Dai and Schuster, 2013; Wang et al., 2013) as regularized plane-wave LSM. Alternatively, trim statics can be applied to the common-image gathers (CIGs) to align migrated reflections with one another (Huang et al., 2014b).

If there are no velocity errors and noise issues, strategies 1 and 2 give similar LSM images. However, if the migration velocity model has significant errors, then the overdetermined strategy cannot find a common reflectivity model with sharp interfaces that explains all of the shot gathers. The result is a smeared migration image. Therefore, the underdetermined approach often is preferred because the prestack LSM images can be aligned with one another by, e.g., trim statics, before stacking.[2]

15.3 Implementation of LSM

The implementation of LSM now is described for reverse time migration and diffraction-stack migration. Typically, diffraction-stack migration provides images with fewer artifacts because it only smears reflections along the

ellipses in Figure 13.2. In contrast, RTM automatically generates upgoing reflections from reflectors, so residuals also are smeared along the rabbit ears and cigars in Figure 13.2 to give rise to unwanted migration artifacts. These artifacts can be avoided by using a smooth model for the migration velocity and by eliminating the diving and direct waves (McMechan, 1983; Loewenthal et al., 1987).

15.3.1 Least-squares reverse time migration

Least-squares reverse time migration (LSRTM) is implemented by solving the wave equation for three types of right-hand sides (RHSs). The first type has the time history of the actual source $F(\mathbf{x}, t)$ on the RHS so that the solution to

$$\nabla^2 D(\mathbf{x}, t)_o - s(\mathbf{x})_o^2\ddot{D}(\mathbf{x}, t)_o = \overbrace{F(\mathbf{x}, t)}^{\text{source term}}, \tag{15.12}$$

gives the "downgoing" field $D(\mathbf{x}, t)_o$ in the smooth slowness model denoted by $s(\mathbf{x})_o$. The equation $(\nabla^2 - s(\mathbf{x})_o^2\partial^2/\partial t^2)D(\mathbf{x}, t)_o = F(\mathbf{x}, t)$ is symbolized by $\mathcal{L}[D_o] = F$, and its solution is $D_o = \mathcal{L}^{-1}[F]$.

The second type of wave equation is the one in which the RHS time history is given by $\ddot{D}(\mathbf{x}, t)_o$ and the source strength is $-2s(\mathbf{x})_o\delta s(\mathbf{x})$:

$$\nabla^2 U(\mathbf{x}, t) - s(\mathbf{x})_o^2\ddot{U}(\mathbf{x}, t) = \overbrace{-2s(\mathbf{x})_o\delta s(\mathbf{x})^{(k)}\ddot{D}(\mathbf{x}, t)_o}^{\text{exploding reflectors}}. \tag{15.13}$$

The solution in equation 15.13, compactly represented as $\mathcal{L}^{-1}[-2s(\mathbf{x})_o\delta s(\mathbf{x})^{(k)}\ddot{D}(\mathbf{x}, t)_o]$, is the upgoing scattered field $U(\mathbf{x}, t)^{(k)}$ emanating from exploding reflectors. Each explosion is initiated by the downgoing field $\ddot{D}(\mathbf{x}, t)_o$ when it encounters a nonzero slowness perturbation $\delta s(\mathbf{x})^{(k)}$. Note, the iteration index k is denoted as a superscript.

The third type of solution corresponds to the backward extrapolation of the residual wavefield[3] $\Delta r(\mathbf{g}, t)$ at $\mathbf{g}$ on the recording surface to get the upgoing residual wavefield $\Delta r(\mathbf{x}, t)$ at depth. Here, a single shot gather is assumed so that the index for the shot is silent. In this case, the residual traces $\Delta r(\mathbf{g}, t)$ at the surface act as virtual sources so that the residual wavefield at depth is expressed compactly as

$$\Delta r(\mathbf{x}, t) = \hat{\mathcal{L}}^{-1}[\Delta r(\mathbf{g}, t)], \tag{15.14}$$

in which the hat denotes that the solution of the wave equation is computed by temporally marching the self-adjoint FD code backward from the final time in the recorded traces to zero time. If the governing equation is real and

---

[2] Plane-wave migration images for different p values provide a more even and less noisy illumination of the subsurface than from migrated shot gathers. Hence, statics estimates or migration velocity analysis from plane-wave migration might be more reliable than from shot-gather migration.

[3] The residual is computed by subtracting the predicted traces from the recorded data at the surface.

Box 15.3.1 Preconditioned Steepest-descent Pseudocode for LSRTM

Estimate $s(\mathbf{x})_0$, $w(t)$, and C

Compute $D = \mathcal{L}^{-1}[F]$
$\delta s(\mathbf{x}) \leftarrow \sum_t p^{\text{obs}}(\mathbf{x}, t) D(\mathbf{x}, t)$

for $k = 0 : K$
$pp(\mathbf{g}, t) \leftarrow \mathcal{L}^{-1}[-2s(\mathbf{x})_o \delta s(\mathbf{x}) \ddot{D}(\mathbf{x}, t)_o]$
$\Delta r(\mathbf{g}, t) = pp(\mathbf{g}, t) - p(\mathbf{g}, t)^{\text{obs}}$

$\Delta r(\mathbf{x}, t) = \hat{\mathcal{L}}^{-1}[\Delta r(\mathbf{g}, t)]$
$\gamma(\mathbf{x}) \leftarrow 2s(\mathbf{x})_0 \sum_t \Delta r(\mathbf{x}, t) D(\mathbf{x}, t)$
$\delta s(\mathbf{x}) = \delta s(\mathbf{x}) - \alpha C(\mathbf{x}) \gamma(\mathbf{x})$
end

Estimate smooth slowness model, source
wavelet & diagonal preconditioner C
(see Chapter 11).
Solve equation 15.12 with slowness $s(\mathbf{x})_0$.
Migrate recorded reflection data $p^{\text{obs}}(\mathbf{g}, t)$;
$p^{\text{obs}}(\mathbf{x}, t)$ is the backward-extrapolated data.

Start LSM iterations.
Predict reflection data with eq. 15.13.
Compute residual at geophones.
Stop if $\frac{\|\Delta r\|_2}{\|U^{\text{obs}}\|_2} < \epsilon$.
Back propagate residual in reverse time.
Migrate residual & compute step length α.
Update slowness perturbation.

---

not self-adjoint, i.e., $\mathcal{L} \neq \mathcal{L}^\dagger$, then the adjoint wave equation (discussed in Chapter 16) is used to extrapolate the residuals.

To begin the LSM iterations, the direct and diving waves first are muted (or adaptively subtracted) from the data, and the result is migrated to get an estimate of the starting slowness perturbation $\delta s(\mathbf{x})^{(0)}$. To avoid rabbit-ear artifacts in the migration image, the forward- and back-propagation operations always employ the smooth background slowness $s(\mathbf{x})_o$. As will be discussed in section 19.2.6, the source wavelet needs to be estimated from the data and traces are normalized to a maximum value of 1, otherwise there will be nonzero residuals from the mismatch between the predicted and observed wavelets.

In practice, the LSRTM image is computed iteratively by a preconditioned conjugate gradient or Quasi-Newton method, but for simplicity, the pseudocode in Box 15.3.1 describes a preconditioned steepest-descent method for a single shot gather.

A nondiagonal preconditioner for a conjugate-gradient LSM method is used by Cabrales-Vargas and Marfurt (2013) to penalize rough solutions (see Exercise 8 in section 15.11). Other preconditioners are discussed in Chapter 19.

15.3.2 Diffraction-stack LSM

Diffraction-stack least-squares migration (Nemeth et al., 1999; Duquet et al., 2000) is free from rabbit ear artifacts because, unlike RTM, it does not generate upgoing reflections from downgoing fields. Therefore, the above pseudocode is valid for diffraction-stack LSM, except the solutions $\mathcal{L}^{-1}[F]$ and $\mathcal{L}^{-1}[-2s(\mathbf{x})_o \delta s(\mathbf{x}) \ddot{D}(\mathbf{x})]$ to equations 15.12 and 15.13 are obtained by multiplying the right-hand sides by the asymptotic Green's function and integrating over space and time. Appendix 15B contains a MATLAB® code for diffraction-stack LSM applied to simple reflector models.

15.4 Problems with LSM

The two most significant challenges with LSM are image sensitivity to the accuracy of the migration velocity model and computational cost. Another challenge is that the LSM algorithm can create false reflectors from the multiples if LSM is applied separately to each shot gather.

15.4.1 LSM sensitivity to velocity errors

The migration velocity model must be accurate enough so that the events along a common horizon in the CIG are flattened to within a half wavelength of one other. Otherwise the stacked CIGs will blur the summed LSM reflectivity image and spoil the potential improvement in spatial resolution. This suggests the need to combine a velocity inversion method such as migration velocity analysis (MVA), waveform inversion, or traveltime tomography

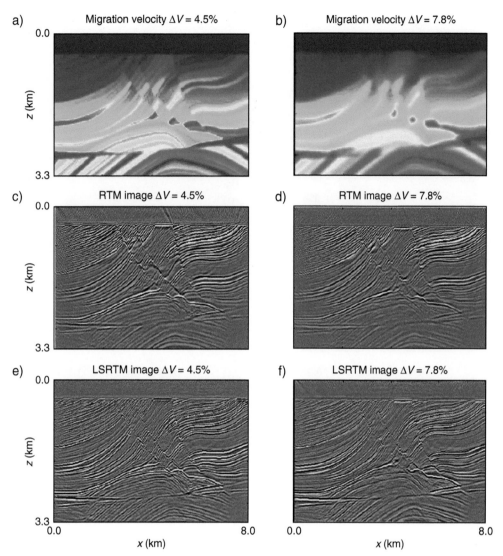

Figure 15.2. RTM and LSRTM images for the Marmousi migration velocity model with an RMS velocity error of (a) $\Delta V = 4.45\%$ and (b) $\Delta V = 7.81\%$. Illustrations courtesy of Gaurav Dutta.

to improve both the migration velocity and the reflectivity models iteratively. Regularization terms or constraints (Wang and Sacchi, 2007) also can be used to partly align the reflection events in the CIGs, but iteratively improving the velocity model is preferred.

To quantify the sensitivity of LSM to velocity errors empirically, Figures 15.2 to 15.4 present the results of synthetic simulations comparing RTM and LSRTM for different migration velocity errors. It is evident that LSRTM images show an improvement over standard RTM images only when the error in the velocity model is less than approximately 8%, where the blurring increases with increasing reflector depth. For velocity errors exceeding 10%, RTM might be preferred over LSRTM for the Marmousi model. Figure 15.4 suggests that LSRTM converges faster for increasing accuracy of the migration velocity, and

typically, around 20–30 iterations are required for acceptable images. However, larger velocity errors lead to more blurring and slower convergence rates.

15.4.2 Computational cost of LSM

Least-squares RTM is $O(3N)$ times costlier than RTM, where N is the number of LSM iterations. To reduce the cost of wave-equation LSM to acceptable levels, Appendix 15B shows how shot gathers can be encoded and blended together to form one supergather (Romero et al., 2000; Dai and Schuster, 2009; Tang and Biondi, 2009). This means that just one encoded supergather needs to be migrated at each iteration, rather than sequentially migrating hundreds of shot gathers per iteration. There are at least five strategies for encoding the shot gathers and blending them into

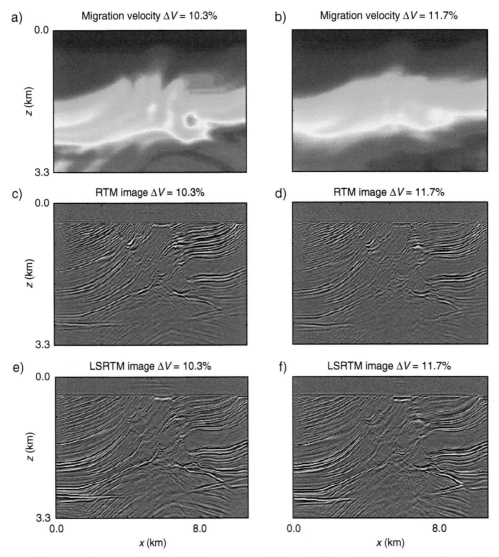

Figure 15.3. Same as Figure 15.2, except RMS velocity errors are $\Delta V = 10.3\%$ and $\Delta V = 11.7\%$. Illustrations courtesy of Gaurav Dutta.

one supergather or several subsupergathers. The benefit is to reduce the $O(N)$ cost of LSRTM to range from 8 to 0.1 times the cost of standard RTM.

15.5 Numerical results

The iterative LSM algorithm is applied to a variety of synthetic shot gathers and field data to show its benefits compared to standard migration.

15.5.1 3D point-scatterer model

For the model with a point scatterer buried at a depth of 500 m, synthetic shot gathers are generated by a diffraction-modeling method. Both Kirchhoff migration and LSM are applied to these data recorded on the surface. Figure 15.5a depicts the Kirchhoff migration image of a depth slice

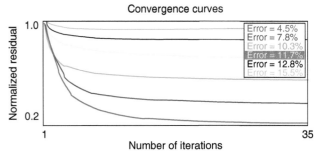

Figure 15.4. Normalized data residual versus iteration number for LSRTM with different RMS errors in the migration velocity model. After Dutta et al. (2014).

and shows many artifacts resulting from aliasing and limited aperture. These artifacts sometimes are referred to as acquisition-footprint noise.

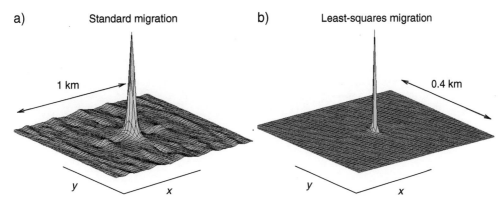

Figure 15.5. Point-scatterer responses of the 3D prestack (a) Kirchhoff migration and (b) LSM operators for a point scatterer buried at the depth of 500 m below the recording surface. The data set consists of 176 shot gathers, each with 176 traces recorded at the surface level $z = 0$, and the vertical axis represents the migration amplitude. Plots created by Xin Wang for Huang et al. (2014a).

In contrast, the LSM image in Figure 15.5b shows fewer artifacts compared to those in Figure 15.5a. This example demonstrates that LSM can reduce aliasing artifacts and achieve spatial resolution in accordance with the full bandwidth of the source spectrum, as long as the migration velocity model is accurate.

15.5.2 Partial compensation for poor source and receiver sampling

If the receiver or source intervals are widened to be larger than the apparent horizontal wavelength, then the migration image will contain aliasing artifacts, as shown in Figure 15.6a for poorly sampled traces and shot lines. These artifacts result from uncanceled migration ellipses, which become worse with coarser source and receiver distributions. In comparison, the LSM image in Figure 15.6b partly suppresses many of these artifacts and still provides high resolution in the migration image. This is because the migration artifacts are forward modeled at each iteration to give corresponding artifacts in the predicted data. Such data-domain noise increases the misfit error, so the LSM image will tend to find the reflectivity model with fewer aliasing artifacts. However, if the trace spacing is too large, then LSM will not eliminate the severe aliasing artifacts.

15.5.3 Poststack migration of Gulf of Mexico data

A marine data set recorded in the Gulf of Mexico (courtesy of ExxonMobil Corporation) is processed where the 2D stacked section is used as the input traces into the LSM algorithm (Nemeth et al., 1999). The poststack migration image is shown in Figure 15.7a, and the LSM image after 15 iterations is shown in Figure 15.7b. As in the

synthetic data examples, the LSM images have reflectivity strengths that are better balanced and some migration artifacts are suppressed. The CDP interval for these data is 25 m, so these data are not aliased, and consequently, the acquisition-footprint is negligible.

Figure 15.8 zooms into the white boxes to reveal better resolution in the LSM images. This is not surprising for vertical resolution because the LSM method performs a wavelet deconvolution step. However, there is better lateral resolution in the LSM images as delineated by the more highly resolved fault structures. The fault is more clearly defined, layers are thinner, and there is better interface continuity, partly because poststack LSM is immune to the misalignment issues suffered by prestack LSM for an inaccurate velocity model.

15.5.4 Prestack migration of Gulf of Mexico data

Marine seismic data are recorded in the Gulf of Mexico (courtesy ExxonMobil Corporation), using 515 shots with a 37.5-m interval, in which the source-receiver offsets are from 198 m to 6 km, with a 12.5-m receiver spacing. The trace length is 10 s with a 2-ms sampling interval. Prior to migration, the source wavelet is estimated by stacking early arrivals from the near-offset traces. The velocity model is obtained by waveform inversion of the early arrivals.

The data are transformed into plane-wave gathers (Wang et al., 2013) and migrated by a plane-wave, diffraction-stack migration method and its LSM implementation is denoted as plane-wave LSM (PLSM). In this case, the underdetermined approach is used where each plane-wave gather enjoys a separate LSM, and if the regularization term in equation 15.11 is used, then this is denoted as regularized plane-wave LSM (RPLSM). See Appendix 15B for details.

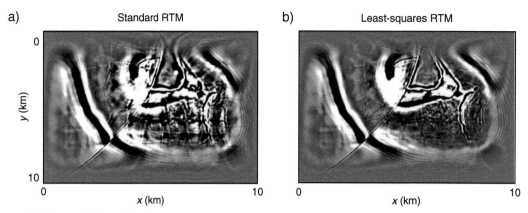

Figure 15.6. Depth slices of (a) standard RTM and (b) LSRTM images for the 3D SEG/EAGE salt model. There are 45 shot gathers, 200 receivers per shot, nine shots along each sail line, and a total of five sail lines. After Dutta et al. (2014).

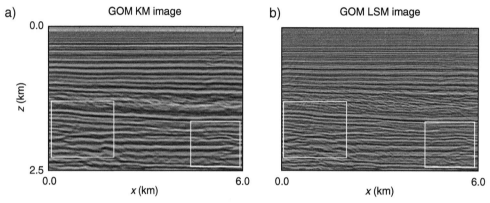

Figure 15.7. Poststack migration images for Gulf of Mexico (GOM) data computed by (a) standard Kirchhoff-like migration and (b) LSM after 30 iterations. After Nemeth et al. (1999).

Figures 15.9a–15.9d show the conventional Kirchhoff migration (KM), plane-wave Kirchhoff migration (PKM), PLSM, and RPLSM images, respectively. The quality of the KM and PKM images is comparable, and the shallow reflectors are highly resolved with PKM, although the deep reflector images contain more artifacts. Figure 15.10 shows the two zoom views of PKM, PLSM, and RPLSM images, which are marked as boxes in Figure 15.9. Similar to the synthetic results, Figure 15.10 shows that the PLSM and RPLSM images are of better quality in the shallow region (image I) than the KM image. Also, the PLSM image has slightly higher quality than the RPLSM image, which indicates the velocity at shallow depth is accurate. However, for the deep image (image II), the PLSM image shows a much higher level of noise, and the RPLSM provides a better quality image with fewer artifacts. It also shows more reflector continuity but with lower resolution. For comparison, the image quality of PKM and RPLSM are the best.

By analyzing the CIGs of PKM and RPLSM (Wang et al., 2013), it is found that RPLSM increases the prestack image resolution more than KM. However, after stacking the final image is blurred, which is a symptom of an inaccurate velocity model. A trim statics technique might

be needed to provide a better stacked image. In addition, the high-resolution prestack images can be used to correct the velocity model by migration velocity analysis.

15.6 LSM with a crosscorrelation objective function

Instead of finding the reflectivity model that minimizes the L_2 norm of the data residual, Zhang et al. (2013) propose finding the reflectivity model that minimizes the weighted sum of the zero-lag crosscorrelation of the predicted $\hat{d}(t)_{s,g}$ and observed $\hat{d}(t)_{s,g}^{\text{obs}}$ normalized traces:

$$\epsilon = -\sum_{s,g,t} \hat{d}(t)_{s,g} \hat{d}(t)_{s,g}^{\text{obs}}. \tag{15.15}$$

Here, the hat symbol indicates that the trace associated with the source-geophone index (s, g) is normalized by the L_2 norm of that trace; e.g., $\hat{d}(t)_{s,g} = \frac{d(t)_{s,g}}{\|d(t)_{s,g}\|}$, where $d(t)_{s,g}$ is the unnormalized trace. If the predicted and observed traces perfectly match one another, then $\epsilon = -1$, otherwise $-1 < \epsilon$.

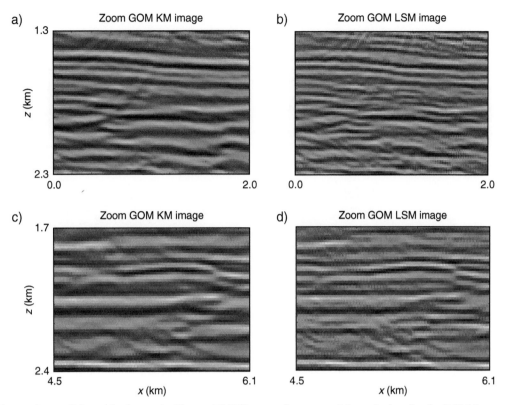

Figure 15.8. Zoom views of the white boxes in Figure 15.7 illustrate better spatial resolution for the LSM images. After Nemeth et al. (1999).

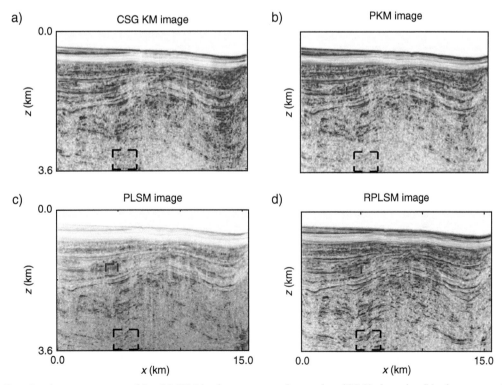

Figure 15.9. Migration images computed by (a) KM in the common shot gather (CSG) domain, (b) plane-wave Kirchhoff migration (PKM), (c) plane-wave least-squares migration (PLSM), and (d) regularized plane-wave least-squares migration (RPLSM). After Wang et al. (2013).

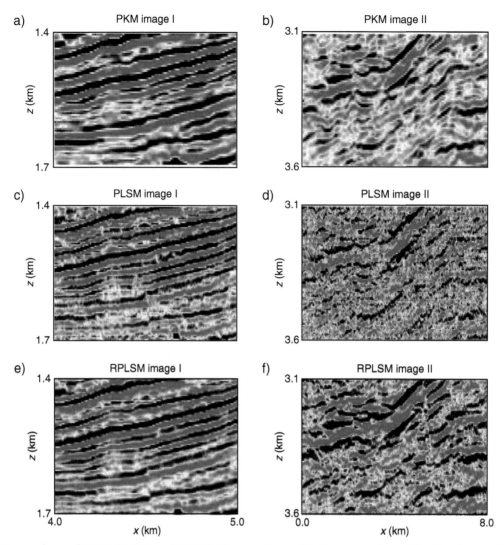

Figure 15.10. Zoom views of PKM, PLSM, and RPLSM images. Image I is the zoom view of the blue box and image II is the zoom view of the black box. After Wang et al. (2013).

The corresponding iterative LSM method requires the gradient of equation 15.15:

$$\frac{\partial \epsilon}{\partial s(\mathbf{x})} = -\sum_{s,g,t} \frac{1}{\|d(t)_{s,g}\|} \frac{\partial d(t)_{s,g}}{\partial s(\mathbf{x})} \overbrace{[\alpha_{s,g}\hat{d}(t)_{s,g} - \hat{d}(t)_{s,g}^{\text{obs}}]}^{\text{weighted residual}},$$

(15.16)

in which $\alpha_{s,g} = \sum_t \hat{d}(t)_{s,g}\hat{d}(t)_{s,g}^{\text{obs}}$ and $\frac{\partial d(t)_{s,g}}{\partial s(\mathbf{x})}$ is the Fréchet derivative of the data (see Chapter 11). The interpretation of equation 15.16 is that the gradient is computed by a zero-lag correlation between the back-propagated weighted residual and the forward-modeled source field.

Instead of predicting both amplitudes and phases of events, correlation-based LSM is tasked mainly to match the phase of the observed events. The benefit is that migration artifacts associated with improper modeling of geometrical spreading or attenuation should be lessened.

As an example, Figure 15.11a is a reflectivity section from the Marmousi model, and Figure 15.11b is the LSRTM image obtained by standard LSRTM. Here, the input traces are computed by a viscoacoustic modeling algorithm with the Q model shown in Figure 16.1. The target reservoir, indicated by the deepest black arrow, is delineated better in the phase-inverted LSRTM image with balanced amplitudes. However, these are not the true amplitudes needed for amplitude-versus-offset analysis, which highlights a limitation of this method.

15.7 LSRTM with internal multiples

If the background velocity model $v(x, y, z)$ is updated during the LSRTM iterations, then this procedure is classified as a nonlinear LSRTM. Unlike a smooth background, a background velocity model with sharp reflectors will enable the modeling of multiple reverberations from the sharp

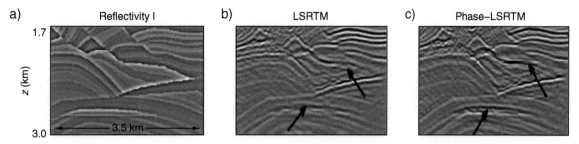

Figure 15.11. (a) Reflectivity, (b) LSRTM, and (c) phase-based LSRTM images of a section of the Marmousi model. After Dutta et al. (2014).

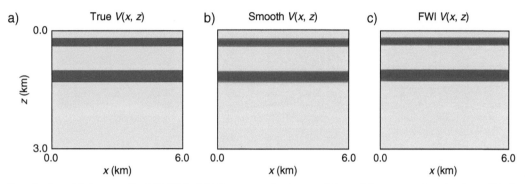

Figure 15.12. Interbed multiples test for LSRTM: (a) The true velocity model used for generating the data, (b) the smooth velocity model often used in RTM and LSRTM, and (c) the hybrid FWI velocity model. After AlTheyab (2013).

interfaces, and therefore allow for their migration. This is not possible with LSRTM and a smooth velocity model.

This capability is illustrated with data generated for the model in Figure 15.12a, where there are two shallow interbed multiples generators, and a deep anticline. The hybrid FWI velocity model in Figure 15.12c has sharp boundaries automatically sharpened by a LSRTM method (AlTheyab et al., 2013). Figure 15.13 shows the RTM and LSRTM results using the smooth and hybrid FWI velocity models. Results based on the smooth model have a false reflector interfering with the anticline image. This false reflector is a result of interbed multiples, which are not taken into account by modeling with a smooth background model. The same artifact still occurs when using the hybrid FWI velocity model for RTM. However, interbed multiples are taken into account in the LSRTM inversion, if the sharp reflectors are used in the background velocity model. As a result, the LSRTM image in Figure 15.13c shows an accurate estimate of the deep anticline without the false reflector induced by the multiples. Other nonlinear RTM methods for imaging multiples are presented by Malcolm et al. (2011), Berkhout (2012), Davydenko et al. (2012), Fleury and Snieder (2012), and Soni and Verschuur (2013).

15.8 Trim statics and LSM

If the common reflectors in two prestack migration images are misaligned in depth by more than a half-wavelength for different shot gathers, then adding them together will lead to a smeared image. This will be true for both the overdetermined (see equation 15.3) and the underdetermined (see equation 15.9) migration images if there are significant errors in the migration velocity model. To alleviate this problem, a trim-statics shift can be used to align the prestack migration images with one another prior to stack. The benefit is a more coherent migration image in the presence of inaccurate migration velocities, but the liability might be an erroneous positioning of the reflector image.

One such alignment procedure is an adaptive stacking method. Consider misaligned reflector images in the two prestack migration images denoted as $m(x,z)^A$ and $m(x,z)^B$. The common reflector in both images should be stacked coherently together, so an arbitrary pixel at (x,z) in $m(x,z)^A$ should stack coherently with its most similar counterpart in $m(x,z)^B$ near a small neighborhood around (x,z). This compares to conventional stacking of the event at (x,z) in both the $m(x,z)^A$ and $m(x,z)^B$ images. For a pair of pixels at (x,z) and $(x+\delta x,z+\delta z)$, the similarity based on the pixel values of (x,z) and $(x+\delta x,z+\delta z)$ alone generally is not reliable.

A more telling similarity might be the average amplitude or reflector slope within small image patches, of the extent of a few wavelengths, surrounding (x,z) and $(x+\delta x,z+\delta z)$. A pairwise stacking, between images $m(x,z)^A$ and $m(x,z)^B$, is selected when each pixel is stacked with

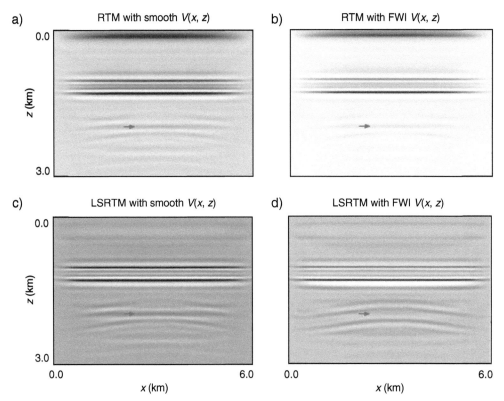

Figure 15.13. Migration images in (a) and (b) migrated with, respectively, the Figure 15.12a smooth velocity model and the Figure 15.12b velocity model with sharp boundaries defined by hybrid FWI (AlTheyab et al., 2013). Figures (c) and (d) are obtained by LSRTM using the smooth-velocity and FWI-velocity models, respectively. The false flat reflector (highlighted by blue arrows) in (a–c) is generated by incorrect imaging of the interbed multiples from shallow layers. In (d), the false reflector is attenuated and the deep anticline is imaged properly. Figure courtesy of Abdullah AlTheyab.

its best counterpart.[4] A four-fold stacking, among images $m(x,z)^A$, $m(x,z)^B$, $m(x,z)^C$, and $m(x,z)^D$, is achieved by two levels of pairwise stacking, e.g., stack $(m(\mathbf{x})^A, m(\mathbf{x})^B)$ together and stack $(m(\mathbf{x})^C, m(\mathbf{x})^D)$ together, and then stack the two stacked images together. This generalizes to stacking any number of images, termed stacking by trim statics. This stacking procedure can be carried out after all of the prestack LSM images are computed, or it can be done after every few iterations. The results shown in Figure 15.14 were obtained after the prestack LSM images were computed (Huang et al., 2014b).

Figures 15.14a and 15.14b contrast the two methods of stacking produced by least-squares Kirchhoff plane-wave migration of plane-wave gathers for 31 different incident angles (Wang et al., 2013). In Figure 15.14a, there are reflectors truncated laterally, although the one with trim statics in Figure 15.14b has much better lateral continuity of reflectors. For this example, it is quite evident that the latter image is superior to the former in terms of interface continuity.

The liability of trim statics is the danger that the interfaces are broken by actual faulting and the statics corrections might destroy this valuable information. In this case, the statics shifts can be used to estimate the depth shift between common reflectors in different CIGs, and this depth residual can be used to update the velocity model (Stork, 1991 and 1992). The trim-statics LSM image in Figure 15.14b can be used as the *pilot* image from which the depth residuals can be computed for the other CIGs.

15.9 Artifact reduction with LSM

Migration artifacts can be reduced in the migration image by a local slant stack and filtering of the migration image (G. Dutta, personal communication, 2015). An iterative conjugate-gradient method is used to approximate a least-squares inverse to the local slant-stack operation. The workflow consists of the following steps.

1. Migrate the data by standard migration or LSM to get the migration image $m(\mathbf{x})$.
2. Multiply the migration image by the small window $w(x,z)^i$ to get the local image $m(\mathbf{x})^i = w(x,z)^i m(\mathbf{x})$. Typically, the window height and width are about one

---

[4]The best counterpart is defined to be the patch in $m(x + \delta x, z + \delta z)^B$ that gives the most energetic sum after stacking into the patch at $m(x,z)^A$.

a)
LSM

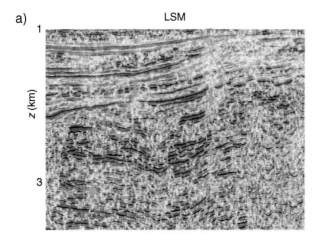

b)
LSM + trim statics

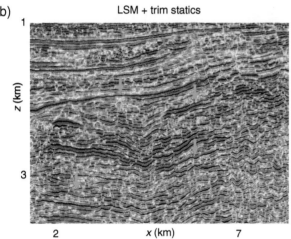

Figure 15.14. (a) Images of LSM and (b) LSM plus trim statics after 10 iterations of LSM for 31 p-values. The data set is recorded by a marine seismic survey in the Gulf of Mexico. Note the improved coherence around the blue dashed line or the green arrows in (b) compared to (a). After Huang et al. (2014b).

to two wavelengths, and the windows can be either contiguous or have an overlap up to 50%.

3. Apply a local slant stack to $m(\mathbf{x})^i$ to get $\hat{m}(p,z_o)^i = R[m(\mathbf{x})^i] = \int m(x, px + z_o)^i dx$, where the integration is over the support of the ith window.

4. Mute undesirable noise and dips in $\hat{m}(p,z_o)^i$ by $\bar{M}(p,z_o)^i = \hat{w}(p,z_o)^i \hat{m}(p,z_o)^i$, where $\hat{w}(p,z_o)^i$ is the muting window in the (p,z_o) domain that mutes out all but the dominant dips. The threshold value of the muting window is determined by trial and error.

5. Use an approximate least-squares inverse so that we get the locally filtered image $\bar{M}(x,z)^i = R[\bar{M}(p,z_o)^i]^{-1}$. The approximate inverse is by an iterative conjugate-gradient method with about 10–15 iterations.

6. Repeat all of the above steps to get $\bar{M}(x,z)^i$ for all values of i, and combine these locally filtered images to get the filtered migration image.

15.9.1 Numerical results

The above filtering scheme is first tested on LSRTM images migrated from 3D synthetic data associated with the SEG/EAGE salt model (G. Dutta, personal communication, 2015). Then, it is applied to aliased data from a marine experiment in the Gulf of Mexico.

Three-dimensional SEG/EAGE salt model

Synthetic data are generated for the SEG/EAGE salt model by simulations of the 3D acoustic wave equation. To induce aliasing artifacts into the migration image, only 45 coarsely spaced shots are migrated, each shot having around 40,000 receivers evenly distributed on the surface. There are a total of five sail lines with each sail line having nine shots.

Figure 15.15 compares the standard RTM, LSRTM, and the filtered LSRTM images. The RTM image in Figure 15.15a suffers from strong backscattering noise because of the presence of the salt body. There is a strong acquisition footprint in the depth slices, the reflector amplitudes are weak, and there is significant high-frequency noise caused by migrating the undersampled shot gathers. Figure 15.15b shows the LSRTM image with some improvements over the standard RTM image, but the aliasing noise is still prominent and is severe below the salt body. The filtered LSRTM image, shown in Figure 15.15c, mostly is free from aliasing noise, the signal-to-noise ratio (S/N) is high, and the salt boundaries are delineated better when compared to the standard RTM and LSRTM images.

Gulf of Mexico field-data example

The effectiveness of filtered LSRTM also is demonstrated on a 2D OBS dataset from the Gulf of Mexico. There are 26 OBS nodes at a spacing of 402.5 m and the shot spacing for the 360 shots is at an interval of 50 m. By reciprocity, the number of shot gathers used during RTM is only 26 and each shot is recorded by 360 receivers. The migration velocity model is obtained by an FWI method.

The standard RTM and LSRTM images after 10 iterations are shown in Figures 15.16a and 15.16b, respectively. It can be seen from these figures that the standard LSRTM image has better balanced amplitudes and better resolution than the standard RTM image. However, both these images suffer from very low S/N and strong aliasing artifacts caused by sparse shot sampling. The filtered RTM and LSRTM images, shown in Figure 15.16c and 15.16d, respectively, have fewer aliasing artifacts and a much better S/N than the standard RTM and LSRTM images. It is much easier to delineate the reflectors in the filtered LSRTM image than in the standard LSRTM image.

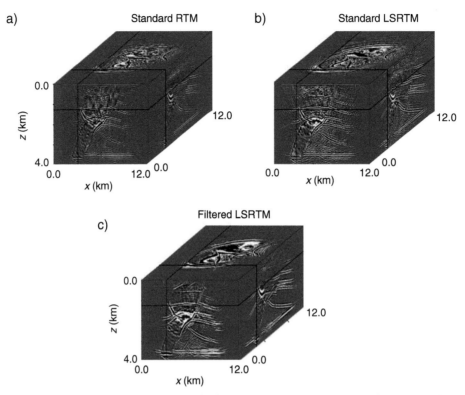

Figure 15.15. Comparison between images from (a) standard RTM, (b) standard LSRTM after 10 iterations, and (c) filtered (also denoted as prior conditioned by Dutta et al., 2015) LSRTM after 10 iterations. Only 45 shots are used to migrate the whole volume. After Dutta et al. (2015).

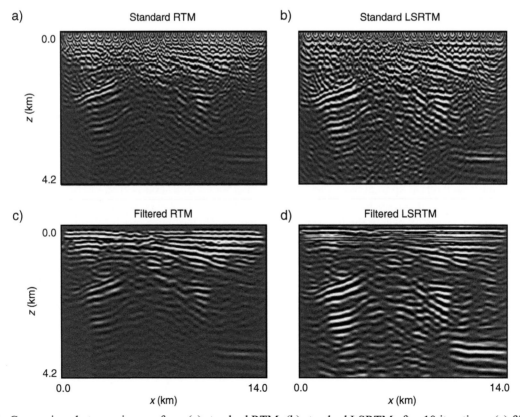

Figure 15.16. Comparison between images from (a) standard RTM, (b) standard LSRTM after 10 iterations, (c) filtered RTM, and (d) filtered LSRTM after 10 iterations. After Dutta et al. (2015).

The disadvantages of filtering migration images are that the filtering can more than double the computational cost of LSRTM and the final result can be sensitive to the choice of the muting window in the slant-stack domain. Currently, the threshold parameter for muting certain dips is by trial and error.

15.10 Summary

The iterative least-squares-migration method and its numerical implementation are described. For the method of steepest descent, LSM can be described as a sequence of iterative migrations of the data residuals. The migration operator $\mathbf{L}^\dagger$ remains the same at each iteration, so LSM is classified as a linearized inversion method. For fast convergence, it is important to compensate for geometric spreading by an effective preconditioner, and regularization helps suppress high-frequency noise and artifacts in the LSM image.

Least-squares migration can provide reflectivity images with fewer migration artifacts, compensation for attenuation loss from Q (see Chapter 16), and with higher spatial resolution than standard migration. In some cases, the spatial resolution of the LSM image can be doubled compared to standard migration if the velocity model is sufficiently accurate. Such models can be obtained by MVA or some tomographic method such as full-waveform inversion. Ideally, MVA and LSM should be combined so that both the velocity and reflectivity models are updated iteratively.

The major cost barrier to wave equation LSM is mitigated by combining encoded shot gathers into either one supergather or several sub-supergathers. A requirement for the successful use of LSM or encoded LSM is that significant free-surface multiples should be eliminated prior to imaging and the migration velocity must be accurate. Empirical results suggest that the migration velocity must have less than 5% RMS error, otherwise the final reflectivity image can be blurred. A more general rule is that migration events from a common reflector in the CIG must be flattened to within a half-wavelength of one another.

15.11 Exercises

1. Explain why diffraction-stack migration only smears reflections along the ellipses in Figure 13.2.
2. Explain why RTM smears reflections energy along cigars, ellipses, and rabbit ears.
3. Describe the workflow of a diffraction-stack migration algorithm that smears reflections exclusively along the rabbit ears. Why would this be useful for updating long-wavelength components of the velocity model for FWI?
4. Describe the workflow of a diffraction-stack migration algorithm that smears first-order interbed multiples

along their associated ellipses. Why would this be useful for updating the migration image compared to primary migration?
5. Run the prestack LSM code for a point scatterer. Compare the performance of this code to one that contains a diagonal preconditioning matrix for geometric spreading compensation.
6. Write an iterative prestack LSM code that uses the conjugate gradient (CG) method rather than the method of steepest descent (SDM). Compare the performance of CG LSM to that of SDM. Include the preconditioning term from the previous exercise.
7. Repeat exercise 6, except use a regularization term to reduce high-frequency noise in the migration image.
8. Test the sensitivity of the zero-offset LSM to 5% and 10% errors in the velocity model for point-scatterer and fault models.
9. Repeat exercise 8 using a *prestack* LSM code.
10. In the presence of migration velocity errors, it might be useful to apply LSM to individual shot gathers, and then correct for velocity errors by flattening the events in the common image gather before coherently summing up the corrected images. The above procedure can be repeated for each iteration. Comment on the potential merits and drawbacks of this strategy compared to migration velocity analysis at each iteration to update the migration velocity. Use numerical results to reinforce your arguments.
11. Run the prestack LSM code in the LSM computational labs for the salt model.
12. Cabrales-Vargas and Marfurt (2013) apply a roughness constraint $\mathbf{R}$ using a preconditioner rather than solving the regularized normal equations

$$[\mathbf{L}^\dagger\mathbf{L} + \eta^2\mathbf{R}]\mathbf{m} = \mathbf{L}^\dagger\mathbf{d}. \qquad (15.17)$$

Substituting $\mathbf{z} = \mathbf{Rm}$ into the above equation gives

$$[(\mathbf{R}^{-1})^\dagger\mathbf{L}^\dagger\mathbf{L}\mathbf{R}^{-1} + \eta^2\mathbf{I}]\mathbf{z} = (\mathbf{R}^{-1})^\dagger\mathbf{L}^\dagger\mathbf{d}. \qquad (15.18)$$

The inverse to the roughness operator is a smoothing operator such as an integral, so approximate $\mathbf{R}^{-1} \approx \mathbf{P}$ to get

$$[\mathbf{P}^\dagger\mathbf{L}^\dagger\mathbf{L}\mathbf{P} + \eta^2\mathbf{I}]\mathbf{z} \approx \mathbf{P}^\dagger\mathbf{L}^\dagger\mathbf{d}. \qquad (15.19)$$

where η^2 is conveniently set to zero and the new normal matrix is symmetric and solvable by a CG method (see Chapter 4). Setting $\tilde{\mathbf{L}} = \mathbf{LP}$ the above equation becomes

$$[\tilde{\mathbf{L}}^\dagger\tilde{\mathbf{L}}]\mathbf{z} \approx \tilde{\mathbf{L}}^\dagger\mathbf{d}. \qquad (15.20)$$

Solve for $\mathbf{z}$ and recover the model by $\mathbf{m} = \mathbf{P}^\dagger\mathbf{z}$. This procedure is used for interpolation, regularization of irregularly sampled sources and receivers, and for minimizing aliasing artifacts. Compare the advantages and disadvantages of this reconditioning method to solving the regularization equation 15.17.

15.12 Computational labs

The LSM Computational Toolkit contains least-squares RTM and Kirchhoff codes.

Appendix 15A:
Diffraction-stack LSM MATLAB codes

Assuming a discretized distribution of reflectivity and source/receiver locations, equation 10.30 can be rewritten as

$$d(\mathbf{g}, \mathbf{s}, t) = [\mathbf{Lm}]_{g,s,t} = \alpha \sum_{\mathbf{x}} w(t - \tau_{gx} - \tau_{sx}) m(\mathbf{x}),$$

(15.21)

in which α describes geometrical-spreading effects that can be taken outside the integral in the far-field approximation. The integration over model space coordinates is approximated by a summation over grid values of the discretized reflectivity model.

The MATLAB function code that implements diffraction stack LSM for a 2D point scatterer reflectivity model is given below.

```
%%%%%%%%%%%%%%%%%%%%%%%%%%%%%%%%%%%%%%%%%%%%%%%%%%%%%%
% Single Scattering Diffraction 2D Prestack Modeling and
% 2D Diffraction Stack Migration.
% Source on surface at (sx,0) and geophones at (gx,0).
% Homogeneous velocity model with velocity c and
% reflectivity model R(i,j)
%
%  Solve L*R = D for R.
%
% functions- input- TIME.m, ricker.m, forw.m, mig.m
% (nx,nz)   - input- Dimensions of Model
% (dx,dz)   - input- Spatial Sampling Intervals
%(dt,sx,fr)- input- Time sampling interval, source x-index,
%                   source wavelet frequency
% W(t)      -output- Ricker Wavelet with Central freq=fr
% D(x,t)    -output- Shot gather for a source at (sx,0)
%
%%%%%%%%%%%%%%%%%%%%%%%%%%%%%%%%%%%%%%%%%%%%%%%%%%%%%%
clear all; np=200;sx=1;nx=50;nz=nx;c=1000;dt=.01;dx=7;dz=dx;fr=20;
[rick]=ricker(np,fr,dt);              % Ricker Source Wavelet
nt=round(sqrt((dx*nx)^2+(dz*nz)^2)*2/c/dt+1)
nd2=round(nt)+2; W=zeros(2*nt,1);
W(nt:nt+np-1)=rick(1:np);             % Time Shift Wavelet
R=zeros(nx,nz);R(round(nx/2),round(nz/2))=1; % Define Refl. Model

[TGX]=TIME(R,nx,nz,nt,dx,dz,dt,c,sx,W,nd2);  % Traveltime Table
[DTRUE]=forw(R,nx,nz,nt,dx,dz,dt,c,sx,W,nd2,TGX);
  % Compute Shot Gather
D=-DTRUE;R1=R*0;                       % Residual: L*0-D
nit=30;
for i=1:nit;
[R]=mig(D,nx,nz,nt,dx,dz,dt,c,sx,W,nd2,TGX);
  % L^{\dagger} D ;Migrate Res.
```

```
[D]=forw(R,nx,nz,nt,dx,dz,dt,c,sx,W,nd2,TGX);% L R ;Compute CSG
alpha=R(:)'*R(:)/(D(:)'*D(:));          % Compute Step Length
R1=R1-alpha*R;                          % Update Reflectivity
[D]=forw(R1,nx,nz,nt,dx,dz,dt,c,sx,W,nd2,TGX)-DTRUE;% New Residual
res(i)=D(:)'*D(:);mx=max(abs(R1(:)));
mesh([1:nx]*dx,[1:nz]*dz,R1'/mx);
xlabel('X (m)');ylabel('Depth (m)');title(['Migration Image
  (iter #, residual) =',...
num2str(i),', ' num2str(res(i))]);
pause(1)
end
```

The forward-modeling subroutine that implements equation 15.21 is

```
%%%%%%%%%%%%%%%%%%%%%%%%%%%%%%%%%%%%%%%%%%%%%%%%%%%%%%%%%%%%%
% SUBROUTINE forw.m
%%%%%%%%%%%%%%%%%%%%%%%%%%%%%%%%%%%%%%%%%%%%%%%%%%%%%%%%%%%%%
function [D]=forw(R,nx,nz,nt,dx,dz,dt,c,sx,W,nd2,TGX)
%
% Compute diffraction stack response D(gx,t) of
% source at sx & reflectivity distribution given by R
%
D=zeros(nx,nt); M=zeros(nx,nz);
for gx=1:nx;                   %Loop Over Traces
  for t=1:nt;                  %Loop over time sample/trace
    M=W(t-TGX(:,:,gx)-TGX(:,:,sx)+nd2).*R;
    D(gx,t)=sum(M(:));
  end;
end;
x=[1:nx]*dx;
t=[0:nt-1]*dt; imagesc(x*dx,t,D')
xlabel('X (m)');ylabel('Time (s)')
```

The adjoint of the forward-modeling operator $\mathbf{L}^\dagger$ applied to the data as described by equation 10.47, can be written as

$$\mathbf{m}(\mathbf{x})^{\mathrm{mig}} = [\mathbf{L}^\dagger \mathbf{d}]_x = \alpha \sum_{g,s} \sum_t w(t - \tau_{gx} - \tau_{sx}) d(\mathbf{g}, \mathbf{s}, t),$$

(15.22)

where the summation is now over data-space coordinates rather than the model-space coordinates (x, z). The argument in $w(t - \tau_{gx} - \tau_{sx})$ describes an ellipse in model space coordinates for fixed τ, $\mathbf{x}_g$, and $\mathbf{x}_s$ values in a homogeneous medium.

The MATLAB code that implements equation 15.22 is given below.

```
%%%%%%%%%%%%%%%%%%%%%%%%%%%%%%%%%%%%%%%%%%%%%%%%%%%%%%%%%%%%%%%
% SUBROUTINE mig.m
%%%%%%%%%%%%%%%%%%%%%%%%%%%%%%%%%%%%%%%%%%%%%%%%%%%%%%%%%%%%%%%
function [R]=mig(D,nx,nz,nt,dx,dz,dt,c,sx,W,nd2,TGX)
%
% Compute diffraction stack migration of D(gx,t)
%
R=zeros(nx,nz);
for gx=1:nx;gx                 %Loop Over Traces
  for t=1:nt;                  %Loop Over Time Samples
    R=W(t-TGX(:,:,gx)-TGX(:,:,sx)+nd2)*D(gx,t)+R;
  end;
end;
imagesc([1:nx]*dx,[1:nz]*dz,R');
xlabel('X (m)');ylabel('Depth (m)')
```

The following two codes *ricker.m* and *TIME.m* are needed for forward modeling and migration with the code *forw.m*.

```
%%%%%%%%%%%%%%%%%%%%%%%%%%%%%%%%%%%%%%%%%%%%%%%%%%%%%%
% SUBROUTINE TIME.m
%%%%%%%%%%%%%%%%%%%%%%%%%%%%%%%%%%%%%%%%%%%%%%%%%%%%%%
function [TGX]=TIME(R,nx,nz,nt,dx,dz,dt,c,sx,W,nd2)
%
% Compute Traveltime Table
%
x=[1:nx];z=[1:nz];[X,Z]=meshgrid(x,z);
zz=(dz*Z).^2;X=(dx*X);        % Compute X & Z Matrices
D=zeros(nx,nt);cnst=1/c/dt;   %Define Constants
TGX=zeros(nx,nz,nx);
for gx=1:nx;                  %Loop Over Traces
xx=dx*gx-X;xx=xx.*xx;
TGX(:,:,gx)=round(sqrt(xx+zz)*cnst+1);gx
end;
```

The *ricker.m* code for the source wavelet is below.

```
%%%%%%%%%%%%%%%%%%%%%%%%%%%%%%%%%%%%%%%%%%%%%%%%%%%%%%
% SUBROUTINE ricker.m
%%%%%%%%%%%%%%%%%%%%%%%%%%%%%%%%%%%%%%%%%%%%%%%%%%%%%%
function [rick]=ricker(np,fr,dt)    %Ricker Wavelet
npt=np*dt;
t=(-npt/2):dt:npt/2;
rick1=(1-t .*t * fr^2 *pi^2  ) .*exp(- t.^2 * pi^2 * fr^2 ) ;
rick =rick1(round(np/2)-round(1/fr/dt)+1:np);
l=length(rick);
if l<np;
rick2=[rick zeros(1,np-l)];
end
l=np;rick=rick2;
plot([0:l-1]*dt,rick);xlabel('Time (s)');
title([num2str(fr),' Hz Ricker Wavelet']);pause(1);
```

Implementation of LSM with regularization

The $N \times N$ regularization matrix $\mathbf{C}$ in equation 10.41 can be implemented in the LSM MATLAB code by noting that the precursor to the regularized system of normal equations is given by the regularized modeling equations

$$\begin{bmatrix} \mathbf{L} \\ \eta\mathbf{C} \end{bmatrix} [\mathbf{m}] = \begin{bmatrix} \mathbf{d} \\ \mathbf{0} \end{bmatrix}. \tag{15.23}$$

Multiplying this equation by $[\mathbf{L}^\dagger \ \ \eta\mathbf{C}^\dagger]$ gives

$$\begin{bmatrix} \mathbf{L}^\dagger & \eta\mathbf{C}^\dagger \end{bmatrix} \begin{bmatrix} \mathbf{L} \\ \eta\mathbf{C} \end{bmatrix} [\mathbf{m}] = \begin{bmatrix} \mathbf{L}^\dagger\mathbf{d} \end{bmatrix}, \tag{15.24}$$

which gives the normal equations in equation 10.41. Therefore, in the method of steepest descent, the $M \times N$ modeling matrix $\mathbf{L}$ is replaced by the $(M + N) \times N$ matrix on the left side of equation 15.23. The $M \times 1$ data vector $\mathbf{d}$ gets replaced by the $(M + N) \times 1$ vector on the right side of equation 15.23, where $\mathbf{0}$ is an $N \times 1$-vector of zeros. Typically, the damping parameter is about 1% of the maximum value of the diagonal element in $\mathbf{L}^\dagger\mathbf{L}$, and it is decreased gradually in value as the iterations proceed.

Appendix 15B:
Multisource LSM with encoding

To reduce the cost of LSM, all of the S shot gathers can be phase or frequency encoded and summed together to give an encoded supergather

$$\mathbf{D} = \sum_i P_i\mathbf{d}_i = \sum_i P_i\mathbf{L}_i\mathbf{m} = \mathbf{Lm}, \tag{15.25}$$

in which P_i is the encoding operator and the encoded modeler[5] $\mathbf{L}$ of supergathers is given by $\mathbf{L} = \sum_i P_i\mathbf{L}_i$. The role of P_i is to produce dissimilarity between shot gathers so that they are mutually uncorrelated in some sense. For example, if P_i is the random variable with values ± 1 then ideally $\langle\mathbf{d}_i^\dagger P_i^\dagger P_j\mathbf{d}_j\rangle = \mathbf{d}_i^\dagger\langle P_i P_j\rangle\mathbf{d}_j = \mathbf{d}_i^\dagger\mathbf{d}_j\delta_{ij}$, where δ_{ij} is the Kronecker delta function and $\langle \ \rangle$ indicates ensemble averaging over different realizations of the random variable.

The LSM image associated with the encoded supergather can be obtained by finding the model $\mathbf{m}$ that minimizes the supergather misfit function $\|\mathbf{Lm} - \mathbf{D}^{obs}\|^2$ with the iterative formula

$$\mathbf{m}^{(k+1)} = \mathbf{m}^{(k)} - \mathbf{L}^\dagger[\mathbf{Lm}^{(k)} - \mathbf{D}^{obs}],$$

$$= \mathbf{m}^{(k)} - \sum_i \mathbf{L}_i^\dagger P_i^\dagger P_i \overbrace{[\mathbf{L}_i\mathbf{m}^{(k)} - \mathbf{d}_i^{obs}]}^{\mathbf{r}_i}$$

$$+ \overbrace{\sum_{i\neq j}\sum_j \mathbf{L}_i^\dagger P_i^\dagger P_j[\mathbf{L}_j\mathbf{m}^{(k)} - \mathbf{d}_j^{obs}]}^{crosstalk},$$

$$= \mathbf{m}^{(k)} - \sum_i \mathbf{L}_i^{(k)\dagger}\mathbf{r}_i^{(k)} + crosstalk, \tag{15.26}$$

where the same background velocity is used at each iteration but the encoding functions change at each iteration. For a sufficient number of iterations, the crosstalk terms incoherently sum together to become small compared to the coherently stacked migration image (Dai, 2012a, 2012b; Dai et al., 2012) and the result reduces to that of standard migration in equation 15.3. The benefit is that one supergather migration by a wave-equation method requires no more computational cost than the migration of a single shot gather. Therefore, there is a significant cost savings if the number of iterations in equation 15.26 is much less than the number of shot gathers.

There are a number of different encoding strategies.

1. Random time series: P_i represents a white-noise series that, in the time domain, is convolved with each trace

---

[5]For a finite-difference solution to the wave equation, predicting one supergather is computed efficiently by simultaneously exciting all the encoded sources.

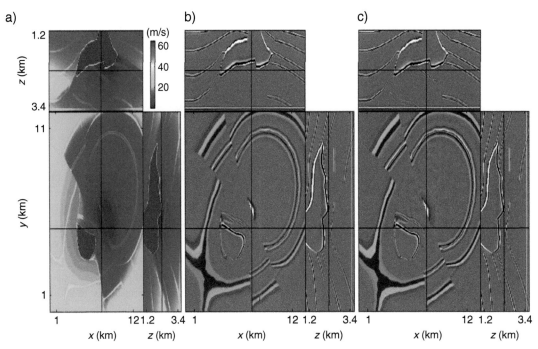

Figure 15.17. Portions of the 3D (a) velocity model, (b) standard OWEM image, and (c) multisource LSM image, where the modeling and migration schemes are those for the one-way wave equation. The multisource image required 1/40th the cost of the standard OWEM image in (b). For this example, there are 4096 shot gathers in this marine OBS survey (Huang and Schuster, 2012).

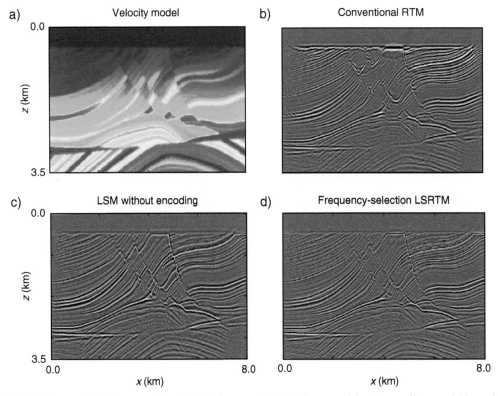

Figure 15.18. (a) Velocity model, (b) conventional RTM image, (c) LSM image without encoding, and (d) multisource LSM image with frequency selection. The multisource image required 0.1 times the cost of the image in panel (c), and 3.2 times the cost of the conventional RTM image in (b). For this example, there are 400 shot gathers with 201 traces per shot gather with a marine acquisition geometry (Dai et al., 2013). The time-shifting plus polarity encoding scheme only works for a fixed acquisition geometry, although the frequency-selection strategy works well for both marine and land geometries. After Dai et al. (2013).

of the ith shot gather (Romero et al., 2000). The resulting shot gathers then are blended together to get one supergather, and this supergather is migrated by a wave-equation migration method for many sources. This procedure can be repeated at each iteration with a different set of white-noise sources, and the migration images are stacked together. It is valid for a fixed acquisition geometry, but the procedure will have difficulties in its implementation with a marine geometry.

2. Frequency selection: P_i is a narrow bandpass filter that, in the time domain, is convolved with each trace of the ith shot gather. The passbands do not overlap so the time-domain representations of P_i and P_j convolved with one another are approximately zero unless $i = j$ (Huang and Schuster, 2012; Dai et al., 2013). The filtered shot gathers then are blended together to get one supergather. This procedure is equally effective for both land and marine data.

3. Random polarity: P_i is a random variable with value either $+1$ or -1 and multiplies each trace in the ith shot gather (Krebs et al., 2009). These randomly polarized shot gathers then are blended, i.e. stacked, together to get one supergather. This procedure is valid for a fixed acquisition geometry, but it will have difficulties in implementation with a marine geometry.

4. Random time shift: Each trace in the ith shot gather is convolved with $\delta(t - \tau_i)$ such that τ_i is a random time shift (Dai and Schuster, 2009; Tang and Biondi, 2009). These shifted traces then are blended together to get one supergather. This procedure is valid for a fixed acquisition geometry, but it will have implementation difficulties with a marine geometry.

5. Plane-wave encoding: Shot gathers are time shifted linearly with respect to source-receiver offset and summed together to form a plane-wave source with a specified slowness value (Etgen, 2005; Zhang et al., 2005; Vigh and Starr, 2008; Vigh et al., 2009). This procedure is applicable for both land and marine acquisition geometries.

The encoding scheme for the supergather $\mathbf{D}$ is distinct at each iteration so that the crosstalk between different migrated shot gathers acts as noise while the prestack migration images $\mathbf{L}_i^\dagger \mathbf{d}_i$ reinforce one another. A random encoding scheme similar to Romero et al. (2000) can be used to reduce the cost of multisource LSRTM to be around that of standard RTM. However, the real benefit is that the cost of multisource LSM (Dai and Schuster, 2009; Dai et al. 2012; Dai, 2012a, 2012b) can be reduced to be nearly the same cost as RTM, but with the LSM benefits of higher resolution and fewer migration artifacts. An alternative is a plane-wave encoding scheme (Etgen, 2005), which for plane-wave LSM can require fewer iterations (Dai and Schuster, 2013; Wang et al., 2013) than standard LSM.

An example of using the frequency-selection encoding is shown in Figure 15.17, which compares the standard one-way, wave-equation migration (OWEM) image in Figure 15.17b to the multisource LSM images in Figure 15.17c, obtained after 50 iterations. Here, the migration scheme is the split-step migration of Stoffa et al. (1990). In comparison, this multisource LSM image is slightly sharper overall and has more clearly delineated linear features. The quality of the multisource LSM is deemed somewhat better than that of the standard OWEM image, except that Figure 15.17c required about 1/40th the computational cost of Figure 15.17b.

The frequency-encoding scheme also can be applied in the space-time domain with an RTM algorithm (Dai et al., 2013). The results are shown in Figure 15.18, where each shot gather is computed by a finite-difference solution to the space-time wave equation for a mono-frequency source and a marine acquisition geometry.

Chapter 16: Viscoacoustic Least-Squares Migration

This chapter presents the equations for viscoacoustic least-squares migration. We also introduce the adjoint-state approach for deriving the formula for the viscoacoustic gradient of the misfit function. Viscoacoustic least-squares migration is important for media with low values of Q.

16.1 Theory of viscoacoustic least-squares migration

The previous chapter presented formula 15.1 for iterative least-squares migration (LSM) as

$$\mathbf{m}^{(k+1)} = \mathbf{m}^{(k)} - \alpha \mathbf{PL}^{\dagger}[\mathbf{Lm}^{(k)} - \mathbf{d}]$$

$$- \text{ gradient of regularization term.} \qquad (16.1)$$

If viscoacoustic effects are accounted for in the modeling operator $\mathbf{L}$, then the Hessian inverse $[\mathbf{L}^{\dagger}\mathbf{L}]^{-1}$ estimated by iterative LSM compensates for the effects of attenuation suffered by the observed data $\mathbf{d}$. This requires an accurate estimate of the attenuation model, the modeling and adjoint operations, and the gradient that account for viscoacoustic effects in the data (Blanch and Symes, 1995; Dutta et al., 2013). The next three sections present the derivations of these operations for a viscoacoustic medium.

16.1.1 Viscoacoustic Born modeling equations

For the sake of algebraic simplicity, we define the following parameters

$$\kappa = K; \quad \tau = \frac{\tau_\epsilon}{\tau_\sigma} - 1,$$

so that the viscoacoustic modeling equations 9.28 become

$$\frac{\partial p}{\partial t} = -\kappa(\tau + 1)\nabla \cdot \mathbf{u} - r + f(\mathbf{x}_s, t),$$

$$\frac{\partial r}{\partial t} = -\frac{1}{\tau_\sigma}(r + \tau\kappa\nabla \cdot \mathbf{u}),$$

$$\frac{\partial \mathbf{u}}{\partial t} = -\frac{1}{\rho}\nabla p. \qquad (16.2)$$

The goal in Born modeling is to find the perturbed wavefield $\delta p(\mathbf{x}, t)$ in terms of the first-order perturbations in the medium parameters. Defining ρ_0, κ_0, τ_{σ_0}, and τ_0 as the background model parameters and $\delta\rho$, $\delta\kappa$, $\delta\tau_\sigma$, and $\delta\tau$ as their small perturbations, the perturbed model can be expressed as

$$\rho = \rho_0 + \delta\rho; \; \kappa = \kappa_0 + \delta\kappa;$$

$$\tau_\sigma = \tau_{\sigma_0} + \delta\tau_\sigma; \; \tau = \tau_0 + \delta\tau. \qquad (16.3)$$

The viscoacoustic equations now can be written as

$$\frac{\partial \delta p}{\partial t} = -[\delta\kappa(\tau + 1) + \kappa\delta\tau]\nabla \cdot \mathbf{u} - \kappa(\tau + 1)\nabla \cdot \delta\mathbf{u} - \delta r,$$

$$\frac{\partial \delta r}{\partial t} = -\frac{1}{\tau_\sigma}(\delta r + (\kappa\delta\tau + \tau\delta\kappa)\nabla \cdot \mathbf{u} + \tau\kappa\nabla \cdot \delta\mathbf{u})$$

$$+ \frac{\delta\tau_\sigma}{\tau_\sigma^2}(r + \tau\kappa\nabla \cdot \mathbf{u}),$$

$$\frac{\partial \delta\mathbf{u}}{\partial t} = -\frac{1}{\rho}\nabla\delta p + \frac{\delta\rho}{\rho^2}\nabla p, \qquad (16.4)$$

where terms second-order in the perturbation variables have been neglected under the Born approximation. To simplify equation 16.4, we make the following assumptions:

- The density is constant so that $\delta\rho = 0$.
- The material relaxation parameters are constant so that $\delta\tau = 0$ and $\delta\tau_\sigma = 0$.

Equation 16.4 thus simplifies to

$$\frac{\partial \delta p}{\partial t} + \delta r + \kappa(\tau + 1)\nabla \cdot \delta\mathbf{u} = -\delta\kappa(\tau + 1)\nabla \cdot \mathbf{u},$$

$$\left(\frac{\partial}{\partial t} + \frac{1}{\tau_\sigma}\right)\delta r + \frac{\tau}{\tau_\sigma}\kappa\nabla \cdot \delta\mathbf{u} = -\delta\kappa\frac{\tau}{\tau_\sigma}\nabla \cdot \mathbf{u},$$

and

$$\frac{1}{\rho}\nabla\delta p + \frac{\partial \delta\mathbf{u}}{\partial t} = 0. \qquad (16.5)$$

This system of equations can be represented in matrix-vector notation as

$$
\overbrace{
\begin{bmatrix}
\frac{\partial}{\partial t} & 1 & \kappa(1+\tau)\frac{\partial}{\partial x} & \kappa(1+\tau)\frac{\partial}{\partial z} \\[6pt]
0 & \frac{\partial}{\partial t}+\frac{1}{\tau_\sigma} & \frac{\tau}{\tau_\sigma}\kappa\frac{\partial}{\partial x} & \frac{\tau}{\tau_\sigma}\kappa\frac{\partial}{\partial z} \\[6pt]
\frac{1}{\rho}\frac{\partial}{\partial x} & 0 & \frac{\partial}{\partial t} & 0 \\[6pt]
\frac{1}{\rho}\frac{\partial}{\partial z} & 0 & 0 & \frac{\partial}{\partial t}
\end{bmatrix}}^{\mathbf{A}}
\overbrace{
\begin{pmatrix}
\delta p \\ \delta r \\ \delta u_x \\ \delta u_z
\end{pmatrix}}^{\mathbf{w}}
$$

$$
= \overbrace{
\begin{pmatrix}
-\delta\kappa(\tau+1)\nabla\cdot\mathbf{u} \\[6pt]
-\delta\kappa\frac{\tau}{\tau_\sigma}\nabla\cdot\mathbf{u} \\[6pt]
0 \\[6pt]
0
\end{pmatrix}}^{\mathbf{f}},
\tag{16.6}
$$

or

$$
\mathbf{A}\mathbf{w}=\mathbf{f},
\tag{16.7}
$$

where $\mathbf{A}$ is the 4×4 operator matrix in equation 16.6. The solution to the above equations is the Born approximation, in which the source fields represented by the 4×1 source vector $\mathbf{f}$ are excited at the locations of the model perturbations, and the source time history at these perturbations is associated with the background fields at these points. Equation 16.7 must be solved to get the predicted seismograms at the surface. These predicted seismograms are subtracted from the observed data to get the residual vector $\Delta\mathbf{d}$. To back propagate these residuals, we now derive the adjoint modeling equations for a viscoacoustic medium.

16.1.2 Viscoacoustic adjoint equations

Recalling from Box 10.2.2.2 that the adjoint of the real function $f(x)(\partial/\partial x)$ is $-[\partial f(x)]/\partial x$, the explicit expression for the adjoint of $\mathbf{A}$ can be obtained from equation 16.6 as the 4×4 adjoint matrix

$$
\mathbf{A}^\dagger = -
\begin{bmatrix}
\frac{\partial}{\partial t} & 0 & \frac{\partial}{\partial x}\frac{1}{\rho} & \frac{\partial}{\partial z}\frac{1}{\rho} \\[6pt]
-1 & \frac{\partial}{\partial t}-\frac{1}{\tau_\sigma} & 0 & 0 \\[6pt]
\frac{\partial}{\partial x}\kappa(1+\tau) & \frac{\partial}{\partial x}\frac{\tau}{\tau_\sigma}\kappa & \frac{\partial}{\partial t} & 0 \\[6pt]
\frac{\partial}{\partial z}\kappa(1+\tau) & \frac{\partial}{\partial z}\frac{\tau}{\tau_\sigma}\kappa & 0 & \frac{\partial}{\partial t}
\end{bmatrix}.
\tag{16.8}
$$

Let $\mathbf{v}=(v_1,\ v_2,\ v_3,\ v_4)^T$ be the adjoint-state vector associated with equation 16.8 such that

$$
\mathbf{A}^\dagger\mathbf{v}=\Delta\mathbf{d},
\tag{16.9}
$$

or as an explicit system of equations

$$
\frac{\partial v_1}{\partial t}+\nabla\cdot\left(\frac{1}{\rho}(v_3,v_4)\right)=-\Delta d(\mathbf{x}_g,t;\mathbf{x}_s),
$$

$$
v_1-\frac{\partial v_2}{\partial t}+\frac{v_2}{\tau_\sigma}=0,
$$

$$
\nabla\kappa(1+\tau)v_1+\nabla\left(\frac{\tau}{\tau_\sigma}\kappa v_2\right)+\frac{\partial(v_3,v_4)}{\partial t}=0,
\tag{16.10}
$$

where, for convenience, we assume the special case of the pressure-field residual $\Delta\mathbf{d}=(\Delta d,0,0,0)^T$. If both pressure and particle-velocity residuals are available, then the residual vector is given as $\Delta\mathbf{d}=(\Delta d,0,\Delta u_x,\Delta u_z)^T$. It is not possible to record any memory variable (see equation 9.23) data (because it is something which is not a physical quantity like pressure or particle velocity), so the memory residual is 0.

The next section shows how the solutions to the forward and adjoint equations are used to compute the viscoacoustic gradient.

16.1.3 Viscoacoustic gradient

The L_2 misfit function is defined as

$$
\epsilon(\mathbf{m})=\frac{1}{2}(\mathbf{w}(\mathbf{m})-\mathbf{d},\mathbf{w}(\mathbf{m})-\mathbf{d}),
\tag{16.11}
$$

in which $\mathbf{w}(\mathbf{m})$ (see equation 16.7) and $\mathbf{d}$ are the predicted and recorded data, respectively, and $\mathbf{m}$ is the predicted model. For convenience, we assume a single source and a single receiver and a space-time formulation where all quantities are real valued. The model that minimizes this misfit function is found by employing the gradient given by

$$
\frac{\partial\epsilon(\mathbf{m})}{\partial m_i}=\left(\frac{\partial\mathbf{w}(\mathbf{m})}{\partial m_i},\mathbf{w}(\mathbf{m})-\mathbf{d}\right),
\tag{16.12}
$$

in which $\partial\mathbf{w}(\mathbf{m})/\partial m_i$ is the Fréchet derivative. As shown in Chapter 11, the expression for the Fréchet derivative is found by expressing the solution as an integral of weighted Green's functions, and perturbing the solution with respect to the parameter (or parameters) of interest. This approach is straightforward and simple to implement for a small number of equations of motion such as the acoustic wave equation. If there are many equations of motion, such as the elastic first-order equations of motion, then the integral function approach can be algebraically tedious. A more systematic approach is the adjoint-state method (Lailly, 1983; Plessix, 2006; Fichtner et al., 2009; Fichtner, 2011). Instead of starting with an integral solution, it starts and ends with the partial differential equations of motions.

Following Dutta and Schuster (2014), the starting point for the adjoint-state method is to take the Fréchet derivative of the system of modeling equations 16.7 and get

$$\mathbf{A}(\mathbf{m}) \frac{\partial \mathbf{w}(\mathbf{m})}{\partial m_i} + \frac{\partial \mathbf{A}(\mathbf{m})}{\partial m_i} \mathbf{w}(\mathbf{m}) = 0, \quad (16.13)$$

which can be rearranged to give

$$\frac{\partial \mathbf{w}(\mathbf{m})}{\partial m_i} = -\mathbf{A}(\mathbf{m})^{-1} \frac{\partial \mathbf{A}(\mathbf{m})}{\partial m_i} \mathbf{w}(\mathbf{m}). \quad (16.14)$$

Plugging equation 16.14 into equation 16.12 gives the gradient

$$\frac{\partial \epsilon(\mathbf{m})}{\partial m_i} = -\left(\mathbf{A}(\mathbf{m})^{-1} \frac{\partial \mathbf{A}(\mathbf{m})}{\partial m_i} \mathbf{w}(\mathbf{m}), \overbrace{\mathbf{w}(\mathbf{m}) - \mathbf{d}}^{\Delta \mathbf{d}} \right),$$

$$= -\left(\overbrace{\frac{\partial \mathbf{A}(\mathbf{m})}{\partial m_i} \mathbf{w}(\mathbf{m})}^{\text{exploding reflector}}, \overbrace{\{\mathbf{A}(\mathbf{m})^{-1}\}^{\dagger} \Delta \mathbf{d}(\mathbf{m})}^{\mathbf{v} = \text{back-propagated residual}} \right),$$

$$(16.15)$$

in which $\Delta \mathbf{d} = \mathbf{w}(\mathbf{m}) - \mathbf{d}$ is the residual vector. In the context of viscoelastic migration, the term $\mathbf{v} = \{\mathbf{A}(\mathbf{m})^{-1}\}^{\dagger} \Delta \mathbf{d}(\mathbf{m})$ is interpreted as the solution of the adjoint equation 16.9 with the residual seismograms acting as virtual sources. As we know from Chapter 11, this is equivalent to back propagation of the recorded data. The other term $(\partial \mathbf{A}(\mathbf{m})/\partial m_i) \mathbf{w}(\mathbf{m})$ is denoted as the exploding reflector because it represents the downgoing source field weighted by the strength $\partial \mathbf{A}(\mathbf{m})/\partial m_i$ of the perturbation at the trial image point. If the perturbation is zero, then there is no exploding reflector at that point.

The $\partial \mathbf{A}(\mathbf{m})/\partial m_i$ term in equation 16.15 can be obtained by taking the derivative of equation 16.8 with respect to a model parameter. For example, assume the variation of the model parameter $m_i \to \kappa$, so

$$\frac{\partial \mathbf{A}}{\partial \kappa} = \begin{bmatrix} 0 & 0 & (1+\tau)\frac{\partial}{\partial x} & (1+\tau)\frac{\partial}{\partial z} \\ 0 & 0 & \frac{\tau}{\tau_\sigma}\frac{\partial}{\partial x} & \frac{\tau}{\tau_\sigma}\frac{\partial}{\partial z} \\ 0 & 0 & 0 & 0 \\ 0 & 0 & 0 & 0 \end{bmatrix}, \quad (16.16)$$

so that the viscoacoustic gradient in equation 16.15 becomes

$$\frac{\partial \epsilon}{\partial \kappa} = -\left(\begin{bmatrix} 0 & 0 & (1+\tau)\frac{\partial}{\partial x} & (1+\tau)\frac{\partial}{\partial z} \\ 0 & 0 & \frac{\tau}{\tau_\sigma}\frac{\partial}{\partial x} & \frac{\tau}{\tau_\sigma}\frac{\partial}{\partial z} \\ 0 & 0 & 0 & 0 \\ 0 & 0 & 0 & 0 \end{bmatrix} \begin{pmatrix} p \\ r \\ u_x \\ u_z \end{pmatrix}, \begin{pmatrix} v_1 \\ v_2 \\ v_3 \\ v_4 \end{pmatrix} \right),$$

$$= -\int_0^T \overbrace{\left[v_1(1+\tau) + v_2 \frac{\tau}{\tau_\sigma} \right]}^{\text{back-propagated residuals}} \overbrace{\nabla \cdot \mathbf{u}}^{\text{source}} dt, \quad (16.17)$$

in which $v_1 = (\{\mathbf{A}(\mathbf{m})^{-1}\}^{\dagger} \Delta \mathbf{d}(\mathbf{m}))_1$ and $v_2 = (\{\mathbf{A}(\mathbf{m})^{-1}\}^{\dagger} \Delta \mathbf{d}(\mathbf{m}))_2$ are solution components of the adjoint equations. The term in the square bracket of equation 16.17 is obtained from the back-propagated residual and $\nabla \cdot \mathbf{u}$ is the divergence of the forward-propagated particle-velocity field that emanates from the source. The summation over time represents the zero-lag correlation between these forward- and back-propagated fields.

16.1.4 Algorithm for Q LSRTM

The following steps are carried out for numerically implementing Q LSRTM by a preconditioned conjugate-gradient method, where a diagonal preconditioning matrix $\mathbf{C}$ is assumed.

- Form the misfit function ϵ, given by

$$\epsilon = \frac{1}{2} ||\mathbf{L}\mathbf{m}^{(i+1)} - \mathbf{d}^{\text{obs}}||^2,$$

in which $\mathbf{L}$ represents a linear modeling operator and $\mathbf{L}\mathbf{m}^{(i+1)}$ is the predicted data given by the solution to equation 16.5, $\mathbf{d}^{\text{obs}}$ represents the recorded seismogram or the pressure data, $\mathbf{m}$ represents the reflectivity image, and i represents the iteration index.

- Compute the gradient given by

$$\mathbf{g}^{(i+1)} = \mathbf{L}^{\dagger} \left[\mathbf{L}\mathbf{m}^{(i+1)} - \mathbf{d}^{\text{obs}} \right] = \mathbf{L}^{\dagger} \delta \mathbf{d}^{(i+1)},$$

where $\delta \mathbf{d}$ represents the data residual for the predicted and observed data, which is back propagated by using the adjoint equations in 16.10. According to equation 16.17, the adjoint residual wavefield is crosscorrelated with the weighted background field at the trial image point $\mathbf{x}$ to give, at zero lag, the perturbation in bulk reflectivity $\delta \kappa(\mathbf{x})$ at each iteration.

Assuming density to be constant, i.e., $\delta\rho = 0$, the perturbation in bulk reflectivity can be scaled suitably to give the perturbation in the reflectivity image δm as

$$\kappa = \rho v^2 \Rightarrow \delta\kappa = 2\rho v\delta v$$

$$\Rightarrow \delta m = \frac{\delta v}{v} = \frac{\delta\kappa}{2\rho v^2}.$$

- Update the gradient using the conjugate-gradient formula as

$$\mathbf{dk}^{(i+1)} = \mathbf{Cg}^{(i+1)} + \beta\mathbf{dk}^{(i)},$$

in which β is given by

$$\beta = \frac{\left(\mathbf{g}^{(i+1)}\right)^\dagger \mathbf{Cg}^{(i+1)}}{\left(\mathbf{g}^{(i)}\right)^\dagger \mathbf{Cg}^{(i)}},$$

and $\mathbf{dk}$ is the conjugate direction vector.

- Compute the step length α:

$$\alpha = \frac{\left(\mathbf{dk}^{(i+1)}\right)^T \mathbf{g}^{(i+1)}}{\left(\mathbf{Ldk}^{(i+1)}\right)^\dagger \left(\mathbf{Ldk}^{(i+1)}\right)}.$$

- Iteratively update the reflectivity image

$$\mathbf{m}^{(i+2)} = \mathbf{m}^{(i+1)} + \alpha\mathbf{dk}^{(i+1)},$$

in which the background velocity model is kept fixed.

16.2 Numerical results

Figures 16.1 and 16.2 show the models and the migration images for the Marmousi model with attenuation. Here, the parameter that indicates attenuation is the variable Q, where decreasing values of Q indicate greater attenuation (see Exercise 6 in section 11.6). The input data are generated by viscoacoustic modeling (see Chapter 9) of the velocity and attenuation models in Figures 16.1a and 16.1b respectively, and the smoothed models used for migration are shown in Figures 16.1c and 16.1d. These synthetic data then are migrated by acoustic and viscoacoustic RTM to give the images shown in Figures 16.2a and 16.2c, respectively. In both results, the reflectivity images are blurred somewhat by the attenuation in the data. To compensate for amplitude loss, acoustic and viscoacoustic LSM are applied to the same data, and the results are plotted in Figures 16.2b and 16.2d. Zoomed sections are shown in Figure 16.3, where it is evident that Q LSRTM with Q compensation correctly accounts for the attenuation loss when compared to acoustic LSRTM.

16.3 Summary

Viscoacoustic least-squares migration can provide reflectivity images with fewer migration artifacts and higher spatial resolution than standard migration for a medium with significant attenuation. In some cases, the spatial resolution of the LSM image can be more than doubled compared to standard migration if Q compensation

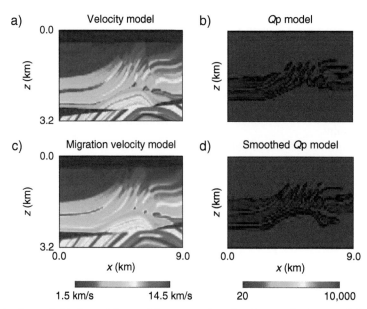

Figure 16.1. The true (a) velocity and (b) Q models used for generating the observed Marmousi data. Smoothed (c) velocity and (d) Q models used for RTM and LSRTM. After Dutta et al. (2013).

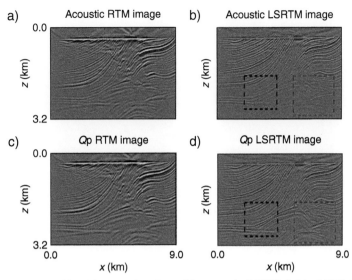

Figure 16.2. Migration images computed by (a) acoustic RTM, (b) acoustic LSRTM, (c) Q RTM, and (d) Q LSRTM. After Dutta et al. (2013).

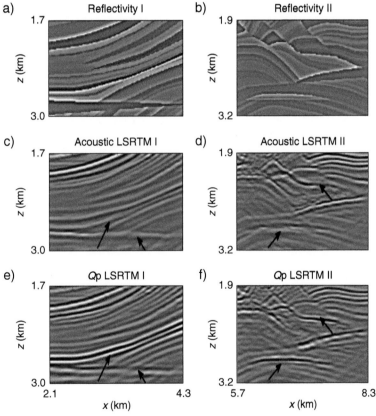

Figure 16.3. Zoomed sections of the black (left) and blue (right) boxes in Figure 16.2. (a and b) True reflectivity models. The acoustic LSRTM images are shown in (c) and (d), and viscoacoustic LSRTM images are shown in (e) and (f). After Dutta et al. (2013).

is provided. However, these improvements require highly accurate velocity and Q models so that the specified reflection events in the CIG are flattened to be within about one-half of a wavelength from one another.

16.4 Computational labs

1. Review the viscoacoustic migration lab in the Computational Toolkit. Answer all questions.

Chapter 17: Least-Squares Migration Filtering

The least-squares migration method is not only for high-resolution imaging of the reflectivity distribution, but it also can be used for interpolation and for filtering coherent noise. We now explore noise filtering with least-squares migration, denoted as least-squares migration filtering (LSMF), in which the kinematics and/or particle motion of predicted events are used to separate signal from coherent noise (Nemeth et al., 2000).

The key idea is borrowed from Thorson and Claerbout (1985) and illustrated in Figure 17.1, where the signal $\mathbf{d}_{\text{sig}}$ (solid curve) is intermingled with coherent noise $\mathbf{d}_{\text{noise}}$ (dashed curve). Some of the dips in the signal are the same as in the noise, so the traditional FK transform will not separate them fully in the FK domain. Without complete separation, muting noise also will destroy the signal before transforming back to the $x - t$ domain. Therefore, a transform is needed that distinguishes the actual moveout of the coherent noise from the signal. Such a transform is achieved by decomposing the modeling operator $\mathbf{L}$ into one that models the signal and another that models the coherent noise. Then, an LSM algorithm can be used as a least-squares migration filter to separate the coherent noise from the signal.

17.1 Least-squares migration filtering

Nemeth et al. (2000) proposes a LSMF scheme for separating coherent noise from the signal in seismic data: decompose the forward-modeling operator into a sum of both signal and noise modeling operators $\mathbf{L} = \mathbf{L}_{\text{sig}} + \mathbf{L}_{\text{noise}}$, and solve the resulting system of equations

$$\mathbf{d} = \mathbf{d}_{\text{sig}} + \mathbf{d}_{\text{noise}} = \mathbf{L}_{\text{sig}}\mathbf{m}_{\text{sig}} + \mathbf{L}_{\text{noise}}\mathbf{m}_{\text{noise}} \quad (17.1)$$

for the signal's reflectivity distribution $\mathbf{m}_{\text{sig}}$ by an iterative LSM method. The noise-free data then can be generated by $\mathbf{d}_{\text{sig}} = \mathbf{L}_{\text{sig}}\mathbf{m}_{\text{sig}}$. Another option is to assume that the noise and signal models are the same, i.e., $\mathbf{m}_{\text{sig}} = \mathbf{m}_{\text{noise}}$, but retain the separate signal and modeling operators in the above equation to solve $\mathbf{d} = [\mathbf{L}_{\text{sig}} + \mathbf{L}_{\text{noise}}]\mathbf{m}$.

The least-squares solution to equation 17.1 can be found by finding the model that minimizes the misfit function

$$\epsilon = ||\mathbf{L}_{\text{sig}}\mathbf{m}_{\text{sig}} + \mathbf{L}_{\text{noise}}\mathbf{m}_{\text{noise}} - \mathbf{d}||^2 \quad (17.2)$$

to obtain

$$\begin{bmatrix} \mathbf{m}_{\text{sig}} \\ \mathbf{m}_{\text{noise}} \end{bmatrix} = \begin{bmatrix} \mathbf{L}_{\text{sig}}^{\dagger}\mathbf{L}_{\text{sig}} & \mathbf{L}_{\text{sig}}^{\dagger}\mathbf{L}_{\text{noise}} \\ \mathbf{L}_{\text{noise}}^{\dagger}\mathbf{L}_{\text{sig}} & \mathbf{L}_{\text{noise}}^{\dagger}\mathbf{L}_{\text{noise}} \end{bmatrix}^{-1} \begin{bmatrix} \mathbf{L}_{\text{sig}}^{\dagger} \\ \mathbf{L}_{\text{noise}}^{\dagger} \end{bmatrix}\mathbf{d}. \quad (17.3)$$

In practice, this solution is computed by a regularized conjugate-gradient method with preconditioning.

An example of LSMF of PP and PS reflections in seismic data is presented by Wang (1997a) and Yu and Wang (1999), in which the particle-velocity components $\mathbf{u} = (u, w)$ of the PP and PS reflections recorded at the geophone location $\mathbf{g}$ for a source at $\mathbf{s}$ are given by

$$\mathbf{u}(\mathbf{s}, \mathbf{g}, t)^{\text{PP}} = A(\mathbf{s}, \mathbf{g}, t)^{\text{PP}} \overbrace{(\cos\theta, \sin\theta)}^{\hat{\mathbf{n}}^{\text{P}}};$$

$$\mathbf{u}(\mathbf{s}, \mathbf{g}, t)^{\text{PS}} = A(\mathbf{s}, \mathbf{g}, t)^{\text{PS}} \overbrace{(\cos\alpha, -\sin\alpha)}^{\hat{\mathbf{n}}^{\text{S}}}, \quad (17.4)$$

in which the unit vectors for the PP and PS particle motions are defined as $\hat{\mathbf{n}}^{\text{P}} = (\cos\theta, \sin\theta)$ and $\hat{\mathbf{n}}^{\text{S}} = (\cos\alpha, -\sin\alpha)$, respectively. The PP and PS incidence angles θ and α are measured with respect to the horizontal axis. The amplitude terms

$$A(\mathbf{s}, \mathbf{g}, t)^{\text{PP}} = \sqrt{(u^{\text{PP}})^2 + (w^{\text{PP}})^2}$$

and

$$A(\mathbf{s}, \mathbf{g}, t)^{\text{PS}} = \sqrt{(u^{\text{PS}})^2 + (w^{\text{PS}})^2} \quad (17.5)$$

are those for the PP and PS arrivals.

The values of θ and α as a function of the event's arrival time can be determined by one of the following procedures: hodogram analysis, a local slant stack of the data, or by computing the incidence angles from the traveltime function $\tau(\mathbf{s}, \mathbf{x}, \mathbf{g})$ for reflections and its derivatives $(\partial\tau/\partial x, \partial\tau/\partial z)$ for given source $\mathbf{s}$, geophone $\mathbf{g}$, and trial-image $\mathbf{x}$ points. In the latter case, the S-component motion is assumed to be perpendicular to the angle of incidence.

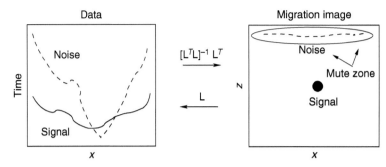

Figure 17.1. Shot gather $\mathbf{d} = \mathbf{d}_{\text{sig}} + \mathbf{d}_{\text{noise}}$ recorded in the $x-t$ domain with both signal $\mathbf{d}_{\text{sig}}$ (solid curve) and coherent noise $\mathbf{d}_{\text{noise}}$ (dashed curve). The physics-based transform $[\mathbf{L}^T\mathbf{L}]^{-1}\mathbf{L}^T$ separates the coherent noise from the signal in the $x-z$ domain of the migration image, so the noise can be muted and the result inverse transformed by $\mathbf{L}_{\text{sig}}$ to derive the signal only. If $\mathbf{L}^T$ is the migration operator, then this procedure is known as LSMF.

The PP and PS modeling equations under the Born approximation are defined as

$$\mathbf{u}^P(\mathbf{g},\mathbf{s},\mathbf{x},t) = \int B(\mathbf{g},\mathbf{s},\mathbf{x})^{PP} s(t - \tau_{sx}^P - \tau_{xg}^P)$$
$$\times \, m(\mathbf{x})^P \hat{\mathbf{n}}^P dx \longrightarrow \mathbf{d}_{PP} = \mathbf{L}_{PP}\mathbf{m}_P;$$

$$\mathbf{u}^S(\mathbf{g},\mathbf{s},\mathbf{x},t) = \int B(\mathbf{g},\mathbf{s},\mathbf{x})^{PS} s(t - \tau_{sx}^P - \tau_{xg}^S)$$
$$\times \, m(\mathbf{x})^S \hat{\mathbf{n}}^S dx \longrightarrow \mathbf{d}_{PS} = \mathbf{L}_{PS}\mathbf{m}_S, \quad (17.6)$$

in which $s(t)$ is the second time derivative of the source wavelet, and $m(\mathbf{x})^P$ and $m(\mathbf{x})^S$ are the PP and PS reflectivity models. Note the unit vectors $\hat{\mathbf{n}}^P$ and $\hat{\mathbf{n}}^S$ are implicit functions of $\mathbf{s}$, $\mathbf{g}$, and $\mathbf{x}$. The functions $B(\mathbf{g},\mathbf{s},\mathbf{x})^{PS}$ and $B(\mathbf{g},\mathbf{s},\mathbf{x})^{PP}$ account for geometrical spreading and attenuation in the PS and PP reflections, respectively. For a source at $\mathbf{x}$ and geophone at $\mathbf{x}'$, the P and S traveltime fields $\tau_{xx'}^P$ and $\tau_{xx'}^S$ are computed by a finite-difference solution to the eikonal equation for the P- and S-velocity models, respectively.

The PP and PS migration operators are formed by applying the transposes of the forward-modeling operators in equation 17.6 to the data:

$$m(\mathbf{x})^P = \int\int\int s(t - \tau_{sx}^P - \tau_{xg}^P) \overbrace{B(\mathbf{s},\mathbf{x},\mathbf{g})^{PP}\hat{\mathbf{n}}^P}^{\text{PP reflection}} \cdot \mathbf{u} \, dx_g dx_s dt$$
$$\longrightarrow \mathbf{m}_P = \mathbf{L}_{PP}^\dagger \mathbf{d}$$

and

$$m(\mathbf{x})^S = \int\int\int s(t - \tau_{sx}^S - \tau_{xg}^P) \overbrace{B(\mathbf{s},\mathbf{x},\mathbf{g})^{PS}\hat{\mathbf{n}}^S}^{\text{PS reflection}} \cdot \mathbf{u} \, dx_g dx_s dt$$
$$\longrightarrow \mathbf{m}_S = \mathbf{L}_{PS}^\dagger \mathbf{d}. \quad (17.7)$$

The above equation filters PP waves from PS waves according to their distinct kinematic *and* particle-motion characteristics. The input traces consist of the two components of data $\mathbf{u}$ recorded at the geophones.

Inserting $\mathbf{L}_{PP} \rightarrow \mathbf{L}_{\text{sig}}$ and $\mathbf{L}_{PS} \rightarrow \mathbf{L}_{\text{noise}}$ into equation 17.3 gives $\mathbf{m}_{\text{sig}}$ and $\mathbf{m}_{\text{noise}}$. The filtered data then can be computed by forward modeling $\mathbf{L}_{sig}\mathbf{m}_{\text{sig}}$ to get $\mathbf{d}_{\text{sig}} = \mathbf{u}^P$. In practice, no matrix storage or inversion is needed because the solution $\mathbf{m}_{\text{sig}}$ is obtained by an iterative gradient method.

17.2 Numerical results

The LSMF method now is used to separate PP and PS arrivals from one another in both synthetic data and field traces recorded in the North Sea.

17.2.1 LSMF of PS and PP reflections for a Graben model

Yu and Wang (1999) and Wang (1997a) use equations 17.3 to 17.7 to separate PP and PS reflections from one another. A finite-difference solution to the elastic wave equation is used to compute the line-source response of the 2D graben model in the upper right illustration in Figure 17.2a. A constant V_P/V_S ratio is used to calculate the S-velocity model and Figure 17.2a and 17.2b show the horizontal- and vertical-component common receiver gathers (CRGs). The receiver position is at $x = 500$ m and for any one shot 201 geophones are located on the surface with the sampling interval of 25 m. The PS converted waves in the horizontal component are mixed with strong PP waves.

The LSMF method then is applied to these data to give the predicted z-component PP and x-component PS common-receiver gathers in Figure 17.3a and 17.3b. These predictions compare very well with the actual traces in Figure 17.3c and 17.3d that are computed by a diffraction-stack modeling method. Although artifacts exist for the early arrivals, most of the PP and PS waves are separated correctly. In comparison, the FK-filtered CRGs in the bottom row of Figure 17.3e and 17.3f are polluted with crosstalk noise. Both the PP and PS arrivals overlap one other in the

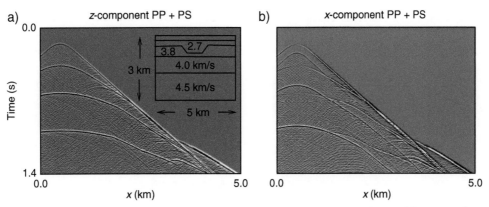

Figure 17.2. (a) The z-component and b) x-component receiver gathers computed by a finite-difference solution to the elastic wave equation. The graben velocity model is in the upper right of (a). Compiled from Yu and Wang (1999).

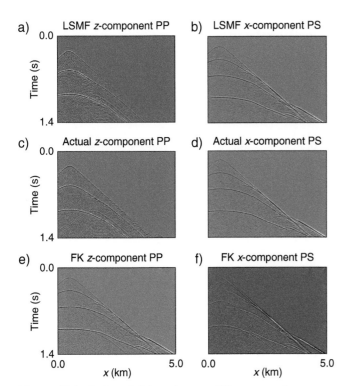

Figure 17.3. Left and right columns of figures are for vertical-PP and horizontal-PS component receiver gathers, respectively. The LSMF receiver gathers along the top row closely match the actual common-receiver gathers in the middle row; in comparison, the FK results in the bottom row do not achieve a good separation of PP and PS components. After Yu and Wang (1999).

FK domains so that a dip filter cannot separate them easily except for the shallow part.

17.2.2 LSMF of Valhall data

Yu and Wang (1999) work with the North Sea Valhall data set, acquired by PGS Reservoir Service AS and donated to UTAM by Amerada Hess. As they note, the data were recorded by multicomponent geophones deployed on the ocean bottom, with an eight-station geophone array and 25-m element spacing. Three particle-velocity geophones and one hydrophone were included in each station, and there was an 11.5-s data recording length, with a 2-ms sample interval. The source vessel traveled a shot line that was directly over and parallel to the fixed receiver array, and there was an 8-km offset on each side of the array center. After each shot line was completed, the receiver array was moved 200 m and fixed in the next array position. The source and receiver positions were inline with one another for the data to be processed.

Figure 17.4a and 17.4b show a common-receiver gather with the vertical and horizontal components of the original data. Yu and Wang (1999) note the different types of unwanted noise in the original data, for instance the interface waves that obscure the PP and PS reflections in the horizontal and vertical component traces. Figure 17.4c and 17.4d illustrate LSMF applied to multicomponent data. As seen, the strongest reflections are recovered. Yu and Wang (1999) compare this with the original data and show that the PP and PS waves "are mostly resolved, while much of the unwanted noise is eliminated." They also note that the PP and PS waves "are not separated as well as in the case of synthetic data." They surmise that a likely cause of this imperfect separation is that the records are a sum of both upgoing waves and downgoing waves, but the modeling operator does not take this into consideration. Another factor is that the migration velocity model is a layered homogeneous model, which is not accurate enough for the larger offsets in the data. They conclude that "compared with the FK filtering results" shown in Figure 17.4e and 17.4f, "the LSMF method appears to give significantly better results."

The Kirchhoff migration images for the horizontal and vertical components of 16 common receiver gathers are shown in Figure 17.5a and 17.5b. The layers

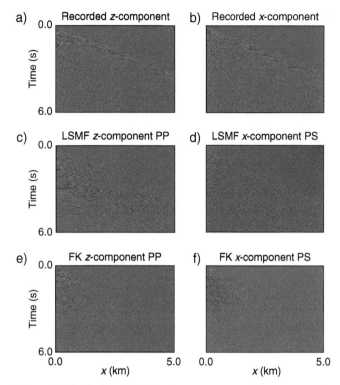

Figure 17.4. Left and right columns are z- and x-component common receiver gathers from the Valhall data set. The original common receiver gathers are in (a–b), the LSMF common receiver gathers are in (c–d), and the ones separated by FK are in (e–f). After Yu and Wang (1999).

(at depth between 3000 m and 4500 m) are resolved in both components. As Yu and Wang (1999) note, there is a noticeable improvement in the LSMF images compared to the single-component migration results shown in Figure 17.5a and 17.5b.

17.3 Problems with LSMF

There are two significant problems with LSMF.

1. LSMF is more than an order of magnitude more expensive than standard migration because it requires many iterations of a conjugate-gradient method. As discussed in Appendix 15A, this cost can be reduced by using encoded multisource technology. The multisource inversion strategy means that overdetermined LSM must be used, which, unlike underdetermined LSM, also requires an accurate velocity model.

2. Another limitation of LSMF is that it requires an accurate modeling operator and an accurate estimate of the migration velocity model. In the underdetermined mode, it is implemented separately for each shot gather (or receiver gather), so it might not be so sensitive to the accuracy of the velocity model. However, $\mathbf{L}_{\text{sig}}$ and

$\mathbf{L}_{\text{noise}}$ should include as much of the physics as possible, especially the kinematics of events. Otherwise, the noise and signal regions in Figure 17.1 will overlap and give incomplete separation. This problem is denoted as crosstalk. A partial remedy to crosstalk is regularized LSMF, in which the regularization parameter penalizes the incorrect physics of, for example, mode conversion in the water column.

The above two problems and their partial solutions now are tested with synthetic data.

17.3.1 Encoded multisource LSMF

Instead of $\mathbf{L} = \mathbf{L}_{\text{sig}} + \mathbf{L}_{\text{noise}}$, we create an encoded supergather $\mathbf{d}$ and supergather modeling operator $\mathbf{L}$ (see Appendix 15A):

$$\mathbf{d} = \sum \mathbf{E}^i \mathbf{d}^i,$$

$$\mathbf{L} = \sum_i \mathbf{E}^i [\mathbf{L}^i_{\text{sig}} + \mathbf{L}^i_{\text{noise}}], \qquad (17.8)$$

in which superscript i indicates the ith shot gather and $\mathbf{E}^i$ defines the encoding matrix for the ith shot gather. The corresponding equations to be solved by multisource LSMF are (AlTheyab, 2011)

$$0 = \mathbf{L}_{\text{sig}} \mathbf{P}_{\text{sig}} \mathbf{s}_{\text{sig}} + \mathbf{L}_{\text{noise}} \mathbf{P}_{\text{noise}} \mathbf{s}_{\text{noise}}$$

and

$$0 = \eta \mathbf{W} \mathbf{s}_{\text{noise}}, \qquad (17.9)$$

in which

$\mathbf{P}_{\text{sig}}$ is the diagonal preconditioning operator $[\mathbf{P}_{\text{sig}}]_{ii} = 1/[\mathbf{L}^\dagger_{\text{sig}} \mathbf{L}_{\text{sig}}]_{ii}$,

$\mathbf{P}_{\text{noise}}$ is the diagonal preconditioning operator $[\mathbf{P}_{\text{noise}}]_{ii} = 1/[\mathbf{L}^\dagger_{\text{noise}} \mathbf{L}_{\text{noise}}]_{ii}$,

$\mathbf{s}_{\text{sig}}$ is the preconditioned *signal*-reflectivity function such that $\mathbf{m}_{\text{sig}} = \mathbf{P}_{\text{sig}} \mathbf{s}_{\text{sig}}$, and

$\mathbf{s}_{\text{noise}}$ is the preconditioned *noise*-reflectivity function such that $\mathbf{m}_{\text{noise}} = \mathbf{P}_{\text{noise}} \mathbf{s}_{\text{noise}}$,

Here, $\mathbf{W}$ is a diagonal operator that penalizes mode conversion in purely acoustic media such as the water column. That is, $\mathbf{W}_{ii} = 1$ if the ith pixel is in the water column, otherwise it is zero,

The term η is the damping parameter set equal to 0.1 for the results that follow below.

The above LSMF algorithm now is applied to marine PP + PSP data, in which the signals correspond to calculated PP reflections and coherent noise corresponds to the converted PSP reflections. These converted waves are

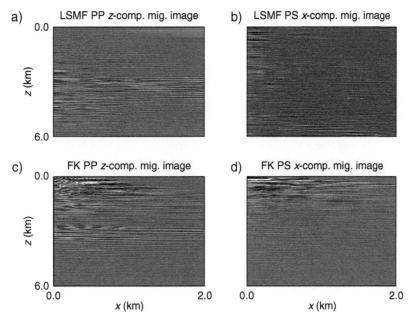

Figure 17.5. Left and right columns are z- and x-component migration images obtained by Kirchhoff migration of the separated data such as those in Figure 17.4. Each image is computed from the corresponding 16 common receiver gathers. The LSMF images in the top row have more continuity and fewer artifacts than those obtained by migrating the data separated by FK. After Yu and Wang (1999).

recorded by pressure hydrophones near the free surface, where a P wave emanates downward from the source, converts to an upgoing PS reflection at a sedimentary interface, and then converts to a PSP wave as it enters the water column from below. The shear-particle motion is that for a SV wave, and the simulations emulate multiple-free data recorded by a hydrophone streamer just below the free surface.

Figure 17.6a to 17.6d depict the background velocities and reflectivities of the test model. The PP modes and PSP modes share the acoustic water layer at the top of the model, which cannot support the propagation of shear waves, and the reflectivity models are shown in Figure 17.6c and 17.6d. Single-source shot gathers are generated for 700 source points evenly distributed along the top surface, where recording hydrophones also are distributed evenly. Time-domain Born forward modeling is used to generate both the PP and the PSP data to give the PP + PSP pressure fields.

All 700 shot gathers are encoded by random time delays and blended together (see equation 17.9) to yield one supergather (see Appendix 15B). Only two finite-difference simulations are required either to generate the supergather or to migrate it at each iteration. A preconditioned conjugate-gradient method is used to solve equations 17.9 for the reflectivity models $\mathbf{m}_{PP}$ and $\mathbf{m}_{PSP}$, and then the ith shot gathers are recovered by the forward-modeling operations

$$\mathbf{d}_{PP}^i = \mathbf{L}_{PP}^i \mathbf{m}_{PP} \quad \text{and} \quad \mathbf{d}_{PPS}^i = \mathbf{L}_{PSP}^i \mathbf{m}_{PSP}. \quad (17.10)$$

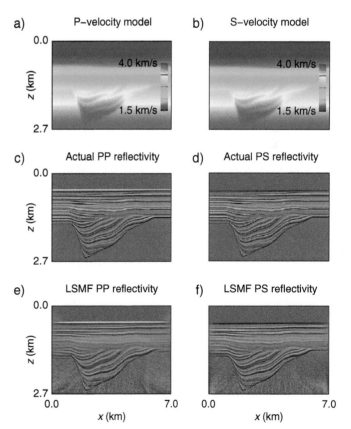

Figure 17.6. P- and S-velocity models are shown in (a) and (b), respectively; and the P- and S-reflectivity models are in (c) and (d), respectively. The PP and PSP reflectivity models recovered by LSMF are, respectively, in (e) and (f). After AlTheyab (2011).

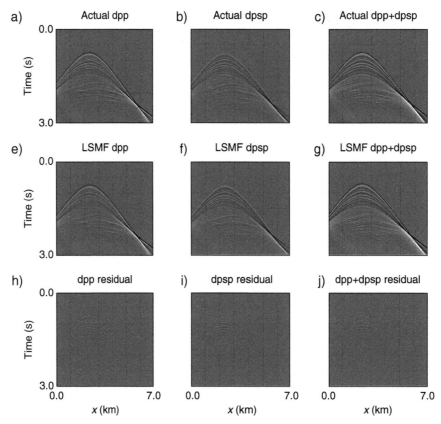

Figure 17.7. The ideal results (first row), LSMF separation results (second row), and the difference between the actual and LSMF shot gathers (third row). All plots have the same grayscale values. After AlTheyab (2011).

The migration operation is the exact adjoint of the time-domain Born forward modeling, and a smooth version of the actual velocity model is used for modeling and migration.

Figure 17.6e to 17.6f display the inverted $\mathbf{m}_{PP}$ and $\mathbf{m}_{PSP}$ models after 50 encoded iterations (200 iterations in total). Most of the reflectivities are recovered, as seen by comparison with the actual reflectivity models in Figure 17.6c and 17.6d. Some crosstalk noise, however, is prominent in the deeper parts. Figure 17.7 shows the ideal separation results, the LSMF results, and their differences. The ideal separation results are modeled using the true reflectivity models in Figure 17.6c and 17.6d. Most of the PP and PSP events in Figure 17.7d to 17.7e are well separated by the LSMF method, and the data residual in Figure 17.7g to 17.7i is less than 10% of the input data. Most of the residual energy is related to the shallower events, where more iterations and a better preconditioning will reduce the residuals.

Multisource LSMF achieved acceptable results with much reduced cost, which is about the same as standard migration of all 700 shot gathers. In terms of the IO cost, standard LSMF requires reading and migrating the 700 shot gathers for every iteration. Multisource LSMF, on the other hand, reads the data only at the re-encoding iterations. The

rest of the iterations use the encoded supergathers which are stored in memory. The multisource forward modeling is applied to all of the sources at once, which reduces the computational cost of forward modeling from 700 modeling experiments to one modeling simulation. This is also true for migration.

However, the above simulation was narrowly designed to test the performance of the encoding strategy. The almost perfect separation results are overly optimistic because the input data were generated by the same Born modeling code that performed migration. A true test of the algorithm is its performance in separating signal from coherent noise in field data.

17.4 Summary

The LSMF method can be used to separate coherent signal from coherent noise as long as the modeling operators can be approximated accurately. Here, the physics of wave propagation is used to predict the kinematics of both the noise and signal, and an iterative least-squares procedure is used for the separation. Separation accuracy is enhanced if both the moveout and the particle motions of the signal are used to distinguished the signal from the noise. LSMF also can be used to separate surface waves from body waves and to separate multiples from primaries.

Results with both synthetic data and Valhall field data demonstrate that the PP and PS reflections can be separated accurately by the LSMF method, but some crosstalk noise is always extant. The Valhall results show that the PP and PS events are better resolved in the horizontal and vertical components, respectively, although much of the unwanted noise also is eliminated. It also is shown that inverting a supergather of encoded shot gathers can reduce the computational time of LSMF to be about that of standard migration. This assumes an accurate velocity model for overdetermined LSMF to work well. It also assumes an accurate approximation to the converted-wave modeling operators. Unfortunately, both of these assumptions will not always be satisfied for field-data examples.

Chapter 18: Migration Deconvolution[1]

Chapter 15 showed that the migration image can be related to the data by $[\mathbf{L}^\dagger \mathbf{L}]\mathbf{m} = \mathbf{L}^\dagger \mathbf{d}$. Substituting $\mathbf{m}^{\text{mig}} = \mathbf{L}^\dagger \mathbf{d}$ into this normal equation yields the relationship between the actual model and migration image:

$$[\mathbf{L}^\dagger \mathbf{L}]\mathbf{m} = \mathbf{m}^{\text{mig}}, \tag{18.1}$$

which says that $[\mathbf{L}^\dagger \mathbf{L}]$ blurs the actual reflectivity model $\mathbf{m}$ into the migration image $\mathbf{m}^{\text{mig}}$. Stronger off-diagonal values of $[\mathbf{L}^\dagger \mathbf{L}]$ lead to more blurring. Physically, blurring is caused partly by the migration operator not correcting for a number of effects: defocusing of the wavefield across interfaces with strong velocity contrast, poor source-receiver geometry, attenuation, and geometrical spreading. These effects mostly can be compensated for by applying the Hessian inverse to the migration image

$$\mathbf{m} = [\mathbf{L}^\dagger \mathbf{L}]^{-1}\mathbf{m}^{\text{mig}}, \tag{18.2}$$

to give a more resolved estimate of the reflectivity model. An approximation to this inverse is the migration deconvolution filter (Schuster and Hu, 2000; Hu et al., 2001; Yu et al., 2006) which assumes a layered medium localized about the trial image point. Its computational cost is no more than that of one migration. An advantage over least-squares migration is that the input to migration deconvolution processing is the 3D migration image, not the data set, which is a five-dimensional cube in two shot coordinates, two receiver coordinates, and time.

18.1 Migration Green's function

Each column of the Hessian matrix $[\mathbf{L}^\dagger \mathbf{L}]$ can be interpreted as the point-scatterer response of the migration operator. For example, assume a point scatterer embedded in the background model so that the reflectivity model $m(\mathbf{x})$ is zero everywhere except at $\mathbf{x}_i$. In this case,

$m(\mathbf{x}) = m(\mathbf{x}_i)\delta(\mathbf{x} - \mathbf{x}_i)$, which says that the ith column vector of $\mathbf{L}^\dagger \mathbf{L}$ in equation 18.1 is the point-scatterer response of the migration operator for a point scatterer at $\mathbf{x}_i$. The kernel associated with $[\mathbf{L}^\dagger \mathbf{L}]$ is known as the migration Green's function (Schuster, 1997; Schuster and Hu, 2000), or is known in the engineering community as the point spread function (Jansson, 1997).

To clarify the physical meaning of the migration Green's function, we examine the special cases of a point scatterer and a fault model.

Point-scatterer model

For a point scatterer at $\mathbf{x}_o$ with scattering strength $m(\mathbf{x}_o)$, the data residual $\Delta P(\mathbf{g}|\mathbf{s})$ in equation 11.9 can be replaced by the Born approximation $\omega^2 W(\omega) \int G(\mathbf{g}|\mathbf{x}_o')G(\mathbf{x}_o'|\mathbf{s})m(\mathbf{x}_o')dx_o'$ to give the migration equation for a single frequency

$$m(\mathbf{x})^{\text{mig}}$$

$$= \int \omega^4 |W(\omega)|^2 \sum_g \sum_s \overbrace{G(\mathbf{g}|\mathbf{x})^* G(\mathbf{x}|\mathbf{s})^* G(\mathbf{g}|\mathbf{x}_o)G(\mathbf{x}_o|\mathbf{s})}^{\Gamma(\mathbf{x}|\mathbf{x}_o)}$$

$$\times m(\mathbf{x}_o')d\mathbf{x}_o',$$

$$= \int \Gamma(\mathbf{x}|\mathbf{x}_o')m(\mathbf{x}_o')d\mathbf{x}_o', \tag{18.3}$$

in which $\Gamma(\mathbf{x}|\mathbf{x}_o')$ is interpreted as the migration response at the trial image point $\mathbf{x}$ for the point scatterer at $\mathbf{x}_o'$ (Schuster, 1997). If $\Gamma(\mathbf{x}|\mathbf{x}_o')$ is computed and saved, then this allows for rapid computation of migration images for different reflector models (Schuster and Hu, 2000; Lecomte et al., 2003; Toxopeus et al., 2008) as weighted sums of migration Green's functions.

If there is only one trace and one scatterer such that $m(\mathbf{x}_o') = \delta(\mathbf{x}_o - \mathbf{x}_o')m(\mathbf{x}_o)$ and $G(\mathbf{x}|\mathbf{x}') = e^{i\omega\tau_{xx'}}/|\mathbf{x} - \mathbf{x}'|$, then applying $-|W(\omega)|^{-2}\omega^{-2}$ as a preconditioner and integrating equation 18.3 over all frequencies gives

$$m(\mathbf{x})^{\text{mig}} = \frac{m(\mathbf{x}_0)\ddot{\delta}(\tau_{sx_o} + \tau_{x_o g} - \tau_{sx} - \tau_{xg})}{|\mathbf{x}_o - \mathbf{x}_g|\,|\mathbf{x}_o - \mathbf{x}_s|\,|\mathbf{x} - \mathbf{x}_s|\,|\mathbf{x}_g - \mathbf{x}|}. \tag{18.4}$$

[1]Much of Chapter 18 is based on the work of Yu et al. (2006): Yu, J., J. Hu, G. T. Schuster, and R. Estill, 2006, Prestack migration deconvolution: GEOPHYSICS, **71**, no. 2, S53–S62, http://dx.doi.org/10.1190/1.2187783. The author would like to thank his coauthors and GEOPHYSICS for their kind permission to use this work in Chapter 18.

This formula says that, for a single trace, the point-scatterer response $\Gamma(\mathbf{x}|\mathbf{x}_0)$ of the migration operator is an ellipse, with foci at the source and receiver points, and the ellipse intersects the point scatterer as shown in Figure 10.4a. If there are numerous traces associated with different source-receiver pairs, then the migration response describes an ensemble of intersecting ellipses, in which the common intersection point is at the location of the scatterer as shown in Figure 10.4b.

If the source-receiver pair has zero offset, then the resulting traces sometimes are known as zero-offset or poststack data. In this case, equation 18.4 becomes

$$m(\mathbf{x})^{\text{mig}} = \frac{m(\mathbf{x}_0)\ddot{\delta}(2\tau_{x_o g} - 2\tau_{xg})}{|\mathbf{x}_o - \mathbf{g}|^2 |\mathbf{x} - \mathbf{x}_s|^2}, \qquad (18.5)$$

in which the migration response describes a circle[2] with the center at the geophone location. For many zero-offset traces, the migration response is an ensemble of intersecting circles that can be described as "smiles." The smile becomes more flattened and the horizontal resolution decreases as the depth of the scatterer increases. For a dense uniform distribution of zero-offset (nonzero-offset) source-receiver pairs, the ensemble of circles (ellipses) forms a migration "butterfly" (see Figure 10.4b).

Fault model

Assume a discrete series of point scatterers that form the dashed fault interface shown in Figure 18.1. In this case, the migration response $m(\mathbf{x})^{\text{mig}}$ is the weighted summation of the point-scatterer responses

$$m(\mathbf{x})^{\text{mig}} = \sum_{\omega} \sum_{\mathbf{x}_0'} \Gamma(\mathbf{x}|\mathbf{x}_0') m(\mathbf{x}_0'), \qquad (18.6)$$

in which the weight $m(\mathbf{x}_i)$ is the reflectivity strength at the $\mathbf{x}_i$ point of the interface. An example of an image computed by equation 18.6 with a Ricker source wavelet is depicted in Figure 18.1. Instead of a faulted interface, the migration response is a blurred representation of it. Note the upturned edges of the migration image along the fault boundary, which are a result of the finite aperture of the zero-offset traces. A wider aperture will increase the resolution of the image at the edges of the fault.

Lecomte et al. (2003) show how migration modeling can be used to assess the resolution and illumination properties for different survey geometries. Similarly, Toxopeus et al. (2008) present an efficient migration modeling method, in which $\Gamma(\mathbf{x}|\mathbf{x}_0)$ is computed using a concatenation of two filters in the wavenumber domain—an angle filter with the minimum and maximum angles of wave

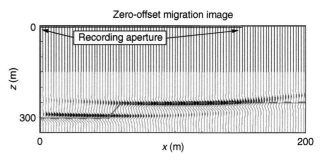

Figure 18.1. The zero-offset migration response of a faulted interface (dashed red line) buried at a depth of 300 m below a recording array of length 150 m. Note the curled migration artifacts from the truncated recording aperature. After Schuster and Hu (2000).

propagation, and a bandpass filter that honors the range of recorded frequencies. As an example, Figure 18.2a shows the prestack migration image from field data, Figure 18.2b is the hypothetical geological model, and Figure 18.2c is the modeled migration image using the reflectivity in Figure 18.2b and the efficiently computed migration Green's function. The reflectivity model can be adjusted until the simulated migration image matches the actual migration image.

18.2 Approximations to $[\mathbf{L}^\dagger \mathbf{L}]^{-1}$

The preconditioned steepest-descent solution to the normal equations for LSM is

$$\mathbf{m}^{(k+1)} = \mathbf{m}^{(k)} - \alpha \mathbf{P} \mathbf{L}^\dagger [\mathbf{L}\mathbf{m}^{(k)} - \mathbf{d}], \qquad (18.7)$$

in which $\mathbf{P}$ is the approximate inverse to $[\mathbf{L}^\dagger \mathbf{L}]$. Next, several ways to compute this preconditioning operator are discussed.

18.2.1 Hessian inverse by $\delta_{ij}/[\mathbf{L}^\dagger \mathbf{L}]_{ij}$

The simplest preconditioner is to apply the inverse to the diagonal terms of the Hessian matrix as discussed in section 11.4. Alternatively, Sacchi et al. (2007) use an inexpensive stochastic procedure for computing the diagonal component of the inverse Hessian. Their preconditioned image is displayed in Figure 18.3c, in which the preconditioner $P(x, z)$ is shown in Figure 18.3b. Notice the increased illumination beneath the salt compared to the original image in Figure 18.3a.

18.2.2 Hessian inverse by a nonstationary matching filter

A nonstationary matching filter can be used to approximate the inverse Hessian (Guitton, 2004; Aoki and

---

[2]This assumes a homogeneous medium.

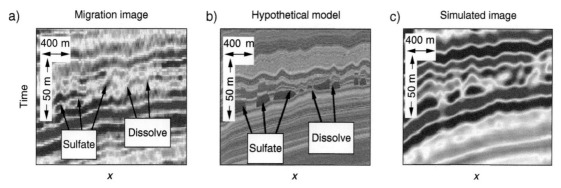

Figure 18.2. (a) Prestack migration image, (b) hypothetical geological model, and (c) simulated image computed by applying the migration Green's function to the reflectivity model associated with (b). After Toxopeus et al. (2008).

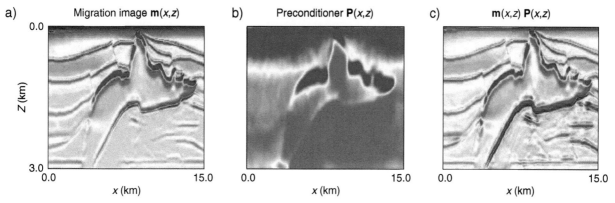

Figure 18.3. (a) Standard migration image, (b) an image of the illumination preconditioner $P(x,z)$, and (c) the migration image with illumination compensation. After Sacchi et al. (2007).

Schuster, 2009; Dai and Schuster, 2009). The idea is illustrated in Figure 18.4 and described in five steps.

1. An input reflectivity model $\mathbf{m}$ is defined, then the synthetic data are generated by $\mathbf{d} = \mathbf{Lm}$ and migrated to get $\mathbf{m}_{mig} = \mathbf{L}^{\dagger}\mathbf{d}$. The input reflectivity model can be obtained by taking the original data, migrating it to get the migration image, and then skeletonizing it to a line model of reflector interfaces denoted by $\mathbf{m}$. The smooth background velocity model is used to compute the traveltimes needed for the $\mathbf{L}$ and $\mathbf{L}^{\dagger}$ operators.

2. A nonstationary filter $\mathbf{F}$ is computed such that it approximates $[\mathbf{L}^{\dagger}\mathbf{L}]^{-1}$, i.e., $\mathbf{Fm}_{mig} \approx \mathbf{m}$. This filter can be found by defining a small window, e.g., about two to three traces wide and three wavelengths long in the dashed box in Figure 18.4a and 18.4b. To simplify, let $\mathbf{F}^p$ be the filter in the pth window, with depth-offset dimensions so it can be represented by the 2×3 filter $\mathbf{F}^p = [a\, c\, e; b\, d\, f]$. The filter coefficients must satisfy

$$\mathbf{F}^p * \mathbf{m}^p_{mig} = \mathbf{m}^p, \qquad (18.8)$$

in which the $*$ denotes convolution only in depth (not in offset), $\mathbf{m}^p$ is the vector that represents the discrete

reflectivity trace centered in the pth window, and $\mathbf{m}^p_{mig}$ represents the three migration traces in that window.

3. We know that a convolution operation is commutative so that $\mathbf{m} * \mathbf{F} = \mathbf{F} * \mathbf{m}$. This means that the matrix $\mathbf{F}$ can be reformed into a vector, and the vector $\mathbf{m}_{mig}$ can be formulated as a convolution matrix. Therefore, reformulating $\mathbf{F}$ as a 6×1 vector and $[\mathbf{m}_{mig}]$ as a convolution matrix yields the 6×1 vector $\mathbf{f}^p = [a\, b\, c\, d\, e\, f]^T$ and the normal equations are given by

$$[\mathbf{m}^p_{mig}]^{\dagger}[\mathbf{m}^p_{mig}]\mathbf{f}^p = [\mathbf{m}^p_{mig}]^{\dagger}\mathbf{m}^p, \qquad (18.9)$$

in which $[\mathbf{m}^p_{mig}]$ is the convolution matrix that contains the coefficients for three migration traces, with each trace being M samples long, and $\mathbf{m}^p$ is the vector that contains one reflectivity trace. The filter equations for a small window are depicted in Figure 18.4c.

4. The filter $\mathbf{f}^p$ is found for all the predefined windows by solving equation 18.8 for all values of the window index p.

5. The above filter is found for synthetic migration images that closely resemble the actual migration image obtained from field data. These synthetic images are generated from the same source-receiver configuration as the original field experiment. Therefore, the

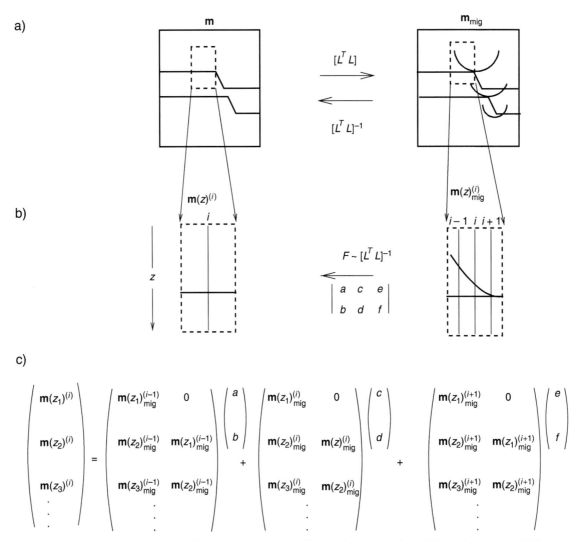

Figure 18.4. (a) Reflectivity model **m** and migration image $\mathbf{m}_{mig}$, (b) windowed version of these images, and (c) system of equations to find the filter coefficients (a, b, c, d, e, and f) that approximate the deconvolution effects of the inverse Hessian.

application of these nonstationary filters to the field migration image might be an acceptable approximation to the actual inverse Hessian.

Example

An example that illustrates the effectiveness of the matching filter is given for the Marmousi model shown in Figure 18.5a. Here, the velocity model is that of a complex structure, which then is smoothed to define the background velocity model $v(\mathbf{x})$. The zero-offset data $\mathbf{d}^{Marm.}$ associated with this model are generated and then migrated with a diffraction-stack method to give the migration image shown in Figure 18.5b. Notice the migration artifacts associated with the defocusing effects in the complex part of the velocity model.

To construct the approximate inverse to the Hessian matrix, it is recognized that the Hessian operators

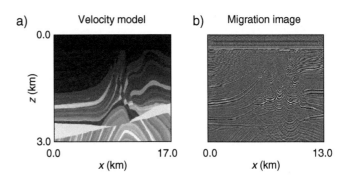

Figure 18.5. (a) Marmousi-2 velocity model and (b) zero-offset migration image obtained by migrating the zero-offset data for this reflectivity model (Aoki and Schuster, 2009).

depend only on the smooth background velocity model $\mathbf{x}$ of the Marmousi model, not the reflectivity model. Therefore, a grid of scatterers is superimposed on $v(\mathbf{x})$ to give the reflectivity model **m** shown in Figure 18.6a. An

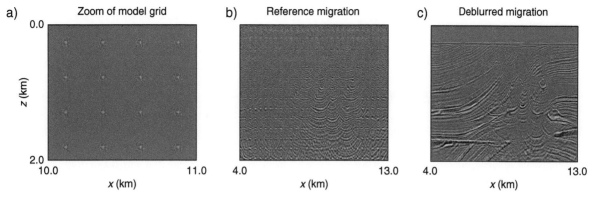

Figure 18.6. (a) Zoom view of grid model denoted as **m**, and (b) associated migration image denoted as $\mathbf{m}_{\text{mig}}$; note the defocusing associated with the complex part of the model. These two images are used to estimate the deblurring filter $\mathbf{F} \approx [\mathbf{L}^\dagger\mathbf{L}]^{-1}$, which is then used to deblur the Marmousi migration image $\mathbf{L}^\dagger\mathbf{d}^{\text{Marm.}}$ in Figure 18.5b to give the image in (c) (Aoki and Schuster, 2009).

eikonal traveltime method (Qin et al., 1992) is employed to compute the traveltime tables; diffraction-stack modeling is used to compute the zero-offset data **d**; and then these data are migrated to give $\mathbf{m}_{\text{mig}} = \mathbf{L}^\dagger\mathbf{d}$ shown in Figure 18.6b. The procedure described in Figure 18.4 is used to estimate the filter $\mathbf{F} \approx [\mathbf{L}^\dagger\mathbf{L}]^{-1}$, and this filter then is applied to the Marmousi migration image $\mathbf{L}^\dagger\mathbf{d}^{\text{Marm.}}$ to give the deblurred image shown in Figure 18.6c. There is a noticeable reduction of artifacts in the migration image, so **F** is a good approximation to $[\mathbf{L}^\dagger\mathbf{L}]^{-1}$ in this example.

18.2.3 Migration deconvolution

Another means for efficiently estimating the reflectivity model using equation 18.2 is by migration deconvolution (Hu et al., 2001; Yu et al., 2006). The migration-deconvolution (MD) filter applied to the migration image in Yu et al. (2006) approximates the LSM estimate of reflectivity, except the input data for MD is a 3D migration image rather than a 5D prestack data set for LSM.

The direct inverse of $[\mathbf{L}^\dagger\mathbf{L}]$ is computationally infeasible for large models, so we assume a local $v(z)$ medium and recording aperture that is sufficiently wide. In this case, we can approximate equation 18.6 in the frequency domain by a convolution in the x- and y-coordinates:

$$m(x,y,z)^{\text{mig}} = \int_{V_o} \Gamma(x - x_0, y - y_0, z|0,0,z_0)m(x,y,z_0)dV_0.$$

$$(18.10)$$

A Fourier transform applied in the x and y coordinates yields

$$\hat{m}(k_x,k_y,z)^{\text{mig}} = \int \hat{\Gamma}(k_x,k_y,z|0,0,z_0)\hat{m}(k_x,k_y,z_0)dz_0,$$

$$(18.11)$$

in which the hat symbol indicates a function in the k_x-k_y-z domain. Instead of a three-dimensional integral (or summation), equation 18.10 is reduced to the 1D integration over the z-coordinate in equation 18.11. For any fixed wavenumber vector, the inverse to this integral is now feasible.

As Yu et al. (2006) note, application of the inverse operator $[\int dz_0\hat{\Gamma}(k_x,k_y,z|0,0,z_0)]^{-1}$ to the migration image $\hat{m}^{\text{mig}}$ in equation 18.11 yields $\hat{m}$, the deconvolved section in the wavenumber-depth domain. The final deconvolved spatial-domain image is achieved by applying an inverse Fourier transform in the frequency and wavenumber domains. Appendix 18A gives details for the numerical computation of $\hat{m}(k_x,k_y,z_0)$.

Migration Green's function calculation

Equation 18.12 is the discretized form of equation 18.11:

$$\hat{m}(k_x,k_y,z_i)^{\text{mig}} = \sum_{j=-\frac{N}{2}+i+1}^{\frac{N}{2}+i} \hat{\Gamma}(k_x,k_y,z_i|0,0,z_{0j})\hat{m}(k_x,k_y,z_{0j})\triangle z.$$

$$(18.12)$$

Here, the kernel $\hat{\Gamma}(k_x,k_y,z|0,0,z_0)$ is the Fourier transform of the migration Green's function (Hu et al., 2001; Yu et al., 2006). As Yu et al. (2006, S55) note, "it is a function of the acquisition geometry parameters and velocity model." Solving this system of equations and applying the inverse to the migration image are the key steps for migration deconvolution.

Referring to Figure 18.7 and equation 18.11, Yu et al. (2006, S55) note, there are two parameters used to construct the inverse of the migration Green's function.

1. The parameter N represents the length of the MD filter in the z-coordinate and defines the number of neighboring depth levels around the current depth (indicated

CDP

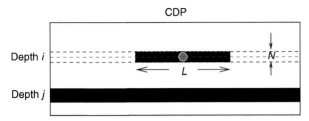

Figure 18.7. Diagram shows increasing aperture width L with depth. Parameter N represents the filter length defining the neighboring depth levels around the current depth indicated by the horizontal dashed red line. Parameter L is the aperture width needed to calculate the migration Green's function at the central position (red circle). Figure and description adapted from Yu et al. (2006).

by the dashed red line). The value of N influences the spatial resolution of the MD image, where a smaller value of N leads to less computational time but often worse resolution in the MD image. Empirical tests suggest acceptable results if N is set to an odd number ranging between 5 and 17.

2. The parameter L defines the width of the trace aperture for the calculation of the migration Green's function at the center point (marked by a solid circle). The value of L varies with depth, where larger L values typically lead to better resolution in the MD image. Appendix 18A offers more details.

Yu et al. (2006, S56) note that "for a medium with a laterally varying velocity, several reference $v(z)$ profiles are used to construct different MD filters for different regions of the image. The different regions have a 5% overlap, and the MD filtered images are blended together along the overlap zones. The MD filter works better if applied to migrated common-offset gathers in order to satisfy the assumption of lateral shift invariance."

18.3 Iterative migration deconvolution

An iterative procedure (Sjoeberg et al., 2003) can be used to find the solution to $[\mathbf{L}^\dagger \mathbf{L}]\mathbf{m} = \mathbf{m}^{mig}$. For example, the iterative preconditioned steepest-descent solution (replace $\mathbf{L}$ in equation 3.20 by $\mathbf{L}^\dagger \mathbf{L}$) is

$$\mathbf{m}^{(k+1)} = \mathbf{m}^{(k)} - \alpha \mathbf{P} \overbrace{(\mathbf{L}^\dagger \mathbf{L} \mathbf{m}^{(k)} - \mathbf{m}^{mig})}^{\text{migration residual}}$$

$$+ \text{ gradient of regularization term}, \quad (18.13)$$

in which $\mathbf{P}$ is the preconditioning term estimated by the local nonstationary filters or by the migration deconvolution filter described in the previous section. For linear inversion,

$[\mathbf{L}^\dagger \mathbf{L}]$ remains the same at each iteration, although in nonlinear inversion, $[\mathbf{L}^\dagger \mathbf{L}]$ gets updated at each iteration (see Chapter 26). One advantage of this approach over inversion in the data domain is that the input is a 3D migration image rather than a 5D prestack data set; this assumes that the overdetermined strategy is used, in which all of the shot records are migrated and stacked together at each iteration. Once the stacked 3D migration image is computed from the recorded data, the field data are not required for iterations in equation 18.13, so that the IO demands can be reduced considerably.

18.4 Numerical tests

Next, synthetic data and field data will be tested with the migration-deconvolution algorithm described in Hu et al. (2001) and Yu et al. (2006). As Yu et al. (2006, S54) note, "the synthetics were generated for a point-scatterer model, a meandering-stream model, and the SEG/EAGE salt model. The field data were from a marine survey in Alaska. Except for the SEG/EAGE salt model, a Kirchhoff migration code was used to image these data, and the migration Green's function was computed using a bending raytracing code. The Alaska field data were time migrated so the MD filter in the (x, y, z) domain was computed as an operator than the (x, y, t) domain."

18.4.1 Point-scatterer model

The migration images of point-scatterer models are shown in the left column of Figure 18.8 (Yu et al., 2006). As described in Yu et al. (2006), "Traces were generated with a 3×3 array of sources and an 11×11 array of receivers with point scatterers buried at 1, 3, 5, and 7 km depths; the primary reflections were computed by ray tracing. This coarse acquisition geometry was selected to generate aliasing artifacts in the migration image."

Applying the MD filter to the migration sections in the left column gives the deconvolved images shown in the right column of Figure 18.8. Compared with the results of Kirchhoff migration, Yu et al. (2006, S56) note that "MD decreases artifacts in the migration image and improves the horizontal spatial resolution by more than 20%" (see Figure 18.9). They add that "this is not surprising because the coarse acquisition geometry in this example leads to severe migration artifacts."

18.4.2 Meandering-stream model

In this example, Yu et al. (2006, S56–S57) compute a synthetic data set for a meandering-stream model. They use a "coarse acquisition geometry with one shot line that

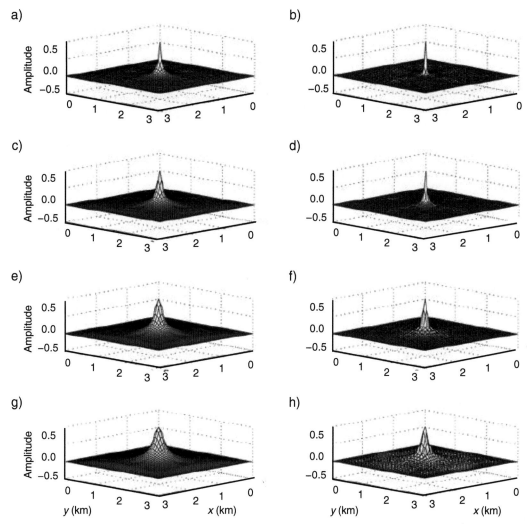

Figure 18.8. The 3D survey geometry consists of a 3 × 3 array of point sources and an 11 × 11 array of geophones in a 9-km² area and point scatterers are located at the depths 1, 3, 5, and 7 km in (a–b), (c–d), (e–f), and (g–h), respectively. Migration images are on the left, and the corresponding MD results are shown in the right column. Note that migration deconvolution reduces the migration artifacts and improves the spatial resolution. Image and description adapted from Yu et al. (2006).

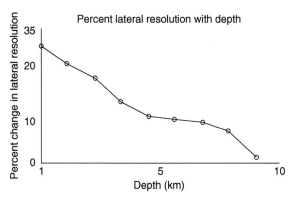

Figure 18.9. Percent improvement in horizontal spatial resolution versus scatterer depth after MD filtering to the migration images in Figure 18.8. The MD images at shallow depths show the most improvement in resolution. After Yu et al. (2006).

intersects the middle location of the crossline direction. The shot line generates five common-shot gathers with a shot interval of 750 m in the inline direction. For each shot, an 11 × 7 array of receivers is activated with a receiver inline spacing of 300 m and a crossline spacing of 428 m, similar to that for a 3D land acquisition geometry. The meandering stream is buried at a depth of 3.6 km" (see Figure 18.10a).

Figure 18.10b shows the 3D prestack Kirchhoff migration image. Yu et al. (2006) note that the stream channel is difficult to map because of recording-footprint noise. Figure 18.10c shows the corresponding prestack MD image. Here, as Yu et al. (2006, S57) note, "the migration Green's function is generated using the same coarse acquisition geometry described above. Compared to the Kirchhoff image, prestack migration deconvolution clearly produces a higher resolution image that more accurately resembles the true model."

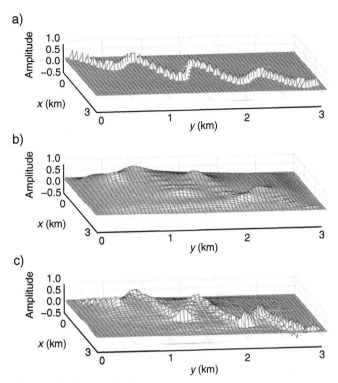

Figure 18.10. (a) The 3D meandering stream model at z = 3.6 km. (b) The 3D prestack migration and (c) prestack migration deconvolution images of (a). This comparison demonstrates that MD can provide a significant improvement in image quality compared to standard migration. After Yu et al. (2006).

18.4.3 Converted-wave marine field data

Next, the MD algorithm will be tested on 2D prestack time migration, with a data-recording length of 12 s and an 8-ms sampling interval. In this example, the final migration image is computed from converted PS data by PS migration.

Figure 18.11a shows the PS prestack time migration (PSTM) image after spiking deconvolution and Figure 18.11b shows the result after wavelet deconvolution. For comparison, the migration and MD images are shown in Figure 18.11c and 18.11d, respectively. Yu et al. (2006, S57) note that "in the shallow part (above 4.0 s), [there] is some unwanted coherent noise in the migration image." The PS-wave migration deconvolution result noticeably improves the migration quality, reduces artifacts, and increases spatial resolution. Comparing the prestack time migration and migration deconvolution images in the two panels, the MD result has less noise and provides more detailed information about the subsurface formation as indicated in the box area.

18.4.4 3D Alaska field data

Yu et al. (2006) apply Kirchhoff time migration to prestack migration images computed from 3D marine data,

recorded in an offshore survey near Alaska. They apply a 3D MD prestack filter to the 651×91 traces that compose the stacked migrated cube; the estimated reflectivity at subsurface point (x, y, t) is represented by the value of the migrated trace at that point. Inline- and crossline-direction trace intervals are 50 m and 25 m, respectively. Each trace has a recording length of 5 s with a temporal sampling interval of 2 ms.

Yu et al. (2006, S59) note that "to construct the MD filter, slices of the 3D prestack time-migration image cube are input at the crossline and inline intervals of 50 m." Figure 18.12a "shows the time slice of the 3D PSTM cube at 1.2 s." Figure 18.12b illustrates the corresponding 3D MD result. Figure 18.13 shows the Kirchhoff migration and MD images in a crossline direction. In these slices, the MD image provides a better resolution of the fault, as indicated by the ovals.

18.5 Summary

This chapter shows that $[\mathbf{L}^\dagger\mathbf{L}]$ is a model resolution function that estimates the migration image $\mathbf{m}^{\text{mig}}$ as a blurred version of the actual reflectivity image $\mathbf{m}$, i.e., $\mathbf{m}^{\text{mig}} = [\mathbf{L}^\dagger\mathbf{L}]\mathbf{m}$. A wider aperture and a denser distribution of receivers and sources provide a more diagonally dominant $[\mathbf{L}^\dagger\mathbf{L}]$, and so gives a more accurate image of the reflectivity distribution. Estimating the reflectivity distribution with $\mathbf{L}^\dagger\mathbf{d}$ is known as standard migration, while $[\mathbf{L}^\dagger\mathbf{L}]^{-1}\mathbf{L}^\dagger\mathbf{d}$ and $[\mathbf{L}^\dagger\mathbf{L}]^{-1}\mathbf{m}^{\text{mig}}$ are known as LSM and MD images, respectively.

The analytic form of $[\mathbf{L}^\dagger\mathbf{L}]^{-1}$ can be derived for a homogeneous medium in the far-field approximation, and suggests inexpensive approximations to the inverse. One such approximation is the reciprocal of the diagonal elements of $[\mathbf{L}^\dagger\mathbf{L}]$, and the other is a nonstationary linear matching filter. Both of these approaches can be shown to accelerate convergence for iterative least-squares migration or waveform inversion. Another procedure is to inexpensively approximate the migration deconvolution operator $[\mathbf{L}^\dagger\mathbf{L}]^{-1}$ using a local $v(z)$ assumption. As Yu et al. (2006, S60) note, to account for strong lateral velocity variations, multi-reference migration Green's functions can be employed by subdividing the migration image cube into regions approximated by different $v(z)$ profiles. The final MD image is a blended combination of subdivided MD images. Tests on synthetic data and 3D SEG/EAGE salt data show significant improvements in image quality due to suppression of migration artifacts and increased spatial resolution. An advantage of MD compared to 3D least-squares migration is that the 3D input volume is just three dimensions in (x, y, z) compared to the five dimensions for the data input to LSM. It is straightforward to implement MD in a target-oriented mode so that it can be computed with fast workstations.

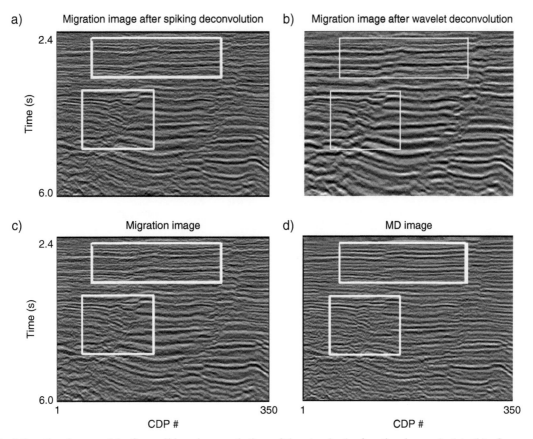

Figure 18.11. Migration images (a) after spiking deconvolution of the standard migration image in (c), (b) after wavelet deconvolution of (c), and (d) after MD filtering of (c). The MD image seems to give the most detail about the subsurface formation. After Yu et al. (2006).

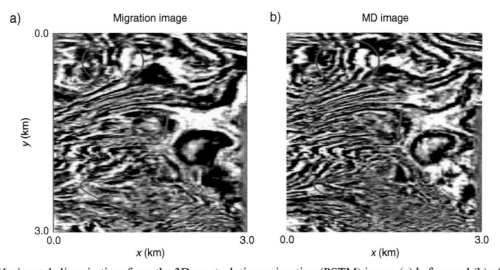

Figure 18.12. Horizontal slices in time from the 3D prestack time migration (PSTM) image (a) before and (b) after MD is applied. Notice the improvements in spatial resolution. After Yu et al. (2006).

The MD filter can be applied efficiently, according to Yu et al. (2006, S60), "in a target-oriented mode, where only a small target volume of the subsurface is deconvolved. Further cost reductions can be accomplished by reducing the trace aperture length L, as well as calculating the MD filter only along coarse depth levels followed by interpolation." An iterative approach can provide a more accurate estimate of the inverse Hessian, but at the added

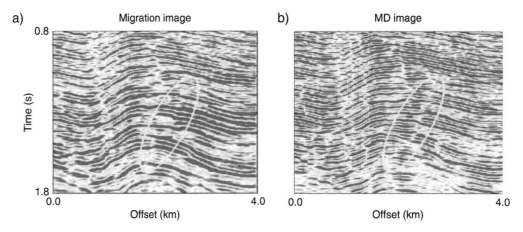

Figure 18.13. Zoom view of (a) PSTM and (b) MD images along the inline direction. After Yu et al. (2006).

cost for the number of iterations. Such costs can be reduced by encoding and blending shot gathers into supergathers, and iteratively migrating to reduce the residual (see Chapter 15).

Finally, MD will not correct blurring problems caused by inaccurate velocity models or by the presence of strong multiples in the data. In some cases, MD might worsen the associated migration artifacts.

18.6 Exercises

1. What is the interpretation of the ith column of $[\mathbf{L}^{\dagger}\mathbf{L}]$ in model-space coordinates?

2. What is the interpretation of the ith row of $[\mathbf{L}^{\dagger}\mathbf{L}]$ in model-space coordinates?

3. Write the pseudocode for MD described in Hu et al. (2001).

4. In traveltime tomography, the slowness estimate is given by $\delta\mathbf{s} = [\mathbf{L}^{\dagger}\mathbf{L}]^{-1}\mathbf{L}^{\dagger}\delta\mathbf{t}$. Define $\mathbf{L}^{\dagger}\delta\mathbf{t} = \delta\mathbf{s}^{\mathrm{mig}}$ so that the new problem in the image domain is to solve $[\mathbf{L}^{\dagger}\mathbf{L}]\delta\mathbf{s} = \delta\mathbf{s}^{\mathrm{mig}}$ for $\delta\mathbf{s}$. State the advantages and disadvantages of traveltime tomography in the image domain compared to standard traveltime tomography in the data domain. Denote the procedure for computing $\delta\mathbf{s} = [\mathbf{L}^{\dagger}\mathbf{L}]^{-1}\delta\mathbf{s}^{\mathrm{mig}}$ as traveltime tomography deconvolution.

5. Write a code for traveltime tomography deconvolution. Compare its performance to that of standard traveltime tomography.

6. In the previous exercise, what is the interpretation of a column of $[\mathbf{L}^{\dagger}\mathbf{L}]$? What is the interpretation of a row of $[\mathbf{L}^{\dagger}\mathbf{L}]$? What is the interpretation of $\delta\mathbf{s}^{\mathrm{mig}}$?

7. The point-scatterer response of the migration operator is a butterfly (Schuster and Hu, 2000). What is the response of the diffraction migration operator to a diving wave?

8. Use the MATLAB® codes for forward and backward modeling in Chapter 15 to estimate the reflectivity model by a preconditioned, iterative migration-deconvolution method (see equation 18.13). Compare the performance of this approach to LSM.

9. Contrast the merits and liabilities of LSM against iterative MD.

10. The interpretation of the point-scatterer response of the migration operator in section 18.1 implicitly assumed that the Green's function for migration only accounted for the direct wavefield. However, if the background velocity contains sharp velocity contrasts, then the Green's function used in RTM also will account for reflections. Describe the point-scatterer response of the RTM migration operator that accounts for reflection events from a layer beneath the actual diffractor (see Chapter 13).

Appendix 18A:
Numerical implementation of MD

Equation 18.12 can be expressed as an $N \times N$ system of equations:

$$
\begin{pmatrix} \tilde{m}(\mathbf{k}, z_1)^{\mathrm{mig}} \\ \tilde{m}(\mathbf{k}, z_2)^{\mathrm{mig}} \\ \vdots \\ \tilde{m}(\mathbf{k}, z_N)^{\mathrm{mig}} \end{pmatrix}
$$

$$
= \begin{bmatrix} \tilde{\Gamma}(\mathbf{k}, z_1 \mid 0,0,z_1) & \tilde{\Gamma}(\mathbf{k}, z_1 \mid 0,0,z_2) & \cdots & \tilde{\Gamma}(\mathbf{k}, z_1 \mid 0,0,z_N) \\ \tilde{\Gamma}(\mathbf{k}, z_2 \mid 0,0,z_1) & \tilde{\Gamma}(\mathbf{k}, z_2 \mid 0,0,z_2) & \cdots & \tilde{\Gamma}(\mathbf{k}, z_2 \mid 0,0,z_N) \\ \vdots & \vdots & \ddots & \vdots \\ \tilde{\Gamma}(\mathbf{k}, z_N \mid 0,0,z_1) & \tilde{\Gamma}(\mathbf{k}, z_N \mid 0,0,z_2) & \cdots & \tilde{\Gamma}(\mathbf{k}, z_N \mid 0,0,z_N) \end{bmatrix}
$$

$$
\begin{pmatrix} \tilde{m}(\mathbf{k}, z_1) \\ \tilde{m}(\mathbf{k}, z_2) \\ \vdots \\ \tilde{m}(\mathbf{k}, z_N) \end{pmatrix}.
\tag{18.14}
$$

As Yu et al. (2006) note, "empirical tests suggest that N should be chosen so that $|z_1 - z_N|$ is several wavelengths long. The elements of the above matrix are the values of the migration Green's function, which is a function of the recording geometry, velocity structure, and the frequency content of the seismic wavelet."

Yu et al. (2006) give the following steps for the numerical implementation of migration deconvolution (changes to the original text are given in brackets):

1. Prepare traveltime tables consistent with the field acquisition geometry and migration velocity model; compute the migrated image and its Fourier transform to give $\tilde{m}(\mathbf{k}, z_i)^{\text{mig}}$ on the left side of equation [18.14].
2. Calculate the migration Green's functions [$\tilde{\Gamma}(\mathbf{k}, z_i | 0, 0, z_j)$] and construct the matrix in equation [18.14].
3. Solve equation [18.14] to give the deblurred reflectivity estimate [$\tilde{m}(\mathbf{k}, z_i)$] at the current ith depth level; add a damping parameter to the matrix diagonal prior to inversion [as discussed in a later section.]
4. Set $i \rightarrow i + 1$ and repeat the above three steps for each depth level until the deepest level is finished.

> The estimates of the calculated $\tilde{m}(\mathbf{k}, z_i)$ at a specific value of $(\mathbf{k}, z_i)$ are averaged to give the final image value. The final deblurred section is obtained by applying a Fast Fourier transform (FFT) to the averaged values of $\tilde{m}(\mathbf{k}, z_i)$ to give $m(x, y, z_i)$. This inversion procedure is roughly equivalent to the first iteration of an overlapping block-diagonal Jacobi method; however, more effective methods such as conjugate gradients [applied to a large system of normal equations] can be used as well.

Selecting the value of N

As Yu et al. (2006) state, the MD filter length N (the dimension of the matrix in equation 18.14), must be chosen so that the filter is at least as tall as several wavelengths (see Figure 18.7). They note that "empirical tests suggest that N depends on the acquisition geometry and migration operators used in the previous imaging steps. We usually select N to be an odd integer value between 7 and 17; the optimal value is chosen by trial and error after testing with several data subsets" (Yu et al., 2006, S56). For $N = 1$, the MD filter is approximately the same as the reciprocal of the Hessian's diagonal (Nemeth et al., 1999).

Selecting the value of L

As Yu et al. (2006) note, the other important parameter for the MD filter is the width of the aperture denoted by L, which is denoted as the window width of the filter. Larger values of L will lead to a MD filter that attempts to spike wider migration butterflies (Schuster and Hu, 2000), which might be unnecessary if most migration artifacts are localized. If L is too small, it indicates that only a small number of points around the current reference location is used. A 15-trace Hamming taper is applied to each side of the window.

Selecting damping parameters

The numerical inversion of the matrix in equation 18.14 can be unstable when the matrix is ill-conditioned, as Yu et al. (2006) note. They use the following regularization strategy. First, compute the condition number of the matrix in equation 18.14. If the matrix is ill-conditioned, a damping parameter is added to the diagonal. The damping parameter is a positive scalar with approximately 1% of the value of the maximum diagonal component.

Selecting the source wavelet

The source wavelet is needed to form the system of equations to be inverted. For these examples, Yu et al. (2006) use a Ricker wavelet with a bandwidth approximating that of the actual data.

Yu et al. (2006) note that the MD operation can be applied to each migrated common-offset gather or to the final stacked migration image. For numerical results delineated here, they use the latter strategy.

Part VI

Waveform Inversion

Chapter 19: Acoustic Waveform Inversion and its Numerical Implementation

Waveform tomography inverts seismic traces for the earth's elastic parameters. Unlike traveltime tomography, it utilizes both the amplitude and phase information of all arrivals rather than only the traveltimes of selected events. Although elegant in theory, waveform inversion is not always used in exploration geophysics because it is computationally expensive (often more than an order of magnitude more expensive than migration), it requires an expert user to get it to work well, and sometimes it does not work at all. The most challenging problem is that the iterative nonlinear inversions tend to get stuck in a local minimum. Fortunately, the increasing speed of computers, more effective inversion strategies, and a greater demand for accurate lithology information will increase its use in the future.

There are several reasons why waveform inversion can provide highly detailed information about the earth model:

1. Compared to traveltime data, the waveform amplitudes can be more sensitive to variations in some model parameters. For example, replacement of brine by gas in a sedimentary rock might not change the propagation velocity or the associated traveltimes of reflected waves significantly, but it can change the amplitude of reflections significantly to produce "bright spots" (Nur and Wang, 1988). Bright-spot technology has been used widely in the Gulf of Mexico to pinpoint hydrocarbon reserves that otherwise would be hidden from seismic view.

2. There is a much larger quantity of information contained in the waveform data than in the corresponding traveltime data for a specified event. For example, a seismogram might contain the traveltime information from one diving wave, but also will contain all types of arrivals in the trace. This means that there are fewer velocity models that will fit all of the waveforms compared to the sparse traveltime data.

The overabundance of information in waveform data is both a blessing and a curse. It is a blessing because it is so rich in information, but it is also a curse because it leads to a highly nonlinear relationship between the model and the data. This means that the misfit function might contain many local minima or long twisting valleys that can lure the gradient optimizer to an incorrect model. Moreover, a successful waveform inversion demands that the forward and adjoint modeling of synthetic data should closely honor both the dynamics and kinematics of the recorded arrivals. Modeling that neglects important physics in the actual wave propagation can lead to tomograms with misleading errors. The following set of examples compare the pseudolinear nature of traveltime misfit functions to the nonlinear nature of waveform misfit functions.

Example 19.0.1. Pseudolinear traveltime misfit function with quasimonotonic character

Seismograms are generated for a two-layer medium with a rigid surface at the top, where the first layer has a thickness $d = 0.25$ km and velocity $V = 1.0$ km/s. The second layer velocity is $\gg 1$ km/s so that strong multiples are generated. Figure 19.1a shows a shot gather with a 10-Hz Ricker wavelet source. The primary reflection traveltimes $t^{obs}(x)$ are picked and displayed in Figure 19.1c, and are used to generate the traveltime misfit function in Figure 19.1d for different values of V. Figure 19.1d shows that the misfit function monotonically decreases as the hypothetical velocity V approaches the correct velocity of 1.0 km/s. Thus, a gradient optimization method will converge quickly to the global minimum.

The next example demonstrates the bumpy character of a highly nonlinear misfit function.

Example 19.0.2. Highly nonlinear waveform misfit function

In contrast to the traveltime misfit function, the waveform misfit function in Figure 19.1b has many local minima between the correct velocity of 1.0 km/s and the starting model velocity of 1.5 km/s. Hence a gradient optimization method will get stuck in a local minimum well before it reaches the global minimum. The reason for so many local

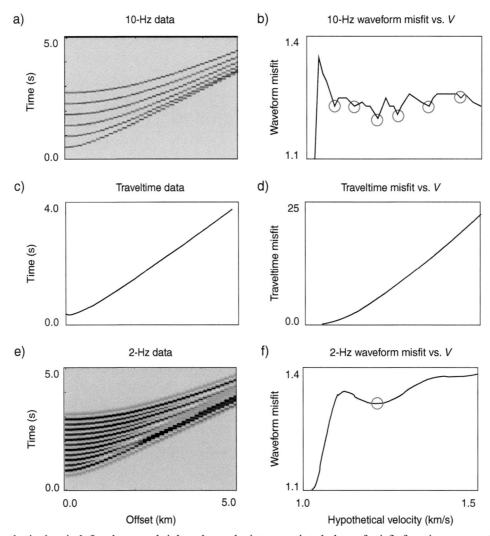

Figure 19.1. Synthetic data in left column and right column depicts associated plots of misfit functions versus hypothetical velocity values of the first layer in the two-layer model. The correct value of V is 1.0 km/s, where the misfit functions tend to zero. Notice the fewer local minima (red circles) for the 2-Hz data than for the 10-Hz data.

minima is that the traces are quite wiggly with respect to time, and slight changes in the hypothetical value of V will time shift the seismograms. A velocity change that shifts the wiggly seismograms by about a period or two will yield a similar-looking seismogram and a misfit function with about the same value as before the shift. This is known as the cycle-skipping problem and leads to numerous local minima in the misfit function.

How can we avoid creating misfit functions that are dense in local minima or characterized by flat valleys or plains? One partial remedy is multiscale inversion, i.e., mute portions of the data, skeletonize the data, and/or run it through a low-pass filter so both the data and the inverted model are much simpler. The misfit function is now simpler, with less of a chance for cycle skipping, so an iterative gradient method might get to a model $\mathbf{m}_o$ which is close to the global minimum. Using $\mathbf{m}_o$ as the new starting model, begin a gradient search on the data with more complexity, higher frequencies (Bunks et al., 1995), and models with

smaller grid spacings (Nemeth et al., 1997). A similar strategy is first to invert the near source-receiver offset traces to find the velocity model that predicts data with no cycle skipping. Then, wider offset traces can be inverted to refine the model (Al-Yaqoobi and Warner, 2013). The key is to gradually open the offset and time windows of the data until the observed data are explained without cycle skipping. An example is shown in Figure 19.2 and the details of this multiscale method are described in section 21.3.

The next example demonstrates a multiscale strategy by low-pass filtering the seismograms shown in Figure 19.1a.

Example 19.0.3. Mildly nonlinear waveform misfit function

The seismograms shown in Figure 19.1a are low-pass filtered to give the seismograms shown in Figure 19.1e. These simpler traces give rise to the simpler waveform

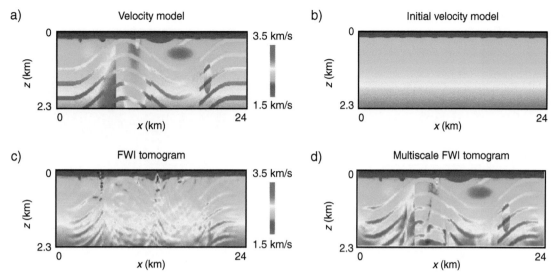

Figure 19.2. (a) Velocity model, (b) initial model at the start of the FWI iterations, (c) standard FWI tomogram, and (d) multiscale FWI tomogram after 20 iterations of a nonlinear Gauss-Newton method (AlTheyab and Wang, 2013) where the offset and time windows of the data are increased gradually to avoid cycle skipping (Asnaashari et al., 2012; Almomin and Biondi, 2013; Al-Yaqoobi and Warner, 2013; AlTheyab, 2015). The acquisition geometry consisted of evenly spaced shots and geophones over a 10-km width, and the source wavelet is peaked at 10 Hz. Images courtesy of Abdullah AlTheyab.

misfit function in Figure 19.1f that has many fewer local minima compared to that of the unfiltered data. Thus, a gradient search method will make good progress in getting to the global minimum.

The final example demonstrates the sensitivity of the data to changes in the model.

Example 19.0.4. Finite-difference solution

A finite-difference solution to the wave equation is used to generate 10 shot gathers for a layered $v(z)$ model corresponding to the blue line in Figure 19.3a. These data were inverted by a simple waveform inversion method denoted by AlTheyab (2015) as Occam-Born inversion, to give the smooth velocity profile depicted as the green line in Figure 19.3a. The predicted shot gathers are shown in Figure 19.3c. The green $v(z)$ profile is very different than the actual $v(z)$ (blue curve), yet the shot gathers in Figure 19.3c and 19.3b are almost identical to one another. Full-waveform inversion also is applied to the observed data to give the magenta $v(z)$ profile in Figure 19.3a, which is still far from the actual velocity at deeper depths, yet gives seismograms in 19.3d that are almost identical to the observed ones in Figure 19.3b.

Example 19.0.4 illustrates that a large range of velocity models can explain much of the data (Jannane et al., 1989) if the velocity variations change more rapidly than the dominant wavelength (200–700 m) and there is an insufficient recording aperture and shot spacing. The partial remedies are to collect data with a higher source frequency, a smaller shot spacing, and a wider recording aperture so that the

deeper reflections can be explained by only one velocity model. The shallow reflections that accurately explain the shallow ($z < 0.5$ km) velocities in Figure 19.3a have an offset-to-depth ratio of greater than 4:1, and the deeper reflections have an offset-to-depth ratio of less than 2:1. This suggests that traces with offset-to-depth ratios greater than 4:1 for deeper reflections are more likely to provide a successful inversion of the deep velocities[1].

This chapter provides the basic strategy for numerically implementing standard waveform inversion. Detailed examples are given in the computational labs for waveform inversion, and its practical application to field data is given in later chapters.

19.1 Numerical implementation of waveform inversion

Waveform inversion seeks to reconstruct the earth model parameters, e.g., velocity and density, from the waveform data. In most cases, the waveform inversion algorithm will consist of minimizing a waveform misfit function by a gradient method, in which the background velocity model is updated every specified number of iterations (AlTheyab, 2015). The slowness update formula by steepest descent is given in the frequency domain in

---

[1]It should be noted that velocity errors throughout the model and unaccounted modeling of the physics lead to calculated traveltime errors that increase with reflector depth. Therefore, inverting deep reflections requires the extra burden of accurately inverting both shallow and deep velocities.

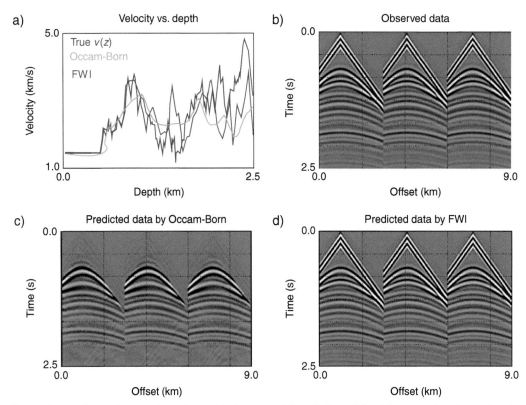

Figure 19.3. Illustration of the problem of data insensitivity to model variations. The (a) true and estimated $v(z)$ velocity models, (b) observed shot gathers generated by finite-difference solutions to the acoustic wave equation for different line sources in a layered $v(z)$ model, shot gathers generated by the (c) Occam-Born $v(z)$ and (d) FWI $v(z)$ models. Here, the dominant period of the source wavelet is about 0.15 s and the dominant wavelengths range between 200 m and 700 m. Figures were computed by Abdullah AlTheyab.

equation 11.5 as[2]

$$s(\mathbf{x})^{(i+1)} = s(\mathbf{x})^{(i)} - \alpha 2 s(\mathbf{x})^{(i)}$$

$$\times \sum_{\omega} \omega^2 \sum_{s} \left\{ \sum_{g} [\Delta P(\mathbf{g}, \mathbf{s}) G(\mathbf{x}|\mathbf{g})^*]^* \right\}$$

$$\times W(\omega) G(\mathbf{x}|\mathbf{s}), \qquad (19.1)$$

or equivalently

$$s(\mathbf{x})^{(i+1)} = s(\mathbf{x})^{(i)} - \alpha \overbrace{2s(\mathbf{x})^{(i)} \sum_{s} u(\mathbf{x}, \mathbf{s}, t) \otimes d(\mathbf{x}, \mathbf{s}, t)|_{t=0}}^{\text{residual migration}},$$

$$(19.2)$$

in which α is the step length that also absorbs the 2π factor. The forward-modeled, downgoing wavefield $d(\mathbf{x}, \mathbf{s}, t)$ and the upgoing residual $u(\mathbf{x}, \mathbf{s}, t)$ (which represents the backward-modeled upgoing reflections) are given by

$$d(\mathbf{x}, \mathbf{s}, t) = -\int g(\mathbf{x}, t - t'|\mathbf{s}, 0) \ddot{w}(t') dt' \qquad (19.3)$$

---

[2]The gradient should be a real function in the spatial domain after summation over all frequencies, so it is identical to its complex conjugate.

and

$$u(\mathbf{x}, \mathbf{s}, t) = \int \sum_{g} g(\mathbf{x}, t' - t|\mathbf{g}, 0) \Delta p(\mathbf{g}, \mathbf{s}, t') dt'. \quad (19.4)$$

Equation 19.2 says the slowness is updated by a zero-lag crosscorrelation between the back-propagated residual wavefield $u(\mathbf{x}, \mathbf{s}, t)$ and the forward-propagated wavefield $d(\mathbf{x}, \mathbf{s}, t)$.

The pseudocode for the FWI method is described in Box 19.1.1 as a simple application of the steepest descent method. In practice, often a preconditioned conjugate gradient or quasi-Newton method is used.

In Box 19.1.1, α is the step length computed at the kth iteration and $\mathbf{C}$ is the left preconditioner, such as the reciprocal to the diagonal of the Hessian (see Chapter 11). Here, $\mathbf{L}(\mathbf{s})$ is the solution to the wave equation

$$\nabla^2 P(\mathbf{x}, t) - s(\mathbf{x})^2 \ddot{P}(\mathbf{x}, t) = \overbrace{F(\mathbf{x}, t)}^{\text{source term}}, \qquad (19.5)$$

for the source term described by $F(\mathbf{x}, t)$. The slowness update $\mathbf{ds} = -\alpha \mathbf{C} \mathbf{L}^T \Delta \mathbf{r}$ is computed by RTM migration of the residuals in equation 19.2.

Box 19.1.1 Pseudocode for Preconditioned FWI

Choose starting slowness model $\mathbf{s}^{(1)}$ Estimate source wavelet

$\mathbf{p}^{(1)} = \mathbf{L}(\mathbf{s}^{(1)})$ Compute predicted data on recording surface

    for $k = 1 : K$ Loop over k

       $\mathbf{pp} = \mathbf{p}^{(k)}$

       $\Delta\mathbf{r} = \mathbf{pp} - \mathbf{p}^{obs}$ Compute residual on recording surface

       $\mathbf{ds} = -\alpha\mathbf{C}\mathbf{L}^T\Delta\mathbf{r}$ Estimate α, $\mathbf{C}$, and migrate residual

       $\mathbf{s}^{(k+1)} = \mathbf{s}^{(k)} + \mathbf{ds}$ Update slowness

       $\mathbf{p}^{(k+1)} = \mathbf{L}(\mathbf{s}^{(k+1)})$ Update predicted data

       $\Delta = \mathbf{p}^{(k+1)} - \mathbf{p}^{obs}$ Stop if $\dfrac{\|\Delta\|_2}{\|\mathbf{p}^{obs}\|_2} < \epsilon$

   end

19.2 Expediting convergence

Unfortunately, the FWI code in the previous section is too simple for successful inversion of realistic seismic data. Extra ingredients are needed to increase the chances for convergence, several of which are given below.

19.2.1 Conjugate-gradient and quasi-Newton gradient methods

The nonlinear conjugate gradient and limited-memory quasi-Newton methods can offer considerable speedup compared to the method of steepest descent for FWI (Mora, 1987, 1989; Zhou et al., 1995, 1997; Pratt et al., 1998; Plessix, 2006; Plessix et al., 2010; Métivier et al., 2012). These methods benefit by preconditioning of the adjoint operator and regularization.

19.2.2 Starting model

Waveform inversion of reflection data with limited source-receiver offsets and missing low frequencies is not suitable for reconstructing the long-wavelength components of the slowness field. Such components most often are needed to avoid cycle skipping and getting stuck in a local minimum.

The long-wavelength components of the velocity distribution down to intermediate depths can be estimated by inverting the diving-wave arrivals in the data, similar to refraction tomography or direct-arrival traveltime tomography (e.g., Luo and Schuster, 1991a; Pratt and Goulty, 1991; Zhou et al., 1995; Prieux et al., 2013; Sheng et al., 2006). For a marine seismic experiment with towed hydrophones, the problem is that diving waves often require an offset-to-depth ratio of more than 4:1 to be recorded as first arrivals.

If the maximum source-receiver offset is 12 km, the early-arrival diving waves only provide the long-wavelength velocity model to depths of no more than about 2 to 4 km. Below that depth, inversion of reflections are prone to cycle-skipping problems unless the starting model is accurate to that depth. Potential remedies to this problem are adaptive multiscale FWI (see section 19.2.5), travel-time inversion of deeper reflections (Prieux et al., 2013), migration velocity analysis (Symes and Carazzone, 1991; Stork, 1992; Sava and Biondi, 2004; Sava and Fomel, 2006; Symes, 2008; Almomin, 2011; Almomin and Biondi, 2012; Tang et al., 2013), or tomographically inverting reflections along the rabbit ear wavepaths (Mora, 1989; Prieux et al., 2013). It can be very useful to constrain the model velocities with information such as well logs, which can supply the missing low-wavenumber information about the velocity model (Lazaratos et al., 2013).

19.2.3 Preconditioning

An ill-posed problem often leads to slow convergence with a gradient optimization method. Instead of a round contour at the misfit's minimum, the global minimum might reside at the bottom of a long narrow valley. Preconditioning in the form of an approximation to $[\mathbf{L}^\dagger\mathbf{L}]^{-1}$ is recommended to deform the long valley into a bullseye. However, regularization still is needed because it ensures the final model estimate is reasonably close to the a priori guess about the true model (e.g., nearby well logs or smoothness requirements provide a reasonable model constraint).

An approximation to $[\mathbf{L}^\dagger\mathbf{L}]^{-1}$ is the diagonal of the Hessian inverse proposed by Beydoun and Mendes (1989) or the illumination compensation terms (Duquet et al., 1998; Rickett, 2003) discussed in section 11.4. A more expensive but theoretically more effective preconditioner is the migration-deconvolution approach of Hu et al. (2001) and Yu et al. (2006) discussed in Chapter 18.

Another preconditioning approach (Fomel et al., 2002) is to estimate the inverse Hessian, after the Nth iteration of a conjugate-gradient method, by a weighted sum of the N conjugate vectors $\mathbf{p}_i$

$$[\mathbf{L}^\dagger\mathbf{L}]^{-1} \approx \sum_{i=1}^{N} \frac{\mathbf{p}_i\mathbf{p}_i^\dagger}{\mathbf{p}_i^\dagger\mathbf{L}^\dagger\mathbf{L}\mathbf{p}_i}. \tag{19.6}$$

The inverse matrix cannot be stored explicitly for large problems, but individual components can be computed by storing the conjugate vectors and computing only row-vector multiplications when multiplying $[\mathbf{L}^\dagger\mathbf{L}]^{-1}$ by the vector associated with the migrated residual. A similar equation is used to estimate the model resolution matrix to identify regions of low illumination and uncertainty in a migration image.

Finally, the model can be conditioned so its spectral shape in depth is similar to that of the impedance profile recorded in a nearby well (Lazaratos et al., 2013). For example, if the logged impedance profile is $I(z)$, then the smoothed spectral shape of this function can be imposed upon the velocity model by a shaping filter. In practice, model shaping is obtained by applying the frequency domain filter $\omega^{1/2}\tilde{I}(\omega)/A^{1/2}(\omega)$ to the data spectrum and the filter $\omega^{1/2}/A^{1/2}(\omega)$ to the source wavelet, where $\tilde{I}(\omega)$ is the spectrum of $I(z)$ and $A^{1/2}(\omega)$ depends on the specifics of the inversion problem. Data shaping is equivalent to encouraging the reconstructed impedance profile to have the same spectral shape as that computed from the well log. According to Lazaratos et al. (2013, p. 2429), an additional benefit is that "it naturally increases the contribution of the lower-frequency part of the spectrum, leading to better convergence properties in the presence of local minima of the objective function." They also note that "We can significantly reduce the number of iterations required for the convergence of the FWI process by guaranteeing that, from the very first iteration, the inversion generates subsurface models with the desired frequency spectrum." This procedure can be very important for supplying low-wavenumber information about the model.

19.2.4 Subspace decomposition

The data (e.g., picked traveltimes) might have different units than other data types (e.g., resistivity measurements). Also, the decomposition of the FWI gradient becomes the sum of a weak rabbit ear gradient and a strong ellipse (see Chapter 13). Unless the gradients are balanced optimally in magnitude, the update might concentrate only on one gradient while ignoring the other. This is characteristic of misfit functions with long narrow valleys, with the consequent slow convergence rate for gradient-search methods.

In this case, the gradient vector γ consists of sensitive γ_{sens} and less sensitive γ_{insens} components:

$$\gamma = (\gamma_{\text{sens}}, \gamma_{\text{insens}})^T. \tag{19.7}$$

These two components will be referred to as sub gradients (Kennett et al., 1988). Therefore, two scalar step lengths should be determined, κ_{sens} for the sensitive gradient and κ_{insens} for the insensitive gradient.

These two step lengths can be determined by first computing both the insensitive and sensitive gradients. Then solve for the optimal κ_{sens} and κ_{insens} that minimize $\epsilon = \epsilon(\kappa_{\text{sens}}, \kappa_{\text{insens}})$. Here, ϵ is the waveform misfit function. A simple Newton method (see Chapters 2 and 3) can be used to solve for the two scalar step lengths, which requires the numerical inversion of a 2×2 matrix. These two scalar step lengths then can be used to scale the two gradients so the updated slowness is given by

$$\Delta\mathbf{s}(\mathbf{x}) = (\kappa_{\text{sens}}\gamma_{\text{sens}}, \kappa_{\text{insens}}\gamma_{\text{insens}})^T. \tag{19.8}$$

This idea can be generalized easily to the decomposition of the gradient into any number of sub gradients.

19.2.5 Adaptive multiscale FWI

A naive iterative method attempts to reduce simultaneously both the high- and low-spatial wavenumbers of the data residuals. However, the high-wavenumber residuals can converge at a dramatically different rate than low-wavenumber residuals. The multigrid method (Briggs, 1987) suggests that the overall rate of convergence can be increased for solving certain partial differential equations by primarily reducing the low-wavenumber residuals on a coarse grid, and then reducing the high-wavenumber residuals on a finer grid. The iterations are performed on a sequence of models in which the grids become cyclically refined and then coarsened. This iterative strategy is denoted as the multigrid method. For FWI, a similar combination of adaptive multiscale-like procedures often is used to mitigate the cycle-skipping problem.

Bunks et al. (1995) suggest a frequency-domain multiscale strategy for waveform inversion.

1. The initial iteration should be performed on a smoothed velocity model with few unknowns. After about five iterations the convergence rate likely will stall, and so the gridded velocity model should be refined by a factor of two. The data should be low-pass filtered so the minimum wavelengths are on the same scale as the gridpoint spacing.

2. Smooth the model after refining again by halving the grid spacing, and begin new iterations until convergence stalls. This strategy approximately follows the

parsimonious refinement strategy suggested by Sirgue and Pratt (2004) in the frequency domain and Boonyasiriwat et al. (2009) in the time domain. Inversion can be efficiently carried out in the frequency domain by first computing space-time domain solutions (Sirgue et al., 2007 and 2008).

3. Refine the grid by a factor of two and repeat steps 2 and 3 until acceptable convergence.

Applying a similar multiscale strategy to traveltime data (Nemeth et al., 1987) produces speedups in convergence and is an important ingredient for successful use of full-waveform inversion. Variations in the multiscale strategy include using early-arrival events (Sheng et al., 2006; Buddensiek et al., 2008) and traces with a small source-receiver offset (Al-Yaqoobi and Warner, 2013), and gradually widening the offset and time window of admissible data with the increase in the number of iterations. For the early iterations, low wavenumbers in the model can be reconstructed by smearing the residuals along the rabbit ear and banana wavepaths. Later iterations can smear the residuals along the ellipses, banana, and rabbit ear wavepaths.

Figure 19.2c shows the failure of FWI converging prematurely to a local minimum; in this case, cycle skipping is unavoidable because the initial velocity model in Figure 19.2b is too far from the actual model in Figure 19.2a. In contrast, Figure 19.2d is the tomogram that is inverted gradually by successively selecting and inverting subsets of the data without cycle skipping (AlTheyab, 2015). To avoid cycle skipping, AlTheyab initially inverts the data using small source-receiver offsets and short time windows, which is similar to the multiscale approach of Al-Yaqoobi and Warner (2013). In this case, cycle skipping is largely avoided but only the shallow velocities are updated because of the limited time window. After the residual is reduced to an acceptable level, the offset and time windows for each shot gather are widened[3] and FWI is again applied, except to estimate the velocity model to moderate depths. This procedure is repeated until all of the data is inverted. There are some incorrect updates in the final tomogram, which indicate that some events are still cycle skipped. For this example, more data are incorporated into the subset after every 20 iterations of iterative Gauss-Newton FWI.

To increase the velocity update along the low-wavenumber rabbit ears associated with reflections, AlTheyab et al. (2013) included a linear LSM loop to be interior to the nonlinear outer loop of FWI (see Box 21.1.1). This inner loop allowed the rabbit ear reflection gradient to be activated without being dominated by the stronger gradient associated with the diving wave.

---

[3]Common-offset gathers are used in practice.

19.2.6 Estimation of the source wavelet

The implementation of equation 19.2 demands knowledge of the source wavelet $w(t)$, for which there are several methods for estimating $w(t)$.

1. The source wavelet can be inverted from the data by considering that each time sample of $w(t)$ is the unknown to be inverted (see Exercise 1, under the topic "Source wavelet estimation" in the Computational Toolkit and Appendix 22B). The source wavelet is inverted so that the predicted data best agree with the observed data for the early arrivals. Inversion of the velocity model and source wavelet can be computed separately, simultaneously, or sequentially.

2. An inversion strategy can be devised that is somewhat insensitive to knowledge of the source wavelet (Lee and Kim, 2003; Yu et al., 2014). See Exercise 6.

3. The reflection from the sea floor can be isolated and stacked over several traces to get the source wavelet. See the topic "Source wavelet estimation" in the Computational Toolkit.

4. The direct wave can be windowed and integrated over time to give the source wavelet. The free-surface reflection interferes with the direct arrival for hydrophones near the sea surface so the recorded first arrival is the superposition of the direct arrival $w(t)$ and free-surface reflection $-w(t + \delta t)$, in which δt is the time lag of the free-surface reflection relative to the direct arrival. The direct-arrival waveform can be estimated from $w(t) - w(t + \delta t)$ by either deconvolution or integration.

5. An objective function can be designed in which knowledge of the source wavelet is not needed (Lee and Kim, 2003; Sheng, 2004). See the exercises at the end of this chapter.

Warner et al. (2013a) suggest that the missing low frequencies in seismic data can be created by using a sparse L_1 norm deconvolution to spike the data, then the deconvolved data are convolved with a wavelet with the missing low frequencies. Here, the original bandlimited source wavelet is assumed to be known. The downshifted frequency data can be used to create a new misfit function and FWI is used to estimate the missing low-wavenumber information in the velocity model. The resulting low-wavenumber tomogram will be the starting model to apply FWI to the original data. This approach seemed to give promising improvements for several examples, but further tests are needed to determine if it is robust and effective for the general case.

19.2.7 Ignoring amplitudes

Seismic waves are strongly affected by the elastic, attenuation, and anisotropic characteristics of the earth.

However, current modeling methods for FWI do not take these effects fully into consideration, and so there will be strong data residuals because of our inadequate modeling ability. The next chapters show how phase-like inversion methods still can provide good resolution in the velocity model without having to fully explain amplitudes.

One approach for correcting the amplitude and phase mismatches between predicted and observed data is the matched filter approach suggested by Warner and Guasch (2014). Here, a matched filter (see Chapter 18) is used to match the observed trace with the predicted trace, and then the gradient of the objective function is used to update both the velocity model and filter coefficients. If a particular model provides a perfect match to the field data, then the matching filter will be a delta function of unit amplitude at zero lag. Therefore, an objective function can be created that measures the deviation of the filter from a zero-lag delta function, and a conventional adjoint formulation is used to find the earth model that minimizes this functional. Some of the benefits with this approach is that the amplitudes of the predicted traces do not need to be modeled accurately, and for the examples presented, it mitigates problems with cycle skipping. Because the method works by adapting one dataset to another using Wiener filters, Warner and Guasch (2014) refer to it as adaptive wavefield inversion.

19.3 Numerical tests

A working MATLAB® code for inverting a velocity model from a shot gather is given in the online Computational Toolkit. This code is used to invert 200 acoustic seismograms for the velocity model shown in Figure 19.4. The input data are a 200-trace CSG for a 20-Hz Ricker wavelet line source centered at the surface of the velocity model. The reconstructed velocity model is shown in Figure 19.5, and the plot of the normed residual versus iteration number is in Figure 19.6. In this case, the predicted seismograms almost match the observed seismograms on a wiggle for wiggle basis, yet Figure 19.5 suggests that the high-wavenumber parts of the model are reconstructed properly but the low-wavenumber parts of the model are mostly absent.

19.4 Summary

Iterative waveform inversion can be described as iteratively migrating waveform residuals into the medium, where the slowness field is updated by this migration image. The potential benefit of FWI is that it can, in theory, provide a much more detailed estimate of the earth's velocity and density model than any current geophysical method.

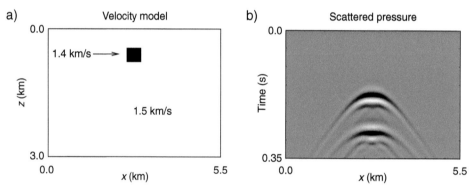

Figure 19.4. (a) Velocity model and (b) CSG pressure seismograms after muting of the direct waves. The shot gather is for a point source on the surface directly above the scatterer and shooting into 200 geophones evenly distributed over 5.5 km on the surface.

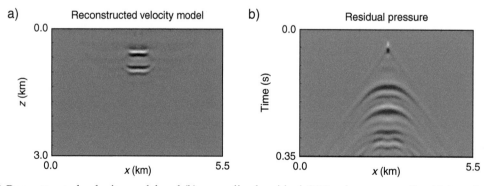

Figure 19.5. (a) Reconstructed velocity model and (b) normalized residual CSG seismograms after 11 iterations of the waveform inversion code. The initial model is a homogeneous half-space with velocity 1.5 km/s.

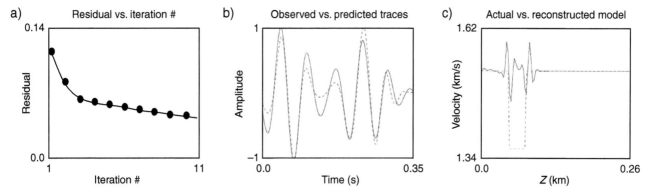

Figure 19.6. (a) Norm of CSG residual versus iteration number, (b) comparison between observed and synthetic seismograms after 11 iterations. Observed seismogram is indicated by dashed line, and synthetic seismogram is represented by the solid line. (c) Comparison between actual and reconstructed velocity profiles along a vertical slice through the center of the scatterer. The predicted and observed seismograms are calculated at the surface above the center of the scatterer. Although the high-wavenumber components (i.e., edges of scatterer) of the model appear to be well reconstructed, the low-wavenumber parts (i.e., velocity of scatterer) are not recovered.

The main obstacles to achieving this benefit fully are the following:

- The waveform misfit function is highly nonlinear so the inversion tends to get stuck in a local minimum. A partial remedy is that the starting model should be close enough to the actual model to avoid the cycle-skipping problem. Traveltime tomography or migration velocity analysis can be used to obtain the initial model, where the recorded reflection traveltimes can be used as a constraint in the misfit function.

- There can be an inherent nonuniqueness problem in which many different models can almost fit the same data. A good starting model is needed so that cycle skipping is avoided. In the absence of a good starting model, a multiscale approach is needed where low-frequency, short-offsets, and early-arrival events are fitted first. As the iterations proceed and there is no cycle skipping, then larger subsets of the data can included. Regularization based on a priori knowledge about the model, especially the low-wavenumber information from well logs, is also important.

- The important physics that governs the actual wave propagation sometimes is not included in the simulations. If an acoustic FWI method is used, then the strong surface waves should be filtered from the data prior to inversion.

Compared to migration, waveform tomography is less robust, more computationally expensive, and often requires expert-user intervention to get it to work. Thus, future research should aim toward mitigating these problems and attempt to make tomography as effective and as easy to use as migration. The payoff will be more accurate estimates of lithology than provided by migration, traveltime tomography, or amplitude-versus-offset (AVO) studies.

19.5 Exercises

1. Consider the 1D wave equation

$$\frac{1}{c^2}\frac{\partial^2 p(z,t|z_s,0)}{\partial t^2} - \frac{\partial^2 p(z,t|z_s,0)}{\partial x^2} = \delta(z-z_s)w(t),$$
$$(19.9)$$

and the source-perturbed wave equation

$$\frac{1}{c^2}\frac{\partial^2(p(z,t|z_s,0)+\delta p(z,t|z_s,0))}{\partial t^2}$$
$$- \frac{\partial^2(p(z,t|z_s,0)+\delta p(z,t|z_s,0))}{\partial x^2}$$
$$= \delta(z-z_s)[w(t)+\delta w(t)]. \qquad (19.10)$$

Show that the relationship between the source perturbation $\delta w(t)$ and data perturbation δp is given by

$$\delta p(z,t|z_s,0) = \int G(z_s,t'|z,t)\delta w(t')dt'. \quad (19.11)$$

Now show that if $z = z_g$,

$$\frac{\delta p(z_g,t|z_s,0)}{\delta w(t')} = G(z_g,t|z_s,t'), \qquad (19.12)$$

so the update formula for estimating the wavelet is

$$w(t)^{(k+1)} = w(t)^{(k)} - \alpha\frac{\partial p(z_g,t|z_s,0)}{\partial w(t')}\Delta p(z_g,t|z_s,0),$$
$$(19.13)$$

in which $\Delta p(z_g,t|z_s,0)$ is the data residual. Discuss how this wavelet inversion procedure might be incorporated into an FWI workflow.

2. Define the autocorrelation residual $\Delta r(\mathbf{g}, \mathbf{s}) = P^{\mathrm{cal}}$ $(\mathbf{g}, \mathbf{s})P^{\mathrm{cal}}(\mathbf{g}, \mathbf{s})^* - P^{\mathrm{obs}}(\mathbf{g}, \mathbf{s})P^{\mathrm{obs}}(\mathbf{g}, \mathbf{s})^*$. Find the gradient formula for $\sum_g \sum_s |\Delta r(\mathbf{g}, \mathbf{s})|^2$ and interpret its physical meaning. Do we need to estimate the phase of the source wavelet from the data to compute the predicted autocorrelogram? What are the advantages and disadvantages of autocorrelation waveform inversion (AWI) compared to FWI?

3. Define the source and receiver statics as the phase-shift operation $e^{i\omega(\tau_s + \tau_g)}$ and the recorded trace as $p(\mathbf{g}, \mathbf{s})e^{i\omega(\tau_s + \tau_g)}$, which is the product of the actual trace $p(\mathbf{g}, \mathbf{s})$ and the source-receiver statics. In this case, what is the advantage of AWI compared to FWI?

4. Assume that the early arrivals are windowed from the data to give the direct arrival trace $W(\mathbf{g}, \mathbf{s})$. Define the deconvolution misfit function (Sheng, 2004) as

$$\Delta r(\mathbf{g}, \mathbf{s}) = \frac{P^{\mathrm{cal}}(\mathbf{g}, \mathbf{s})W^{\mathrm{cal}}(\mathbf{g}, \mathbf{s})^*}{|W^{\mathrm{cal}}(\mathbf{g}, \mathbf{s})|^2 + \epsilon} - \frac{P^{\mathrm{obs}}(\mathbf{g}, \mathbf{s})W^{\mathrm{obs}}(\mathbf{g}, \mathbf{s})^*}{|W^{\mathrm{obs}}(\mathbf{g}, \mathbf{s})|^2 + \epsilon},$$
(19.14)

in which $1 \gg \epsilon > 0$ is a small damping parameter. Find the gradient formula for $\sum_g \sum_s \Delta r(\mathbf{g}, \mathbf{s})^2$. What are the advantages and disadvantages of this objective function for inversion compared to FWI and AWI? Comment about its ability to suppress statics.

5. Same as previous question, except assume that the windowed event is that of a shallow reflection arrival.

6. Yu et al. (2014) define the "convolution" misfit function as

$$\Delta r(\mathbf{g}, \mathbf{s}) = P^{\mathrm{cal}}(\mathbf{g}, \mathbf{s})W^{\mathrm{obs}}(\mathbf{g}, \mathbf{s}) - P^{\mathrm{obs}}(\mathbf{g}, \mathbf{s})W^{\mathrm{cal}}(\mathbf{g}, \mathbf{s}),$$
(19.15)

and $W^{\mathrm{obs}}(\mathbf{g}, \mathbf{s})$ is the estimated observed wavelet. Derive the gradient formula for this misfit function so that the "convolution" misfit function avoids division and the selection of ϵ. Here,

- W^{calc} can be a Ricker wavelet whose frequency band overlaps with the data spectrum.
- The extracted source wavelet does not need to be very accurate.
- This misfit can be transformed into a Wiener filter by multiplying Δr with $W^{\mathrm{obs}}(\mathbf{g}, \mathbf{s})^*$ or $W^{\mathrm{cal}}(\mathbf{g}, \mathbf{s})^*$ and selecting an ϵ for division by $|W^{\mathrm{obs}}(\mathbf{g}, \mathbf{s})|^2 + \epsilon$ or $|W^{\mathrm{cal}}(\mathbf{g}, \mathbf{s})|^2 + \epsilon$.

7. The phase is defined as $\phi = Im[lnP]$. Show that the Fréchet derivative of the phase is given by

$$\frac{\partial \phi}{\partial s(\mathbf{x})} = Im\left[\frac{\partial lnP}{\partial s(\mathbf{x})}\right] = \frac{\left|\frac{\partial P}{\partial s(\mathbf{x})}\right|}{|P|}\sin(\phi' - \phi), \quad (19.16)$$

in which ϕ' is the phase of $\partial P/\partial s(\mathbf{x})$. Is the magnitude of the source wavelet needed?

8. From the previous problem, derive the gradient for the phase misfit function $\Delta\phi = \phi^{\mathrm{cal}} - \phi^{\mathrm{obs}}$ to give a wave equation phase inversion (WPI) method. Discuss the advantages and disadvantages of WPI compared to FWI (Luo and Schuster, 1991a; Schuster and Quintus-Bosz, 1993).

9. Try different starting models for the example in Figure 19.4. Does the convergence rate accelerate as the starting model becomes closer to the actual model?

10. Create a MATLAB code for one of the preconditioning strategies mentioned in this chapter. Use a model similar to the one in Figure 19.4, except include a deeper scatterer where the geometrical spreading effects are noticeably different than those for the shallow scatterer. Use waveform inversion to invert the associated CSG. Does the preconditioning term accelerate convergence in this example?

11. Invert the data associated with the Figure 19.4 model, except apply a multiscale strategy. One such strategy might be to use low-pass filtered data for the early iterations, and then use unfiltered data for the later iterations. In the early iterations, applying a low-pass filter to the model also might be useful. Does the multiscale strategy avoid the cycle-skipping problem and accelerate convergence in this example?

19.6 Computational labs

1. Estimate the source wavelet by windowing about the reflection arrival in the *Source Wavelet Extraction* lab under the topic "Source wavelet estimation" in the Computational Toolkit.

2. Apply multiscale FWI to the 1D model in the *Multiscale FWI: 1D Model* lab.

3. Use FWI to invert the source wavelet in the *Inversion for Source Wavelet* lab under the topic "Source wavelet estimation" in the Computational Toolkit.

4. Use FWI to invert the rectangular model or the 2D Marmousi model in the Computational Toolkit under the topic "FWI."

Chapter 20: Wave-Equation Inversion of Skeletonized Data

Chapter 19 described how waveform inversion estimates the velocity model that minimizes the waveform misfit function. However, the data misfit function can be very sensitive to the accurate prediction of amplitudes, which is difficult to achieve with modeling methods that do not describe viscoelastic and anisotropic effects fully. Moreover, a poor starting model will promote cycle skipping and convergence to a local minimum.

To mitigate these problems, other types of data can be inverted that can be modeled more accurately and might enjoy a more quasilinear relationship between the model and the data. For example, the traveltime misfit function in Figure 19.1d is much less bumpy than the waveform misfit function shown in Figure 19.1c. We can think of the less complex traveltimes as data *skeletonized* from the more complicated seismograms. The strategy is initially to invert the skeletonized data to get close to the global minimum with no cycle skipping, then invert the waveforms for the finer details of the model.

A difficulty in inverting skeletonized data is that it is not straightforward to find the Fréchet derivative for the skeletonized data. For example, if the ith skeletonized data sample is denoted by D_i, then the velocity field is updated by

$$c(\mathbf{x})^{(k+1)} = c(\mathbf{x})^{(k)} - \alpha\gamma(\mathbf{x}),$$
$$= c(\mathbf{x})^{(k)} - \alpha \sum_i \frac{\partial D_i}{\partial c(\mathbf{x})} \Delta D_i, \qquad (20.1)$$

in which ΔD_i is the skeletonized data residual and $c(\mathbf{x})$ is the velocity. It is straightforward to compute the Fréchet derivative $\partial D_i/\partial c(\mathbf{x})$ if D_i is the *pressure field* (see equation 10.23) or the *phase* (see equation 19.16), because these data types appear explicitly in the governing equations such as the Helmholtz wave equation or the space-time wave equation. But how is the Fréchet derivative computed for other data types, such as $\partial m(\mathbf{x}')/\partial c(\mathbf{x})$ for inverting common-image migration gathers $m(\mathbf{x}')$, or $\partial\,\text{semb}(v_{\text{NMO}}, t_0)/\partial c(\mathbf{x})$ for inverting the semblance function $\text{semb}(v_{\text{NMO}}, t_0)$ in normal moveout (NMO) velocity semblance gathers? These types of data do not appear

explicitly in the governing equations. The answer is to use the implicit function theorem.

20.1 Implicit function theorem

Skeletonized data in equation 20.1, such as traveltimes $D_i \to \delta\tau$, are not explicit functions of the model variables $c(\mathbf{x})$, so it is difficult to find the expression for the Fréchet derivative. In this case, the implicit function theorem (Luo and Schuster, 1991a, 1991b) can be used to determine $\partial\delta\tau/\partial c$.

The first step in deriving the implicit function theorem is to define an equation of constraint

$$\dot{f}(c, \delta\tau) = 0, \qquad (20.2)$$

that connects the c and $\delta\tau$ variables, in which $f(c, \delta\tau)$ is called the connective function (Luo and Schuster, 1991a, 1991b). For example, a constraint equation can be obtained by crosscorrelating the observed $p(t)^{\text{obs}}$ and predicted traces $p(t)^{\text{pred}}$

$$f(c, \delta\tau) = \int p(t)^{\text{obs}} p(t + \delta\tau)^{\text{pred}} dt, \qquad (20.3)$$

to give the correlation traces $f(c, \delta\tau)$ depicted Figure 20.1a. At the peak of the correlated wavelet, the derivative of the function satisfies the constraint equation

$$\dot{f} := \left.\frac{\partial f}{\partial\delta\tau}\right|_{\delta\tau=\delta\tau^*} = \left.\int p(t)^{\text{obs}}\dot{p}(t + \delta\tau)^{\text{pred}} dt\right|_{\delta\tau=\delta\tau^*} = 0, \qquad (20.4)$$

in which $\delta\tau^*$ is the time lag that aligns the red trace with the black one in Figure 20.1a. The variation of $\delta\tau(c)^*$ with respect to trial velocity values c is described by the dashed curve[1] in Figure 20.1b.

The vector $d\mathbf{r} = (dc, d\delta\tau)$ tangent to the dashed curve is shown as the red arrow in Figure 20.1b, and it is

---

[1] The correct velocity model will yield a predicted trace identical to the observed trace, so that $\delta\tau^* = 0$. The dashed curve in Figure 20.1b suggests this velocity model has not been found.

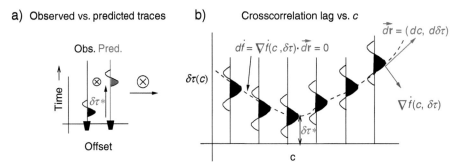

Figure 20.1. (a) Observed $p(t)^{\text{obs}}$ and predicted $p(t)^{\text{pred}}$ traces and (b) the correlated traces $f(c, \delta\tau) = p(t)^{\text{obs}} \otimes p(t)^{\text{pred}}$ as a function of the predicted velocity c. Here, $\delta\tau$ is the lag variable and $\delta\tau^*$ is the stationary lag time that aligns the red trace with the black one in (a). The value of $\dot{f}(c, \delta\tau) = 0$ does not change along the dashed curve; hence, $d\dot{f}(c, \delta\tau) = \nabla\dot{f} \cdot dr = 0$ for points along the dashed curve.

perpendicular to the gradient $\nabla\dot{f}(c, \delta\tau)$ (blue arrow) such that

$$df = \nabla\dot{f} \cdot dr = \frac{\partial\dot{f}}{\partial c}dc + \frac{\partial\dot{f}}{\partial\delta\tau}d\delta\tau = 0. \quad (20.5)$$

Rearranging the above equation yields the Fréchet derivative

$$\frac{\partial\delta\tau}{\partial c} = -\frac{\partial\dot{f}/\partial c}{\partial\dot{f}/\partial\delta\tau}, \quad (20.6)$$

which is satisfied at $\delta\tau = \delta\tau^*$ and gives the desired form for explicitly computing $\partial\delta\tau/\partial c$ in terms of the Fréchet derivatives[2] of $\dot{f}$. The above equation can be generalized to multidimensional functions $\dot{f}(x_1, x_2, x_3, \ldots) = 0$ of arbitrary dimension[3]:

$$\frac{\partial x_i}{\partial x_j} = -\frac{\partial\dot{f}/\partial x_j}{\partial\dot{f}/\partial x_i}, \quad (20.7)$$

and is the key result from the implicit function theorem. Equations 20.6 and 20.7 now will be used to estimate the Fréchet derivatives of skeletonized data. See https://www.youtube.com/watch?v=xtgTckGMuWE for an enlightening tutorial on the implicit function theorem for a multidimensional functional. For more than one connective functional, see Chapter 24.4.

20.2 Examples of skeletonized inversion

Several examples of skeletonized wave-equation inversion now will be described. In all cases, a simpler type of data is identified that leads to a simpler objective function with faster convergence, but less resolution than FWI. These objective functions can have the added benefit of not being very sensitive to the accurate modeling of amplitudes.

20.2.1 Wave-equation traveltime tomography

Let $p(\mathbf{g}, t|\mathbf{s}, 0)$ represent a seismic trace recorded by a crosshole experiment, and the goal is to invert the transmission traveltime data by modeling and inverting the wave equation.[4] The observed and predicted traces at one geophone are depicted in Figure 20.1a, and the goal is to find the velocity distribution that minimizes the sum of the squared traveltime residuals

$$\epsilon = 1/2 \sum_{s,g} \overbrace{(\tau(\mathbf{g}, \mathbf{s}) - \tau(\mathbf{g}, \mathbf{s})^{\text{obs}})}^{\Delta\tau(\mathbf{g},\mathbf{s})}{}^2, \quad (20.8)$$

in which $\tau(\mathbf{g}, \mathbf{s})$ are the traveltimes predicted by a numerical solution to the wave equation for a source at $\mathbf{s}$ and geophone at $\mathbf{g}$.

Replacing D_i by $\tau(\mathbf{g}, \mathbf{s})$ in equation 20.1 and deriving the Fréchet derivative $\partial\tau(\mathbf{g}, \mathbf{s})/\partial c(\mathbf{x})$ from a crosscorrelation connective function (see equation 20.46 in Appendix 20A) gives the formula of steepest descent for estimating the velocity distribution:

$$c(\mathbf{x})^{(k+1)} = c(\mathbf{x})^{(k)} - \alpha \sum_{s,g} \frac{\partial\tau(\mathbf{g}, \mathbf{s})}{\partial c(\mathbf{x})}\Delta\tau(\mathbf{g}, \mathbf{s}),$$

$$= c(\mathbf{x})^{(k)} - \alpha\frac{1}{c^3(\mathbf{x})}$$

$$\times \sum_{s,g} \int dt\, \overbrace{\dot{g}(\mathbf{x}, t|\mathbf{g}, 0) \star \dot{p}(\mathbf{x}, t|\mathbf{s}, 0)}^{\text{migration kernel}}\,\overbrace{\Delta\tilde{\tau}(\mathbf{g}, t|\mathbf{s})}^{\text{data}}. \quad (20.9)$$

Here, $\Delta\tilde{\tau}$ is the pseudotraveltime residual

$$\Delta\tilde{\tau}(\mathbf{g}, t|\mathbf{s}) = \frac{-2}{E}\dot{p}(\mathbf{g}, t - \Delta\tau|\mathbf{s}, 0)^{\text{obs}}\Delta\tau(\mathbf{g}, \mathbf{s}), \quad (20.10)$$

---

[2] The formal definition of the Fréchet derivative of the functional $f(c)$ for c in a Banach space of functions is $\delta f[c(\mathbf{x})]/\delta c(\mathbf{x}) = \lim_{\epsilon\to 0}\{f[c(\mathbf{x}) + \epsilon g(\mathbf{x})] - f[c(\mathbf{x})]\}/\epsilon$ for some test function $g(\mathbf{x})$.

[3] The dashed curve $\tau(c)$ in Figure 20.1 can also represent the two-dimensional contour of an N-dimensional functional $f(c, \tau, x_1, x_2, \ldots)$, in which all the x_i variables are kept fixed. Hence, equation 20.6 is still valid.

[4] Here, it is assumed that the source frequency is not high enough to satisfy the high-frequency assumption of ray-based traveltime tomography. Therefore, a wave-equation method should be used for inverting traveltimes.

which is the recorded trace weighted by the associated traveltime residual.[5] The gradient in equation 20.9 is similar to the formula for RTM except the reflection traces are weighted by the traveltime residual $\Delta\tau(\mathbf{g},\mathbf{s})$. In other words, the velocity is updated by smearing the traveltime residuals along the wavepaths associated with the rabbit ears, bananas, and ellipses described in Chapters 12 and 13. The significant velocity updates mostly will be along the wavepaths where the associated traveltime residuals are large. This implies that strong shallow reflections with difficult-to-predict amplitudes will not contribute strongly to the gradient, as long as the observed shallow reflections are predicted kinematically.

Inverting traveltimes with equation 20.9 is denoted (Luo and Schuster, 1991a, 1991b) as wave-equation traveltime tomography (WT). The results from a WT case history are shown in Figure 20.2 and the workflow is given in Box 20.2.1. Synthetic traces in Figure 20.2b are generated by a finite-difference solution to the acoustic wave equation for the blue velocity profile shown in Figure 20.2a. The associated first-arrival traveltimes are picked and inverted using the WT algorithm described above to give the purple WT profile, which serves as the starting model for FWI to give the WTW tomogram in Figure 20.2d. The WTW tomogram provides the most coherent RTM image in Figure 20.2e, and the predicted early arrivals show a good match with the data in Figure 20.2f.

To blend WT with FWI, we can use the wave equation traveltime and waveform (WTW) misfit function (Luo and Schuster, 1991a; Zhou et al., 1995; Zhou et al., 1997)

$$\epsilon = \frac{1-\alpha}{2}\sum_{s,g}[w_{s,g}^{\tau}\Delta\tau(\mathbf{g},\mathbf{s})]^2 + \frac{\alpha}{2}\sum_{s,g,t}[w_{s,g,t}^{p}\Delta p(\mathbf{g},\mathbf{s},t)]^2,$$
(20.11)

in which $0 \le \alpha \le 1$ can be varied gradually from 0 to 1 as the iterations proceed, and $w_{s,g}^{\tau}$ and $w_{s,g,t}^{p}$ are weighting functions related to the reliability and normalization[6] of the data. If there is more than one traveltime pick per trace, then the traveltime residuals, the summations, and traveltime weights will have an additional index that denotes the different events per trace. If $\alpha = 1/2$, the estimated velocity model will honor both the kinematics and amplitudes of the observed data democratically.

To avoid manual identification of reflections in traces, the reflection data can be extrapolated down to the trial reflector depth z_o. Similarly, the source field can be forward propagated down to this same depth. In this case, the forward- and back-propagated traces at the depth z_o can be

correlated with one another, and only the events near lag zero should be considered. This is because the direct wave and back-propagated reflections from z_o should be nearly coincident in time at this depth z_o (Zhang et al., 2012) for sufficiently small errors in the velocity model.

A generalized misfit function can be created by setting $\alpha = 1/2$ in equation 20.11, $w_{s,g}^{\tau} = \Delta p(\mathbf{g},\mathbf{s},t)$ and $w_{s,g,t}^{p} = \Delta\tau(\mathbf{g},\mathbf{s})$ to give

$$\epsilon = \frac{1}{2}\sum_{s,g,t}[\Delta\tau(\mathbf{g},\mathbf{s})\Delta p(\mathbf{g},\mathbf{s},t)]^2,$$
(20.12)

in which the gradient will be a blend of both traveltime and waveform gradients that can be weighted differently at each iteration. As the traveltime residual gets small for some events, these events become less important in the inversion despite having a non-negligible amplitude residual. This might be important for ignoring strong shallow reflections in favor of updating deep velocities with later reflection arrivals.

The formulation of Luo and Schuster (1991a) inverts transmission traveltimes, but a phase-inversion method (Sun and Schuster, 1993) replaces the predicted trace $d(t)^{\text{pred}}$ spectrum $D(\omega)^{\text{pred}} = |D(\omega)^{\text{pred}}|e^{i\omega\phi^{\text{pred}}}$ with $\tilde{D}(\omega)^{\text{pred}} = |D(\omega)^{\text{obs}}|e^{i\omega\phi^{\text{pred}}}$, in which $|D(\omega)^{\text{obs}}|$ is the observed magnitude spectrum. Here, the trace is assumed to be normalized to the maximum amplitude in that trace. The corresponding misfit function for one trace in the frequency domain is

$$\epsilon = 1/2|\tilde{D}^{\text{pred}} - D^{\text{obs}}|^2 = |D^{\text{obs}}|^2 - |D^{\text{obs}}|^2\cos(\phi^{\text{pred}} - \phi^{\text{obs}}).$$
(20.13)

In this case, the Fréchet derivative with respect to the velocity perturbation depends only on the predicted phase, not the predicted amplitude. Compare this to the zero-lag correlation proposed by Routh et al. (2011), in which the objective function in the frequency domain becomes

$$\epsilon = \tilde{D}^{\text{pred}}D^{\text{obs}*} \approx |D^{\text{obs}}|^2 e^{i(\phi^{\text{pred}} - \phi^{\text{obs}})}$$
(20.14)

if the observed spectrum replaces the predicted magnitude spectrum. In both cases, the magnitude spectrum of the observed data does not need to be fitted, only the phase spectra should be explained. A similar phase-inversion method can be obtained by normalizing each trace by its magnitude spectrum.

Other phase-inversion methods have been developed, except they are computed in the space-frequency or space-Laplace domains (Woodward, 1992; Herman, 1992; Shin and Min, 2006). Another phase-like inversion method is by Zhang and Wang (2009), who apply a $\tau - p$ transform to the data, and then invert for the velocity distribution that best focuses the energy around the source position. It relaxes the need to know the source wavelet or the exact amplitudes of the events, and the predicted model is largely

---

[5]The traveltime residual is also the stationary lag time $\delta\tau^*$ illustrated in Figure 20.1b.

[6]To ensure that the misfit functions are unitless and balanced, the weight functions $w_{s,g}^{\tau}$ and $w_{s,g,t}^{p}$ might include normalization terms such as $1/\sum_{s',g'}[\tau(\mathbf{g}',\mathbf{s}')^{\text{obs}}]^2$ and $1/\sum_{s',g',t'}[p(\mathbf{g}',\mathbf{s}',t')^{\text{obs}}]^2$, respectively.

Box 20.2.1 Workflow for Wave-Equation Traveltime Tomography

1. Window events of interest by weighting the observed and calculated traces: $\tilde{p}(\mathbf{g}, \mathbf{s}, t)^{\text{obs}} = w(\mathbf{g}, \mathbf{s}, t)p(\mathbf{g}, \mathbf{s}, t)^{\text{obs}}$ and $\tilde{p}(\mathbf{g}, \mathbf{s}, t)^{\text{pred}} = w(\mathbf{g}, \mathbf{s}, t)p(\mathbf{g}, \mathbf{s}, t)^{\text{pred}}$. The window function $w(\mathbf{g}, \mathbf{s}, t)$ is tapered just before and after the event of interest. For notational convenience we replace $p(\mathbf{g}, t|\mathbf{s}, 0)$ with $p(\mathbf{g}, \mathbf{s}, t)$.

2. Correlate $\tilde{p}(\mathbf{g}, \mathbf{s}, t)^{\text{obs}}$ and $\tilde{p}(\mathbf{g}, \mathbf{s}, t)^{\text{pred}}$ in each window to obtain the traveltime residuals $\Delta\tau(\mathbf{g}, \mathbf{s})$.

3. Migrate the weighted traces $\Delta\tau(\mathbf{g}, \mathbf{s})\dot{p}(\mathbf{g}, \mathbf{s}, t + \Delta\tau)^{\text{obs}}$ in equation 20.9 to get the image $m(\mathbf{x})$.

4. Update velocity model $c(\mathbf{x}) = c(\mathbf{x}) - \eta m(\mathbf{x})$. Repeat steps 1–4 until convergence, where η is the step length. However, WT can suffer from cycle-skipping problems if there are multiple events in the windowed trace.

Benefits: Wave-equation traveltime tomography overcomes the high-frequency limitation of ray-based tomography to provide more realistic estimates of velocity models. There are fewer local minima compared to a waveform misfit function if events are windowed properly, so convergence is relatively more robust and faster.

Liabilities: Wave-equation traveltime tomography is much more expensive than ray-based traveltime tomography. Ray-based traveltime tomograms often provide an adequate starting model for FWI as long as the rays reach the depth of interest with enough angular diversity. For transmission tomography, event windowing is easy. For reflection tomography, event identification can be tedious unless an automated WT method is used (Zhang et al., 2015a, 2015b).

---

insensitive to predicting amplitudes accurately. This algorithm is related to the source-focusing inversion method of Sun (1991) who back-projected the data to the source position and uses an iterative gradient method to find the velocity model that maximizes the weighted-entropy objective function around the source position (see Exercise 2). The advantages of this approach are that there is no significant need to 1) know the source wavelet, 2) accurately model waveforms, and 3) pick the traveltimes. The penalty, however, is that WT is not likely to achieve the full resolution of FWI because the velocity is updated mainly along the long wavepaths between the source and the receivers, and so it cannot achieve high-wavenumber resolution at deep depths.

20.2.2 Early-arrival waveform tomography

Another type of skeletonized inversion is to only invert the early arrivals,[7] in which the later arrivals in Figure 19.1a are muted to get the early arrivals in Figure 20.3a. The resulting misfit function reduces to the simple one in Figure 20.3b, which suggests that many local minima can be bypassed using early arrival waveform tomography (EWT). Moreover, the elastic events not explained by an acoustic modeler, such as surface waves in land data, can be muted out as well.

An example showing the effectiveness of EWT is demonstrated in Sheng (2004) and Sheng et al. (2006), in

which seismograms are computed for the acoustic velocity model in Figure 20.4a, and the first-arrival traveltimes are inverted by ray-based tomography (Nemeth et al., 1997) to get the Figure 20.4c tomogram. The input data were computed for 21 sources and 51 geophones evenly located on the surface with source and geophone intervals of 10 m and 4 m, respectively. A Ricker wavelet with 60-Hz peak frequency is the source wavelet, and Figure 20.4b depicts a typical shot gather. The wavelength of the undulating interface is estimated to be about 40 m, which violates the high-frequency assumption of ray tracing (Bleistein et al., 2001) for a 60-Hz source. The computational grid dimension is 401×121 gridpoints.

Figure 20.4c and 20.4d show the traveltime and EWT tomograms, respectively, and suggest that traveltime tomography recovers the long-wavelength features, but the short-wavelength details are blurred. In contrast, the EWT tomogram provides a very accurate estimate of both the coarse and finely detailed features in the actual model. Unlike EWT, ray-based tomography performs poorly because the high-frequency assumption of ray-based tomography is violated with this model. The EWT method, with the workflow described in Box 20.2.2, reduces both the traveltime and waveform residuals by more than an order of magnitude after 25 iterations.

20.2.3 Wave-equation inversion of surface waves

Surface waves are often the dominant arrivals in a land CSG, as illustrated by the events in Figure 20.5. Typically,

---

[7]An early arrival is one that arrives within several periods of the first arrival. The time window initially is narrow to avoid cycle skipping, but as the iterations proceed, the window can be widened to admit more arrivals.

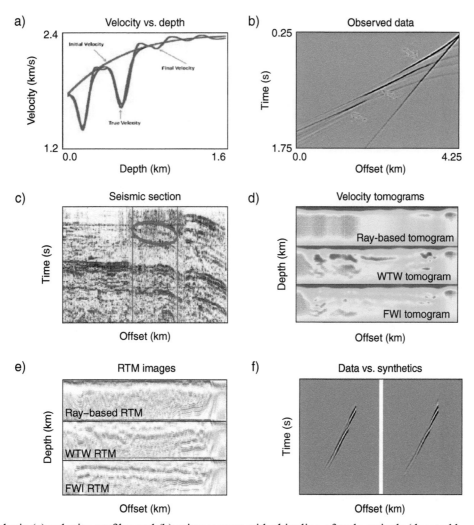

Figure 20.2. Synthetic (a) velocity profiles and (b) seismograms with shingling of early arrivals (denoted by green arrows) associated with low-velocity zones. The purple profile in (a) is computed by applying WT to the first-arrival traveltimes associated with the synthetic traces. A land seismic section is shown in (c), and the associated velocity tomograms in (d). The WTW tomogram has the most character compared to the ray-based and FWI tomograms. The FWI tomogram used the ray-based tomogram as the starting model. Figure (e) depicts the RTM images and (f) compares the windowed early-arrival field record to that of the synthetics using the WTW tomogram. (a–f) Adapted from Shen et al. (2012).

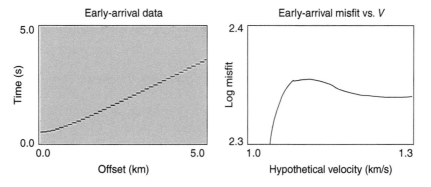

Figure 20.3. Same as Figures 19.1a and 19.1c, except all events but the first reflection arrivals are muted.

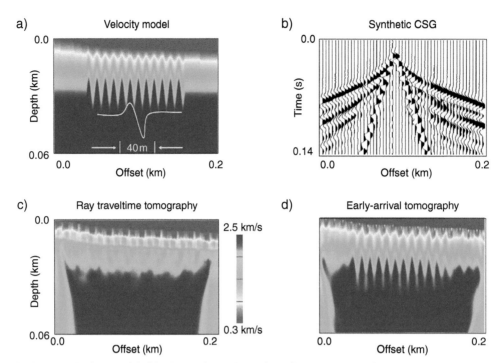

Figure 20.4. Synthetic (a) velocity model, (b) shot gather, (c) ray-based tomogram, and (d) EWT tomogram. Unlike EWT, the velocity model is too rough to satisfy the high-frequency assumption of ray-based tomography to obtain an accurate tomogram. Illustrations adapted from Sheng (2004).

Box 20.2.2 Workflow for Early-Arrival Waveform Tomography

1. Estimate source wavelet and initial model. Window early-arrival events in observed and calculated traces: $\tilde{p}(\mathbf{g}, \mathbf{s}, t) = W(\mathbf{s}, \mathbf{g}, t) p(\mathbf{g}, \mathbf{s}, t)$.
2. Compute waveform residual $\Delta r(\mathbf{g}, \mathbf{s}, t) = \tilde{p}(\mathbf{g}, \mathbf{s}, t) - \tilde{p}(\mathbf{g}, \mathbf{s}, t)^{\text{obs}}$.
3. Migrate weighted traces $\Delta r(\mathbf{g}, \mathbf{s}, t)$ to get image $m(\mathbf{x})$.
4. Update velocity model $c(\mathbf{x}) = c(\mathbf{x}) - \alpha m(\mathbf{x})$. Repeat steps 1–4, and gradually open up early-arrival window with an increase in iterations. There is also the option of a source-receiver offset window that gradually becomes wider with increasing iterations to avoid cycle skipping (Almomin and Biondi, 2013; Al-Yaqoobi and Warner, 2013;

AlTheyab, 2015). If an acoustic code is used for forward modeling, the window should be narrow enough to disallow strong shear-wave events.

Benefits: There are fewer local minima compared to a waveform misfit function, so convergence is somewhat more robust and faster. The strong elastic effects of surface waves for land data are avoided. This is somewhat akin to a multiscale method, in which more complex events are admitted into the inversion with increasing number of iterations.

Liability: The EWT only inverts for shallow- to intermediate-depth velocities. Wider offsets lead to the estimation of deeper velocities.

---

explorationists consider surface waves to be noise, which is unfortunate because they contain a great deal of information about the near-surface geology. Recently there have been efforts (Baumstein et al., 2011; Perez-Solano et al., 2012) to use correlation-based objective functions to invert surface waves for near-surface velocity information.

However, there are many surface-wave cycles in the traces of Figure 20.5, so the waveform misfit functions for these data are likely to be highly nonlinear with respect to changes in the shear velocities. Therefore, we should look for a means to simplify the data. One such reduction is to extract the dispersion velocity $C(\omega)^{\text{obs}} = \omega / k(\omega)$ curve for the fundamental mode in Figure 20.6, and use it to reconstruct the shear-velocity distribution.

A surface-wave inversion algorithm that uses the wave equation to invert the dispersion curve is presented next.

1. Form the misfit function ϵ

$$\epsilon = 1/2 \sum_{\omega}(k(\omega) - k(\omega)^{obs})^2, \qquad (20.15)$$

so the iterative solution is given by

$$c(\mathbf{x})^{(k+1)} = c(\mathbf{x})^{(k)} - \alpha\gamma(\mathbf{x}),$$

$$= c(\mathbf{x})^{(k)} - \alpha \sum_{\omega} \Delta k(\omega)\frac{\partial k(\omega)}{\partial c(\mathbf{x})}. \qquad (20.16)$$

Here, $k(\omega)^{obs}$ is the dispersion curve for the fundamental mode picked from the data. An alternative approach is to transform the dispersion curve $k(\omega)^{obs}$ into the phase velocity $C(\omega)^{obs} = \omega/k(\omega)^{obs}$ curve, and use the misfit function

$$\epsilon = \frac{1}{2}\sum_{\omega}(C(\omega) - C(\omega)^{obs})^2 \qquad (20.17)$$

to find the S-velocity distribution.

Land shot gather

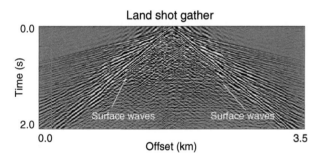

Figure 20.5. Common-shot gather recorded by a land survey.

2. The Fréchet derivative $\partial k(\omega)/\partial c(\mathbf{x})$ is obtained by recognizing that the maximum value of the crosscorrelation satisfies a constraint equation similar to that in equation 20.4. In this case, the predicted magnitude spectrum $U(k,\omega|\mathbf{s},0)$ computed by a solution to the elastic wave equation is correlated with the observed magnitude spectrum $U(k,\omega|\mathbf{s},0)^{obs}$ of the vertical-component traces in a common-shot. For example,

$$\dot{f}(\Delta k, c(\mathbf{x}))|_{\Delta k = \Delta k^*}$$

$$= \int \dot{U}(k + \Delta k^*, \omega|\mathbf{s},0)\, U(k,\omega|\mathbf{s},0)^{obs} dk = 0, \qquad (20.18)$$

in which $\dot{U} = \frac{\partial U(\Delta k, \omega|s,0)}{\partial \Delta k}$, Δk^* is the stationary wavenumber that aligns the traces associated with the predicted and observed magnitude spectra, and the dot denotes the derivative with respect to the wavenumber Δk. The spectrum $U(k,\omega|\mathbf{s},0)$ is obtained by applying a 2D Fourier transform to the filtered shot gather $u(\mathbf{g},t|\mathbf{s},0)$ that mostly contains surface waves.

The above equation says that $\dot{f}$, the wavenumber derivative of the crosscorrelation between the observed and predicted spectra at a fixed frequency, is zero at the lag value equal to the wavenumber residual $\Delta k(\omega)^*$. This is the wavenumber shift in which the computed and observed magnitude spectra $U(\Delta k,\omega|\mathbf{s},0)$ of the fundamental modes will be aligned with one another for maximum correlation. Thus, equation 20.18 serves as the constraint equation which can be used to obtain the Fréchet derivative $\partial\Delta k/\partial c$ in equation 20.16. Therefore, the denominator in equation 20.6 takes the form

$$\frac{\partial \dot{f}(\Delta k(\omega,\mathbf{s}), c(\mathbf{x}))}{\partial \Delta k}\bigg|_{\Delta k = \Delta k^*}$$

$$= \int \ddot{U}(\omega, k + \Delta k^*|\mathbf{s})\, U(\omega, k|\mathbf{s})^{obs}\, dk, \qquad (20.19)$$

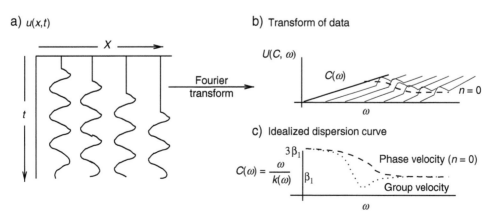

a) $u(x,t)$

b) Transform of data

c) Idealized dispersion curve

Figure 20.6. (a) Common shot gather, and (b) actual $C(\omega) - \omega$ spectrum of the data and (c) idealized dispersion curve for the fundamental Rayleigh mode ($n = 0$) for a two-layered elastic medium with a free surface. Here, the dispersion velocity is $C(\omega) = \omega/k(\omega)$.

and the numerator is

$$\frac{\partial \dot{f}(\Delta k(\omega, \mathbf{s}), c(\mathbf{x}))}{\partial c(\mathbf{x})}\bigg|_{\Delta k = \Delta k^*}$$

$$= \int \frac{\partial \dot{U}(\omega, k + \Delta k^*|\mathbf{s})}{\partial c(\mathbf{x})} \, U(\omega, k|\mathbf{s})^{\mathrm{obs}} \, dk, \quad (20.20)$$

so that from equation 20.6 the Fréchet derivative becomes

$$\frac{\partial \Delta k}{\partial c} = -\frac{\partial \dot{f}/\partial c}{\partial \dot{f}/\partial \Delta k}\bigg|_{\Delta k = \Delta k^*}$$

$$= -\frac{\int \dfrac{\partial \dot{U}(\omega, k + \Delta k|\mathbf{s})}{\partial c(\mathbf{x})} \, U(\omega, k|\mathbf{s})^{\mathrm{obs}} \, dk}{\int \ddot{U}(\omega, k + \Delta k|\mathbf{s}) \, U(\omega, k|\mathbf{s})^{\mathrm{obs}} \, dk}\bigg|_{\Delta k = \Delta k^*}.$$

$$(20.21)$$

The term $\partial \dot{U}/\partial c(\mathbf{x})$ can be interpreted as the monofrequency migration response at the trial image point $\mathbf{x}$ for a source at $\mathbf{s}$ and wavenumber k. Therefore, the gradient in equation 20.16 is computed by migrating the spectral data weighted by the data residual $\Delta k(\omega)$ into the medium.

3. Use the gradient update formula in equation 20.16 to update iteratively the velocity model $c(\mathbf{x})$.

A possible procedure for carrying out this inversion is to inverse transform the residual dispersion curves into the space-time domain, and then carry out the velocity updates by finite-difference solutions to the elastic wave equation. An alternative approach is to compute the wavefields by a finite-difference solution to the elastic wave equation, and then use a Fourier transform in the frequency and space-wavenumber domains to get $U(\omega, k + \Delta k|\mathbf{s})$. Knowing these wavefields allows for the calculation of the Fréchet derivatives.

Surface-wave inversion example

An example of inverting for the S-velocity distribution by skeletonized surface-wave inversion is presented next. A shot gather computed by a finite-difference solution to the 2D elastic wave equation is shown in Figure 20.7a for the three-layer model in Figure 20.7f (red line), where the traces are the vertical-component particle-velocity measurements on the free surface. The source is a vertical-component point source. An FK transform is applied to the shot gather to give the spectrum shown in Figure 20.7b, which then is transformed into the phase-velocity spectrum depicted in Figure 20.7c. The blue dots corresponds to the measured curve and the red dots represent the actual phase-velocity curve. The paucity of low-frequency and long-offset traces prevented an accurate estimate of the phase velocities at low frequencies.

The misfit function in equation 20.17 is used to compute the formula of steepest descent

$$c(\mathbf{x})^{(k+1)} = c(\mathbf{x})^{(k)} - \alpha \gamma(\mathbf{x}),$$

$$= c(\mathbf{x})^{(k)} - \alpha \sum_{\omega} \Delta C(\omega)^{(k)} \frac{\partial C(\omega)}{\partial c(\mathbf{x})} - \beta \frac{\partial R(\mathbf{x})}{\partial c(\mathbf{x})},$$

$$(20.22)$$

for reconstructing the S-velocity profile, in which $R(\mathbf{x})$ is a regularization term with the regularization parameter β. For a layered medium, there are only a few unknowns, so the Fréchet derivative $\frac{\partial C(\omega)}{\partial c(\mathbf{x})}$ can be computed by the finite-difference formulation

$$\frac{\partial C(\omega)}{\partial c_i} \approx \frac{C(\omega)_{c + \delta c_i} - C(\omega)_c}{\delta c_i}, \quad (20.23)$$

in which c is the reference S-velocity model and δc_i is the perturbed velocity in the ith layer. Two finite-difference simulations are required to compute $\frac{\partial C(\omega)}{\partial c_i}$, one for the reference S-velocity model and one for the reference model with the S-velocity in the ith layer perturbed by δc_i. The shot gathers from these two simulations in the space-time domain are FK transformed to get the two dispersion spectra. Then, the fundamental mode is identified to get $k(\omega)_c$ and $k(\omega)_{c + \delta c_i}$, and these dispersion curves are used to get the phase-velocity curves $C(\omega)_c$ and $C(\omega)_{c + \delta c_i}$. These phase velocities then are inserted into equation 20.23 to get the approximation to the Fréchet derivative. The normalized RMS residual for $\Delta C(\omega)^{(k)}$ in Figure 20.7d also is computed, and equation 20.22 is used to update the S velocity. The fundamental mode is largely insensitive to the P-velocity and density variations (Aki and Richards, 1980), so their values are not updated iteratively. For an N-layer velocity model, only $2N$ finite-difference simulations are computed for each iteration.

Discretizing the model into four unknown layers, the steepest-descent algorithm after 50 iterations gives the phase-velocity curve in Figure 20.7e and the blue S-velocity profile in Figure 20.7f. In this case, the regularization function $R(\mathbf{x})$ is a roughness penalty function $R(\mathbf{x}) = \frac{1}{2}\sum_z (\frac{c(\mathbf{x})}{\partial z})^2$ that encourages solutions which smoothly vary in depth.

A seismic land survey was carried out near the Red Sea coast in Saudi Arabia to give the recorded shot gather shown in Figure 20.8a. The geophone spacing was 1 m, the source was a hammer on a metal plate, and the dominant frequency in the traces was about 40 Hz. An FK transform is applied to the Figure 20.8a shot gather and the phase-velocity curve for the fundamental mode is picked and displayed as the red dots in Figure 20.8c. Using a five-layer velocity model, these phase velocities are inverted

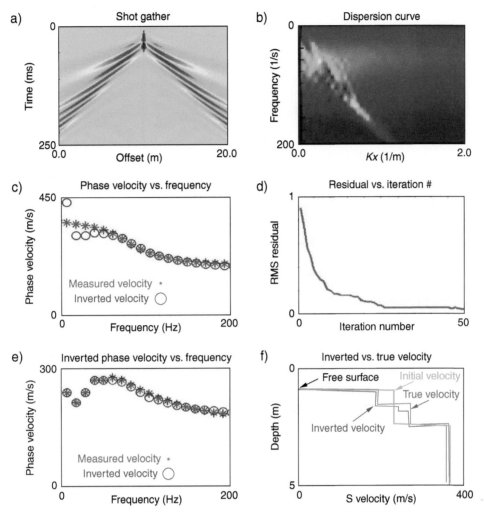

Figure 20.7. Surface-wave inversion results from a land survey near the Red Sea. (a) CSG for the vertical particle-velocity traces $u(g, t)$, (b) its Fourier transform $U(k, \omega)$, (c) phase-velocity curve $C(\omega)$ for the fundamental mode, (d) normalized residual versus iteration number, (e) inverted phase velocity denoted by blue line, and (f) inverted S-velocity model. The true model denoted by the red line in (f) consists of three layers with a free surface. After Zhang et al. (2015c).

using the steepest-descent formula in equation 20.22 to give the predicted blue points in Figure 20.8c. The background P-velocity values for the elastic modeling were obtained from a P-velocity traveltime tomogram inverted from the refraction P-wave arrivals, and a constant density model is assumed. Figure 20.8d shows the initial velocity model depicted by the green curve and the inverted profile is in blue. This reconstructed velocity profile provides a positive velocity gradient for these sediments.

The skeletonized procedure for inverting the fundamental mode of surface waves can be extended to models with lateral S-velocity variations by assuming a quadratic lateral variation in the velocity $c(\mathbf{x})_i$ in the ith layer:

$$c(\mathbf{x})_i = c_i + \gamma_i x + \zeta_i x^2, \qquad (20.24)$$

in which c_i, γ_i, and ζ_i are unknown constants that are to be inverted for by the steepest-descent formula 20.22. Here,

x is the lateral offset coordinate along the model. Instead of inverting for just one unknown in each layer, three unknowns are to be inverted, which triples the computational cost. However, the total computational cost is quite affordable for reconstructing velocity profiles with no more than several dozen layers.

Finally, a sensitivity matrix easily can be computed to assess the sensitivity of the data to changes in the S-velocity profile. The elements of the sensitivity matrix are the computed Fréchet derivatives $\frac{\partial C(\omega_j)_i}{\partial c_i}$ for different frequencies and layer numbers. As an example, Figure 20.9 plots these values for the five-layer model in Figure 20.8d. These values can be used to assess which layer velocities have the least uncertainty. If the actual velocity uncertainties are desired, then the diagonal values of the Hessian inverse can be plotted. To reduce computational costs, Li et al. (2017) develop an adjoint approach to inverting the dispersion curves for the shear-velocity model.

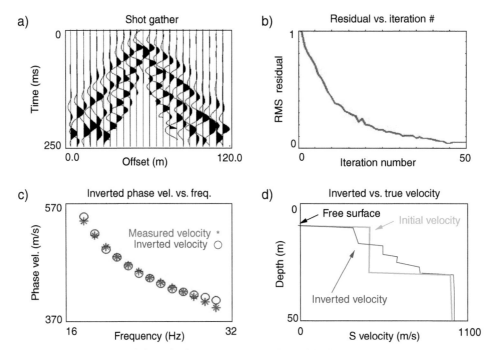

Figure 20.8. (a) CSG for the vertical particle-velocity traces $u(g, t)$, (b) residual versus iteration number, (c) measured (red) and predicted (blue) phase-velocity curves $C(\omega)$ for the fundamental mode, and (d) inverted S-velocity model. After Zhang et al. (2015c).

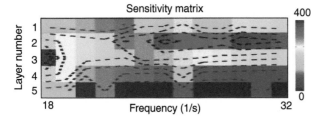

Figure 20.9. Sensitivity matrix of Fréchet derivative values for the five-layer model in Figure 20.8d. As expected, higher frequencies in the data are influenced mainly by the S-velocities in the shallower layers. After Zhang et al. (2015c).

20.3 Alternative objective functions

Other correlation-based methods have been developed to reduce the sensitivity of the objective functions to the accuracy in modeling recorded amplitudes. These include the objective function of Van Leeuwen and Mulder (2010), who use the weighted norm of the cross-correlation function (see row V of Table 20.1), i.e.,

$$\epsilon = \frac{1}{2} \sum_x \sum_\tau \left[\overbrace{\sum_t W_\tau p(x,t)^{\mathrm{obs}} p(x,t+\tau)^{\mathrm{pred}}}^{\text{crosscorrelation}} \right]^2 ,$$

(20.25)

in which $p(x, t)$ is the time-domain trace indexed by x, and the weight W_τ is applied to each time sample to make ϵ less sensitive to noise and amplitude spectra differences between the observed and predicted waveforms. This weighting function also favors small phase shifts between the observed and predicted arrivals, and it mitigates the stringent requirement to estimate the source wavelet or the correct amplitudes of arrivals. Masoni et al. (2013) suggest a Gaussian weight for $W = e^{-\alpha \tau^2}$ to smoothly penalize the correlation amplitudes away from zero lag, in which α is a parameter that controls the width of the Gaussian function. For a simple two-layer model, they show that the Gaussian weight leads to an objective function with fewer local minima than a classical misfit function. This objective function is more robust in the presence of noise.

A special case of equation 20.25 is obtained by setting W_τ to be a normalization term for the predicted and observed traces, $\sum_\tau \longrightarrow 1$, and $\tau = 0$ to give the zero-lag objective function of Baumstein et al. (2011) and Routh et al. (2011):

$$\epsilon = \sum_x \left[\overbrace{\sum_t p(x,t)^{\mathrm{obs}} p(x,t)^{\mathrm{pred}}}^{\text{dot product two traces}} \right]^2 .$$

(20.26)

The objective functions in equations 20.25 and 20.26 are phase-like functionals (see equation 20.14) and can be more robust than the classical waveform misfit function, but they

Table 20.1. Properties of different objective functions.

Objective function	Comments	Amplitude sensitivity	Phase sensitivity	Convergence robustness	Model resolution
I. L_2 Data FWI $\sum_i W_i(d_i - d_i^{obs})^2$ $W_i = 1$ $i \rightarrow$ time + trace index	L_2 waveform inversion Tarantola (1984a, 1984b, 1987) Mora (1987, 1989)	High	High	Low	High
$W_i =$ Early arrival window	Sheng (2004)	High	High	Mod.	Mod.
$W_i =$ Expanding box window	Yaqoobi and Warner (2013)	High	High	Mod.-High	Mod.
II. L_1 Data FWI $\sum_i |d_i - d_i^{obs}|$	L_1 waveform inversion Souza et al. (2013)	Mod.-High	High	Low	High
III. Phase inversion $\sum_i(\phi_i - \phi_i^{obs})^2$	Effective inversion of kinematics of events	Low	High	Mod.	Mod.
$\phi_i \rightarrow$ Trace phase $i \rightarrow$ Freq. & trace index	Woodward (1989, 1992) Sun and Schuster (1993) Routh et al. (2011)				
IV. Regularized trace FWI $\sum_i(f_i * d_i - g_i * d_i^{obs})^2$	Phase-like inversion	Low	High	Mod.	Mod.-High
Trace normalization: $f_i* = 1/$energy-in-trace $g_i* = 1/$energy-in-trace	Shen (2010) Yu et al. (2014)				
Envelope misfit: $g_i, f_i \rightarrow$ Hilbert transform	Low-frequency estimation Chi et al. (2013)	Mod.	Mod.	Mod.	Mod.
Source decon: $g_i, f_i \rightarrow$ decon filter for early arrival in reference trace	No source estimate needed Lee and Kim (2003) Sheng (2004)	Low	High	Mod.	Mod.-High
V. Correlation optimization $\sum_i(W_id_i \otimes W_id_i^{obs})^2$ $W_i =$ First-arrival window $W_i =$ Reflection window	Phase-like inversion Luo and Schuster (1991a) van Leeuwen and Mulder (2010) Routh et al. (2011)	Low	High	Mod.-High	Mod.
VI. Image FWI $\sum_i(\{[\mathbf{L}^\dagger\mathbf{L}]\mathbf{m}\}_i - \mathbf{m}_i^{mig})^2$ Inversion of migration residual	Simpler data Stork (1991), Sjoeberg et al. (2003) Symes and Carrazone (1991) Bulcao et al. (2013)	Mod.-High	High	Mod.-High	Mod.-High

might lead to less resolution. However, the resulting tomograms can provide a good starting model for FWI with reduced chances for cycle skipping.

Bozdag et al. (2011) applies the Hilbert transform to seismic traces and computes the instantaneous phase and envelope misfit functions to estimate the kernel sensitivity functions for global seismic tomography. They show that objective functions based on the envelopes of seismic waveforms can reduce the nonlinearity of the inverse problem. Wu et al. (2014) and Chi et al. (2014) successfully use the envelope objective function for FWI. They claim that this procedure might be able to retrieve ultra-low frequency information from acoustic records to reduce the starting-model dependence of FWI. However, long-offset records still are needed to make up for the lack of low-frequency information in the data.

Finally, Lee and Kim (2003) and Sheng (2004) replace the observed traces in the misfit function by deconvolved traces (see row IV in Table 20.1). They select a master trace from a shot gather to deconvolve the other traces in the shot gather. Deconvolution is weighted correlation in the time domain, and eliminates the need to know the source wavelet. A related procedure by Yu et al. (2014) also reduces the need to know the exact source wavelet.

20.4 Summary

Reducing the complexity of data can lead to objective functions with reduced complexity and less sensitivity to amplitudes in seismic data. The simplicity of the skeletonized objective function can promote faster convergence rates, but it also can lead to a loss in model resolution. It is important to choose the type of skeletonized data that is reasonably sensitive to changes in model parameters and is insensitive to amplitude values, but also reduces the tendency to getting stuck in a local minimum. A good preliminary test for sensitivity is to plot the skeletonized objective function against variations in a few model parameters.

The Fréchet derivative of the skeletonized data is difficult to derive because the skeletonized data variables do not appear explicitly in the governing equations (e.g., the pressure variable appears in the wave equation but V_{NMO} does not). However, the implicit function theorem can be used to compute the skeletonized Fréchet derivative as long as some constraint equation is developed that depends on the field variable and the skeletonized data variable.

There are many skeletonized objective functions that can be more effective than a waveform misfit function, and their number is limited only by our imagination.

20.5 Exercises

1. What are the limitations and benefits of estimating the velocity model by WT compared to FWI? Which should be more robust and which one should provide the highest resolution? Which one emphasizes velocity updates along the rabbit ear wavepaths and largely ignores updating along banana wavepaths? Explain.

2. Assume a single shot gather in which the source is located at $\mathbf{s}$. The goal is to design an objective function that indicates whether the back-propagated wavefield focuses at the source position $\mathbf{s}$ at the excitation time $t = 0$. If the velocity model is correct, then the migrated wavefield will be focused tightly at $\mathbf{s}$ at $t = 0$. Otherwise, it will be smeared around $\mathbf{s}$. Denote the

back-projected receiver wavefield as $p_g(\mathbf{x}, t)$, so the image at the source position (at time zero) is given by $m(\mathbf{x})|_{\mathbf{x}=\mathbf{s}} = p_g(\mathbf{s}, 0)$. Assume the probability density function (Sun, 1991)

$$P(\mathbf{x}) = [m(\mathbf{x})]^2 / \int [m(\mathbf{x}')]^2 d\mathbf{x}'^2, \qquad (20.27)$$

in which $\int P(\mathbf{x}')d\mathbf{x}'^2 = 1$. Show that the entropy function H_s defined as

$$H_s = -\int P(\mathbf{x}) \ln[P(\mathbf{x})] d^2\mathbf{x}, \qquad (20.28)$$

can be used to quantify smear in the back-projected image. Here, the integration is over the velocity model.

3. The source-focusing objective function ϵ_s used by Sun (1991) is represented by

$$\epsilon_s = e^{H_s/H_0} G_s, \qquad (20.29)$$

in which $G_s = \int P(\mathbf{x})|\mathbf{x} - \mathbf{s}|^2 d\mathbf{x}^2$ and $H_0 = lnA$ when A is the area of integration. The focusing function for a number of different shot gathers is

$$\epsilon = \sum_s e^{H_s/H_0} G_s. \qquad (20.30)$$

Show that

$$\frac{\partial H_s}{\partial c(\mathbf{x})} = \int (-1 - ln(P_s(\mathbf{x}'))) \frac{\partial P_s(\mathbf{x}')}{\partial c(\mathbf{x})} d\mathbf{x}'^2,$$

$$\frac{\partial G_s}{\partial c(\mathbf{x})} = \int \frac{\partial P_s}{\partial c(\mathbf{x})} |\mathbf{x}' - \mathbf{x}|^2 d\mathbf{x}'^2. \qquad (20.31)$$

Also find the explicit expression for $\frac{\partial P_s(\mathbf{x}')}{\partial c(\mathbf{x})}$.

4. Figure 20.10 depicts the entropy objective functions for a uniform background slowness s_o and different perturbed slowness models s. There are 19 sources spaced at 20 m and 32 receivers spaced at 10 m in a crosswell geometry. Ray tracing is used to generate the shot gathers. For a single shot gather, Figure 20.10a shows the source objective functions for velocities perturbed from the actual slowness value s_o; the objective-function values are shown in Figure 20.10b as a function of the slowness perturbation. Write a code to duplicate these results (see Figure 20.11).

5. Discuss the benefits and liabilities of Sun's source inversion (Sun, 1991) with those of Zhang and Wang (2009). The objective function of Zhang and Wang (2009) is the back-propagated wavefield at the source location weighted by a function that depends on the actual shot time of the source.

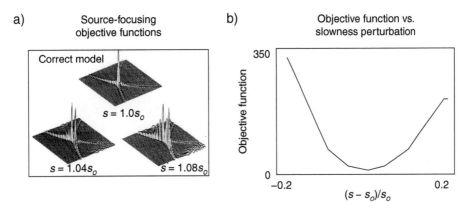

Figure 20.10. Entropy objective functions for different values of the perturbed slowness s, in which s_o is the actual slowness value in the homogeneous velocity model. Adapted from Sun (1991).

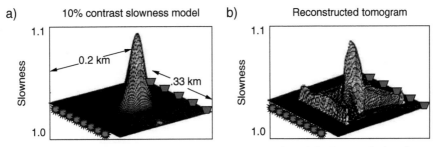

Figure 20.11. Slowness distributions for the (a) actual and (b) reconstructed models. Transmission data were generated and inverted by ray tracing for a crosswell geometry with 19 sources (stars) and 32 receivers (quadrilaterals), where the background velocity is 2 km/s. Adapted from Sun (1991).

6. Another example of skeletonized data is the normal moveout (NMO) velocity V_{NMO} as a function of zero-offset, two-way traveltime τ. For a fixed value of τ, the optimal value of V_{NMO} is the one that maximizes the amplitude of the quasisemblance function $S(V_{\text{NMO}}, c)_\tau$ defined by

$$S(V_{\text{NMO}}, c)_\tau = A \int dx\, p\left(x, \sqrt{\tau^2 + x^2/V_{\text{NMO}}^2}\right), \quad (20.32)$$

in which A is an energy normalization term, $p(x,t)$ represents the traces in a common-midpoint gather (CMG) with midpoint coordinate x, and $c = c(\mathbf{x}')$ is the earth's velocity distribution. We consider the semblance functional to be a function of the velocity distribution because changes in $c(\mathbf{x}')$ will lead to changes in the semblance panel. Derive an algorithm for inverting $c(x,z)$ from a semblance panel by using an objective function similar to that from equation 20.25. In this case, the predicted and observed data are the predicted and observed semblance panels.

7. Examples of a CMG and a semblance panel are shown in Figure 20.12. Here, the optimal value of V_{NMO} for a given τ is the one in which the predicted hyperbola

given by $t = \sqrt{\tau^2 + x^2/V_{\text{NMO}}^2}$ best matches the traveltime moveout of the reflection event in the CMG. In this case, the reflection amplitudes coherently sum along this hyperbola to give a large value of semblance.

For a fixed value of τ, $S(V_{\text{NMO}}, c)_\tau$ can be thought of as a trace in the semblance panel with V_{NMO} acting as a virtual time coordinate, in which the peak value of $S(V_{\text{NMO}}, c)_\tau$ enjoys the stationary property

$$\left.\frac{\partial S(V_{\text{NMO}}, c)_\tau}{\partial V_{\text{NMO}}}\right|_{V_{\text{NMO}}=V_{\text{NMO}*}} = \dot{S}(V_{\text{NMO}}^*, c)_\tau = 0. \quad (20.33)$$

This equation now serves as the connective equation between skeletonized data V_{NMO} and the model $c(\mathbf{x}')$, so the Fréchet derivative is

$$\frac{\partial V_{\text{NMO}}}{\partial c(\mathbf{x}')} = -\frac{\dfrac{\partial \dot{S}(V_{\text{NMO}}, c)_\tau}{\partial c(\mathbf{x}')}}{\dfrac{\partial \dot{S}(V_{\text{NMO}}, c)_\tau}{\partial V_{\text{NMO}}}}. \quad (20.34)$$

Show that the above expression can be used with a gradient-optimization algorithm to find the velocity model that minimizes the misfit function

$$\epsilon = 1/2 \sum_{t_0} \overbrace{(V_{\text{NMO}}(\tau) - V_{\text{NMO}}(\tau)^{\text{obs}})^2}^{\text{data residual}}, \quad (20.35)$$

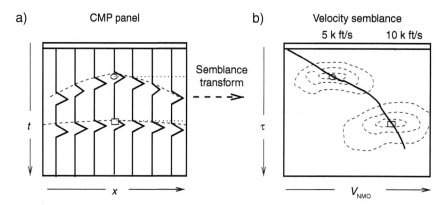

Figure 20.12. (a) Common-midpoint gather and (b) associated semblance $S(V_{NMO}, t_0)$ panel. The points that satisfy the equation $dS/dV_{NMO} = 0$ coincide with parts of the solid line in (b) and represent the maximum values of the semblance panel for any fixed value of τ.

for example, by a formula of steepest descent:

$$c(\mathbf{x})^{(k+1)} = c(\mathbf{x})^{(k)} - \alpha \gamma(\mathbf{x}),$$

$$= c(\mathbf{x})^{(k)} - \alpha \sum_\tau \Delta V_{NMO}(\tau) \frac{\partial V_{NMO}(\tau)}{\partial c(\mathbf{x})}.$$

$$(20.36)$$

Here, $\Delta V_{NMO}(\tau) = V_{NMO}(\tau) - V_{NMO}^{obs}(\tau)$, the maximum amplitude of $S(V_{NMO}(\tau))$ is picked from the semblance panel and is denoted by $V_{NMO}(\tau)^{obs}$, and the one predicted using the wave equation[8] is given by $V_{NMO}(\tau)$.

8. To calculate $\partial V_{NMO}/\partial c(\mathbf{x})$, equation 20.33 says that the following quantities must be computed:

$$\frac{\partial \dot{S}(V_{NMO}, c)}{\partial V_{NMO}} = A \int dx\, \ddot{p}\left(x, \sqrt{\tau^2 + x^2/V_{NMO}^2}\right),$$
$$(20.37)$$

and

$$\frac{\partial \dot{S}(V_{NMO}, c(\mathbf{x}))}{\partial c(\mathbf{x})} = A \int dx\, \frac{\partial \dot{p}(x, \sqrt{\tau^2 + x^2/V_{NMO}^2})}{\partial c(\mathbf{x})},$$
$$(20.38)$$

in which the dot indicates differentiation with respect to V_{NMO}, and the explicit form of the Fréchet derivative already has been derived. Explicitly derive the above expression.

9. Can the algorithm in the previous two exercises be adjusted to perform 2D traveltime tomography, without having to pick traveltimes? Simultaneously inverting all panels from all CMGs might yield a useful 2D velocity model, but one that is less accurate than standard traveltime tomography because the semblance

panels simplify the traveltime moveout function to be hyperbolic. Generalize this algorithm to a higher-order moveout function, in which the background moveout function is generated by ray tracing.

Appendix 20A: Gradient of the traveltime misfit function

To find the velocity model $c(\mathbf{x})$ associated with the traveltime data, we can use the following algorithm:

1. **Misfit function.** Form the misfit function ϵ

$$\epsilon = 1/2 \sum_{g,s} (\tau(\mathbf{g}, \mathbf{s}) - \tau(\mathbf{g}, \mathbf{s})^{obs})^2, \qquad (20.39)$$

in which the summation is over the geophone positions and $\tau(\mathbf{g}, \mathbf{s})$ is the predicted transmission traveltime for a source at $\mathbf{s}$ and a geophone at $\mathbf{g}$. The iterative steepest-descent solution is given by

$$c(\mathbf{x})^{(k+1)} = c(\mathbf{x})^{(k)} - \alpha \gamma(\mathbf{x}),$$

$$= c(\mathbf{x})^{(k)} - \alpha \sum_{g,s} \Delta\tau(\mathbf{g}, \mathbf{s}) \frac{\partial \tau(\mathbf{g}, \mathbf{s})}{\partial c(\mathbf{x})}, \quad (20.40)$$

in which $\Delta\tau(\mathbf{g}, \mathbf{s}) = \tau(\mathbf{g}, \mathbf{s}) - \tau(\mathbf{g}, \mathbf{s})^{obs}$ is the traveltime residual. In practice, we use a preconditioned conjugate-gradient method described in Appendix 20B.

2. **Fréchet derivative** $\partial\tau(\mathbf{g}, \mathbf{s})/\partial c(\mathbf{x})$. To determine the Fréchet derivative $\partial\tau(\mathbf{g}, \mathbf{s})/\partial c(\mathbf{x})$, the first step is to form a constraint functional (see equation 20.2) that relates the waveform data $p(\mathbf{x}, t \mid \mathbf{s}, 0)$ to the traveltime residual $\Delta\tau(\mathbf{g}, \mathbf{s})$. Such a constraint functional is given by the crosscorrelation between the computed trace and

---

[8]A finite-difference solution to the wave equation is used to generate synthetic data; these synthetic data are reassembled into CMGs; and velocity analysis is used to determine the NMO velocity $V_{NMO}(\tau)$ as a function of zero-offset, two-way traveltime.

the differentiated observed data (see Figure 20.1a):

$$\dot{f}(c(\mathbf{x}), \Delta\tau(\mathbf{g}, \mathbf{s}))$$
$$= \int dt\, p(\mathbf{g}, t|\mathbf{s})^{\text{obs}} \dot{p}(\mathbf{g}, t + \Delta\tau|\mathbf{s}, 0) = 0, \quad (20.41)$$

in which the dot indicates time differentiation of the trace. The above equation says that $\dot{f}$, the time derivative of the crosscorrelation between the observed and predicted traces, is zero at the lag value equal to the traveltime residual $\Delta\tau(\mathbf{g}, \mathbf{s})$. This is the time shift in which the computed and observed first arrivals will be aligned with one another for maximum correlation. Thus, equation 20.41 serves as the constraint equation which can be used to obtain the Fréchet derivative $\partial\Delta\tau/\partial c$.

Therefore, the denominator in equation 20.6 takes the form

$$E = -\frac{\partial \dot{f}(c(\mathbf{x}), \Delta\tau(\mathbf{g}, \mathbf{s}))}{\partial \Delta\tau}$$

$$= -\int dt\, p(\mathbf{g}, t|\mathbf{s}, 0)^{\text{obs}} \ddot{p}(\mathbf{g}, t + \Delta\tau|\mathbf{s}, 0),$$

$$= \int dt\, \dot{p}(\mathbf{g}, t|\mathbf{s}, 0)^{\text{obs}} \dot{p}(\mathbf{g}, t + \Delta\tau|\mathbf{s}, 0), \quad (20.42)$$

and the numerator becomes

$$\frac{\partial \dot{f}(c(\mathbf{x}), \Delta\tau(\mathbf{g}, \mathbf{s}))}{\partial c(\mathbf{x})}$$

$$= \int dt\, p(\mathbf{g}, t|\mathbf{s}, 0)^{\text{obs}} \frac{\partial \dot{p}(\mathbf{g}, t + \Delta\tau|\mathbf{s}, 0)}{\partial c(\mathbf{x})},$$

$$= -\int dt\, \dot{p}(\mathbf{g}, t - \Delta\tau|\mathbf{s}, 0)^{\text{obs}} \frac{\partial p(\mathbf{g}, t|\mathbf{s}, 0)}{\partial c(\mathbf{x})}, \quad (20.43)$$

in which integration by parts and a change of variables $t + \Delta\tau \mapsto t$ are used. Here, $\partial p(\mathbf{g}, t|\mathbf{s}, 0)/\partial c(\mathbf{x})$ is the Fréchet derivative (see equation 10.25) given by

$$\frac{\partial p(\mathbf{g}, t|\mathbf{s}, 0)}{\partial c(\mathbf{x})} = \frac{2}{c(\mathbf{x})^3} \dot{g}(\mathbf{x}, t|\mathbf{g}, 0) \star \dot{p}(\mathbf{x}, t|\mathbf{s}, 0). \quad (20.44)$$

Substituting equation 20.44 into 20.43, and inserting the result and equation 20.42 into equation 20.6 yields the Fréchet derivative of the predicted traveltime:

$$\frac{\partial \tau(\mathbf{g}, \mathbf{s})}{\partial c(\mathbf{x})} = \frac{-2}{Ec^3(\mathbf{x})} \int dt\, \dot{g}(\mathbf{x}, t|\mathbf{g}, 0) \star \dot{p}(\mathbf{x}, t|\mathbf{s}, 0)$$
$$\cdot \dot{p}(\mathbf{g}, t - \Delta\tau|\mathbf{s}, 0)^{\text{obs}}. \quad (20.45)$$

3. **Misfit gradient.** Inserting the Fréchet derivative in equation 20.45 into equation 20.40 yields the traveltime misfit gradient

$$\gamma(\mathbf{x}) = \frac{1}{c^3(\mathbf{x})} \sum_s \sum_g \int dt\, \overbrace{\dot{g}(\mathbf{x}, t|\mathbf{g}, 0) \star \dot{p}(\mathbf{x}, t|\mathbf{s}, 0)}^{\text{migration kernel}}$$

$$\times \underbrace{\Delta\tilde{\tau}(\mathbf{g}, t|\mathbf{s})}_{\text{data}}, \quad (20.46)$$

in which $\Delta\tilde{\tau}$ is the pseudotraveltime residual

$$\Delta\tilde{\tau}(\mathbf{g}, t|\mathbf{s}) = \frac{-2}{E} \dot{p}(\mathbf{g}, t - \Delta\tau|\mathbf{s}, 0)^{\text{obs}} \Delta\tau(\mathbf{g}, \mathbf{s}), \quad (20.47)$$

which is the recorded trace weighted by the associated traveltime residual. Therefore, the above gradient is similar to that for waveform inversion, except the traces are weighted by the traveltime residuals before they are migrated to update the velocity.

Using the identities (Tarantola, 1987)

$$\int dt\, [f(t) \star g(t)]\, h(t) = \int dt\, g(t)[f(-t) \star h(t)] \quad (20.48)$$

$$g(\mathbf{x}, -t|\mathbf{x}', 0) = g(\mathbf{x}, 0|\mathbf{x}', t), \quad (20.49)$$

we can rewrite equation 20.46 as

$$\gamma(\mathbf{x}) = \frac{1}{c^3(\mathbf{x})} \sum_s \int dt\, \dot{p}(\mathbf{x}, t|\mathbf{s}, 0)\, \dot{p}'(\mathbf{x}, t|\mathbf{s}, 0), \quad (20.50)$$

in which the summation is over the source coordinates. Here, $\dot{p}(\mathbf{x}, t|\mathbf{s}, 0)$ is the time derivative of the forward-modeled field and $\dot{p}'(\mathbf{x}, t|\mathbf{s}, 0)$ is the time derivative of the back-projected residual field defined by

$$p'(\mathbf{x}, t|\mathbf{s}, 0) = -\sum_g g(\mathbf{x}, -t|\mathbf{g}, 0) \star \Delta\tilde{\tau}(\mathbf{g}, t|\mathbf{s}). \quad (20.51)$$

Combining equations 20.50 and 20.51 gives the form of the gradient in equation 20.9, which is interpreted as migrating the weighted traces. Each trace is weighted by the traveltime residual associated with that trace.

If $\Delta\tau$ is small enough then

$$\dot{p}(\mathbf{g}, t - \Delta\tau|\mathbf{s}, 0)^{\text{obs}}$$
$$\approx [p(\mathbf{g}, t|\mathbf{s}, 0)^{\text{obs}} - p(\mathbf{g}, t - \Delta\tau|\mathbf{s}, 0)^{\text{obs}}]/\Delta\tau,$$
$$\approx [p(\mathbf{g}, t|\mathbf{s}, 0)^{\text{obs}} - p(\mathbf{g}, t|\mathbf{s}, 0)]/\Delta\tau,$$
$$= -\Delta p(\mathbf{g}, t|\mathbf{s}, 0)/\Delta\tau. \quad (20.52)$$

Therefore, equation 20.47 can be approximated by $\delta\tilde{\tau}(\mathbf{g}, t|\mathbf{s}) \approx 2\delta p(\mathbf{g}, t|\mathbf{s}, 0)/E$. In this case, the WT algorithm reduces to that of waveform inversion.

Appendix 20B:
Implementation of WT

Forward modeling

In principle, any forward-modeling scheme which simulates wave propagation can be used; in practice, Luo and Schuster (1991a) use the 2–4 staggered-grid finite-difference scheme described in Chapter 8. To use this scheme, we rewrite the acoustic wave equation as

$$\frac{\partial p(\mathbf{x}, t|\mathbf{s}, 0)}{\partial t} = c(\mathbf{x})^2 \, \rho(\mathbf{x}) \nabla \cdot \mathbf{w}(\mathbf{x}, t|\mathbf{s}, 0) + c(\mathbf{x})^2 \, \tilde{s}(t; \mathbf{x}),$$

$$\frac{\partial \mathbf{w}(\mathbf{x}, t|\mathbf{s}, 0)}{\partial t} = \frac{1}{\rho(\mathbf{x})} \nabla p(\mathbf{x}, t|\mathbf{s}, 0), \tag{20.53}$$

in which $\mathbf{w}(\mathbf{x}, t|\mathbf{s}, 0)$ is the particle-velocity vector and the initial conditions are given as

$$p(\mathbf{x}, t = 0|\mathbf{s}, 0) = 0; \quad \mathbf{w}(\mathbf{x}, t = 0|\mathbf{s}, 0) = 0 \quad \text{for } (t \le 0). \tag{20.54}$$

Here, $\tilde{s}$ is

$$\tilde{s}(t; \mathbf{s}) = \int_0^t dt \, s(t; \mathbf{s}), \tag{20.55}$$

in which $s(t; \mathbf{s})$ is the source term in the second-order wave equation.

From this modeling, we can obtain $p(\mathbf{x}, t|\mathbf{s}, 0)$, which will be used in the time correlation with the reverse time propagation field $p'(\mathbf{x}, t|\mathbf{s}, 0)$. As for the time correlation in equation 20.50, we need to multiply the $p(\mathbf{x}, t|\mathbf{s}, 0)$ and $p'(\mathbf{x}, t|\mathbf{s}, 0)$ fields at the same time. We either can choose to store in computer memory the entire history of field $p(\mathbf{x}, t|\mathbf{s}, 0)$, or to recalculate it, backward in time, simultaneously with the calculation of the field $p'(\mathbf{x}, t|\mathbf{s}, 0)$ (Gauthier et al., 1986). We usually choose this last option. For the recalculation of the field $p(\mathbf{x}, t|\mathbf{s}, 0)$, we need to store in the computer the history of the field $p(\mathbf{x}, t|\mathbf{s}, 0)$ at the boundaries, and, of course, the final two states of the field.

Backward propagation

From equation 20.50, $p'(\mathbf{x}, t|\mathbf{s}, 0)$ should satisfy

$$\frac{1}{c(\mathbf{x})^2} \frac{\partial^2 p'(\mathbf{x}, t|\mathbf{s}, 0)}{\partial t^2} - \rho(\mathbf{x}) \nabla \cdot \left[\frac{1}{\rho(\mathbf{x})} \nabla p'(\mathbf{x}, t|\mathbf{s}, 0) \right]$$

$$= \Delta \tau(\mathbf{g}, t|\mathbf{s}). \tag{20.56}$$

In the time correlation of equation 20.50, the field is $\dot{p}'(\mathbf{x}, t|\mathbf{s}, 0)$, so the time derivative must be taken on both sides of the above equation. To use a staggered finite-difference scheme, rewrite equation 20.53 as

$$\frac{\partial \dot{p}'(\mathbf{x}, t|\mathbf{s}, 0)}{\partial t} = c(\mathbf{x})^2 \, \rho(\mathbf{x}) \nabla \cdot \dot{\mathbf{w}}'(\mathbf{x}, t|\mathbf{s}, 0)$$

$$+ c(\mathbf{x})^2 \, \dot{\Delta\tau}(\mathbf{x}, t; \mathbf{s}), \tag{20.57}$$

$$\frac{\partial \dot{\mathbf{w}}'(\mathbf{x}, t|\mathbf{s}, 0)}{\partial t} = \frac{1}{\rho(\mathbf{x})} \nabla \dot{p}'(\mathbf{x}, t|\mathbf{s}, 0),$$

with initial conditions given as

$$\dot{p}'(\mathbf{x}, t = T|\mathbf{s}, 0) = 0; \quad \dot{w}'(\mathbf{x}, t = T + 1/2dt|\mathbf{s}, 0) = 0, \tag{20.58}$$

in which dt is the discretized time step length used in the finite-difference method, and T is the total recording length. The field $\dot{w}'$ is set to zero at $T + 1/2dt$ because $\dot{w}'$ and $\dot{p}'$ are staggered in time. The pseudoresidual $\Delta\tilde{\tau}$ is calculated from equation 20.47 and the $\Delta\tau$ is obtained by crosscorrelating the observed and predicted traces. Because this initial condition is an approximation, we need to attenuate the amplitudes at the end of each trace to make this approximation more reasonable.

Direction of updating the model

Instead of using a steepest-gradient direction, we can use some modified direction for updating the model. In general, this update scheme can be expressed as

$$c^{(k+1)}(\mathbf{x}) = c^{(k)}(\mathbf{x}) - \alpha\phi(\mathbf{x}), \tag{20.59}$$

in which the method of steepest descent is given as

$$\phi(\mathbf{x}) = \gamma(\mathbf{x}), \tag{20.60}$$

and $\gamma(\mathbf{x})$ is the misfit gradient.

Another modification is the use of a preconditioned gradient direction

$$\phi = \gamma(\mathbf{x}) \left[||\mathbf{x} - \mathbf{s}|| \, ||\mathbf{x} - \mathbf{g}|| \right]^{1/2}, \tag{20.61}$$

which compensates for geometrical spreading in one trace. In practice, Luo and Schuster (1991a) use the conjugate-gradient direction

$$\phi^{(k)} = \beta(\mathbf{x})^{(k)} + \lambda\phi^{(k-1)} \quad \text{for } k > 1, \tag{20.62}$$

in which $\beta^{(k)} = \phi^{(k)}$, k is the iteration index and

$$\lambda = \frac{[\beta^{(k)}]^T [\gamma^{(k)}]}{[\beta^{(k-1)}]^T [\gamma^{(k-1)}]}. \tag{20.63}$$

Calculation of the step length

The formula for the estimation of the step length α in the update formula at the kth iteration is

$$\alpha = \frac{[\phi]^T [\gamma(\mathbf{x})]}{[F\phi]^T [F\phi]}, \tag{20.64}$$

in which

$$[\phi]^T [\gamma(\mathbf{x})] = \sum_x [\phi \, \gamma(\mathbf{x})] \tag{20.65}$$

and

$$[F\phi] = \frac{g[c(\mathbf{x}) + \epsilon\phi] - g[c(\mathbf{x})]}{\epsilon}$$
$$= \frac{\delta p(\mathbf{x}, t; \, \mathbf{s})}{\epsilon}. \tag{20.66}$$

Here, $g[c(\mathbf{x})]$ implies forward modeling to get seismograms for the velocity model $c(\mathbf{x})$, and

$$[F\phi]^T [F\phi] = \sum_g \int dt \left[\frac{\delta p(\mathbf{g}, t; \, \mathbf{s})}{\epsilon} \right]^2, \tag{20.67}$$

in which ϵ is estimated by

$$\max \epsilon \cdot \phi \leq \frac{\max c(\mathbf{x})}{100}. \tag{20.68}$$

Chapter 21: Acoustic Waveform Inversion: Case histories

This chapter presents four case histories of acoustic full-waveform inversion (FWI). These cases demonstrate that inverting each type of data requires a different series of processing steps to suppress the nonacoustic effects in the recorded data and to avoid cycle-skipping problems. The first example is the result of applying acoustic FWI to land data, in which the traces are time windowed about the early arrivals to avoid accounting for the elastic surface waves and converted waves. Inverting only the early arrivals minimizes the problem of cycle skipping and is denoted as early-arrival waveform tomography (EWT). The second example applies FWI to streamer data from the Gulf of Mexico, in which both shallow and deep reflection arrivals are emphasized uniformly by embedding an inner loop of least-squares migration (LSM) within the outer loop of nonlinear iterations. The LSM loop corrects for geometrical spreading (and attenuation if an anelastic modeling code is used) effects. Thus, it increases the amplitudes of deep reflections to be nearly the same magnitude as those from shallow reflections, which facilitates imaging below the diving waves. Finally, acoustic FWI is combined with viscoacoustic modeling to take into account the effects of attenuation in crosswell data. In this example, inverting the first arrivals provides a starting velocity model that is sufficiently accurate so the later reflections mostly are not cycle skipped. Unlike the surface-land experiment, the crosswell experiment allows inversion of the "diving waves" at all depths.

21.1 Early-arrival waveform inversion applied to land data

Hanafy and Yu (2013) and Yu and Hanafy (2014) estimate "the near-surface velocity distribution by applying multiscale early arrival waveform inversion (MEWI) to shallow seismic land data. This data set is collected at Wadi Qudaid in western Saudi Arabia with the purpose of characterizing the shallow subsurface for its water storage and reuse potential" (Yu and Hanafy, 2014, 549). Attenuation effects in the data were compensated for by applying an inverse Q-filter to the data, and the source wavelet is estimated by windowing about the first arrivals, flattening

these arrivals for many traces, and stacking as described in section 19.2.6. As Yu and Hanafy (2014, 549) note, EWT (which they call early-arrival waveform inversion, or EWI) then can be used "to invert the processed data for tomograms on different scales starting from a traveltime tomogram as our initial velocity model." Their results indicate that EWT can generate a more highly resolved estimate of the velocity model, compared to traveltime tomography.

21.1.1 Data acquisition

Yu and Hanafy (2014) and Hanafy and Yu (2013) detail a 2D seismic survey carried out at Wadi Qudaid near King Abdullah University of Science and Technology (KAUST). Yu and Hanafy (2014, 552) describe the 2D acquisition geometry, which has one line of vertical-component geophones:

> Along this line, there are 117 receivers with a 2.0 m spacing, and the shots are located at every receiver position, so $117 \times 117 = 13,689$ traces are recorded. In this field experiment, we used a 200 lb weight drop [Fig. 21a] to generate the seismic source energy with 10–15 stacks at each shot location. Each common shot gather (CSG) was recorded for 1 s with a sampling interval of 0.125 ms. Since we only need the early arrivals, arrivals after 0.25 s are muted.

A typical CSG and its picked first-arrival traveltimes (red crosses) are shown in Figure 21.1b (Figure 3 from Hanafy and Yu, 2014). For this data set, Hanafy and Yu (2014, 552) "estimated the dominant wavelength and the dominant frequency of the first arrival head waves to be 6 m and 65 Hz, respectively, where the minimum P-wave velocity was estimated to be 380 m/s." Figure 21.1c (Figure 4 of Hanafy and Yu, 2014) shows "the picked first-arrival times for all traces presented as a 2D matrix," with the data peaked between 65 Hz and 110 Hz.

The shot gathers first are processed to eliminate effects not modeled by a 2D solution to the acoustic wave equation. As described in Hanafy and Yu (2013), Yu and Hanafy (2014), and Yu et al. (2014), a 3D to 2D geometrical

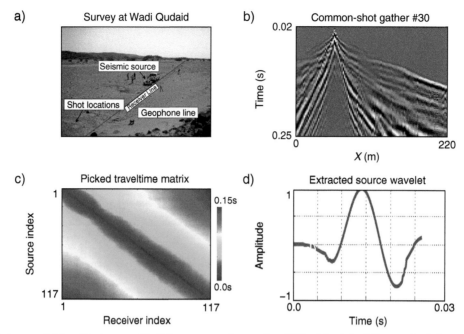

Figure 21.1. (a) Data acquisition (facing south), (b) common-shot gather #30 with picked first-arrival times (red crosses), (c) matrix of picked traveltimes, and (d) source wavelet extracted from a shot gather. Part (a) courtesy Hanafy and Yu (2013), Figure 1, photograph by S. Hanafy, (c). Parts (b–d) courtesy Yu and Hanafy (2014).

spreading adjustment is applied to the data, trace amplitudes are gained to correct for attenuation effects, the traces are normalized, the source wavelet is extracted from the data, and bandpass filtering is used to suppress noise. The details for these processing steps are given below (Yu and Hanafy, 2014).

21.1.2 Data processing

1. To mitigate cycle-skipping problems and the need to model surface waves, the traces are windowed to only admit 3–4 cycles of the early arrivals. Surface waves are excluded by a muting window. The effects of 3D geometrical spreading "are approximately transformed to 2D by multiplying the trace spectrum by $\sqrt{i/\omega}$ in the frequency domain and by multiplying the trace by $\sqrt{t}$ in the time domain (Boonyasiriwat et al. 2010)" (Yu and Hanafy, 2014, 552).

2. Yu and Hanafy (2014) continue that "the attenuation effects in the field data should be corrected because the forward modeling is based on the acoustic wave equation" with no attenuation. They cite Liao and McMechan (1997), who note that the linear attenuation transfer function T of a first arrival propagating in a lossy medium is a function of frequency f, traveltime t, and Q, such that

$$T(f) = e^{-f \int a(x,z)dl}, \qquad (21.1)$$

in which

$$a(x,z) = \frac{\pi}{Q(x,z)v(x,z)}, \qquad (21.2)$$

and the output spectrum is given by

$$R(f) = T(f)S(f). \qquad (21.3)$$

Here, the input $S(f)$ is the spectrum of the first arrival and the integration in equation 21.1 can be approximated by $\int a(x,z)dl \approx \frac{\pi}{Q}\int \frac{1}{v(x,z)}dl = \frac{\pi}{Q}t$; here, t is the picked first-arrival time at the receiver and $\bar{Q}$ is the average Q value in the medium between the source and receiver. Yu and Hanafy (2014) state that the attenuation can be corrected by dividing the trace spectrum $R(f)$ by the factor $T(f)$ in equation 21.1. Here, they note that Q is assumed to be a constant for the early arrivals, and it is also assumed to be independent of f.

Yu and Hanafy (2014, 552) write that "the factor Q can also be written in terms of the centroid frequencies[1] f_r and f_s of the first arrival at the receiver and the source, respectively, as

$$f_r = f_s - \frac{2\pi\sigma_s^2}{Q}t, \qquad (21.4)$$

---

[1]The centroid frequency of the spectrum at the receiver can be defined as $f_r = \sum_i |R(f_i)|f_i/[\sum_j |R(f_j)|]$, where $|R(f_i)|$ is the magnitude spectrum of the first arrival at the frequency f_i.

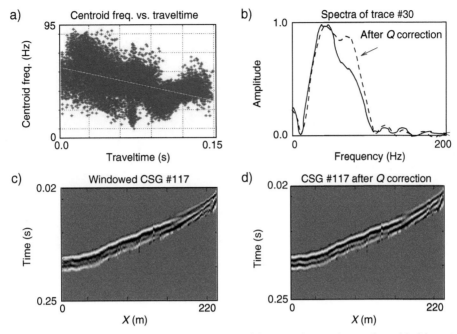

Figure 21.2. (a) Pairs of centroid frequencies and first-arrival traveltimes at the receivers plotted in blue. As Yu and Hanafy (2014, 553) note, "The attenuation factor Q is estimated to be 28 by the best-fit line denoted by the solid yellow line." (b) Spectra of trace 30 before (solid line) and after (dashed line) Q correction, windowed CSG 117 (c) before and (d) after Q correction. The data have been weighted to smoothly reduce the amplitude from 90–120 Hz. Part (a) after Yu and Hanafy (2014), Figure 8. Parts (b–d) after Yu and Hanafy (2014).

where σ_s^2 represents the variance of the source spectrum. After f_r, f_s and σ_s^2 are estimated from the data and the first arrivals are picked, the Q value can be estimated from equation [21.4]. Then, equation [21.1] is applied to the traces to correct the attenuation effects in the frequency domain." They continue that the Q is assumed to be a constant because the early arrivals come from a shallow part of the earth, so the same correction formula is used for all the traces.[2]

3. All traces are normalized to reduce errors from irregular geophone coupling.

4. Near-offset first arrivals within a window of 10–20 traces are averaged, to extract the source wavelet. A cross correlation is applied to several consecutive traces to find the time shift that flattens them to the near-offset arrival, and Figure 21.1d shows the wavelet after stacking the flattened traces. Here, Yu and Hanafy (2014, 553) note that "Since the weight drop is controlled electronically, all shots have similar source wavelets…"

5. Next, "the very near offset traces with source-receiver offsets no greater than 14 m are muted because they contain surface waves and noise even after filtering, and it is difficult to match them with the calculated seismograms. Noise before the picked first arrivals is also muted" (Yu and Hanafy, 2014, 553).

6. Early arrivals are estimated to have a dominant frequency band between 65 Hz and 120 Hz, and the initial filtered traces for EWT have a peak frequency of $f_1 = 18$ Hz because most of the noise and surface waves are below 10 Hz. In this field experiment, the penetration depth of the diving wave is estimated to be $z = 70$ m and the maximum half offset is $h = 116$ m. This leads to $\alpha_{min} = z/\sqrt{h^2 + z^2} = 0.52$. Equation 21.8 in Appendix 21A shows that, $f_2 = 34$ Hz and $f_3 = 65$ Hz are the peak frequencies for the next two multiscale stages of EWT. Therefore, Hanafy and Yu (2014) apply three bandpass filters with increasing pass bands of 0–25 Hz, 0–45 Hz, and 0–75 Hz to the traces in the multiscale strategy. They also apply these filters to the extracted source wavelet in step 4, prior to applying EWT to filtered data.

21.1.3 Estimating and correcting for Q

Figure 21.2b (Figure 8 from Yu and Hanafy, 2014) shows "the centroid frequencies f_r plotted against traveltimes of the first arrivals. The variance σ_s^2 of the source centroid spectra is equal to 312.70, which is the average σ_s^2 value from all the sources (Liao and McMechan, 1997)" (Yu and Hanafy, 2014, 554). Because the dominant peak frequency of the recorded traces is 65 Hz, Yu and Hanafy (2014) use a of 25 ∼ 90 Hz "to calculate f_r, f_s and σ_s^2 to

---

[2] If warranted, a tomography procedure can be used to determine the Q distribution as a function of depth and offset coordinates.

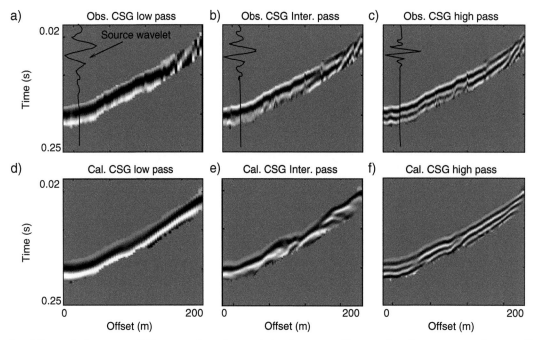

Figure 21.3. (a–c) Recorded traces at different scales after applying low-pass filters to the Q-compensated traces. Panels (d–f) are the same as (a–c), except the traces are calculated by a finite-difference solution to the acoustic wave equation using the FWI tomogram as the velocity model. Illustrations adapted from Yu and Hanafy (2014).

avoid errors from the noise." They estimate the Q value to be about 28 (from Equation 21.4). They note that this "is is a typical value for near-surface soil with significant absorption" (Yu and Hanafy, 2014, 554). They explain that according to equation 21.1, "$1/T(f)$ is applied to the trace spectra to correct for the attenuation effects in the frequency domain. [Figure 21.2c–d] shows CSG #117 before and after the attenuation correction, and [Figure 21.2b] demonstrates the spectrum comparisons of one trace before and after this operation."

Figure 21.3 (adapted from Yu and Hanafy, 2014), shows the (21.3a–c) observed and (21.3d–f) calculated CSGs for three different types of bandpass filters. The traces depicted by the solid black line are the source wavelets after filtering the extracted wavelet in Figure 21.1d.

21.1.4 EWT of the Wadi Qudaid data

Inversion of the picked first-arrival times gives the Figure 21.4a tomogram, which Yu and Hanafy (2014) use as the initial velocity model for EWT at the coarsest scale. They note that "Similarly, the tomogram inverted on the n-th scale is used as the initial velocity model on the $(n+1)$-th scale" (Yu and Hanafy, 2014, 554). They use gridpoint intervals $dx = 4$ m, 2 m, and 1 m, respectively, for the coarsest, intermediate, and finest scales. A total of 2000 time steps is used for the finite-difference simulations (a 2–8 finite-difference solver is used) with a sampling interval

dt equal to 0.125 ms. At the coarsest scale, Yu and Hanafy (2014) used 58 CSGs (all the even-numbered CSGs) rather than 117 CSGs to speed up computation by matching fewer shot gathers. All of the CSGs were used for the other two upscaling operations. For the coarsest scale, they used the pressure rather than its time derivative in the calculation of the low-wavenumber misfit gradient. In the intermediate and finest scales, the time derivative of the pressure was used to update the higher wavenumber part of the velocity model.

Figure 21.4a–b show the traveltime and EWT tomograms obtained from the Wadi Qudaid data. In comparison with the traveltime tomogram, EWT iteratively predicts the early-arrival waveforms with increasing resolution as the low-pass filtered traces are gradually transformed to high-pass data. Yu and Hanafy (2014, 555) note that "Many early arriving events in the synthetic data correlate well with the observed traces" in Figure 21.3c and 21.3f. They show that, from the tomogram at the finest scale, the water table contour of 1550 m/s in the EWT tomogram generally is consistent with the traveltime tomogram, although it is 9% deeper in the EWT tomogram. This suggests that the water storage potential in this wadi might be more than expected from the traveltime tomogram. They point out that a well-log reference of geologic conditions above the 18 m deep water table says that the first layer "consists of loose sand with gravels, and the second layer … consists of compact sand with some gravel and partially to fully saturated with water."

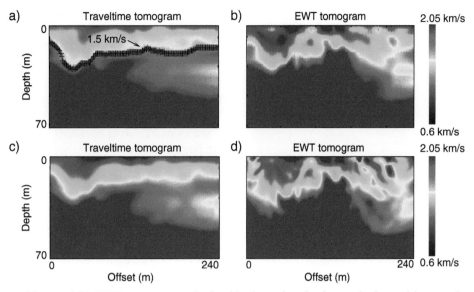

Figure 21.4. (a) Traveltime and (b) EWT tomograms obtained by inverting the first-arrival traveltimes and early-arrival waveforms, respectively, of the Wadi Qudaid data. The black crosses in (a) indicate the velocity contour at 1550 m/s. Panels (c–d) are the same as (a–b), except the input data were computed by a finite-difference solution to the acoustic wave equation for the (b) velocity model. After Yu and Hanafy (2014).

21.1.5 Synthetic data sanity test

Yu and Hanafy (2014) computed synthetics to demonstrate the effectiveness of EWT. They generated a synthetic data set using the final EWT tomogram in Figure 21.4b as the velocity model. First-arrival traveltimes were picked automatically and inverted by traveltime tomography. Figure 21.4c shows the resulting traveltime tomogram, which is similar to the traveltime tomogram in Figure 21.4a. They used the 21.4c tomogram as the starting model, and EWT gives the tomogram in Figure 21.4d after 30 iterations. Yu and Hanafy (2014) note that "It shows highly resolved subsurface structures compared to the traveltime tomogram [Figure 21.4b] and validates EWI's [EWT's] capability for improved resolution compared to traveltime tomography. It also suggests that the extra details in the EWT tomogram are not artifacts, but are representative of the actual geology."

21.1.6 Key points

In the case of shallow land data, the cycle-skipping problem is mitigated by windowing and inverting events within about three to four periods of the first arrival. This also reduces the need for acoustic modeling to explain elastic effects such as surface waves or shear waves. The penalty, however, is that the inverted velocity model is no deeper than the deepest penetration of the early-arrival diving and refracted waves. Wider offsets can provide deeper penetration, so the offset-time window should gradually widen to admit traces with increasing offset as the iterations proceed. However, if an acoustic modeling code is used, the surface-wave arrivals always should be eliminated prior to inversion.

21.2 Acoustic FWI applied to Gulf of Mexico marine data

Geometrical spreading and attenuation weakens the amplitudes of deep reflections relative to shallow reflections. In addition, both deep and shallow reflection wavepaths visit the shallow parts of the velocity model, although only weak reflections visit the deep parts. Unless these factors are compensated for in the iterative inversion, the velocity updates will mostly be for the shallow layers to explain the strong amplitudes of the shallow reflections and diving waves. Ideally, this compensation is achieved by applying the Hessian inverse to the migration image at each iteration, which in practice is too expensive. To reduce this expense, the next section describes an iterative conjugate-gradient method that approximates this Hessian inverse.

21.2.1 Hybrid linear and nonlinear FWI

As an inexpensive alternative to the Hessian inverse, AlTheyab et al. (2013) propose a modified form of acoustic FWI to invert for velocities below the reach of the deepest diving wave. They adjust the FWI algorithm so that an inner loop of iterative linear LSM is contained within the outer loop of nonlinear iterations. These linear iterations strengthen the reflectors in the velocity model, which in turn promotes updating the low-wavenumber velocity

---

Box 21.1.1 Pseudocode for Hybrid Linear-Nonlinear FWI

Choose $\mathbf{s}^{(1)}$	Starting slowness model $\mathbf{s}^{(1)}$
$\mathbf{p}^{(1)} = \mathbf{L}(\mathbf{s}^{(1)})$	Predicted data
$\quad$ for $k = 1 : K$	
$\quad\quad \mathcal{L} = \mathbf{L}(\mathbf{s}^{(k)})$	Define Born modeling operator
$\quad\quad \mathbf{pp} = \mathbf{p}^{(k)}$	with background $\mathbf{s}^{(k)}$
$\quad\quad \delta\mathbf{s} = 0$	
$\quad\quad\quad$ for $i = 1 : I$	LSM with $2 < I < 6$
$\quad\quad\quad\quad \Delta\mathbf{r} = \mathbf{pp} - \mathbf{p}^{\text{obs}}$	Compute residual
$\quad\quad\quad\quad \delta\mathbf{s} = \delta\mathbf{s} - \alpha^{(i)}\mathcal{L}^T\Delta\mathbf{r}$	Migrate residual
$\quad\quad\quad\quad \mathbf{pp} = \mathcal{L}(\delta\mathbf{s})$	Born modeling
$\quad\quad\quad$ end	
$\quad\quad \mathbf{s}^{(k+1)} = \mathbf{s}^{(k)} + \delta\mathbf{s}$	Update slowness
$\quad\quad \mathbf{p}^{(k+1)} = \mathbf{L}(\mathbf{s}^{(k+1)})$	Update predicted data
$\quad\quad \Delta = \mathbf{p}^{(k+1)} - \mathbf{p}^{\text{obs}}$	Stop if $\dfrac{\|\Delta\|_2}{\|\mathbf{p}^{\text{obs}}\|_2} < \epsilon$
$\quad$ end	

---

model along the low-wavenumber reflection wavepaths. If the linear iterations are continued until reasonable convergence before updating the background velocity model, then this hybrid linear and nonlinear strategy can be considered a nonlinear incomplete Gauss-Newton method. It is related closely to the quasi-Newton methods discussed in Bank and Mittleman (1989), Akcelik et al. (2002), Plessix (2006), and Erlangga and Herrmann (2009).

The pseudocode code for the hybrid FWI method is described in Box 21.1.1 as a simple method of steepest descent. In practice, the LSM image is computed iteratively by a preconditioned conjugate-gradient method.

In Box 21.2.1, $\alpha^{(i)}$ is the step length computed at the ith iteration. Here, $\mathbf{L}(\mathbf{s})$ is the solution to the wave equation

$$\nabla^2 P(\mathbf{x}, t)_o - s(\mathbf{x})^2 \ddot{P}(\mathbf{x}, t)_o = \overbrace{F(\mathbf{x}, t)}^{\text{source term}}, \qquad (21.5)$$

for the source term described by $F(\mathbf{x}, t)$, and $\mathcal{L}(\delta\mathbf{s})$ is the solution to

$$\nabla^2 P(\mathbf{x}, t) - s(\mathbf{x})^2 \ddot{P}(\mathbf{x}, t) = \overbrace{2s(\mathbf{x})\delta s(\mathbf{x})\ddot{P}(\mathbf{x}, t)_o}^{\text{exploding reflectors}}, \quad (21.6)$$

where the right side accounts for the strengths and excitation times of the exploding reflectors. In practice, the linear iteration index I is set to 2 for the early nonlinear iterations of the index k. When, for example, $k = 10$, then I is increased to 4 and gradually is increased to a value no

greater than 10 with increasing values of k. This ad hoc strategy is based partly on empirical experience and is similar to increasing the depth of inversion with increasing iteration index.

At the early nonlinear iterations, the number of linear iterations I is small so that the diving waves can update the shallow-velocity model initially. Once the shallow-velocity model is updated accurately, then the deeper velocities can be updated by increasing the value of I so that LSM can compensate for the extreme spreading and attenuation losses suffered by deep reflections. In addition, the interface at depth becomes more sharpened with LSM compared to RTM, so the velocity update along the LSM rabbit ears in Figure 21.5 is more pronounced.

21.2.2 Synthetic two-box model data

The hybrid FWI method is tested next for simulated surface data associated with the two-box model in Figure 21.6a. Here, no diving waves are present and only reflections from the top, bottom, and sides of the boxes are extant. The source-wavelet spectrum is displayed in Figure 21.6b, and the standard FWI tomogram is shown in Figure 21.6c. It is obvious that the high-wavenumber components of the velocity model are reconstructed, but the low- and intermediate-wavenumber components are missing. Apparently, spreading losses weaken the deeper reflections relative to the top reflector and so lessen the ability to update the velocity within the box. In comparison, the

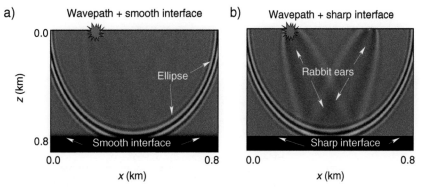

Figure 21.5. Wavepaths for a single trace and a two-layer model with a velocity that varies (a) smoothly and (b) sharply across the interface. Least-squares migration will build a sharp interface compared to RTM, and so its velocity update along the associated rabbit ears will be more pronounced.

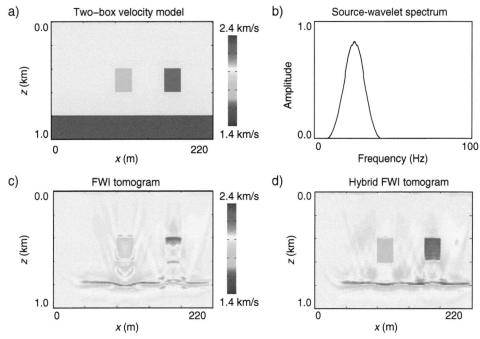

Figure 21.6. (a) Two-box velocity model, (b) the source-wavelet spectrum for forward-modeling the surface acoustic data, (c) standard FWI tomogram, and (d) hybrid FWI tomogram after 100 iterations. The starting model is a homogeneous velocity distribution. Illustrations adapted from AlTheyab et al. (2013).

hybrid FWI tomogram in Figure 21.6d successfully updates the velocities within the boxes and along its sides.

21.2.3 Gulf of Mexico data

Marine seismic data are recorded in the Gulf of Mexico (dataset courtesy ExxonMobil Corporation), using 515 shots with an interval of 37.5 m, where the source-receiver offsets are from 198 m to 6 km, with a 12.5-m receiver spacing. This is the same data set described in section 15.5.4, except the 3D geometrical spreading is transformed to 2D spreading.

A multiscale approach is used by initially bandpass filtering the traces from 0–4 Hz, where there is reliable signal

at 3–4 Hz. At later iterations, the band of admissible frequencies is widened to 10 Hz. Figure 21.7 shows the final tomogram after 50 iterations of the hybrid FWI. The grid size for the tomograms is 301 by 1600 gridpoints in the vertical and horizontal directions, respectively, with a grid spacing of 12.5 m. A 2–8 finite-difference solution to the acoustic wave equation is used to predict the data, a homogeneous density is assumed, and the velocity of the water layer is constrained to be 1500 m/s.

The starting model is obtained by an early-arrival waveform tomography method, and the FWI iterations are halted every five or so nonlinear iterations, depending on the convergence rate. For example, the iterations are stopped if the residual does not decrease by more than 1%

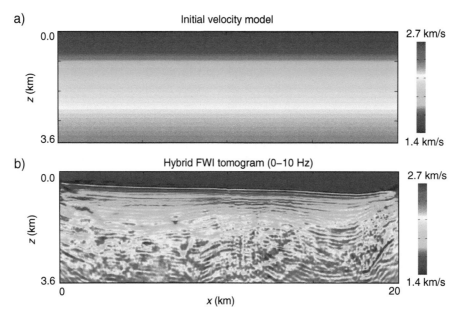

Figure 21.7. (a) Initial velocity model and (b) final hybrid FWI tomogram inverted from the 0–10 Hz data. After AlTheyab et al. (2013), Figure 3 and AlTheyab (2016).

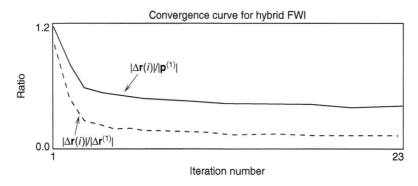

Figure 21.8. Iteration number versus residual ratios. After AlTheyab et al. (2013).

at a nonlinear iteration. The bandwidth of the observed data then is widened by about 20%, a new residual is computed, and the iterations are restarted.

Figure 21.7a shows the starting velocity model, and Figure 21.7b shows the final hybrid-FWI tomogram after 50 iterations. The deeper reflections in the Figure 21.7b tomogram appear to be better focused than those using the conventional FWI approach (Boonyasiriwat, 2007). As shown in Figure 21.8, the hybrid-FWI data residual has decreased by more than 60% compared to the raw data.

To assess the accuracy of the hybrid FWI tomogram, the predicted data are generated using the Figure 21.7b tomogram. For a single shot gather, the predicted traces in Figure 21.9b compare well with the recorded data in Figure 21.9a; this prediction accuracy is about the same for most of the other shot gathers as well. The Figure 21.9c zoom view of the recorded and predicted traces shows excellent agreement at all offset values. The strong direct and refracted waves match well, but they still contain some

large residuals that are stronger than the reflections in some cases. In this case, a possible strategy is to gradually mute out the early arrivals in both the predicted and recorded traces, and only to invert the later arrivals for the deeper velocities. Here, the shallow part of the velocity model is assumed to be sufficiently accurate and no longer needs to be updated.

Figure 21.10a and 21.10b illustrate the wavepaths computed by migrating the early and later arrivals, respectively, in an individual trace. For the early-arrival migration in Figure 21.10a, the curved wavepaths are related to diving waves and do not reach depths below 2 km. Hence, the shallow-velocity model above 2 km is updated mainly along the diving wave trajectories.[3] Both the hybrid FWI and EWT-FWI invert the diving waves, so the tomograms

---

[3] As noted in Chapter 14, the strength of the diving wavepath is $O(1)$ while those for the ellipse and rabbit ear wavepaths are $O(r)$ and $O(r^2)$, respectively, where r denotes the reflection coefficient.

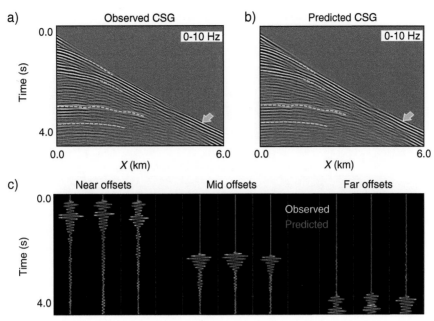

Figure 21.9. A common-shot gather from 0–10 Hz (a) recorded in the survey and the (b) prediction from the hybrid FWI tomogram. The bottom figure shows predicted (red) and observed (yellow) traces from the CSGs (a and b). (a) and (b) adapted from AlTheyab et al. (2013), Figure 5; (c) courtesy of A. AlTheyab.

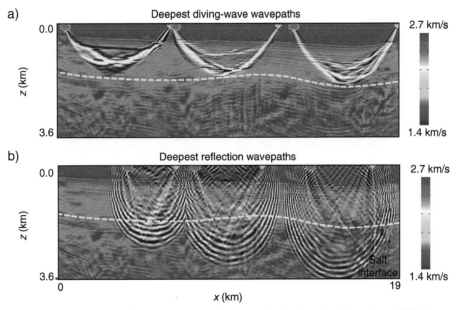

Figure 21.10. Diving and deep reflection wavepaths generated, respectively, for the (a) early and (b) later arrivals at the maximum source-receiver offset of about 6 km. Figure adapted from AlTheyab (2016).

are similar for the shallow section. However, the deep part of the velocity model is updated along the reflection wavepaths of deep reflections by the hybrid FWI approach. For example, see the reflection wavepath in Figure 21.10b that reflects from the salt interface (thick red line).

Figures 21.11 and 21.12 compare the migration images using the EWT-FWI and the hybrid FWI tomograms as the migration velocity models. It appears that the hybrid migration image in Figure 21.11a computed from the hybrid

FWI tomogram generally is better focused than the standard migration image in Figure 21.11a. In Figure 21.12a, the arrows point to the fault reflections that are faint and crosscut continuous reflectors in the standard image. The hybrid image in Figure 21.12b, on the other hand, shows reflection interfaces that sharply terminate against the fault. This indicates geological consistency in the image for the shallow part that can also be seen in Figure 21.12c. In the deeper section, the hybrid migration image in Figure 21.12d

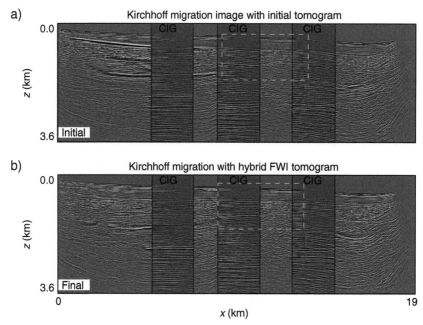

Figure 21.11. Kirchhoff migration results full-bandwidth data (a) with initial starting velocity model and (b) hybrid FWI (0–10 Hz). The colored boxes are for zoom views in Figure 21.12 and the CIGs are plotted in the amber rectangles. After Altheyab et al. (2013).

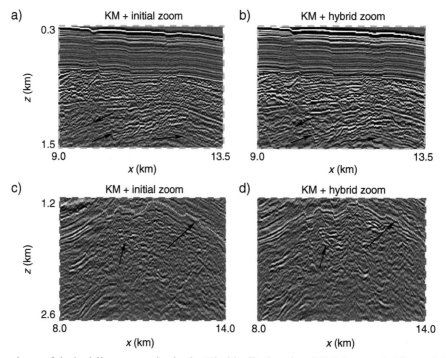

Figure 21.12. Zoom views of dashed-line rectangles in the Kirchhoff migration (KM) images in Figure 21.11. The left and right columns of migration images are obtained using the EWT-FWI and hybrid FWI tomograms, respectively, as migration velocity models. After AlTheyab et al. (2013).

shows more focused dipping features with sharper boundaries. In particular, the reflection interface along the yellow dashed line clearly is more pronounced in the hybrid image than in the standard image in Figure 21.12c.

The amber-colored rectangles in Figure 21.7 depict the common-image gathers (CIG) obtained by migrating the data with the EWT-FWI and the hybrid-FWI velocity models. In the deeper section, the hybrid-FWI CIGs have flatter

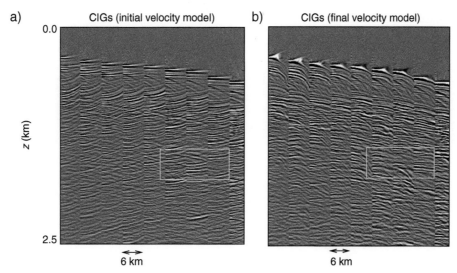

Figure 21.13. The common-image gathers computed from the (a) initial velocity model and (b) final tomogram in Figure 21.7. The far-left and far-right CIGs are near $X = 4$ km and $X = 17$ km, respectively, in the Figure 21.7b tomogram. Note that there are strong common-reflection events in the yellow boxes that are unflattened, suggesting an inaccurate velocity model at this offset position. The double-sided arrow approximates the 6-km range of source positions in the CIG. After AlTheyab et al. (2013), Figure 3 and AlTheyab (2016).

events compared to the EWT-FWI CIGs. This suggests that the hybrid-FWI tomogram is more accurate than the standard-FWI tomogram. There is still room for improvement, as suggested by the curved events in the deeper parts of the CIGs.

21.2.4 Key points

Velocities beneath the reach of diving waves can be updated by smearing residuals along deep reflection wavepaths. These updates can be raised to almost the same strength as updating along shallow reflectors if an LSM algorithm is embedded within the nonlinear FWI loop. LSM compensates for uneven geometrical spreading and illumination so that significant velocity updates can take place along the wavepaths of deep reflections. This does not necessarily eliminate the cycle-skipping problem, but allows for updating velocities below the deepest reach of diving waves. It might be useful to employ a layer-stripping strategy to deepen the depth of velocity updates gradually, as long as the associated reflections pass a no-cycle skip test.

One such cycle-skip test is to assess the phase difference between the predicted and the observed data for one shot gather at the lowest usable frequency (Shah et al., 2012). The data at this low frequency are not cycle skipped if their phase differences vary smoothly and consistently over the different receivers and do not exceed a certain threshold value of, say, $\pi/4$. If the data are cycle skipped, then "…there will be sudden, spatially consistent, 360° jumps in phase" Shah et al. (2012, 1). However, a visual inspection of the EWT and observed shot gathers often is sufficient for the detection of cycle-skipping problems.

21.3 Rolling-offset FWI

Not all of the CIGs associated with the migration image in Figure 21.11 are flattened. As an example, Figure 21.13a and 21.13b depict the CIGs computed with the initial and final velocity models, respectively. There is a noticeable flattening of the common-reflection images in the red box of Figure 21.13b compared to Figure 21.13a. However, there are still strong events in the Figure 21.13b yellow box that are unflattened and are, therefore, not explained by the final velocity model. For these events, the time differences between the near- and far-offset reflections are greater than $T_0/2$, and so stacking these cycle-skipped reflections will blur the final migration image. Here, T_0 is the dominant period of the source wavelet.

Why are there more migrated reflections cycle skipped in the deeper parts compared to the shallower events? The likely reason is that inverting the kinematics of the diving wave can provide an accurate estimate of the velocity model down to about the deepest depth (about 1.5–2.0 km in Figure 21.10) of the diving wave. Thus, the velocity estimate below 1.5 km is likely to be more erroneous, so deeper migrated reflections are more prone to cycle skipping. Also, the depth-to-recording-offset ratio decreases with depth so that velocity errors accumulate and increase with depth.

A promising approach to refining the deeper portion of the velocity model is multiscale inversion (Bunks et al., 1995; Asnaashari et al., 2012; Al-Yaqoobi and Warner, 2013), in which only simple components of the data are inverted initially to avoid cycle skipping, and more complex components are inverted with later iterations. For example,

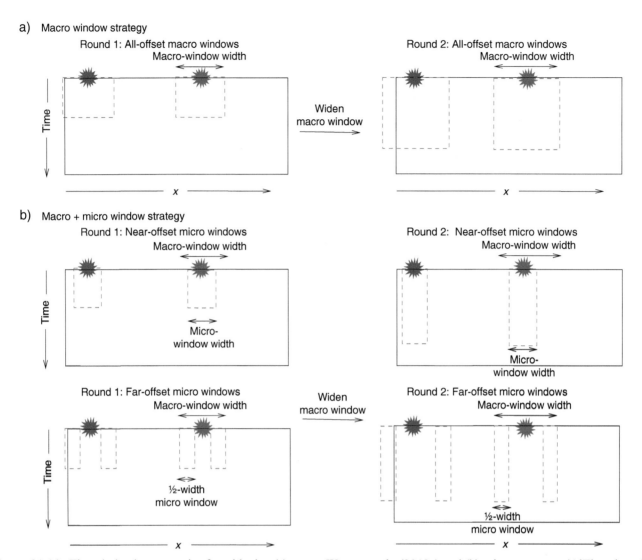

Figure 21.14. The windowing strategies for widening (a) macro Warner et al., (2013a) and (b) micro + macro (AlTheyab and Dutta, 2014) windows of admissible traces (i.e., uncycle-skipped traces) in shot gathers; for simplicity, only two shot gathers are assumed to be in the large solid-line boxes. The strategy for opening micro+macro windows is the key component of rolling-offset FWI, where the final FWI velocity model associated with the far-offset micro-window in Round 1 is subtracted from the background starting model and smoothed to give the new starting model for Round 2. This accurate velocity model from Round 1 allows the size of the macro window to be enlarged and admit more uncycle-skipped traces.

the time- and source-receiver offset windows can be narrow at the early iterations so that fitting the kinematics of short-offset reflections is relatively easy and avoids cycle skipping. Then, the time-offset windows are lengthened gradually, so that the predicted reflections differ from the recorded reflections by no more than half a period. The velocity model again is updated to fit these wider-offset reflections, and as before, avoids cycle skipping between the predicted and recorded reflections. This procedure is repeated iteratively until acceptable convergence. The process of inverting the CSGs over iteratively widened offset-time windows is a variant of multiscale FWI.

AlTheyab and Dutta (2014) developed a variation of multiscale FWI with offset-time windows that improved the convergence rate for their models. They denoted this improved method as *rolling-offset* FWI, as described below.

21.3.1 Workflow for rolling-offset FWI

Figure 21.14a depicts the windowing strategy for multiscale FWI (Warner et al., 2013a) where a macro window is defined during Round 1 that only admits uncycle-skipped traces. The Gauss-Newton full-waveform inversion (GN-FWI) algorithm is applied to the windowed data until acceptable convergence. This provides a better starting model so that the macro-window can be enlarged in Round 2 to admit many more uncycle-skipped traces; FWI can

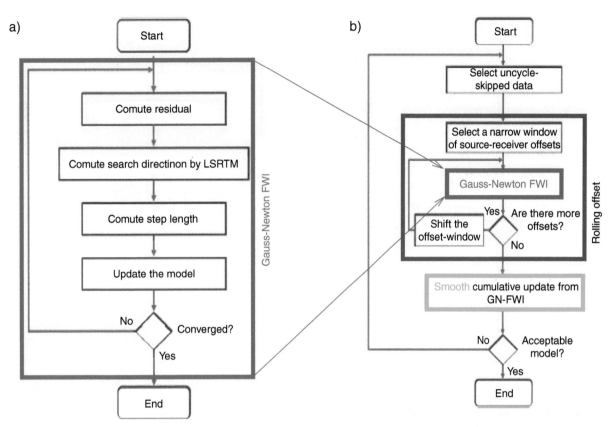

Figure 21.15. Workflows for FWI (a) using incomplete Gauss-Newton optimization and (b) modified workflow of AlTheyab and Schuster (2015). After the velocity model is computed within the magenta rolling-offset box in (b), the updated model is smoothed by a Gaussian filter (green box) to eliminate subwavelength artifacts in the tomogram. Drawn after concepts from AlTheyab (2015).

be applied again and this process is repeated for wider offset-time windows and higher frequencies.

AlTheyab and Dutta (2014) and AlTheyab (2016) recognize that the convergence rate of the above multi-scale strategy could be improved by restricting the velocity updates to the low-wavenumber reflection wavepaths. They devised the macro+micro window strategy shown in Figure 21.14b, which breaks up the macro window Round 1 into several micro windows (about an apparent wavelength wide). These micro windows contain traces at different offsets, ranging from near source-receiver offsets to far source-receiver offsets. Several iterations of FWI are applied to the near-offset traces, the resulting tomogram then is used as the starting model for inverting the traces in the intermediate-offset window, and this process is rolled to the far-offset traces to give the far-offset tomogram. This far-offset tomogram is subtracted from the background starting model and smoothed to ensure there is no wavelength less than the maximum wavelength of the data.[4] This smoothed tomogram then is used to start the Round 2 inversion in which

the macro and micro windows are expanded further in both offset and time.

The workflow for rolling-offset FWI is summarized in Figure 21.15, where Gauss-Newton FWI in Figure 21.15a (red box) is the central part of the workflow. With each pass through the Gauss-Newton FWI block, only a few iterations of the Figure 21.15a FWI algorithm are executed. The block in the Figure 21.15b workflow (labeled 'select uncycle-skipped data') designs the macro-micro window matrix $\mathbf{W}$ in

$$\epsilon = \frac{1}{2}\|\mathbf{W}(\mathbf{d} - \mathbf{d}^{obs})\|^2, \qquad (21.7)$$

in which $\mathbf{d}$ is the predicted (observed) data and $\mathbf{W}$ is the window matrix that excludes (using multiplication by zero) the cycle-skipped events. Here, $\mathbf{W}$ is designed to mask the cycle-skipped data based on frequency, source-receiver offset, and time ranges.

In summary, the rolling-offset FWI algorithm consists of the following steps.

1. Given $\mathbf{m}_1$ (the bad starting model), select uncycle-skipped data by applying the macro-window matrix

---

[4]The longest source wavelength λ^{max} is estimated by dividing the largest velocity in the model by the minimum source frequency. Any velocity component less than λ^{max} is deemed a subwavelength feature.

a) Macro window cuts across + and – polarities

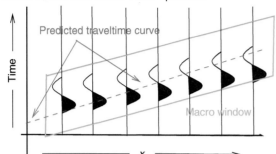

b) Micro window cuts across + polarities

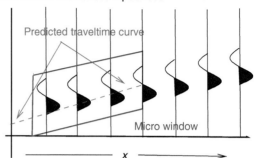

Figure 21.16. (a) Macro- and (b) micro-windowed recorded traces denoted by traces within the green windows. The predicted traveltime curves (dashed red lines) intersect the macro-window recorded traces at both positive and negative amplitudes, although the micro-windowed traces are intersected only along the dark positive lobes.

$\mathbf{W}_{\text{macro}}$ to the data. This macro window is designated with the phrase "macro-window width" in Figure 21.14b.

2. Select the nearest $\lambda/2$ range of offsets by applying the macro-window matrix $\mathbf{W}_{\text{micro}}$ to the data. The near-offset micro windows are the dashed boxes under the phrase *Round 1: Near-offset micro windows* in Figure 21.14b.

3. Use GN-FWI to minimize $\epsilon = \|\mathbf{W}_{\text{micro}}\mathbf{W}_{\text{macro}}(\mathbf{d} - \mathbf{d}^{\text{obs}})\|^2$ and get the tomogram $\mathbf{m}_{1,1}$.

4. Laterally shift the location of the micro-window by $\lambda/2$ to a farther offset by updating $\mathbf{W}_{\text{micro}}$.

5. Use GN-FWI to minimize $\epsilon = \|\mathbf{W}_{\text{micro}}\mathbf{W}_{\text{macro}}(\mathbf{d}^{\text{obs}} - \mathbf{d}^{\text{pred}})\|^2$ and get $\mathbf{m}_{1,2}$. This step assumes we don't have further offsets to roll to, so we exit the inner loop here.

6. Subtract the final and the initial velocity models to get $\mathbf{m}_{\text{diff}} = \mathbf{m}_1 - \mathbf{m}_{1,2}$.

7. Smooth $\mathbf{m}_{\text{diff}}$ with a Gaussian subwavelength filter. This eliminates smile-like artifacts created by the FWI procedure and confines the low-wavenumber velocity updates to be along the reflection wavepaths.

8. Add the smoothed difference to the initial velocity $\mathbf{m}_2 = \mathbf{m}_1 + \mathbf{m}_{\text{diff}}$ in step 9. Repeat steps 1 through 9 until acceptable convergence.

The key advantage of the micro-window approach is illustrated in Figure 21.16. The macro window in Figure 21.16a allows for the predicted arrivals (see dashed red curve) to intersect both the negative (blackened lobes) and positive lobes of the observed arrivals. This means that the velocity updates will be in conflict: decreasing velocity updates associated with the near-offset arrivals and increasing velocity updates for the far-offset arrivals. This conflict will slow down convergence with GN-FWI. To partly cure this problem, the micro window in Figure 21.16b is narrowed so that only the positive lobes are intersected by the dashed red line in the window. Furthermore, the tomogram inverted from traces in the far-offset window is

low-pass filtered so it only contains components associated with the low-wavenumber reflection wavepaths.

Next, an example in which rolling-offset FWI has a much faster convergence rate than the macro-window FWI strategy will be discussed.

21.3.2 Rolling-offset FWI: Synthetic data

Full-waveform inversion now is applied to surface seismic data associated with the Figure 21.17a model. Here, a finite-difference solution to the 2D acoustic wave equation is used to compute the predicted shot gathers with the source wavelet centered at 8 Hz and the maximum source-receiver offset of 6 km. Figure 21.17b depicts the simple starting model, and Figure 21.17c is the tomogram after 300 iterations. In this case, the macro-window FWI strategy in Figure 21.14a is used to invert the data. It is seen that there are many high-wavenumber artifacts below 1 km that do not relate to any feature in the true model. On the other hand, using the macro+micro windowing strategy in Figure 21.14b gives the final tomogram in Figure 21.17d after 100 iterations. This tomogram largely is free from high-wavenumber artifacts while maintaining the high-resolution of the shallow channels. Also, the deeper fast layer is positioned at the correct depth.

For this example, a Gaussian filter is selected so that subwavelength (i.e., wavelengths less than λ^{max}) artifacts in the composite tomogram (green box in Figure 21.15b) are eliminated. This smoothing criterion is consistent with the philosophy of Occam's razor, in which the least-complex subsurface model is favored to explain the data.[5] The elimination of the subwavelength artifacts significantly speeds up convergence in the Figure 21.17 example.

---

[5]Once the low-wavenumber components of the velocity model are estimated accurately, then the conventional GN-FWI method is allowed to reconstruct the high-wavenumber details.

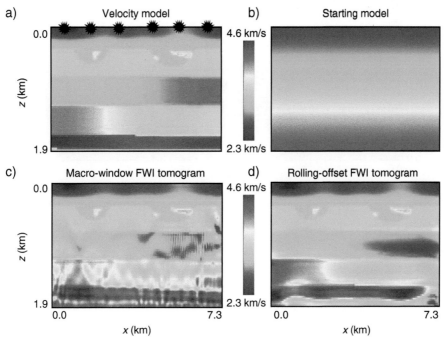

Figure 21.17. The (a) complex velocity model and the (b) starting model for FWI, in which the diving waves are muted prior to inversion. The final tomograms obtained by (c) macro-windowed FWI and (d) rolling-offset FWI. Images adapted from A. Altheyab (2015), Ph.D. thesis presentation.

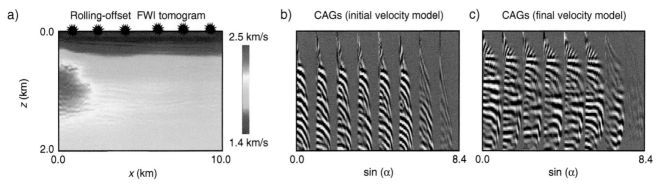

Figure 21.18. (a) Final tomogram using rolling-offset FWI and common-angle gathers (CAGs) computed from a (b) homogeneous velocity model (2000 m/s) and (c) the final tomogram after 40 iterations. Images adapted from AlTheyab and Schuster (2015).

21.3.3 Rolling-offset FWI: 2D Gulf of Mexico data

The marine data associated with the Figure 21.7 tomogram are inverted again, except the rolling-offset FWI algorithm described in Figured 21.15 is used. In this new example, the maximum source-receiver offset is 4 km, the data are low-pass filtered with a maximum frequency of 10 Hz, and the starting model is homogeneous with a velocity of 2000 m/s. This inaccurate-starting model results in unflattened common-angle gathers (CAGs), in which the migrated reflections follow a hyperbolic moveout trajectory

in Figure 21.18b. Stacking these cycle-skipped events in the CAGs will lead to a blurred migration image. However, cycle skipping largely is avoided with rolling-offset FWI that gives the mostly flattened CAGs in Figure 21.18c.

To automatically decide the width of the source-receiver offset window, reflection events can be picked automatically in the Figure 21.19a recorded shot gather and matched to the same events picked in the predicted shot gather of Figure 21.19b. The acceptable size of the source-receiver offset and time window is defined automatically so the traveltimes of the predicted reflections are within one period of the recorded reflections.

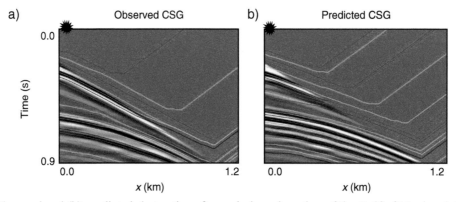

Figure 21.19. (a) Observed and (b) predicted shot gathers for a windowed portion of the Gulf of Mexico data. The colored lines denote the auto-tracked picks of the reflection events in the data. If the reflections tracked along the topmost yellow line in (a) arrive within a period of those in (b), then these events are admitted into the rolling-offset window. Courtesy A. AlTheyab.

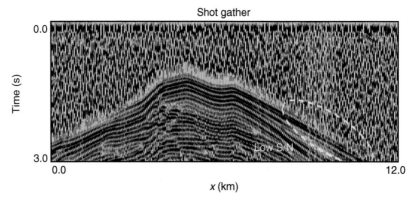

Figure 21.20. Shot gather recorded by the 3D marine survey. Images created from results discussed in AlTheyab (2014).

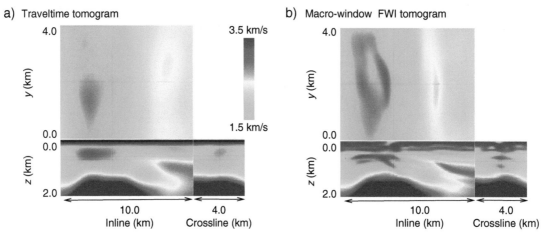

Figure 21.21. (a) Traveltime tomogram inverted from first-arrival traveltimes and (b) tomogram inverted by macro-window FWI. Images created from results discussed in AlTheyab (2014).

21.3.4 FWI with macro windows: 3D marine data

A 3D marine experiment was carried out with marine airguns, and traces were recorded on a 2D grid of recording stations located on the sea floor. The station spacing is 400 m; there are 129 source lines with a 50-m inline spacing of shots; and the survey is over a 16-km by 20-km grid. A portion of a shot gather is shown in Figure 21.20. More than 10,000,000 first-arrival traveltimes were picked and inverted by ray-tracing tomography to give the initial velocity model shown in Figure 21.21a.

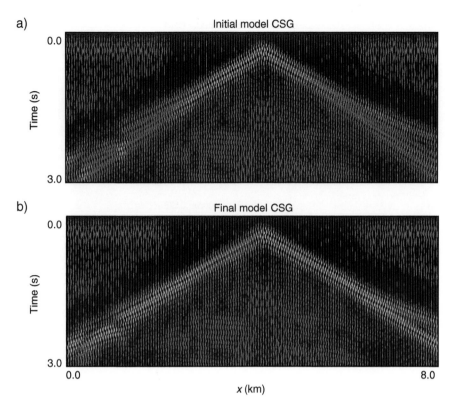

Figure 21.22. Green traces from the predicted shot gather overlaid onto the red traces of the recorded shot gather; here, the predicted traces are computed from the (a) traveltime and (b) macro-window FWI tomograms. The green predicted traces are superimposed on the red recorded traces, and if only a green wiggle is seen, then this means the predicted event almost perfectly fits the recorded trace. Images created from results discussed in AlTheyab (2014).

Gauss-Newton FWI (GN-FWI) with the macro-window strategy outlined in Figure 21.14a is applied to the data according to the following schedule, where Δx denotes the width of the source-receiver offset window for each shot gather and ΔT denotes the window length in time.

1. Estimate source wavelet.
2. Iterations 1–3 of GN-FWI with $\Delta x = 1$ km and $\Delta T = 1.5$ s.
3. Iterations 4–6 of GN-FWI with $\Delta x = 1.5$ km and $\Delta T = 2.0$ s.
4. Iterations 7–9 of GN-FWI with $\Delta x = 2.0$ km and $\Delta T = 2.0$ s.
5. Iterations 10–12 of GN-FWI with $\Delta x = 2.5$ km and $\Delta T = 2.5$ s.
6. Iterations 13–15 of GN-FWI with $\Delta x = 3.0$ km and $\Delta T = 2.5$ s.
7. Iterations 16–18 of GN-FWI with $\Delta x = 3.5$ km and $\Delta T = 3.0$ s.
8. Iterations 19–21 of GN-FWI with $\Delta x = 4.0$ km and $\Delta T = 3.0$ s,

The final tomogram after 40 iterations is shown in Figure 21.21b and contains much more detail than the initial velocity model.

To validate the improved accuracy of the macro-window tomogram, the predicted shot gathers are compared to the recorded shot gathers in Figures 21.22 and 21.23. The green predicted traces overlay the red recorded traces: the greener the overlay, the more accurate the prediction of recorded events. It is obvious that the macro-window FWI traces in Figures 21.22b and 21.23b are greener than the predicted traces in Figures 21.22a and 21.23a computed from the traveltime tomogram. This suggests that the macro-window tomogram in Figure 21.21b might be a significant improvement over the traveltime tomogram in Figure 21.21a.

21.3.5 Key points

The rolling-offset FWI strategy is the extension of rolling frequencies in multiscale FWI (Bunks et al., 1995) to rolling source-receiver offsets and time durations. It is successful at eliminating the cycle-skipping problem in FWI if the reflection events are sufficiently coherent for proper design of the window size. In this case, the kinematics of reflections are inverted without the need for a high-frequency approximation. This is important for estimating the velocities below the deepest penetration of the diving waves. The limitations of rolling-offset FWI are the following.

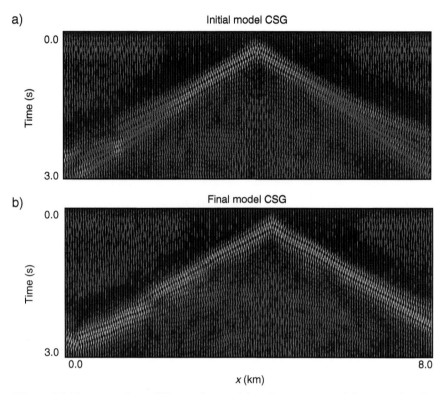

Figure 21.23. Same as Figure 21.22, except for a different shot position. Images created from results discussed in AlTheyab (2014).

1. The design of the rolling-offset window can be user intensive. Creating a robust and fully automated windowing procedure is a programming challenge.
2. It will be difficult to identify coherent reflections in media with significant defocusing and scattering, e.g., below salt. Such environments discourage coherent reflections and so will reduce the effectiveness of reflection FWI methods.
3. Strong multiples, unless they are eliminated or identified, will masquerade as primaries and therefore degrade the accuracy of the tomogram.

21.4 Acoustic FWI applied to crosswell data

The acoustic FWI algorithm is now tested on crosswell data where, as shown in Figure 21.24, a string of sources are placed along a vertical well and the receivers are along a neighboring vertical well. Unlike surface reflection data, crosswell data are characterized by transmitted arrivals penetrating everywhere between the wells, so the cycle-skipping problem largely is eliminated with inversion of early arrivals (Zhou et al., 1995, 1997). A good initial starting model can be obtained from either the sonic log or by traveltime tomography. At the early iterations, the time window only admits the transmitted arrivals and then

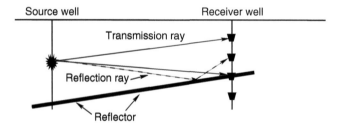

Figure 21.24. A crosswell experimental geometry.

gradually widens in time as the velocity model becomes more accurate. This minimizes the cycle-skipping problem for later reflections because the earliest reflection arrival coincides with the transmitted arrival at the receiver well. Accounting for attenuation effects and normalizing traces reduces the inversion difficulties with errors in the predicted amplitudes, and a multiscale inversion strategy also is important for avoiding cycle skipping.

The acoustic FWI algorithm first is tested on a synthetic crosswell data set, then it is applied to crosswell field data recorded near Friendswood, Texas (Zhou et al., 1995).

21.4.1 Synthetic crosshole data

The wave-equation traveltime and waveform-inversion (WTW) method now is applied to the Figure 21.25a fault

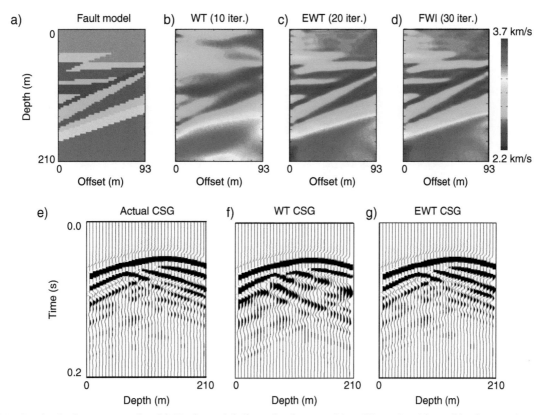

Figure 21.25. Synthetic data test results. (a) Fault model discretized onto a 31×71 mesh with a gridpoint spacing of 3 m. (b) WT tomogram after 10 iterations, (c) EWT tomogram after 20 iterations, where (b) is the starting model at the 10th iteration, and (d) FWI tomogram after 30 iterations where (c) is the starting model at the 20th iteration. Figures (e–f) are the shot gathers generated using the (a–c) velocity models, respectively. Illustration adapted from Zhou et al. (1995).

model. A 31×71 mesh is used to approximate the velocity distribution, with 18 line sources and 36 receivers along the left side and right side of the model, respectively; a 40-gridpoint-wide absorbing sponge zone is added along each boundary. The source wavelet is a Ricker wavelet having a peak frequency of 80 Hz; the starting velocity model is a uniform medium with a velocity of 3000 m/s; and a 2–4 finite-difference solution to the 2D acoustic wave equation is used to generate the data.

Figure 21.25b shows the wave equation traveltime inversion (WT) tomogram after 10 iterations, in which the objective function is the correlation between predicted and "observed" first arrivals (see Chapter 20). After the tenth iteration, the traveltime gradient is turned off and the waveform gradient for the first arrivals is turned on for another 10 iterations, to give the EWT tomogram in Figure 21.25c. For comparison, Figure 21.25d shows the "best" FWI tomogram after 30 iterations, in which the starting model at the 20th iteration is the EWT tomogram in Figure 21.25c. Note that the EWT and FWI tomograms in Figure 21.25c and 21.25d show much better interface definition than the WT (Figure 21.25b) tomogram. This is not surprising because the WT method seeks to fit only the first-arrival traveltimes compared to fitting the waveforms

in the seismograms for the EWT and FWI methods. This means that the first-arrival times can be explained by a smooth velocity model, whereas only a highly detailed fault model will account for the early-arrival waveforms. Luo and Schuster (1991a) show that standard full-waveform inversion failed for this fault model if the starting model was a homogeneous velocity model. This underscores the importance of avoiding cycle-skipping problems by first inverting for the long-wavelength features by traveltime inversion.

Figure 21.25e to 21.25g depict the shot gathers associated with the actual fault model, and the tomograms associated with the WT, EWT, and WTW methods. The EWT shot gather in Figure 21.25g contains almost all of the scattering and reflection events in the actual shot gather in Figure 21.25e. In comparison, the WT shot gather in Figure 21.25f does not correlate as well with the actual shot gather, except for the direct arrivals and some reflection events.

The WTW method can be robust in the presence of zero-mean random noise. This is demonstrated by adding zero-mean random noise to give the noisy input data shown in Figure 21.26a. Applying the WTW method to the noisy data yields the WTW tomogram after 16

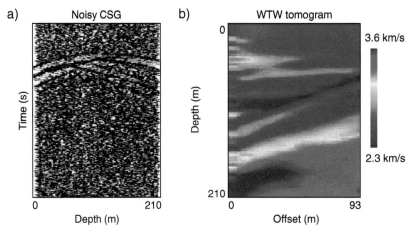

a) Noisy CSG

b) WTW tomogram

Figure 21.26. (a) The same shot gather as in Figure 21.25e, except random noise has been added to the data, and (b) shows the WTW tomogram after 16 iterations with the noisy data as input. Illustration adapted from Zhou et al. (1995).

iterations in Figure 21.26b. The tomogram's accuracy is quite acceptable.

21.4.2 Friendswood crosshole data

The WTW method is applied to a crosshole seismic data set collected by Exxon near its Friendswood, Texas, test site (Chen et al., 1990). The source and receiver wells are 180 m apart, the wells extend to a depth of 300 m, and the source and receiver sampling intervals are 3 m, so that there are 98 sources and 96 receivers. The source consists of a small amount of dynamite, and the seismic data have a usable bandwidth of 80 to 600 Hz. A typical unprocessed shot gather at intermediate depth is shown in Figure 21.27a.

The shot gathers were processed with the following steps.

1. Tube waves are eliminated by median filtering.
2. Free-surface reflections are muted out in the time domain.
3. An 80–600 Hz bandpass filter is applied to the data.
4. Each trace of the seismograms is normalized to its maximum value.
5. Direct arrivals are muted out after the iterations for waveform inversion are started. To ensure that the first-arrival traveltime vector $\mathbf{t}^{obs}$ is predicted accurately, a regularization constraint can be included until $\|\mathbf{t}^{pred}-\mathbf{t}^{obs}\|_2^2$ is less than a specified threshold.

Each predicted shot gather uses a source wavelet extracted from the corresponding observed shot gather; e.g., Figure 21.27b shows the first-arrival source wavelet associated with a trace at intermediate depth. To accommodate the 80–600 Hz bandwidth of the data, a 2D finite-difference mesh of 301×501 gridpoints is used for the forward modeling and back projection, with the same well geometry as in

the Friendswood experiment. Well deviations in the source and receiver wells were corrected by shifting the coordinates of deviated sources and receivers to the appropriate position in the vertical plane of the source-receiver wells. The data were corrected to a 2D format by multiplying the filter $\sqrt{i/\omega}$ by the spectrum of the observed seismograms and scaling the data by $\sqrt{t}$ to approximate geometric spreading. The final processed shot gather associated with Figure 21.27a is shown in Figure 21.27c. Figure 21.27d shows the same gather, except the upgoing waves have been eliminated by f-k filtering.

The WTW method is applied next to the 98 shot gathers of the processed Friendswood data, where the starting model is a homogeneous velocity model of 1800 m/s. Figure 21.28a, 21.28b, and 21.28c show the WTW tomograms after 10, 16, and 46 iterations, respectively. Figure 21.28d shows the Figure 21.28c tomogram after applying an edge-detection algorithm (Zhou et al., 1995). For these WTW tomograms, the waveform gradient is turned on and the traveltime gradient is turned off after the 10th iteration. This means that Figure 21.28a is the WT tomogram after 10 iterations. Figure 21.28b–d are the full waveform inversion tomograms that use the Figure 21.28a WT tomogram as the starting velocity model. An empirical formula (Gardner et al., 1974) is used to compute density from the inverted P-wave velocity.

The final WTW tomogram in Figure 21.28c provides a much finer layer and velocity resolution compared to the WT tomogram in Figure 21.28a. This is verified in Figure 21.29, which compares the smoothed sonic log (solid line) in the source hole to vertical slices of the final WT and WTW tomograms. It is obvious that the vertical resolution of the WTW tomogram is about 1.5–3.0 m compared to the 6.0–12.0-m resolution of the WT tomogram. Note that the WTW velocity profile differs from the sonic log profile by a DC shift in the 200–300 m interval. This highlights a

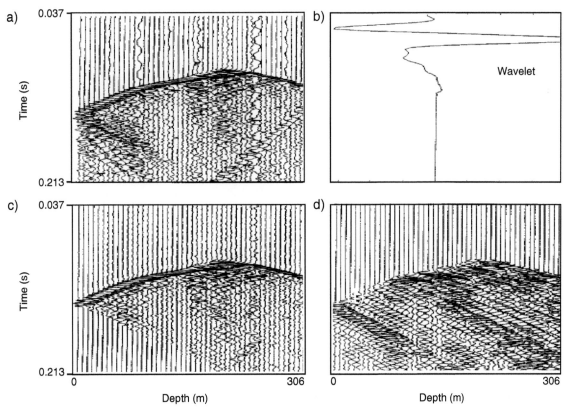

Figure 21.27. A typical shot gather of Friendswood crosshole data collected by Exxon near their Friendswood, Texas, test site. The source depth is 156 m. (a) Raw shot gather; (b) First-arrival wavelet extracted from the (a) shot gather; (c) Figure 21.27a shot gather data after signal processing; (d) Downgoing waves after *f-k* filtering of the Figure 21.27a shot gather. Illustration adapted from Zhou et al. (1995).

potential weakness in the WTW method: it is effective at reconstructing both the high and intermediate wavenumber parts of the model, but it can have difficulty in recovering the low-wavenumber part of the model.

As a final accuracy check, Figure 21.30a and 21.30b show the synthetic shot gathers computed from the velocity field in the 10th iteration WT tomogram (Figure 21.28a) and the final WTW tomogram (Figure 21.28c), respectively. In the WTW synthetic shot gather, both direct waves and reflection arrivals show significant correlations with their counterparts in the observed shot gather shown in Figure 21.30c. For example, downgoing reflection events A, B, C, and D are present in both the real and synthetic shot gathers. Also note that the primary and secondary arrivals around zone G in the field data are matched quite well by similar events in the synthetic WTW gather.

The events not accounted for in the synthetic acoustic gather are depicted in the shot-gather residual shown in Figure 21.30d. Note the large residual associated with the direct wave, which indicates that the synthetic source wavelet did not exactly match the shape and maximum amplitude level of the actual source wavelet. Part of the mismatch in the amplitude level can be attributed to the acoustic finite-difference modeling, which does not take

into account *P-S* conversions or viscoelastic losses in the field data.

In comparison with the WT results, the WT synthetics in Figure 21.30a show a good correlation with the actual direct arrivals in Figure 21.30c. However, the secondary arrivals are almost completely absent because of the smooth nature of the WT tomogram. Inverting just the first-arrival traveltimes is insufficient for reconstructing fine, detailed features of the velocity model.

Figure 21.31 shows the root-mean-square (RMS) traveltime and RMS waveform residuals versus iteration number. Relative to the waveform residual at the 10th iterate, the waveform residual at the 46th iterate decreases by about 30%. Each WTW iteration required about 30 CPU hours on an 80 Mflops computer.

21.4.3 Key points

Unlike surface reflection data, crosswell data are characterized by transmitted arrivals penetrating everywhere between the wells. This means that the cycle-skipping problem largely is eliminated as long as the early arrivals first are inverted to explain the first arrivals kinematically.

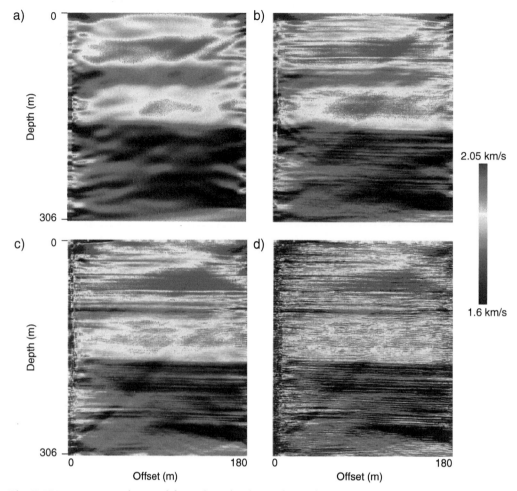

Figure 21.28. The WTW tomograms inverted from the Friendswood crosshole data. (a) WT inversion after 10 iterations. Panels (b–d) are WTW tomograms after 16 iterations, 46 iterations and image enhancement of the tomogram in panel (c), respectively. Illustration adapted from Zhou et al. (1995).

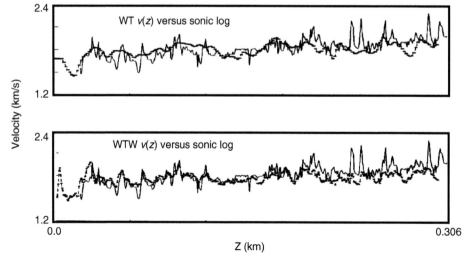

Figure 21.29. Tomogram velocity profiles from the (a) WT and (b) WTW tomograms compared to the sonic log (solid line) in the source well. The $v(z)$ profiles are extracted from the tomograms 12 m from the source well. Illustrations adapted from Zhou et al. (1995).

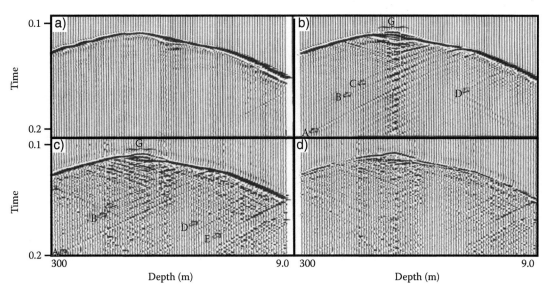

Figure 21.30. Synthetic acoustic common shot gathers associated with the (a) WT and (b) the WTW tomograms in Figure 21.28. The corresponding observed shot gather is in (c), and (d) depicts the seismogram residual for the WTW data. The source location for these common-shot gathers is at the depth 156 m. Illustration adapted from Zhou et al. (1995).

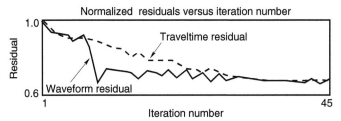

Figure 21.31. The RMS residuals versus iteration number for the WTW inversion of the Friendswood data. Illustration adapted from Zhou et al. (1995).

This typically means that inverting later reflection arrivals will not suffer seriously from the cycle-skipping problem. Accounting for attenuation effects and normalizing traces reduces the inversion difficulties with errors in the predicted amplitudes, and a multiscale inversion strategy is important for avoiding cycle skipping.

21.5 Summary

Several examples of acoustic FWI applied to different data types are presented: shallow land data, deep marine data, and crosswell data. Each data type requires a different strategy for FWI, in which the common goals are to 1) eliminate elastic events not explained by acoustic modeling and 2) avoid getting stuck in a local minimum. For the shallow land data, early arrivals are windowed and inverted so that cycle skipping is avoided and the predicted data mostly match the observed early arrivals. However, the penalty is that there is no update to velocities below the

deepest reach of a diving wave at the maximum source-receiver offset. Even for marine data, the shallow velocities are mostly updated because the diving waves and their wavepaths have strengths of $O(1)$, although those of the deeper reflections have a strength $O(r^2)$ where $1 \gg |r|$. This problem is exacerbated because the deep portions of the model are visited infrequently by seismic arrivals compared to shallow portions of the model. The partial solution is to embed an LSM algorithm within the inner portions of the nonlinear iterations. This typically is not a problem for crosswell data because the transmitted arrivals visit everywhere between the well, so an EWT approach can be used to get a long-wavelength estimate of the velocity model. Such an estimate avoids cycle skipping and getting stuck in a local minimum. The window can be widened gradually in both source-receiver offset and time so that all events can be inverted to give a highly detailed estimate of the velocity model.

All of the field examples in this chapter were for data with no more than moderate complexity, so the FWI algorithm worked reasonably well. However, the unanswered challenge is to create a robust FWI method that will succeed below complex salt bodies and with data that largely contain strong multiples, significant scattering, and incoherent arrivals from deep reflectors.

21.6 Exercises

1. Invert 2D land data with early-arrival FWI under the topic "FWI" in the Computational Toolkit.
2. Invert synthetic crosswell data with multisource FWI under the topic "FWI" in the Computational Toolkit.

3. Invert synthetic marine data with hybrid FWI under the topic "FWI" in the Computational Toolkit.
4. Implement a rolling-offset FWI algorithm with one of the above exercises. Compare its convergence rate with that of standard FWI.

Appendix 21A:
Optimal frequency bands for EWT

In the space-time domain, EWT uses a band of frequencies at each scale so a much wider range of wave numbers than in the frequency domain can be updated. The formula for selecting upscaling frequencies proposed by Sirgue and Pratt (2004) in the frequency domain is

$$f_{n+1} = \frac{f_n}{\alpha_{min}}, \qquad (21.8)$$

where f_n is the current frequency, f_{n+1} is the next frequency to be chosen, and $\alpha_{min} = z/\sqrt{h^2 + z^2}$ is the parameter as a function of the maximum half-offset h and the maximum depth z in the image. The vertical wavenumber range $[k_z^{min}(f_n), k_z^{max}(f_n)]$ is calculated by

$$k_z^{min}(f_n) = \frac{4\pi f_n \alpha_{min}}{c_0}, \qquad (21.9)$$

$$k_z^{max}(f_n) = \frac{4\pi f_n}{c_0}, \qquad (21.10)$$

where c_0 is the smooth background velocity model. Equation 21.8 guarantees the lowest wavenumber to be updated

at the $(n+1)^{th}$ frequency f_{n+1} is equal to the highest wavenumber at the nth frequency f_n. Using equations 21.9 and 21.10 with 21.8, we obtain

$$k_z^{min}(f_{n+1}) = k_z^{max}(f_n). \qquad (21.11)$$

In the Wadi application, this frequency-selection strategy in the time domain is adopted to reduce the overlapped regions of recovered wavenumber components in two neighboring scales. A number of frequencies are used simultaneously for a given bandwidth in time domain waveform inversion (Boonyasiriwat et al., 2009). Here, equation 21.8 is used to choose f_n as the peak frequency for the frequency band in the nth scale. Therefore, low-pass or bandpass filters with proper pass-band and stop-band windows can be applied to seismic data at different scales to control the range of recovered wavenumbers.

A grid size for a given frequency can be determined by the numerical stability and dispersion conditions associated with the finite-difference method at that scale. Here, the numerical dispersion condition for the finite-difference scheme is satisfied by more than ten gridpoints per dominant minimum wavelength (Levander, 1988). A square grid with $dx = dz$ is used. The time step dt can be determined by the 2D numerical stability condition once the space grid size is fixed

$$dt < \frac{dz}{\sqrt{2}c_{max}}, \qquad (21.12)$$

where c_{max} is the maximum velocity.

Chapter 22: Elastic and Viscoelastic Full-Waveform Inversion

This chapter presents the theory of elastic and viscoelastic full-waveform inversion (FWI), which, in principle, reconstructs both the P- and S-wave velocities from the seismic data. Instead of modeling the acoustic wave equation, the modeling and back projection of the data use numerical solutions to either the elastic or viscoelastic wave equations. To account for attenuation, the viscoelastic wave equation is used both to forward propagate and back propagate the wavefields. This means that estimates of the P-wave attenuation Q_P and S-wave attenuation Q_S distributions are needed as input information into the viscoelastic modeling code. These distributions can be estimated by a ray-based inversion scheme or a wave-equation inversion scheme.

22.1 Elastic FWI

Elastic FWI is a straightforward extension of acoustic FWI, except now both the P- and S-wave velocities are inverted from the recorded data (Tarantola, 1987; Mora, 1987 and 1989; Pica et al., 1990; Crase et al., 1992). In this case, the gradient of the objective function is formed by computing solutions of the elastic wave equation. Similar to acoustic FWI, the initial-velocity model can be obtained by either ray tracing or wave-equation traveltime inversion.

The optimization goal is to reconstruct the P- and S-velocity models which predict the observed seismograms $p(\mathbf{g}, t|\mathbf{s}, 0)^{\text{obs}}$ that minimize the *hybrid* misfit function

$$\epsilon = \frac{A(1-\alpha)}{2} \sum_s \sum_g [\Delta\tau_{gs}]^2 + \frac{B\alpha}{2} \sum_s \sum_g \int dt [\Delta p_{gs}(t)]^2. \tag{22.1}$$

Here, $\Delta p_{gs}(t) = p(\mathbf{g}, t|\mathbf{s}, 0) - p(\mathbf{g}, t|\mathbf{s}, 0)^{\text{obs}}$ is the seismogram residual and $p(\mathbf{g}, t|\mathbf{s}, 0)$ is the predicted seismogram after normalization; the recorded seismograms also are normalized. The traveltime residual $\Delta\tau_{gs} = \tau(\mathbf{g}, \mathbf{s}) - \tau(\mathbf{g}, \mathbf{s})^{\text{obs}}$ is the difference between the observed and calculated first-arrival times for a source at $\mathbf{s}$ and a receiver at $\mathbf{g}$. The weight $0 \leq \alpha \leq 1$ is initially set equal to 0, and

gradually changed to the value $\frac{1}{2}$ as the iterations proceed so the traveltimes of specified events also are fitted. The normalization factors $A = 1/(\sum_s \sum_g [\tau(\mathbf{g}, \mathbf{s})^{\text{obs}}]^2)$ and $B = 1/(\sum_s \sum_g \int dt [p(\mathbf{g}, t|\mathbf{s}, 0)^{\text{obs}}]^2)$ are used to balance the two misfit functions. Density as a function of depth can be obtained from the density log in the well or by a simple empirical relation between the P-wave velocity and density (Gardner et al., 1974).

For two-component data in which the vertical $u(\mathbf{g}, t|\mathbf{s}, 0)^{\text{obs}}_z$ and horizontal $u(\mathbf{g}, t|\mathbf{s}, 0)^{\text{obs}}_z$ particle velocities are recorded, the seismogram residual $\Delta p(\mathbf{g}, t)$ is replaced by the particle-velocity residuals $\Delta u(\mathbf{g}, t)_x$ and $\Delta u(\mathbf{g}, t)_z$, in which

$$\Delta u(\mathbf{g}, t|\mathbf{s}, 0)_x = u(\mathbf{g}, t|\mathbf{s}, 0)_x - u(\mathbf{g}, t|\mathbf{s}, 0)^{\text{obs}}_x,$$

$$\Delta u(\mathbf{g}, t|\mathbf{s}, 0)_z = u(\mathbf{g}, t|\mathbf{s}, 0)_z - u(\mathbf{g}, t|\mathbf{s}, 0)^{\text{obs}}_z,$$

and

$$|\Delta p_{gs}(t)|^2 = |\Delta u(\mathbf{g}, t|\mathbf{s}, 0)_x|^2 + |\Delta u(\mathbf{g}, t|\mathbf{s}, 0)_z|^2. \tag{22.2}$$

If the two-component geophones are clamped,[1] then 2D elastic FWI is implemented with the following steps (Mora, 1987; Crase et al., 1992; Zhou et al., 1997):

1. Assume a starting model for the P-wave c_P and S-wave c_S velocity distributions. Assign the density distribution using the well log, or by correlating it with the velocity distribution, e.g., Gardner's relationship (Gardner et al., 1974). The source wavelet also should be estimated according to one of the methods described in section 19.2.6 or Appendix 22B. For the crosswell data example presented in the next section, the initial wavelet is formed by averaging the direct P-wave arrivals in a shot gather.

2. Solve the elastic wave equation with zero initial conditions for each shot point by a finite-difference algorithm

---

[1] A clamped geophone is pressed mechanically against the side of the well casing.

that solves the 2D elastic wave equation for an isotropic medium:

$$\rho\frac{\partial}{\partial t}u_x - \left(\frac{\partial}{\partial x}\sigma_{xx} + \frac{\partial}{\partial z}\sigma_{xz}\right) = 0,$$

$$\rho\frac{\partial}{\partial t}u_z - \left(\frac{\partial}{\partial z}\sigma_{zz} + \frac{\partial}{\partial x}\sigma_{xz}\right) = 0,$$

$$\frac{\partial}{\partial t}\sigma_{xx} = (\lambda + 2\mu)\frac{\partial}{\partial x}u_x + \lambda\frac{\partial}{\partial z}u_z + S_{xx},$$

$$\frac{\partial}{\partial t}\sigma_{zz} = (\lambda + 2\mu)\frac{\partial}{\partial z}u_z + \lambda\frac{\partial}{\partial x}u_x + S_{zz},$$

and

$$\frac{\partial}{\partial t}\sigma_{xz} = \mu\left(\frac{\partial}{\partial x}u_z + \frac{\partial}{\partial z}u_x\right). \quad (22.3)$$

Here, λ and μ are, respectively, the Lamé parameter and shear modulus distributions, S_{xx} and S_{zz} denote the source functions in the well[2] acting as the normal stresses, and $(u_x, u_z, \sigma_{xx}, \sigma_{zz}, \sigma_{xz})$ denote the particle-velocity components and stresses (Aki and Richards, 1980).

3. Calculate the weighted residuals defined in equation 22.2.

4. Solve the elastic wave equation in reverse time from the final recording time T to time zero by using the same finite-difference algorithm for each shot point. Here, the reverse-time seismogram residual is treated as the source time history at the receiver location:

$$\rho\frac{\partial}{\partial t}\hat{u}_x - \left(\frac{\partial}{\partial x}\hat{\sigma}_{xx} + \frac{\partial}{\partial z}\hat{\sigma}_{xz}\right) = \sum_l \hat{\gamma}_l^x,$$

$$\rho\frac{\partial}{\partial t}\hat{u}_z - \left(\frac{\partial}{\partial z}\hat{\sigma}_{zz} + \frac{\partial}{\partial x}\hat{\sigma}_{xz}\right) = \sum_l \hat{\gamma}_l^z,$$

$$\frac{\partial}{\partial t}\hat{\sigma}_{xx} = (\lambda + 2\mu)\frac{\partial}{\partial x}\hat{u}_x + \lambda\frac{\partial}{\partial z}\hat{u}_z,$$

$$\frac{\partial}{\partial t}\hat{\sigma}_{zz} = (\lambda + 2\mu)\frac{\partial}{\partial z}\hat{u}_z + \lambda\frac{\partial}{\partial x}\hat{u}_x,$$

and

$$\frac{\partial}{\partial t}\hat{\sigma}_{xz} = \mu\left(\frac{\partial}{\partial x}\hat{u}_z + \frac{\partial}{\partial z}\hat{u}_x\right), \quad (22.4)$$

Terms $\hat{\gamma}_l^x$ and $\hat{\gamma}_l^z$ denote the reverse-time histories of the residuals computed at the lth receiver location and $\hat{u}_i$ is the ith component of the backward-modeled receiver wavefield.

---

[2] If the source is a vertical component vibrator on the earth's horizontal surface, then only S_{zz} is nonzero.

5. Compute the misfit gradients associated with the Lamé parameters (Mora, 1987; Crase et al., 1992):

$$\frac{\partial\epsilon}{\partial\lambda} = -\sum_{shots}\int_0^T dt\left(\frac{\partial}{\partial x}u_x + \frac{\partial}{\partial z}u_z\right)\left(\frac{\partial}{\partial x}\hat{u}_x + \frac{\partial}{\partial z}\hat{u}_z\right),$$

$$\frac{\partial\epsilon}{\partial\mu} = -\sum_{shots}\int_0^T dt\left[2\left(\frac{\partial}{\partial x}\hat{u}_x\frac{\partial}{\partial x}u_x + \frac{\partial}{\partial z}\hat{u}_z\frac{\partial}{\partial z}u_z\right)\right.$$
$$\left. + \left(\frac{\partial}{\partial z}\hat{u}_x + \frac{\partial}{\partial x}\hat{u}_z\right)\left(\frac{\partial}{\partial z}u_x + \frac{\partial}{\partial x}v_z\right)\right]. \quad (22.5)$$

The summation is over the different shot gathers. In a homogeneous medium with a single scatterer, the term $(\frac{\partial}{\partial x}u_x + \frac{\partial}{\partial z}u_z)$ is proportional to the downgoing source field for a P-wave, and $(\frac{\partial}{\partial x}\hat{u}_x + \frac{\partial}{\partial z}\hat{u}_z)$ is the scattered P-wave residual back propagated from the recorders. The product of these two fields and the integration over time is the traditional imaging condition for elastic-wave migration. See Appendices 22A and 22F for the adjoint-based derivation of the gradients associated with λ, μ, and ρ.

6. Calculate the updates to the P- and S-wave velocities using the formulas

$$\delta c_P = 2c_P\rho\delta\lambda$$

and

$$\delta c_S = -4c_S\rho\delta\lambda + 2c_S\rho\delta\mu. \quad (22.6)$$

The above steps are performed at each iteration, and the subspace method (Kennett et al., 1988) is used to calculate the step length for updating the P- and S-wave velocities. Kennett's method (see section 19.2.4) separates the P- and S-velocity misfit gradients into two subspaces, and calculates the optimal step length for each gradient. The P- and S-velocity values are used as model parameters in the inversion because they are estimated more robustly than the Lamé parameters λ and μ (Tarantola et al., 1985).

22.2 FWI of crosswell hydrophone records

If unclamped sources and receivers are used in a crosswell experiment, the wave propagation through the fluid-filled wells needs to be modeled for elastic full-waveform inversion. Figure 21.24 shows the crosswell experimental geometry, and only volume expansion sources and hydrophone receivers are used in the experiment. The details for the source-wavelet inversion are given in Appendix 22B.

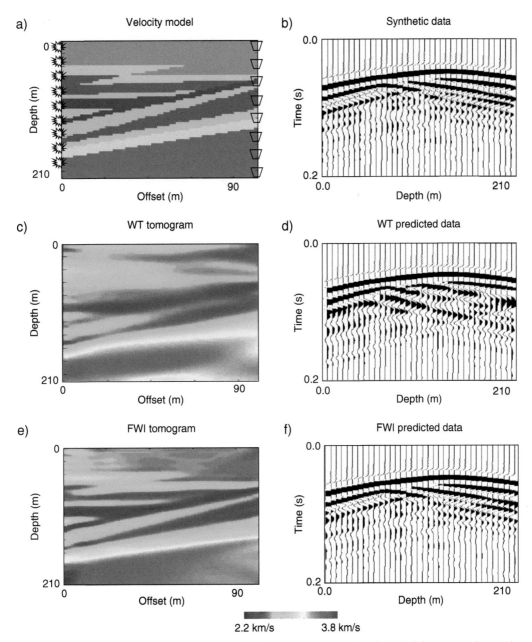

Figure 22.1. Acoustic velocity model, WT tomogram, and FWI tomogram in left column of figures, and associated shot gathers in the right column. In this example, an acoustic forward-modeling code is used to generate both the actual and predicted data sets. It is obvious that the FWI tomogram is noticeably more resolved than the WT tomogram. Figures adapted from Wang (1995).

The crosswell source generates pressure on the wall of the source well, which then excites waves into the earth. Once the seismic waves reach the receiver well, the stresses on the wall generate the fluid pressure in the well, which is recorded by the hydrophones. The modeling of seismic wave propagation within the source well can be accomplished partly by inverting for an equivalent source on the wall of the source well. In comparison, the pressure field generated in the receiver well can be estimated from the stresses on the well's wall by a low-frequency approximation (White and Lessenger,

1988). Details on corrections for borehole effects are given in Appendix 22C.

22.2.1 Acoustic FWI applied to acoustic synthetic data

Figure 22.1a shows the crosswell fault model, where 18 (36) evenly spaced shots (hydrophones) are on the left side (right side) of the acoustic velocity model. Here, the P-wave velocities range from 2300 m/s to 3800 m/s, and

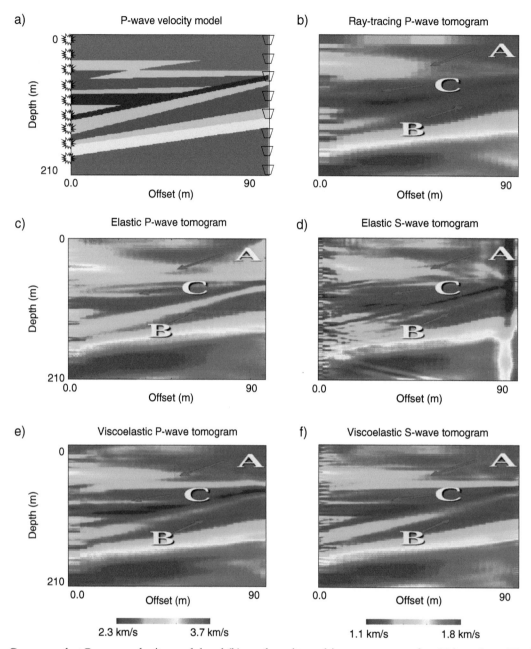

Figure 22.2. Common-shot P-wave velocity model and (b) ray-based traveltime tomogram after 10 iterations. The input data are computed by a FD solution to the 2D viscoelastic wave equation with constant $Q_P = 40$ and $Q_S = 25$. The V_P/V_S ratio is fixed at $V_P/V_S = 2.0$ for any point in the model. Applying elastic FWI and viscoelastic FWI to the input traces gives the tomograms in (c and d) and (e and f), respectively. Figures adapted from Wang (1997b).

the source time history is described by a Ricker wavelet peaked at 60 Hz. The goal is to establish the accuracy of acoustic FWI applied to crosswell data in which there are no significant elastic effects in the traces. Therefore, the data are generated and inverted by a 2D acoustic modeling code, and an example shot gather is shown in Figure 22.1b. The first arrivals are windowed and the wave-equation traveltime inversion (WT) method is used to give the velocity tomogram (after 10 iterations) in Figure 22.1c.

This tomogram estimates the low-wavenumber details in the Figure 22.1a velocity model, but it is unable to recover the high-wavenumber details after 10 iterations. It is evident in the WT shot gather in Figure 22.1d that not all of the arrivals in Figure 22.1b are reconstructed. These details are recovered accurately in the FWI tomogram in Figure 22.1e, where the starting model from the WT tomogram is accurate enough to avoid cycle-skipping problems.

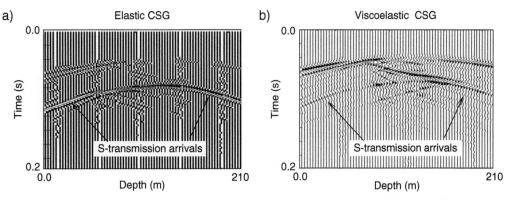

Figure 22.3. Shot gathers generated for the (a) elastic and (b) viscoelastic fault models in Figure 22.2a. Images courtesy of Yue Wang.

22.2.2 Elastic and viscoelastic FWI applied to synthetic viscoelastic data

The viscoelastic S-wave velocity model is a scaled version ($V_S = 0.5V_P$) of the Figure 22.1a P-velocity model, and density is assigned by the empirical formula ($\rho \approx \sqrt{c_P(z)}$). In this example, the "observed" seismograms are generated by a fourth-order, finite-difference solution to the 2D viscoelastic wave equation (see Appendix 22E). Here, the fault model shown in Figure 22.1a is discretized onto a mesh with 121×281 gridpoints, there are 36 sources evenly distributed on the left side of the model, 71 two-component receivers are along the right side of the model, and borehole effects are ignored in the modeling and inversion. The source time history is a Ricker wavelet peaked at 120 Hz, and particle velocities are recorded at the receiver locations.

To account for the attenuation in the data, a viscoelastic modeling code is used both to model and form the misfit gradient. In this case, the FWI algorithm (see Appendix 22D) only inverts for the λ and μ models, in which the correct Q_P and Q_S values are assumed to be known. Nine iterations of FWI inversion reconstruct the P- and S-velocity tomograms shown in Figure 22.2e and Figure 22.2f. The viscoelastic tomograms reveal much finer detail at the interfaces than the elastic tomograms. In the S-velocity tomogram, the interface boundaries are much sharper than those in the P-velocity tomogram because the wavelength of the S-wave is half that of the P-wave.

The elastic P-wave tomogram can explain the amplitude attenuation seen in the P-wave arrivals, but both the P- and S-wave amplitudes cannot be explained simultaneously with an elastic modeling code that does not account for attenuation. In addition, the S-wave transmission arrivals (with a dominant wavelength of about 10 m) in the model shown in Figure 22.2a propagate more than nine wavelengths in the low-velocity zones compared to about four wavelengths for the associated P-waves. Hence, there is more attenuation in the S-waves compared to the P-waves that cannot be accounted for by the elastic modeling and

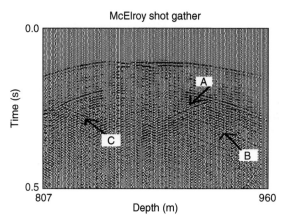

Figure 22.4. A McElroy common-shot gather after data processing. Strong S-wave reflections are denoted by the arrows at A, B, and C.

inversion codes. This example suggests the importance of accounting for viscoelastic effects in data if Q_P, $Q_S \leq 50$ and the S-wave propagation distance is more than nine wavelengths. Shot gathers generated for the elastic- and viscoelastic-fault models in Figure 22.2a are shown in Figure 22.3.

22.3 FWI applied to McElroy crosswell data

Viscoelastic full-waveform inversion (Wang, 1995 and 1997b) now is applied to crosswell data recorded near McElroy, Texas (Harris et al., 1992). There are 201 shots evenly distributed along the source well over the depth range of 167 m. The usable frequency range of the source wavelet is from 200 Hz to 1400 Hz, the lateral offset of the vertical wells is 61 m, and each common-shot gather has 186 traces. The receivers in the experiment are hydrophones which record the pressure field in the fluid-filled receiver well. The P-wave velocity ranges from 4600 m/s to 7200 m/s and the S-wave velocity ranges from 2700 m/s to 4200 m/s. A grid size of 0.208×0.208 m is used to

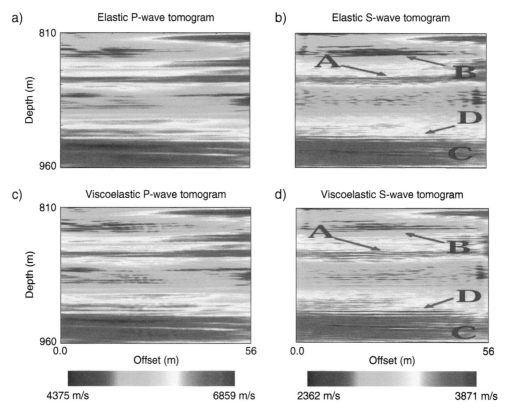

Figure 22.5. The P- and S-velocity tomograms obtained by (a and b) elastic FWI and (c and d) viscoelastic FWI of the McElroy crosswell data. After Wang (1997b).

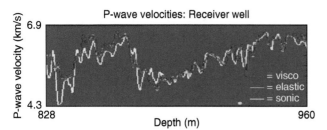

Figure 22.6. Comparison of elastic and viscoelastic P-velocity profiles with P-velocity sonic logs. The tomogram profiles are about 9 m from the receiver well. Image courtesy of Yue Wang.

discretize the unknown velocity model, and it has 295 × 801 gridpoints.

22.3.1 Data processing

The same processing procedure is used as in the elastic inversion of Zhou et al. (1997). A 200 to 1400 Hz band-pass filter is applied to the field data to suppress both the high- and low-frequency noise, and a median filter is applied to both the common-shot and common-receiver gathers to eliminate the tube waves generated in the source and receiver wells. Then the field traces are transformed from 3D to 2D by multiplying their spectra by $\sqrt{i/\omega}$ in the frequency domain (Barton, 1989) and multiplying

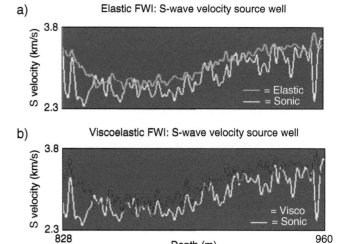

Figure 22.7. Comparison of (a) elastic and (b) viscoelastic S-velocity profiles with the S-velocity sonic log. The tomogram profiles are extracted about 9 m from the wells. Images courtesy of Yue Wang.

each time sample by $\sqrt{t}$ in the time domain. Figure 22.4 shows a common-shot gather after data processing, when the reflections are enhanced in the processed gather.

The initial wavelet is obtained by averaging the wavefronts of the first P-wave arrivals in each common-shot gather. Then the wavelet inversion scheme is used to invert

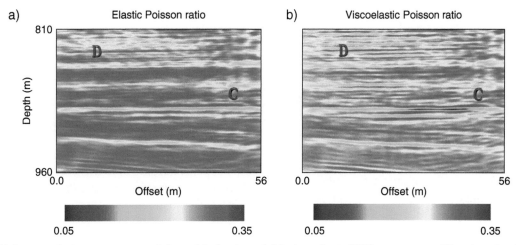

Figure 22.8. Poisson-ratio images computed from (a) elastic and (b) viscoelastic FWI tomograms. The viscoelastic FWI map in (b) appears to have higher resolution than in (a). After Wang (1997b).

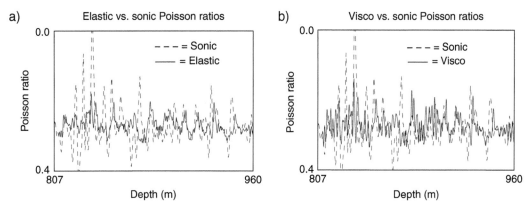

Figure 22.9. Comparison of the Poisson-ratio profiles obtained from the tomograms and the sonic log near the source well. Images modified from Wang (1997b).

for the equivalent source wavelet, which acts on the wall of the source well (Zhou et al., 1997).

The constant values of $Q_P = 80$ and $Q_S = 50$ are estimated from the data by the Liao and McMechan (1997) procedure outlined in Appendix 22D. More accurate Q_P and Q_S distributions could have been reconstructed by ray tracing, but the constant Q assumption is sufficient to show that viscoelastic inversion is superior to elastic inversion for the McElroy data.

22.3.2 Elastic and viscoelastic waveform inversion

Next, the first-arrival traveltimes are picked from the field records and inverted by a ray-based traveltime-inversion scheme. The traveltime tomogram is used as the initial P-velocity model for elastic FWI and the S-velocity initial model is computed by multiplying the P-velocity traveltime tomogram at each pixel by the ratio of the direct S- and P-wave arrival times. The density model is calculated from the P-velocity tomogram by using the same empirical formula in the synthetic tests.

Figure 22.5a and 22.5b shows the elastic P- and S-wave velocity tomograms (Wang, 1995, 1997b; Zhou et al., 1997) that were used as the starting velocity models for the viscoelastic waveform inversion. After two iterations, the strong P- and S-wave transmitted arrivals are suppressed to emphasize velocity details from the reflection arrivals.[3]

Figure 22.5c and 22.5d shows the P- and S-velocity tomograms after four more iterations. The layering at positions A, B, C, and D in the viscoelastic tomograms are more clearly resolved compared with layers in the elastic tomograms. The vertical resolution is about 3 m in the P-velocity tomogram and about 1.5 m in the S-velocity tomogram, which is close to the limits of crosswell imaging (Schuster, 1996).

Figures 22.6 and 22.7 compare the P- and S-velocity profiles from the waveform tomograms with the

---

[3]Inverting the direct waves along their transmission wavepaths primarily reconstructs the long-wavelength components of the tomogram, which can mitigate the cycle-skipping problem in FWI. After the strong direct waves are inverted, they can be either muted or downweighted so that the fine details of the model can be reconstructed more easily from the weaker reflections.

corresponding profiles in the sonic logs. Similar to the synthetic example, the P-wave profiles obtained from either elastic or viscoelastic inversion agree in many places with the sonic P-velocity. However, this is not the case with the elastic or viscoelastic S-velocity tomograms which show many more discrepancies with the S-velocity sonic log, especially at the lower wavenumbers. Nevertheless, the viscoelastic S-velocity profile has significantly fewer high-wavenumber discrepancies than the elastic S-velocity profile, which is consistent with the synthetic results. This suggests that taking the physics of attenuation into consideration is likely to be important with FWI when propagation distances are greater than 10 wavelengths and the Q_P and Q_S values are less than 80 and 50, respectively.

Figure 22.8 shows the Poisson-ratio images computed from the elastic and viscoelastic FWI tomograms. The viscoelastic Poisson-ratio image has higher resolution, so it can provide more useful information about the reservoir's porosity and lithology distributions. Figure 22.9 compares the Poisson-ratio distributions along the source well for the results of elastic and viscoelastic FWI. Relative to the elastic Poisson-ratio curve, the viscoelastic Poisson-ratio curve has a better correlation with that of the sonic log and better spatial resolution. These results were computed with no more than 10 iterations of a conjugate-gradient method.

22.4 Summary

Methods for elastic and viscoelastic full-waveform inversion are presented for inverting seismic data. To avoid the cycle-skipping problem, the long-wavelength features of the P-velocity model are reconstructed by wave-equation traveltime tomography to give a good starting model, and then the short-wavelength features are reconstructed by FWI. Numerical tests show that crosswell FWI is somewhat robust with respect to the starting velocity model for the McElroy crosswell data. After accounting for borehole coupling in the receiver well, elastic FWI is shown to reconstruct the P-velocity model accurately from the McElroy data, but not the S-velocity model. The S-velocity model is reconstructed more accurately with viscoelastic FWI. Test results from both synthetic and field data suggest viscoelastic FWI is more accurate than elastic FWI for propagation distances greater than about 10 wavelengths in attenuative media in which $Q_S < 50$ and $Q_P < 80$.

22.5 Exercises

1. Using Appendix 22A as a template, derive the misfit gradients with respect to ρ and μ in equation 22.5.
2. Prove equation 22.6.
3. Prove equation 22.33.
4. Prove equation 22.36.
5. Show that the second-order elastic wave equation is self-adjoint.
6. Derive the adjoint to the second-order viscoelastic equations. Is the viscoelastic wave equation self-adjoint?

Appendix 22A: Misfit gradient for λ

The elastic misfit gradient associated with λ is derived now[4] in a manner similar to that used for acoustic FWI (see Chapter 19). Appendix 22F uses the adjoint-state procedure to derive the misfit gradients for λ, μ, and ρ.

Assume the harmonic elastic wave equation in a 2D heterogeneous medium so that

$$\omega^2 \rho u_i + \partial_j \{\lambda \partial_k u_k \delta_{ij} + \mu[\partial_i u_j + \partial_j u_i]\} = -f_i, \quad (22.7)$$

in which u_i is the ith component of displacement for a harmonic source oscillating at angular frequency ω with the source function vector described by f_i. Einstein notation is assumed, in which $u_{i,j} = \partial u_i / \partial x_j$ and pairs of common indices indicate summation over the index, e.g., $u_i u_i = u_1^2 + u_2^2$.

We define G_{im} to be the harmonic Green's tensor (Aki and Richards, 1980) for the background medium with the λ, μ, and density ρ distributions that solves the equation

$$\omega^2 \rho G_{im} + \partial_j \{\lambda \partial_k G_{km} \delta_{ij} + \mu[\partial_i G_{jm} + \partial_j G_{im}]\}$$
$$= -\delta_{im} \delta(\mathbf{x} - \mathbf{x}_0), \quad (22.8)$$

in which the Green's tensor with explicit dependence on $\mathbf{x}$ and $\mathbf{x}_0$ is given by $G(\mathbf{x}|\mathbf{x}_0)_{im}$.

Assume that the solution u_i to equation 22.7 is perturbed to be $u_i + \delta u_i$ by a perturbation $\lambda + \delta\lambda$ of the Lamé distribution. In this case, the wave equation to first order in the perturbations $\delta\lambda$ and δu_i is found by taking the first-order perturbation of equation 22.7 with respect to small changes in $\delta\lambda$ to get

$$\omega^2 \rho \delta u_i + \partial_j \{\lambda \partial_k \delta u_k \delta_{ij} + \mu[\partial_i \delta u_j + \partial_j \delta u_i]\}$$
$$= -\partial_j \{\delta\lambda \partial_k u_k \delta_{ij}\}, \quad (22.9)$$

where second-order terms in the perturbation functions have been neglected. Taking the product of the Green's tensor G_{im} with both sides of equation 22.9 and integrating over the entire volume gives

$$\delta u_m = \int G_{im} \partial_j \{\delta\lambda \partial_k u_k \delta_{ij}\} dx^3,$$

$$= \int \partial_j [G_{im} \{\delta\lambda \partial_k u_k \delta_{ij}\}] dx^3 - \int [G_{im,j} \{\delta\lambda \partial_k u_k \delta_{ij}\}] dx^3,$$
$$(22.10)$$

---

[4]The misfit gradients with respect to perturbations in ρ and μ are left as exercises.

in which integration by parts is used to derive the last equation. The leftmost volume integral reduces to a surface integral at infinity, which is assumed to be zero for outgoing waves. In this case, equation 22.10 becomes the Born approximation

$$\delta u(\mathbf{g})_m = -\int [G_{im,j}\{\delta\lambda\partial_k u_k \delta_{ij}\}]dx^3,$$

$$= -\int [\overbrace{G(\mathbf{g}|\mathbf{x})_{im,j}\delta_{ij}}^{\text{extrapolator}}\ \overbrace{\delta\lambda(\mathbf{x})}^{\text{scatterer strength}}\ \overbrace{\partial_k u(\mathbf{x})_k}^{\text{incident field}}]dx^3,$$
$$(22.11)$$

in which $\delta u(\mathbf{g})_m$ denotes the mth component of the perturbed particle velocity recorded at $\mathbf{g}$ due to scattering from the perturbation $\delta\lambda(\mathbf{x})$ at $\mathbf{x}$.

Defining $\delta\lambda = \delta(\mathbf{x} - \mathbf{x}_o)\lambda(\mathbf{x}_o)$ as a perturbation at the point $\mathbf{x}_o$ yields the Fréchet derivative

$$\frac{\delta u(\mathbf{g})_m}{\delta\lambda(\mathbf{x}_o)} = -G(\mathbf{g}|\mathbf{x}_o)_{im,j}\delta_{ij}\partial_k u(\mathbf{x}_o)_k, \qquad (22.12)$$

which in two dimensions becomes

$$\frac{\delta u(\mathbf{g})_m}{\delta\lambda(\mathbf{x})} = -\overbrace{\left(\frac{\partial G(\mathbf{g}|\mathbf{x})_{xm}}{\partial x} + \frac{\partial G(\mathbf{g}|\mathbf{x})_{zm}}{\partial z}\right)}^{\text{extrapolator}}\overbrace{\left(\frac{\partial u(\mathbf{x})_x}{\partial x} + \frac{\partial u(\mathbf{x})_z}{\partial z}\right)}^{\text{downgoing source field}},$$
$$(22.13)$$

where $\mathbf{x}_o$ is conveniently replaced by $\mathbf{x}$, and we assign the indices $1 \to x$ and $2 \to z$. For a single shot gather, we define $\Delta u(\mathbf{g})_m$ as the mth component of the residual, so that the least-squares misfit function is given by

$$\epsilon = \frac{1}{2}\sum_\omega\sum_g [\Delta u(\mathbf{g})_x^*\Delta u(\mathbf{g})_x + \Delta u(\mathbf{g})_z^*\Delta u(\mathbf{g})_z]. \quad (22.14)$$

In this case, the gradient for updating $\lambda(\mathbf{x})$ at $\mathbf{x}$ is given by

$$\frac{\partial\epsilon}{\partial\lambda(\mathbf{x})} = \sum_\omega\sum_\mathbf{g} Re\left[\frac{\partial u(\mathbf{g})_x}{\partial\lambda(\mathbf{x})}\Delta u(\mathbf{g})_x^* + \frac{\partial u(\mathbf{g})_z}{\partial\lambda(\mathbf{x})}\Delta u(\mathbf{g})_z^*\right],$$
$$(22.15)$$

which, after substituting equation 22.13 for the Fréchet derivatives, becomes

$$= -\sum_\omega Re\left[\overbrace{\left(\frac{\partial\hat{u}(\mathbf{x})_x}{\partial x} + \frac{\partial\hat{u}(\mathbf{x})_z}{\partial z}\right)}^{\text{back-propagated residual}}\overbrace{\left(\frac{\partial u(\mathbf{x})_x}{\partial x} + \frac{\partial u(\mathbf{x})_z}{\partial z}\right)}^{\text{downgoing source field}}\right],$$
$$(22.16)$$

in which

$$\frac{\partial\hat{u}_x(\mathbf{x})}{\partial x} + \frac{\partial\hat{u}_z(\mathbf{x})}{\partial z} = \frac{\partial}{\partial x}\overbrace{\sum_g [G(\mathbf{g}|\mathbf{x})_{xx}\Delta u(\mathbf{g})_x^* + G(\mathbf{g}|\mathbf{x})_{xz}\Delta u(\mathbf{g})_z^*]}^{\Delta\hat{u}_x(\mathbf{x}) = x\text{-component of back-propagated residual}}$$

$$+ \frac{\partial}{\partial z}\overbrace{\sum_g [G(\mathbf{g}|\mathbf{x})_{zx}\Delta u(\mathbf{g})_x^* + G(\mathbf{g}|\mathbf{x})_{zz}\Delta u(\mathbf{g})_z^*]}^{\Delta\hat{u}_z(\mathbf{x}) = z\text{-component of back-propagated residual}}.$$
$$(22.17)$$

The summation over frequencies in equation 22.16 shows that the gradient of $\lambda(\mathbf{x})$ is computed by taking the product of the downgoing source field $\nabla\cdot\mathbf{u}(\mathbf{x})$ and the back-propagated residual field $\nabla\cdot\hat{\mathbf{u}}(\mathbf{x})$ and summing over all frequencies. This is similar to the traditional migration imaging condition.

Appendix 22B: Source-wavelet inversion

For the elastic medium, the relationship between the source function and particle displacement is given in Aki and Richards (1980):

$$\rho\ddot{u}_i - \partial_j c_{ijkl}\partial_l u_k = f_i,$$
$$c_{ijkl}\partial_l u_k n_j = T_i,$$
$$u_i = 0 \quad t < 0,$$

and

$$\dot{u}_i = 0 \quad t < 0, \qquad (22.18)$$

in which u_i is the ith component of the displacement, f_i is the body force function, T_i is the traction, and ρ and c_{ijkl} are the density and elastic parameters, respectively. Perturbing the body force f_i and the traction T_i components leads to a perturbed displacement δu_i:

$$\rho\delta\ddot{u}_i - \partial_j c_{ijkl}\partial_l\delta u_k = \delta f_i,$$
$$c_{ijkl}\partial_l\delta u_k n_j = \delta T_i. \qquad (22.19)$$

This new equation has the same form as the elastic wave equation. Therefore, its solution can be obtained in terms of the elastic Green's tensor G_{ij} (Mora, 1987)

$$\delta u_i = \int_v dv G_{ij} * \delta f_j + \int_s ds G_{ij} * \delta T_j, \qquad (22.20)$$

in which the displacement discontinuity term in Green's theorem is neglected. For the fluid-filled borehole, we only consider the source as a volume expansion and set the traction term to be zero.

The adjoint equation corresponding to equation 22.20 is (Tarantola, 1984a)

$$\delta \hat{f_i} = \int dt G_{ij} * \delta u_j. \qquad (22.21)$$

Generally, $\delta \hat{f_i}$ is different from δf_i. However, the preconditioned conjugate gradient is

$$g = D^* C_d^{-1} \Delta d + C_m^{-1} \Delta m, \qquad (22.22)$$

in which D^* is the adjoint operator, C_d^{-1} is the data covariances, Δd is the data misfit, C_m^{-1} represents the model-parameter covariances, and Δm is the model-parameter misfit. We assume a diagonal data covariance. Then, from equation 22.21, the regularized gradient of the source-wavelet inversion algorithm can be expressed as

$$\delta \hat{f_i} = \int dt C_d^{-1} G_{ij} * \delta u_j + C_{f_i - f_{i0}}^{-1} (f_i - f_{i0}), \qquad (22.23)$$

in which f_{i0} is the initial estimate of the wavelet time history. This equation states that the gradient of the source-wavelet inversion scheme can be calculated by back propagating the seismogram residuals and iteratively updating the wavelet estimates. In this case, the P- and S-wave velocities are assumed to be estimated correctly from the traveltime tomograms and the source-wavelet function is reconstructed by using the transmitted waves in the seismogram.

The following steps are used for source-wavelet inversion.

1. Pick the first-arrival traveltimes to invert for the P-velocity distribution.
2. Assign the S-velocity distribution by scaling the P-velocity tomogram with the S/P direct-arrival time ratio, and calculate the elastic parameters λ and μ from the P and S velocities.
3. Set the initial wavelet to be an average of the direct P-wave arrivals in a shot gather and model the elastic wave propagation by a finite-difference solution to the elastic wave equation.
4. Back propagate the seismogram residuals to calculate the gradient in the equation and update the source wavelet by $f_i = f_{i0} + \delta \hat{f_i}$.
5. Set $f_{i0} = f_i$ and repeat the above update procedure until convergence.

For the crosswell situation, we can calculate the elastic parameters from the inverted P- and S-velocity traveltime tomograms. Thus, the source function can be inverted approximately from the direct-wave information in the seismogram.

Appendix 22C: Borehole pressure-field simulation

If the receivers or sources are placed in a borehole, then the elastic response of the borehole should be taken into account (Peng et al., 1993; Dong et al., 1995; Dong and Toksöz, 1995). The pressure field generated in the receiver well can be calculated from the stress components on the wall of the well by a low-frequency assumption (White and Lessenger, 1988)

$$P = -\rho_f \alpha_T^2 \frac{\mu}{\mu + \xi} \frac{(\sigma_{xx} + \sigma_{yy} + \sigma_{zz}) - (1 + \nu)\sigma_{zz}}{E}$$
$$+ \frac{\rho_f \alpha_T}{2\pi a^2} \pi (a_+^2 - a_-^2) v_z, \qquad (22.24)$$

in which $\alpha_T = (\frac{1}{\alpha_f^2} + \frac{\rho_f}{\mu + \xi})^{-1/2}$, and $\xi = \frac{E_c h}{2a}$, and ρ_f is the fluid density. Here, α_f is the acoustic wave velocity in the fluid, E_c is the Young's modulus of the casing, h is the casing thickness, a is the open borehole radius, a_+ and a_- are the borehole radii above and below the caliper change, E and ν are the Young's modulus and Poisson's ratio for the earth medium, respectively, and μ is the shear modulus of the medium. Here, σ_{xx}, σ_{yy}, and σ_{zz}, are the normal stresses, and v_z is the vertical particle velocity of the formation on the wall of the borehole. It is assumed that the low-frequency approximation is appropriate because the borehole diameter is much smaller than the source wavelength.

By using the 2D assumption and ignoring the borehole caliper changes, we simplify equation 22.24 as

$$P = C(\sigma_{xx} - \nu \sigma_{zz}), \qquad (22.25)$$

in which C scales the amplitude of the seismogram. This unknown scaling factor can be treated approximately as a constant, and it can be ignored if the seismogram is normalized to its maximum value.

Back propagation of the waveform residual can be separated into two steps. First, the pressure misfit is back propagated onto the wall of the receiver well to calculate the stress misfit, and then the stress misfit is back propagated into the earth medium to calculate the velocity gradient. The second step can be completed by finite-difference modeling as indicated in equation 22.3. In the first step, we analytically calculate the effective monopole and dipole seismic sources on the wall of the well produced by a pressure source in the well. The formulas can be expressed as (White and Lessenger, 1982; Kurkjian et al., 1992):

$$\sigma(t)_{ij} = \frac{\partial M(t)}{\partial t} \delta_{ij} - \frac{\partial D(t)}{\partial t} \delta_{i1} \delta_{j1},$$

$$M(t) = -2\pi a^2 \alpha_T \frac{\alpha^2}{\beta^2} \frac{\partial P(t)}{\partial t},$$

$$D(t) = -4\pi a^2 \alpha_T \frac{\partial P(t)}{\partial t}, \qquad (22.26)$$

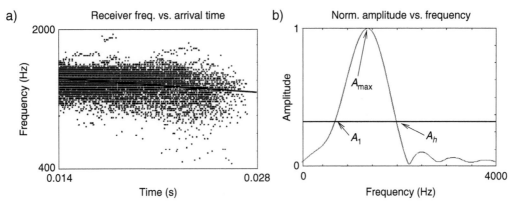

Figure 22.10. (a) The relationship between f_r and t_P. (b) The spectrum of one trace. The illustration in (a) is used to get the slope between f_r and t_P, and (b) is used to get the value of the spectrum's covariance. The Q_P can be estimated from these two values. After Wang (1997b).

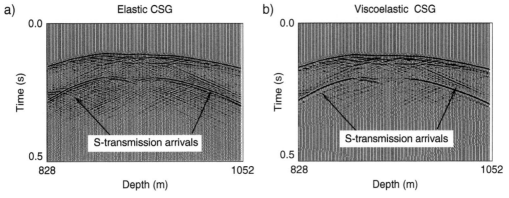

Figure 22.11. Same as Figure 22.3, except the P- and S-velocity tomograms in Figure 22.5 are used as the velocity models. In the case of the viscoelastic model, uniform Q distributions of $Q_P = 80$ and $Q_S = 50$ are assumed. After Wang (1997b).

in which M and D are the monopole and dipole sources, the 1-axis lies along the borehole, δ_{ij} is the Kronecker delta, and α and β are the formation P- and S-wave velocities, respectively. The unknown scalar factor $2\pi a^2 \alpha_T$ can be ignored when doing back propagation, because it will not change the direction of the velocity gradient.

Appendix 22D: Estimation of Q_P and Q_S

According to equation 21.4 and assuming a constant Q_P value in the computation region, the relationship between Q_P and the spectral centroid of the recorded arrival is

$$f_r = f_s + C \int \frac{dl}{V_p(x,z)} = f_s + Ct_p,$$

$$C = \frac{2\pi \sigma_s^2}{Q_p}. \qquad (22.27)$$

The direct P-waves are extracted from the field data set, and the centroid frequencies of their spectra are estimated from the data. Figure 22.10a shows the relationship between f_r and the picked arrival time t_P of the direct wave. The constant C is acquired from the slope of the best-fitting line. To

determine the Q_P distribution, σ_s is extracted from the variance of the spectrum at the receiver location. Figure 22.9b shows the spectrum of the direct P-waves for one trace. The values of A_h and A_l are equal to $A_{\max}/e$, and the covariance of the spectrum is calculated by

$$2\sigma_s^2 = 2\sigma_r^2 = \frac{f(A_h) - f(A_l)}{2}. \qquad (22.28)$$

Here, $f(A_h)$ and $f(A_l)$ are the frequencies at the A_h and A_l positions, and σ_s is assumed to be the same as σ_r, which is the covariance of the spectrum at the receiver location. The average σ_s is estimated to be equal to 444 Hz, and the Q_P value is estimated to be 105. Because the estimated Q_P value is not precise, and the Q_S value is also needed, trial-and-error modeling is used to test the effects of different values of Q_P and Q_S values in the vicinity of the estimated value. The synthetic seismograms are computed to compare with the field data. Figure 22.11a and 22.11b show the synthetic common-shot gathers computed by the elastic and viscoelastic codes using the reconstructed P- and S-velocity tomograms in Figure 22.5a to 22.5d. The attenuation of the S-wave events can be observed in the viscoelastic seismograms by comparison with the elastic seismograms. It is found that $Q_P = 80$ and $Q_S = 50$ in the model give reasonable agreement between the synthetic and observed seismograms. These values are used for viscoelastic waveform inversion.

Appendix 22E: Viscoelastic FWI gradient

The 2D viscoelastic inversion procedure consists of the following steps similar to those presented by Wang (1995). Here, the Q values are assumed to be known and the residuals are modeled and back projected in a viscoelastic medium in which only the elastic parameters μ and λ are updated at each gridpoint.

1. The viscoelastic wave equation for the standard linear model is given by

$$\rho \frac{\partial u_x}{\partial t} = \frac{\partial \sigma_{xx}}{\partial x} + \frac{\partial \sigma_{xz}}{\partial z},$$

$$\rho \frac{\partial u_z}{\partial t} = \frac{\partial \sigma_{zx}}{\partial x} + \frac{\partial \sigma_{zz}}{\partial z},$$

$$\frac{\partial \sigma_{xx}}{\partial t} = \pi \frac{\tau_\epsilon^p}{\tau_\sigma} \left(\frac{\partial u_x}{\partial x} + \frac{\partial u_z}{\partial z} \right) - 2\mu \frac{\tau_\epsilon^s}{\tau_\sigma} \frac{\partial u_z}{\partial z} + r_{xx} + S_{xx},$$

$$\frac{\partial \sigma_{zz}}{\partial t} = \pi \frac{\tau_\epsilon^p}{\tau_\sigma} \left(\frac{\partial u_x}{\partial x} + \frac{\partial u_z}{\partial z} \right) - 2\mu \frac{\tau_\epsilon^s}{\tau_\sigma} \frac{\partial u_x}{\partial x} + r_{zz} + S_{zz},$$

$$\frac{\partial \sigma_{xz}}{\partial t} = \mu \frac{\tau_\epsilon^s}{\tau_\sigma} \left(\frac{\partial u_z}{\partial x} + \frac{\partial u_x}{\partial z} \right) + r_{xz},$$

$$\frac{\partial r_{xx}}{\partial t} = -\frac{1}{\tau_\sigma} \left(r_{xx} + \pi \left(\frac{\tau_\epsilon^p}{\tau_\sigma} - 1 \right) \left(\frac{\partial u_x}{\partial x} + \frac{\partial u_z}{\partial z} \right) \right.$$
$$\left. - 2\mu \left(\frac{\tau_\epsilon^s}{\tau_\sigma} - 1 \right) \frac{\partial u_z}{\partial z} \right),$$

$$\frac{\partial r_{zz}}{\partial t} = -\frac{1}{\tau_\sigma} \left(r_{zz} + \pi \left(\frac{\tau_\epsilon^p}{\tau_\sigma} - 1 \right) \left(\frac{\partial u_x}{\partial x} + \frac{\partial u_z}{\partial z} \right) \right.$$
$$\left. - 2\mu \left(\frac{\tau_\epsilon^s}{\tau_\sigma} - 1 \right) \frac{\partial u_x}{\partial x} \right),$$

and

$$\frac{\partial r_{xz}}{\partial t} = -\frac{1}{\tau_\sigma} \left(r_{xz} + \mu \left(\frac{\tau_\epsilon^s}{\tau_\sigma} - 1 \right) \left(\frac{\partial u_x}{\partial z} + \frac{\partial u_z}{\partial x} \right) \right).$$

$$(22.29)$$

It is solved for each shot point by a fourth-order, finite-difference algorithm (Robertsson et al., 1994). Here, the particle-velocity components are (u_x, u_z), S_{xx} and S_{zz} represent the source wavelets for the special case

of an explosive source, $\pi = \lambda + 2\mu$, r_{ij} is the memory variable, τ_ϵ^P and τ_ϵ^S are the strain-relaxation times for the P and S waves, and τ_σ is the stress-relaxation time.

2. Equation 22.29 can be recast (personal communication with Y. Wang and K. Bube, 2014) in the more compact matrix-vector notation

$$\overbrace{\left[A_t \frac{\partial}{\partial t} - A_x \frac{\partial}{\partial x} - A_z \frac{\partial}{\partial z} - B \right]}^{A} \begin{pmatrix} u \\ \Sigma \\ r \end{pmatrix} = f, \quad (22.30)$$

in which A is the viscoelastic forward-modeling operator and

$$u = \begin{pmatrix} u_x \\ u_z \end{pmatrix}; \quad \Sigma = \begin{pmatrix} \sigma_{xx} \\ \sigma_{zz} \\ \sigma_{xz} \end{pmatrix}; \quad r = \begin{pmatrix} r_{xx} \\ r_{zz} \\ r_{xz} \end{pmatrix}. \quad (22.31)$$

The source time-history term in equation 22.30 is denoted by the 8×1 vector f, and the coefficient matrices are defined as

$$A_t = \begin{bmatrix} \rho & 0 & 0 & 0 & 0 & 0 & 0 & 0 \\ 0 & \rho & 0 & 0 & 0 & 0 & 0 & 0 \\ 0 & 0 & 1 & 0 & 0 & 0 & 0 & 0 \\ 0 & 0 & 0 & 1 & 0 & 0 & 0 & 0 \\ 0 & 0 & 0 & 0 & 1 & 0 & 0 & 0 \\ 0 & 0 & 0 & 0 & 0 & 1 & 0 & 0 \\ 0 & 0 & 0 & 0 & 0 & 0 & 1 & 0 \\ 0 & 0 & 0 & 0 & 0 & 0 & 0 & 1 \end{bmatrix};$$

$$A_x = \begin{bmatrix} 0 & 0 & 1 & 0 & 0 & 0 & 0 & 0 \\ 0 & 0 & 0 & 0 & 1 & 0 & 0 & 0 \\ \pi C & 0 & 0 & 0 & 0 & 0 & 0 & 0 \\ \pi C - 2\mu D & 0 & 0 & 0 & 0 & 0 & 0 & 0 \\ 0 & \mu D & 0 & 0 & 0 & 0 & 0 & 0 \\ \pi F & 0 & 0 & 0 & 0 & 0 & 0 & 0 \\ \pi F - 2\mu H & 0 & 0 & 0 & 0 & 0 & 0 & 0 \\ 0 & \mu H & 0 & 0 & 0 & 0 & 0 & 0 \end{bmatrix};$$

$$A_z = \begin{bmatrix} 0 & 0 & 0 & 0 & 1 & 0 & 0 & 0 \\ 0 & 0 & 0 & 1 & 0 & 0 & 0 & 0 \\ 0 & \pi C - 2\mu D & 0 & 0 & 0 & 0 & 0 & 0 \\ 0 & \pi C & 0 & 0 & 0 & 0 & 0 & 0 \\ \mu D & 0 & 0 & 0 & 0 & 0 & 0 & 0 \\ 0 & \pi F - 2\mu H & 0 & 0 & 0 & 0 & 0 & 0 \\ 0 & \pi F & 0 & 0 & 0 & 0 & 0 & 0 \\ \mu H & 0 & 0 & 0 & 0 & 0 & 0 & 0 \end{bmatrix};$$

$$\mathbf{B} = \begin{bmatrix} 0 & 0 & 0 & 0 & 0 & 0 & 0 & 0 \\ 0 & 0 & 0 & 0 & 0 & 0 & 0 & 0 \\ 0 & 0 & 0 & 0 & 0 & 1 & 0 & 0 \\ 0 & 0 & 0 & 0 & 0 & 0 & 1 & 0 \\ 0 & 0 & 0 & 0 & 0 & 0 & 0 & 1 \\ 0 & 0 & 0 & 0 & 0 & E & 0 & 0 \\ 0 & 0 & 0 & 0 & 0 & 0 & E & 0 \\ 0 & 0 & 0 & 0 & 0 & 0 & 0 & E \end{bmatrix}, \quad (22.32)$$

in which

$$C = \frac{\tau_\epsilon^P}{\tau_\sigma}; \quad D = \frac{\tau_\epsilon^S}{\tau_\sigma}; \quad E = \frac{-1}{\tau_\sigma}; \quad F = E\left(\frac{\tau_\epsilon^P}{\tau_\sigma} - 1\right);$$

$$H = E\left(\frac{\tau_\epsilon^S}{\tau_\sigma} - 1\right). \quad (22.33)$$

3. The linearized, viscoelastic wave equation can be obtained by representing the model parameters μ and $\pi = \lambda + 2\mu$ as perturbations about the background values π_o and μ_o to give $\mu = \mu_o + \delta\mu$ and $\pi = \pi_o + \delta\pi$. Substituting these parameters into equation 22.30 and retaining only the linear perturbation terms gives

$$\overbrace{\left[\mathbf{A}_t\frac{\partial}{\partial t} - \mathbf{A}_x\frac{\partial}{\partial x} - \mathbf{A}_z\frac{\partial}{\partial z} - \mathbf{B}\right]}^{\mathbf{A}}\overbrace{\begin{pmatrix}\delta\mathbf{u}\\\delta\Sigma\\\delta\mathbf{r}\end{pmatrix}}^{\mathbf{w}} = \mathbf{W}\begin{pmatrix}\delta\pi\\\delta\mu\end{pmatrix} = \mathbf{f},$$

$$(22.34)$$

or in more compact form:

$$\mathbf{A}\mathbf{w} = \mathbf{f}. \quad (22.35)$$

The matrix coefficients in $\mathbf{A}$ are evaluated for the background medium, and $\mathbf{W}$ is defined as

$$\mathbf{W} = \begin{bmatrix} 0 & 0 \\ 0 & 0 \\ C\nabla\cdot\mathbf{u} & -2D\frac{\partial u_z}{\partial z} \\ C\nabla\cdot\mathbf{u} & -2D\frac{\partial u_x}{\partial x} \\ 0 & D\left(\frac{\partial u_z}{\partial x} + \frac{\partial u_x}{\partial z}\right) \\ F\nabla\cdot\mathbf{u} & -2H\frac{\partial u_z}{\partial z} \\ F\nabla\cdot\mathbf{u} & -2H\frac{\partial u_x}{\partial x} \\ 0 & H\left(\frac{\partial u_z}{\partial x} + \frac{\partial u_x}{\partial z}\right) \end{bmatrix}. \quad (22.36)$$

The perturbations to the background fields are denoted by $\delta\mathbf{u}$, $\delta\Sigma$, and $\delta\mathbf{r}$, and are small enough so that the primary scattering events provoked by them are much larger than their interactions from multiple scattering. The solution to equation 22.36 is the Born approximation and is used, similar to equation 16.6, to compute the data predicted data at the surface.

4. The adjoint viscoelastic equation now will be derived from the forward-modeling equation 22.30, where we assume that the governing equation is real so that the Hermitian adjoint operator is identical to the adjoint operator. From Box 10.2.1.2, the adjoint of $f(x)\frac{\partial}{\partial x}$ is $-\frac{\partial[f(x)]}{\partial x}$, so the adjoint of the viscoelastic equation in equation 22.34 is

$$\left[-\frac{\partial}{\partial t}\mathbf{A}_t^\dagger + \frac{\partial}{\partial x}\mathbf{A}_x^\dagger + \frac{\partial}{\partial z}\mathbf{A}_z^\dagger - \mathbf{B}^\dagger\right]\mathbf{v} = \Delta\mathbf{d}, \quad (22.37)$$

in which the 8×1 adjoint-state and data-residual vectors are $\mathbf{v}$ and $\mathbf{d}$, respectively. These source time-history components will be determined by the data residuals at the geophones.

5. Equation 16.15 is used to derive the viscoelastic gradient

$$\frac{\partial\epsilon(\mathbf{m})}{\partial m_i} = -\left(\frac{\partial\mathbf{A}(\mathbf{m})}{\partial m_i}\mathbf{w}(\mathbf{m}), \overbrace{\{\mathbf{A}(\mathbf{m})^{-1}\}^\dagger\Delta\mathbf{d}(\mathbf{m})}^{\mathbf{v}}\right),$$

$$(22.38)$$

in which $\mathbf{A}$ is the viscoelastic modeling operator in equation 22.34 and $\{\mathbf{A}(\mathbf{m})^{-1}\}^\dagger\Delta\mathbf{d}(\mathbf{m})$ is the solution to the viscoelastic adjoint equation 22.37. The Fréchet derivative associated with the $m_i \to \mu$ parameter, for example, is

$$\frac{\partial\mathbf{A}}{\partial\mu} = -\frac{\partial\mathbf{A}_x}{\partial\mu}\frac{\partial}{\partial x} - \frac{\partial\mathbf{A}_z}{\partial\mu}\frac{\partial}{\partial z}, \quad (22.39)$$

in which

$$\frac{\partial\mathbf{A}_x}{\partial\mu} = \begin{bmatrix} 0 & 0 & 0 & 0 & 0 & 0 & 0 & 0 \\ 0 & 0 & 0 & 0 & 0 & 0 & 0 & 0 \\ 2C & 0 & 0 & 0 & 0 & 0 & 0 & 0 \\ 2C-2D & 0 & 0 & 0 & 0 & 0 & 0 & 0 \\ 0 & D & 0 & 0 & 0 & 0 & 0 & 0 \\ 2F & 0 & 0 & 0 & 0 & 0 & 0 & 0 \\ 2F-2H & 0 & 0 & 0 & 0 & 0 & 0 & 0 \\ 0 & H & 0 & 0 & 0 & 0 & 0 & 0 \end{bmatrix};$$

$$\frac{\partial\mathbf{A}_z}{\partial\mu} = \begin{bmatrix} 0 & 0 & 0 & 0 & 0 & 0 & 0 & 0 \\ 0 & 0 & 0 & 0 & 0 & 0 & 0 & 0 \\ 0 & 2C-2D & 0 & 0 & 0 & 0 & 0 & 0 \\ 0 & 2C & 0 & 0 & 0 & 0 & 0 & 0 \\ D & 0 & 0 & 0 & 0 & 0 & 0 & 0 \\ 0 & 2F-2H & 0 & 0 & 0 & 0 & 0 & 0 \\ 0 & 2F & 0 & 0 & 0 & 0 & 0 & 0 \\ H & 0 & 0 & 0 & 0 & 0 & 0 & 0 \end{bmatrix}.$$

$$(22.40)$$

6. The viscoelastic gradient in equation 22.38 is used to update the solution iteratively using a gradient optimization method.

Appendix 22F: Elastic FWI gradient

The misfit gradient associated with the elastic wave equation for a 2D isotropic medium is derived next.

1. The viscoelastic equation in equation 22.29 reduces to the isotropic wave equation by setting $\frac{\tau_\epsilon^p}{\tau_\sigma} = \frac{\tau_\epsilon^s}{\tau_\sigma} = 1$ and $r_{ij} = 0$. In this case, equation 22.30 becomes

$$\overbrace{\left[\tilde{\mathbf{A}}_t \frac{\partial}{\partial t} - \tilde{\mathbf{A}}_x \frac{\partial}{\partial x} - \tilde{\mathbf{A}}_z \frac{\partial}{\partial z} \right]}^{\tilde{\mathbf{A}}} \overbrace{\begin{pmatrix} \mathbf{u} \\ \Sigma \end{pmatrix}}^{\mathbf{w}} = \mathbf{f}, \qquad (22.41)$$

where $\tilde{\mathbf{A}}$ is the elastic forward-modeling operator, $\mathbf{w} = (u_x, u_z, \sigma_{xx}, \sigma_{zz}, \sigma_{xz})^T$, and the coefficient matrices are

$$\tilde{\mathbf{A}}_t = \begin{bmatrix} \rho & 0 & 0 & 0 & 0 \\ 0 & \rho & 0 & 0 & 0 \\ 0 & 0 & 1 & 0 & 0 \\ 0 & 0 & 0 & 1 & 0 \\ 0 & 0 & 0 & 0 & 1 \end{bmatrix};$$

$$\tilde{\mathbf{A}}_x = \begin{bmatrix} 0 & 0 & 1 & 0 & 0 \\ 0 & 0 & 0 & 0 & 1 \\ \pi & 0 & 0 & 0 & 0 \\ \lambda & 0 & 0 & 0 & 0 \\ 0 & \mu & 0 & 0 & 0 \end{bmatrix};$$

$$\tilde{\mathbf{A}}_z = \begin{bmatrix} 0 & 0 & 0 & 0 & 1 \\ 0 & 0 & 0 & 1 & 0 \\ 0 & \lambda & 0 & 0 & 0 \\ 0 & \pi & 0 & 0 & 0 \\ \mu & 0 & 0 & 0 & 0 \end{bmatrix}. \qquad (22.42)$$

Substituting the above coefficient matrices into the square brackets of equation 22.41 gives the explicit form for **A**:

$$\tilde{\mathbf{A}} = \begin{bmatrix} \rho\frac{\partial}{\partial t} & 0 & -\frac{\partial}{\partial x} & 0 & -\frac{\partial}{\partial z} \\ 0 & \rho\frac{\partial}{\partial t} & 0 & -\frac{\partial}{\partial z} & -\frac{\partial}{\partial x} \\ -\pi\frac{\partial}{\partial x} & -\lambda\frac{\partial}{\partial z} & \frac{\partial}{\partial t} & 0 & 0 \\ -\lambda\frac{\partial}{\partial x} & -\pi\frac{\partial}{\partial z} & 0 & \frac{\partial}{\partial t} & 0 \\ -\mu\frac{\partial}{\partial z} & -\mu\frac{\partial}{\partial x} & 0 & 0 & \frac{\partial}{\partial t} \end{bmatrix}. \qquad (22.43)$$

2. Substituting the parameters $\mu = \mu_o + \delta\mu$ and $\pi = \pi_o + \delta\pi$ into equation 22.41 and retaining only the linear perturbation terms yields

$$\left[\tilde{\mathbf{A}}_t \frac{\partial}{\partial t} - \tilde{\mathbf{A}}_x \frac{\partial}{\partial x} - \tilde{\mathbf{A}}_z \frac{\partial}{\partial z} \right] \begin{pmatrix} \delta\mathbf{u} \\ \delta\Sigma \end{pmatrix} = \tilde{\mathbf{W}} \overbrace{\begin{pmatrix} \delta\pi \\ \delta\mu \end{pmatrix}}^{\Delta\mathbf{m}}, \qquad (22.44)$$

in which

$$\Delta\mathbf{m} = (\delta\pi, \delta\mu)^T; \quad \tilde{\mathbf{W}} = \begin{bmatrix} 0 & 0 \\ 0 & 0 \\ \nabla\cdot\mathbf{u} & -2\frac{\partial u_z}{\partial z} \\ \nabla\cdot\mathbf{u} & -2\frac{\partial u_x}{\partial x} \\ 0 & \left(\frac{\partial u_z}{\partial x} + \frac{\partial u_x}{\partial z}\right) \end{bmatrix}. \qquad (22.45)$$

The solution to these equations are the fields associated with sources located at the model perturbations; and the source time history at each perturbation is the weighted source field incident at that point. As in the viscoelastic and viscoacoustic cases, this solution is the predicted field that is used to get the data residuals at the surface.

3. The adjoint of the elastic wave equation 22.41 is

$$\overbrace{\left[-\frac{\partial}{\partial t}\tilde{\mathbf{A}}_t^\dagger + \frac{\partial}{\partial x}\tilde{\mathbf{A}}_x^\dagger + \frac{\partial}{\partial z}\tilde{\mathbf{A}}_z^\dagger \right]}^{\tilde{\mathbf{A}}^\dagger} \mathbf{v} = \Delta\mathbf{d}, \qquad (22.46)$$

in which $\mathbf{v}$ is the 5×1 adjoint-state vector, the coefficient matrices are the transposes of the matrices in equation 22.42, and the components of the source time-history are determined by the data residuals $\Delta\mathbf{d}$ at the geophones. The equations are solved to give the back-propagated fields $\mathbf{v}$ in the subsurface.

4. Finally, the elastic gradient is found by replacing **A** by $\tilde{\mathbf{A}}$ in equation 22.38 and using the solution $\mathbf{v}$ in equation 22.46. In this case, the perturbations of $\tilde{\mathbf{A}}$ with respect to μ, λ, and ρ produce

$$\frac{\partial\tilde{\mathbf{A}}}{\partial\mu} = \begin{bmatrix} 0 & 0 & 0 & 0 & 0 \\ 0 & 0 & 0 & 0 & 0 \\ -2\frac{\partial}{\partial x} & 0 & 0 & 0 & 0 \\ 0 & -2\frac{\partial}{\partial z} & 0 & 0 & 0 \\ -\frac{\partial}{\partial z} & -\frac{\partial}{\partial x} & 0 & 0 & 0 \end{bmatrix};$$

$$\frac{\partial \tilde{\mathbf{A}}}{\partial \lambda} = \begin{bmatrix} 0 & 0 & 0 & 0 & 0 \\ 0 & 0 & 0 & 0 & 0 \\ -\frac{\partial}{\partial x} & -\frac{\partial}{\partial z} & 0 & 0 & 0 \\ -\frac{\partial}{\partial x} & -\frac{\partial}{\partial z} & 0 & 0 & 0 \\ 0 & 0 & 0 & 0 & 0 \end{bmatrix},$$

and

$$\frac{\partial \tilde{\mathbf{A}}}{\partial \rho} = \begin{bmatrix} \frac{\partial}{\partial t} & 0 & 0 & 0 & 0 \\ 0 & \frac{\partial}{\partial t} & 0 & 0 & 0 \\ 0 & 0 & 0 & 0 & 0 \\ 0 & 0 & 0 & 0 & 0 \\ 0 & 0 & 0 & 0 & 0 \end{bmatrix}. \qquad (22.47)$$

For example, the gradients with respect to λ, μ, and ρ are obtained by substituting the coefficient matrices in equation 22.47 into equation 22.38 to give

$$\frac{\partial \epsilon(\mathbf{m})}{\partial \lambda} = -\left(\frac{\partial \tilde{\mathbf{A}}(\mathbf{m})}{\partial \lambda} \mathbf{w}(\mathbf{m}), \overbrace{\{\tilde{\mathbf{A}}(\mathbf{m})^{-1}\}^{\dagger} \Delta \mathbf{d}(\mathbf{m})}^{\mathbf{v}} \right),$$

$$= \left(\begin{pmatrix} 0 \\ 0 \\ \nabla \cdot \mathbf{u} \\ \nabla \cdot \mathbf{u} \\ 0 \end{pmatrix}, \begin{pmatrix} v_1 \\ v_2 \\ v_3 \\ v_4 \\ v_5 \end{pmatrix} \right)$$

$$= \int_0^T \overbrace{\left(\frac{\partial u_x}{\partial x} + \frac{\partial u_z}{\partial z} \right)}^{\text{source field}} \overbrace{(v_3 + v_4)}^{\substack{\text{back-propagated} \\ \text{residual}}} dt,$$

$$\frac{\partial \epsilon(\mathbf{m})}{\partial \mu} = \left(\begin{pmatrix} 0 \\ 0 \\ 2\frac{\partial u_x}{\partial x} \\ 2\frac{\partial u_z}{\partial z} \\ \frac{\partial u_x}{\partial z} + \frac{\partial u_z}{\partial x} \end{pmatrix}, \begin{pmatrix} v_1 \\ v_2 \\ v_3 \\ v_4 \\ v_5 \end{pmatrix} \right)$$

$$= 2 \int_0^T \left(v_3 \frac{\partial u_x}{\partial x} + v_4 \frac{\partial u_z}{\partial z} + \frac{1}{2} v_5 \left\{ \frac{\partial u_x}{\partial z} + \frac{\partial u_z}{\partial x} \right\} \right) dt,$$

$$\frac{\partial \epsilon(\mathbf{m})}{\partial \rho} = -\left(\begin{pmatrix} \frac{\partial u_x}{\partial t} \\ \frac{\partial u_z}{\partial t} \\ 0 \\ 0 \\ 0 \end{pmatrix}, \begin{pmatrix} v_1 \\ v_2 \\ v_3 \\ v_4 \\ v_5 \end{pmatrix} \right)$$

$$= -\int_0^T \left(v_1 \frac{\partial u_x}{\partial t} + v_2 \frac{\partial u_z}{\partial t} \right) dt. \qquad (22.48)$$

The second-order elastic wave equation is self-adjoint (see Exercise 5), so back propagating the residuals by a time-reversed solution of the original second-order wave equation is equivalent to solving the adjoint second-order wave equation.

Chapter 23: Vertical Transverse Isotropy FWI

A finely layered isotropic medium with horizontal interfaces is characterized by propagation velocities that depend on the angle of incidence. Waves that only propagate horizontally have the same propagation velocity regardless of azimuthal angle, but if they have a vertical component, then their speed depends on the polar angle of propagation. This type of medium is known as a vertical transverse isotropic (VTI) medium; another type of VTI medium is one in which the anisotropy is intrinsic to the minerals (Thomsen, 1986). The VTI propagation velocities are a function of the rock strength that varies with respect to strain direction.

The equations for inverting VTI parameters in a pseudo-acoustic medium are derived below. In principle, instead of inverting for the acoustic velocity model, VTI full-waveform inversion (FWI) strives to invert for three parameters if density is known. An example is to invert seismic data for the vertical P-wave velocity $V_P(\mathbf{x})$ and the Thomsen parameters $\epsilon(\mathbf{x})$ and $\delta(\mathbf{x})$. Here, the vertical P-wave velocity $V_P(\mathbf{x})$ in a VTI medium is equal to

$$V_P(\mathbf{x}) = c(\mathbf{x})(1 + \delta(\mathbf{x}) \sin^2 \theta \cos^2 \theta + \epsilon(\mathbf{x}) \sin^4 \theta)|_{\theta=0}$$
$$= c(\mathbf{x}), \qquad (23.1)$$

in which $c(\mathbf{x})$ is the isotropic P-wave velocity and θ is the angle of incidence measured with respect to the vertical axis of symmetry (Thomsen, 2013). For horizontally propagating waves we get

$$V_H(\mathbf{x}) = c(\mathbf{x})(1 + \delta(\mathbf{x}) \sin^2 \theta \cos^2 \theta + \epsilon(\mathbf{x}) \sin^4 \theta)|_{\theta=90°}$$
$$= c(\mathbf{x})(1 + \epsilon), \qquad (23.2)$$

where V_H is the horizontal-propagation velocity.

Gholami et al. (2013) show that the wave-speed parameter V_P has a dominant influence on the data, and it strongly influences the kinematics of arrivals over the full range of scattering angles. The two other Thomsen parameters δ and ϵ have a weaker influence on the data over a narrow range of scattering angles. They suggest that a reliable inversion strategy might be to keep the Thomsen parameters δ and ϵ fixed during FWI and only update the dominant parameter V_P, assuming a sufficiently accurate starting model for the

Thomsen parameters. For this reason, a two-step approach sometimes is used for VTI inversion of surface data (Wang et al., 2013): invert for $V_P(\mathbf{x})$ initially using a rough estimate of $\epsilon(\mathbf{x})$ and $\delta(\mathbf{x})$, and then simultaneously invert for $\epsilon(\mathbf{x})$ and $\delta(\mathbf{x})$ by a conventional approach. For surface seismic data, Cheng et al. (2014) note that δ cannot be recovered uniquely so they recommend only inverting for V_P and ϵ.

23.1 Theory

The first-order equations of motion for VTI waves propagating in a pseudoacoustic medium (Duveneck et al., 2008) are given as

$$\frac{\partial v_x}{\partial t} = \frac{1}{\rho} \frac{\partial \sigma_{xx}}{\partial x},$$

$$\frac{\partial v_z}{\partial t} = \frac{1}{\rho} \frac{\partial \sigma_{zz}}{\partial z},$$

$$\frac{\partial \sigma_{xx}}{\partial t} = \rho V_P^2 \left[(1 + 2\epsilon) \frac{\partial v_x}{\partial x} + \sqrt{1 + 2\delta} \frac{\partial v_z}{\partial z} \right] + f_{\sigma_{xx}}, \quad (23.3)$$

and

$$\frac{\partial \sigma_{zz}}{\partial t} = \rho V_P^2 \left[\sqrt{1 + 2\delta} \frac{\partial v_x}{\partial x} + \frac{\partial v_z}{\partial z} \right] + f_{\sigma_{zz}}.$$

Here, v_x and v_z respectively denote the horizontal- and vertical-particle velocity wavefields, σ_{xx} and σ_{zz} define the normal stresses, and ρ is the density of the medium. The Thomsen parameters are defined as ϵ and δ, which describe VTI anisotropy, and V_P represents the vertical P-wave velocity. The imposed source functions are defined as $f_{\sigma_{xx}}$ and $f_{\sigma_{zz}}$.

The above equations can be written in a more compact form as

$$\mathbf{Aw} = \mathbf{f},$$

$$\mathbf{A} = \begin{bmatrix} \frac{\partial}{\partial t} & 0 & \frac{-1}{\rho} \frac{\partial}{\partial x} & 0 \\ 0 & \frac{\partial}{\partial t} & 0 & \frac{-1}{\rho} \frac{\partial}{\partial z} \\ -(1+2\epsilon)\rho V_P^2 \frac{\partial}{\partial x} & -\rho V_P^2 \sqrt{1+2\delta} \frac{\partial}{\partial z} & \frac{\partial}{\partial t} & 0 \\ -\sqrt{1+2\delta}\rho V_P^2 \frac{\partial}{\partial x} & -\rho V_P^2 \frac{\partial}{\partial z} & 0 & \frac{\partial}{\partial t} \end{bmatrix},$$

$$(23.4)$$

in which

$$\mathbf{w} = \begin{bmatrix} v_x & v_z & \sigma_{xx} & \sigma_{zz} \end{bmatrix}^T, \quad \mathbf{f} = \begin{bmatrix} 0 & 0 & f_{\sigma_{xx}} & f_{\sigma_{zz}} \end{bmatrix}^T.$$

Waveform inversion inverts the model parameters $\mathbf{m} = (V_P, \epsilon, \rho, \delta)$ so that the difference between the predicted data $\mathbf{w}(\mathbf{m})$ and the observed data $\mathbf{d}$ is minimized in the sense of the $L2$ norm:

$$J(\mathbf{m}) = \frac{1}{2} \|\mathbf{w}(\mathbf{m}) - \mathbf{d}\|^2 = \frac{1}{2} \{\mathbf{w}(\mathbf{m}) - \mathbf{d}, \mathbf{w}(\mathbf{m}) - \mathbf{d}\}, \tag{23.5}$$

in which $J(\mathbf{m})$ is the misfit function for the model $\mathbf{m}$.

The model parameters are inverted by a gradient-based method, where the misfit gradient $\frac{\partial J(\mathbf{m})}{\partial m_i}$ is

$$\frac{\partial J(\mathbf{m})}{\partial m_i} = \left\{ \frac{\partial \mathbf{w}(\mathbf{m})}{\partial m_i}, \mathbf{w}(\mathbf{m}) - \mathbf{d} \right\}. \tag{23.6}$$

From equation 16.15, we know that $\mathbf{q} = (\mathbf{A}^{-1})^\dagger (\mathbf{w}(\mathbf{m}) - \mathbf{d})$ is the back-propagated wavefield, which is the solution to

$$\mathbf{A}^\dagger \mathbf{q} = \Delta \mathbf{d}, \tag{23.7}$$

and it is the adjoint equation of equation 23.4. Because $\mathbf{A}$ represents the differential operator in equation 23.4, $\mathbf{A}^\dagger$ can be written as

$$\mathbf{A}^\dagger = \begin{bmatrix} -\frac{\partial}{\partial t} & 0 & \frac{\partial}{\partial x}\left[\rho V_P^2(1+2\epsilon)\right] & \frac{\partial}{\partial x}\left(\sqrt{1+2\delta}\,\rho V_P^2\right) \\ 0 & -\frac{\partial}{\partial t} & \frac{\partial}{\partial z}\left(\rho V_P^2 \sqrt{1+2\delta}\right) & \frac{\partial}{\partial z}(\rho V_P^2) \\ \frac{\partial}{\partial x}\left(\frac{1}{\rho}\right) & 0 & -\frac{\partial}{\partial t} & 0 \\ 0 & \frac{\partial}{\partial z}\left(\frac{1}{\rho}\right) & 0 & -\frac{\partial}{\partial t} \end{bmatrix},$$

$$\mathbf{q} = \begin{bmatrix} \hat{v}_x & \hat{v}_z & \hat{\sigma}_{xx} & \hat{\sigma}_{zz} \end{bmatrix}^T,$$

$$\Delta \mathbf{d} = \begin{bmatrix} \Delta d_{v_x} & \Delta d_{v_z} & \Delta d_{\sigma_{xx}} & \Delta d_{\sigma_{zz}} \end{bmatrix}^T.$$

Equation (23.7) can be expanded as

$$-\frac{\partial \hat{v}_x}{\partial t} + \frac{\partial}{\partial x}(\rho V_P^2(1+2\epsilon)\hat{\sigma}_{xx})$$

$$+ \frac{\partial}{\partial x}(\sqrt{1+2\delta}\,\rho V_P^2\,\hat{\sigma}_{zz}) = \Delta d_{v_x},$$

$$-\frac{\partial \hat{v}_z}{\partial t} + \frac{\partial}{\partial z}(\rho V_P^2 \sqrt{1+2\delta}\,\hat{\sigma}_{xx}) + \frac{\partial}{\partial z}(\rho V_P^2\,\hat{\sigma}_{zz}) = \Delta d_{v_z},$$

$$\frac{\partial}{\partial x}\left(\frac{1}{\rho}\hat{v}_x\right) - \frac{\partial}{\partial t}\hat{\sigma}_{xx} = \Delta d_{\sigma_{xx}},$$

$$\frac{\partial}{\partial z}\left(\frac{1}{\rho}\hat{v}_z\right) - \frac{\partial}{\partial t}\hat{\sigma}_{zz} = \Delta d_{\sigma_{zz}}. \tag{23.8}$$

Equation (23.8) is the adjoint equation of equation (23.3).

Similar to equations 16.16 and 16.17, the misfit gradients for the VTI parameters can be calculated as

$$\frac{\partial J}{\partial V_P} = \left\{ \begin{bmatrix} 0 & 0 & 0 & 0 \\ 0 & 0 & 0 & 0 \\ -2(1+2\epsilon)\rho V_P\frac{\partial}{\partial x} & -2\rho V_P\sqrt{1+2\delta}\frac{\partial}{\partial z} & 0 & 0 \\ -2\rho V_P\sqrt{1+2\delta}\frac{\partial}{\partial x} & -2\rho V_P\frac{\partial}{\partial z} & 0 & 0 \end{bmatrix} \begin{bmatrix} v_x \\ v_z \\ \sigma_{xx} \\ \sigma_{zz} \end{bmatrix}, \begin{bmatrix} \hat{v}_x \\ \hat{v}_z \\ \hat{\sigma}_{xx} \\ \hat{\sigma}_{zz} \end{bmatrix} \right\},$$

$$\frac{\partial J}{\partial \epsilon} = \left\{ \begin{bmatrix} 0 & 0 & 0 & 0 \\ 0 & 0 & 0 & 0 \\ -2\rho V_P^2\frac{\partial}{\partial x} & 0 & 0 & 0 \\ 0 & 0 & 0 & 0 \end{bmatrix} \begin{bmatrix} v_x \\ v_z \\ \sigma_{xx} \\ \sigma_{zz} \end{bmatrix}, \begin{bmatrix} \hat{v}_x \\ \hat{v}_z \\ \hat{\sigma}_{xx} \\ \hat{\sigma}_{zz} \end{bmatrix} \right\},$$

$$\frac{\partial J}{\partial \delta} = \left\{ \begin{bmatrix} 0 & 0 & 0 & 0 \\ 0 & 0 & 0 & 0 \\ 0 & \frac{-\rho V_P^2}{\sqrt{1+2\delta}}\frac{\partial}{\partial z} & 0 & 0 \\ -\frac{\rho V_P^2}{\sqrt{1+2\delta}}\frac{\partial}{\partial x} & 0 & 0 & 0 \end{bmatrix} \begin{bmatrix} v_x \\ v_z \\ \sigma_{xx} \\ \sigma_{zz} \end{bmatrix}, \begin{bmatrix} \hat{v}_x \\ \hat{v}_z \\ \hat{\sigma}_{xx} \\ \hat{\sigma}_{zz} \end{bmatrix} \right\},$$

and

$$\frac{\partial J}{\partial \rho} = \left\{ \begin{bmatrix} 0 & 0 & \frac{1}{\rho^2}\frac{\partial}{\partial x} & 0 \\ 0 & 0 & 0 & \frac{1}{\rho^2}\frac{\partial}{\partial z} \\ -(1+2\epsilon)V_P^2\frac{\partial}{\partial x} & -V_P^2\sqrt{1+2\delta}\frac{\partial}{\partial z} & 0 & 0 \\ -V_P^2\sqrt{1+2\delta}\frac{\partial}{\partial x} & -V_P^2\frac{\partial}{\partial z} & 0 & 0 \end{bmatrix} \begin{bmatrix} v_x \\ v_z \\ \sigma_{xx} \\ \sigma_{zz} \end{bmatrix}, \begin{bmatrix} \hat{v}_x \\ \hat{v}_z \\ \hat{\sigma}_{xx} \\ \hat{\sigma}_{zz} \end{bmatrix} \right\}, \tag{23.9}$$

Equation (23.9) can be simplified to be

$$\gamma_{V_P} = \frac{\partial J}{\partial V_P} = -2\int_0^T \left[\left((1+2\epsilon)\rho V_P\frac{\partial v_x}{\partial x}\right.\right.$$

$$+ \rho V_P\sqrt{1+2\delta}\frac{\partial v_z}{\partial z}\right)\hat{\sigma}_{xx}$$

$$+ \left(\sqrt{1+2\delta}\rho V_P\frac{\partial v_x}{\partial x} + \rho V_P\frac{\partial v_z}{\partial z}\right)\hat{\sigma}_{zz}\right]dt,$$

$$\gamma_\epsilon = \frac{\partial J}{\partial \epsilon} = -2 \int_0^T \rho V_P^2 \frac{\partial v_x}{\partial x} \hat{\sigma}_{xx} dt,$$

$$\gamma_\delta = \frac{\partial J}{\partial \delta} = -\int_0^T \left[\frac{\rho V_P^2}{\sqrt{1+2\delta}} \frac{\partial v_z}{\partial z} \hat{\sigma}_{xx} + \frac{\rho V_P^2}{\sqrt{1+2\delta}} \frac{\partial v_x}{\partial x} \hat{\sigma}_{zz} \right] dt,$$

$$\gamma_\rho = \frac{\partial J}{\partial \rho} = \int_0^T \left[\frac{1}{\rho^2} \frac{\partial \sigma_{xx}}{\partial x} \hat{v}_x + \frac{1}{\rho^2} \frac{\partial \sigma_{zz}}{\partial z} \hat{v}_z \right.$$
$$- \left((1+2\epsilon) V_P^2 \frac{\partial v_x}{\partial x} + V_P^2 \sqrt{1+2\delta} \frac{\partial v_z}{\partial z} \right) \hat{\sigma}_{xx}$$
$$\left. - \left(\sqrt{1+2\delta} \, V_P^2 \frac{\partial v_x}{\partial x} + V_P^2 \frac{\partial v_z}{\partial z} \right) \hat{\sigma}_{zz} \right] dt.$$

(23.10)

Equation 23.10 can be used in a gradient optimization scheme to invert for the VTI model parameters.

23.2 Numerical results

The goal of the synthetic tests is to determine empirically the sensitivity of the VTI FWI tomograms to the illumination coverage associated with VSP and surface seismic experiments. For convenience, the density model is assumed to be constant. The last example applies VTI FWI to a 3D marine data set recorded in the Gulf of Mexico (Wang et al., 2014).

23.2.1 Synthetic VSP data

Figure 23.1 shows the V_P, ϵ, and δ models from the BP 2007 anisotropic model in which the tilt angles of the interfaces are ignored. The starting model for VTI FWI is shown in Figure 23.2 and created by smoothing the Figure 23.1 models with a 2D triangle smoothing filter with the height and width of 1500 m and 3000 m, respectively. There are 601 surface shots with a horizontal shot spacing of 50 m at the depth of 10 m. Receivers are all located in boreholes, and a finite-difference solution to the pseudoacoustic VTI wave equation is used to generate the data. The inversion strategy here is to invert for all three parameters $c_p(\mathbf{x})$, $\delta(\mathbf{x})$, and $\epsilon(\mathbf{x})$ because the wide angular coverage of the multi-well VSP data allows for robust estimation of $\epsilon(\mathbf{x})$, and the near-vertically incident direct waves and reflections at depth allow for reliable estimation of $\delta(\mathbf{x})$ and $V_P(\mathbf{x})$.

In the first test, 51 downhole receivers are located in a single VSP well located at $x = 70$ km, and the depths of receivers range from 4 km to 9 km with a receiver interval

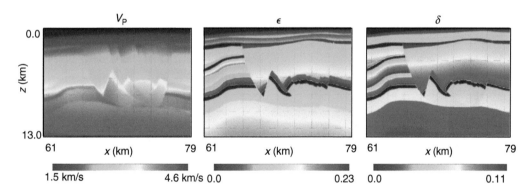

Figure 23.1. Model parameter distributions for V_P, ϵ, and δ. Images courtesy of Ge Zhan.

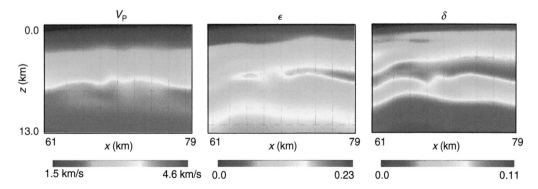

Figure 23.2. Starting models for VTI FWI obtained by smoothing the Figure 23.1 models. Tomograms courtesy of Ge Zhan.

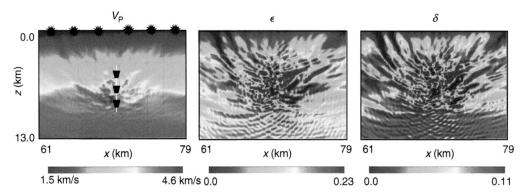

Figure 23.3. The VTI FWI tomograms after inverting the VSP data recorded at the well depicted by the vertical white line with geophone symbols. Tomograms courtesy of Ge Zhan.

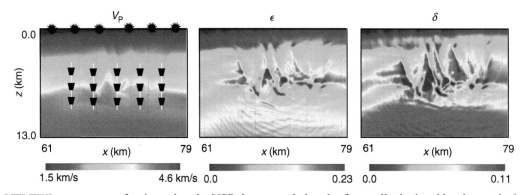

Figure 23.4. VTI FWI tomograms after inverting the VSP data recorded at the five wells depicted by the vertical white lines with the geophone symbols. Tomograms courtesy of Ge Zhan.

of 100 m. By reciprocity, the physical receivers are transformed into virtual sources, and the physical sources are transformed into virtual receivers to give 51 virtual shot gathers, each with 601 virtual traces near the free surface. Three frequencies $f = [3.4, 4.3, 5.5]$ Hz are used for inverting the data, and 30 iterations are used for each frequency. In this example, V_P, V_H, and V_{NMO} are inverted simultaneously (see Exercises 1 and 2), and then the resulting tomograms are converted to the Thomsen parameters.[1] The resulting V_P tomogram in Figure 23.3a is much more accurate than the tomograms in Figure 23.3b and 23.3c because the data are weakly sensitive to variations in δ and ϵ over the limited range of scattering angles (Gholami et al., 2014).

The second test is for multi-well inversion, where two more wells (spaced at horizontal offsets of 2 km) are added to each side of the center well so there is a much wider range of scattering angles than in the single-well test. A total of 255 virtual shot gathers are used as input into the VTI FWI code, and the inverted tomograms are shown in Figure 23.4.

The results show that the wider range of scattering angles give much more accurate δ and ϵ tomograms compared to those in Figure 23.3 for the single-well inversion.

23.2.2   3D Gulf of Mexico data

Three-dimensional OBS data recorded from the Gulf of Mexico are inverted for the VTI parameters[2] by a VTI FWI method (Wang et al., 2014). There are a total of 19,901 shot gathers, the lowest frequency is 3 Hz, and the maximum source-receiver offset is 7 km. The source signature is estimated from the downgoing wavefield on a zero-offset section. An irregular sampling of shots using just 25% of the available shots produced results comparable to inverting all the shot gathers. This is consistent with the results of Boonyasiriwat and Schuster (2010), who invert 3D data with quasi-random shot sampling. They also are partly consistent with the results of Warner et al. (2013b), who use a subset of the original 3D data for FWI.

---

[1]Zhan's empirical tests (Ge Zhan, personal communication, 2014) suggest that the data are more strongly sensitive to changes in V_P, V_H, and V_{NMO} than to changes in the Thomsen parameters. Inverting for V_P, V_H, and V_{NMO} is related to the Type 2 parameterization discussed by Gholami et al. (2013).

[2]In contrast to crosswell data, perturbations in δ do not affect the surface data very much compared to perturbations in ϵ or V_P (Cheng et al., 2014). Hence, we expect poor reliability of the δ tomogram inverted from surface data.

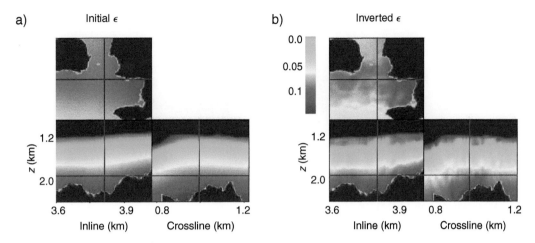

Figure 23.5. (a) Initial and (b) inverted ϵ tomograms estimated from 25% of the 3D OBS data. After Wang et al. (2014).

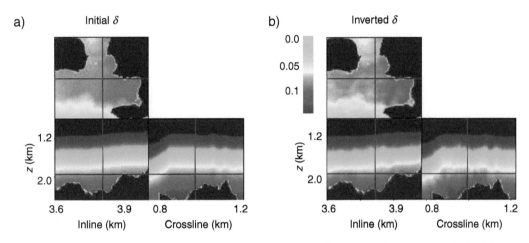

Figure 23.6. Same as Figure 23.5, except the tomograms are for the δ distributions. After Wang et al. (2014).

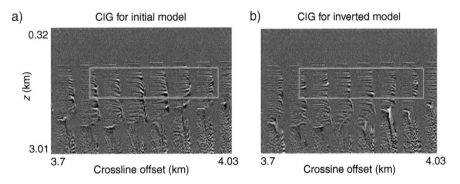

Figure 23.7. Common image gathers (CIGs) using the (a) initial and (b) inverted models. After Wang et al. (2014).

The following two-step procedure is used: 1) the ϵ and δ models are estimated approximately, and then the $V_P(x,y,z)$ model is computed by FWI. 2) Freezing the $V_P(x,y,z)$ model, the $\delta(x,y,z)$ and $\epsilon(x,y,z)$ models are inverted. The workflow consisted of mono-parameter inversion of V_P for 33 iterations, using offset restrictions and layer stripping to avoid cycle skipping, which is then followed by seven iteration of simultaneous inversion ϵ and δ.

Figures 23.5 and 23.6 show the ϵ and δ initial models and the final ϵ and δ tomograms.

To validate the accuracy of the final tomograms, the data are migrated to produce the common-image gathers in Figure 23.7. The artifacts with a hockey stick moveout pattern in the green box of Figure 23.7a are largely eliminated in the CIGs (see Figure 23.7b) migrated with the final VTI model. The flattening of the CIGs indicates that

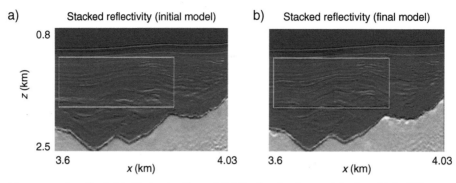

Figure 23.8. Stacked images using the (a) initial-velocity and (b) final-velocity models, in which different colors correspond to different velocities. After Wang et al. (2014).

the final tomograms in Figure 23.6 provide a more accurate VTI model than the initial model. This also is confirmed in Figure 23.8b, which shows stronger reflectivity focusing than seen in the stacked image in Figure 23.8a obtained from the initial-velocity model.

23.3 Extension to TTI media

The VTI modeling and inversion ignore the layer dips and the attendant change in orientation of the Thomsen parameters. For example, if the fine layering of shale deposits conforms to the interface dip, then the vertical propagation velocity V_P will be tilted to be perpendicular to the tilted interfaces. This also means that the δ and ϵ distributions will be for layering tilted at the same angle. Taking this tilted anisotropy into account leads to tilted transverse isotropic (TTI) migration algorithms. Because the migration operation is equivalent to the gradient of the misfit function, then TTI migration can be used for TTI FWI. Warner et al. (2013b) provide a detailed workflow for inverting V_P, assuming that δ and ϵ are estimated by a conventional method, and Vigh et al. (2014b) present a TTI FWI scheme in which V_P and ϵ are inverted in hierarchical stages.

The TTI FWI scheme of Vigh et al. (2014b) is guided by sensitivity tests with surface data (Cheng et al., 2014), in which perturbations in V_P and ϵ change the kinematics of the diving waves significantly more than perturbations in δ (see Figure 23.9). Also, the near-offset reflections are most sensitive to perturbations in the V_P velocity, and not so sensitive to perturbations in δ or ϵ. Thus, the near-offset data should initially be used to only invert for V_P. Cheng et al. (2014) also suggest that, because of the intrinsic ambiguity between δ and depth, only V_P and ϵ should be inverted from surface seismic data which contain both diving waves and reflections. They conclude that "one should only start to invert for ϵ when $V_{P0}[V_P]$ fields are already good enough." (Cheng et al., 2014, 1074).

Therefore, a hierarchical TTI FWI strategy similar to that of Vigh et al. (2014b) is the following.

1. Migrate the data using an initial model for V_P to get an estimate of the layer's tilt angles. The migration method can be isotropic migration if the anisotropy is not too severe. The initial model for $V_P(\mathbf{x})$ can be obtained from refraction inversion, well logs, and/or reflection traveltime tomography. Estimate an initial model for $\delta(\mathbf{x})$ and $\epsilon(\mathbf{x})$ from a combination of well logs, NMO velocity analysis, and reflection tomography.

2. Use FWI to invert for $V_P(\mathbf{x})$ by using a fixed initial estimate of dip angles, $\delta(\mathbf{x})$, and $\epsilon(\mathbf{x})$. TTI modeling is accomplished by solving the TTI wave equation (Zhan et al., 2012).

3. Simultaneously invert for $V_P(\mathbf{x})$ and $\epsilon(\mathbf{x})$, keeping $\delta(\mathbf{x})$ fixed. Other types of parameters can be inverted, such as V_P, V_H, and V_{NMO} (Gholami et al., 2013). Migrate the data again using the updated TTI parameters to get the new tilt angles of interfaces.

4. Repeat above steps until acceptable convergence.

Inverting for orthorhombic or higher-order anisotropy parameters will be even more challenging because a greater number of unknowns per pixel needs to be inverted. There is no doubt that a multistage inversion strategy will be needed to invert initially for the most influential anisotropic parameters, in which the weaker parameters are estimated by a conventional method. In addition, the pixel size of some parameters should be much different than others, as determined by resolution and sensitivity analysis.

23.4 Summary

Inverting for VTI parameters requires the inversion of three VTI parameters per cell compared to acoustic inversion, in which only one parameter is inverted for each pixel; this assumes density is known. The increase in the number of unknowns means that the system of equations has a tendency to become less determined compared to the acoustic case, with the danger that many

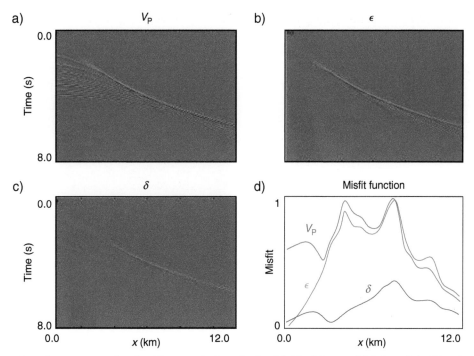

Figure 23.9. Shot-gather changes associated with perturbations in the (a) V_P, (b) ϵ, and (c) δ models. The data misfit functions ($||$original data $-$ perturbed data$||^2$) associated with each perturbation are shown in (d), and suggest that changes in the near-offset surface data are dominated by the V_P perturbations, although the intermediate-offset diving waves and reflections are largely influenced by both ϵ and V_P perturbations. After Cheng et al. (2014).

more models can almost satisfy the same data. Therefore, care must be taken to identify which model parameters strongly control the data and which ones weakly change the data. For the VTI case, the strong model parameter is determined empirically to be the vertical P-wave velocity V_P distribution, and the weaker parameters are ϵ and δ.

Empirical tests suggest that inverting for the V_P tomogram is more robust than inverting for the δ or ϵ distributions. This supports the two-step strategy for VTI inversion. The starting models for δ and ϵ only require an approximate guess. Empirical results suggest that the sequential inversion strategy has a faster convergence rate than simultaneously inverting for all three parameters. In contrast, some researchers empirically conclude that their simultaneous inversion of kinematic VTI parameters (with wide aperture, long offset, and low frequency data) was as effective as a hierarchical approach, and the simultaneous approach is deemed more efficient.

Inverting for higher-order anisotropy parameters will require a multistage inversion strategy to invert initially for the most influential anisotropic parameters, in which the weaker parameters are kept fixed. In addition, the pixel size of some parameters should be much different than others, as determined by resolution and sensitivity analysis.

23.5 Exercises

1. Thomsen (1986) from equation 23.1 defines

$$V_P = c; \quad V_H = V_P(1 + \epsilon);$$

$$V_{NMO} = V_P\sqrt{1 + 2\delta} \approx V_P(1 + \delta), \quad (23.11)$$

where, in the VTI medium, V_P is the vertical P-wave velocity, v_H is the horizontal P-wave velocity by setting $\theta = \pi/2$ in equation 23.1, and V_{NMO} is the short-spread NMO velocity of the P wave. As before, the isotropic velocity is $c = \sqrt{(\lambda + 2\mu)/\rho}$. For weak anisotropy, $V_{NMO} \approx V_P(1 + \delta)$. Rearranging the above gives expressions for δ and ϵ in terms of V_H, V_P, and V_{NMO}:

$$\epsilon = \frac{V_H - V_P}{V_P}; \quad \delta = \frac{V_{NMO} - V_P}{V_P}, \quad (23.12)$$

in which ϵ is interpreted as the fractional difference between the horizontal and vertical velocities, or the anisotropy of the rock (Thomsen, 1986). By substitution of the above formulas, convert equation 23.3 into the equations of motion as a function V_{NMO}, V_P, and V_H.

2. Derive the formulas for the gradients γ_{V_P}, γ_{V_H} and $\gamma_{V_{NMO}}$.

3. Write a 2-4 staggered grid scheme to solve the first-order equations of motion for a VTI medium. Reproduce Figure 1 in Duveneck et al. (2008).

4. Generate surface shot gathers for a simple multi-layered VTI model with a salt-like body. Assume that the background model is VTI even though the reflectors are dipping. Use the Thomsen parameter values given in Duveneck et al. (2008).

5. From the above data, use VTI FWI to invert the data. Compare the results to the tomograms computed by an isotropic FWI algorithm applied to the same data.

6. Compare the convergence rate of simultaneously inverting for the Thomsen parameters versus a multi-stage inversion in which V_P is first inverted for, then δ and ϵ are inverted simultaneously.

7. Convert the TTI RTM code in the Computational Toolkit to TTI FWI.

Part VII

Image-Domain Inversion

Chapter 24: Classical Migration Velocity Analysis

The previous imaging methods can be described as estimating the earth model by predicting synthetic data that best explains *the observed data in the data domain*. In contrast, image-domain inversion finds the velocity model that best explains *the observed migration section in the image domain*. The observed migration image is obtained by migrating the recorded data using an assumed velocity model. Each iteration of image-domain inversion updates both the velocity model and the migration image. One of the advantages of image-domain inversion is that migration untangles crossing events in the data domain and focuses them to the vicinity of the reflecting boundary. Hence, the migration image should have a higher signal-to-noise ratio (S/N) than the original data for a reasonably accurate velocity model.

This chapter presents the theory for classical migration velocity analysis (MVA), which finds the velocity model that best flattens reflections in the common-image gather (Yilmaz and Chambers, 1984; Faye and Jeannot, 1986; Al-Yahya, 1989; Toldi, 1989; Stork, 1992; Lafond and Levander, 1993; Yilmaz, 2001; Jones, 2010; Robein, 2010). It is analogous to the kinematic method of traveltime inversion that finds the velocity model which generates transmission or reflection events that best fit the traveltimes, not amplitudes, in the observed data. Chapter 25 presents a similar MVA method, except migrated reflections are focused in the subsurface-offset image gathers (Xu et al., 1998; Rickett and Sava, 2002; Sava and Biondi, 2004; Robein, 2010). Finally, Chapter 26 presents waveform inversion in the image domain so that both amplitudes and the locations of reflection events match those in the observed migration image.

24.1 Image-domain inversion

The goal of image-domain inversion is to find the velocity model that, ideally, predicts the observed migration image $\tilde{\mathbf{m}}^{\text{obs}} = \mathbf{L}^T \mathbf{d}^{\text{obs}}$. Here, the predicted migration image is given by $\tilde{\mathbf{m}} = \mathbf{L}^T \mathbf{L} \mathbf{m}$, in which $\mathbf{m}$ is an assumed velocity model and $\mathbf{L}$ is the modeling operator with an assumed background velocity model. If the goal is to predict both the locations and waveform amplitudes of the events in the

migration image, then this procedure is denoted in Chapter 26 as waveform inversion in the image domain. If only the locations of the migrated reflections are to be predicted, then the image-domain inversion method is known as an MVA method, such as classical MVA, or a semblance-optimization method (Symes and Carrazone, 1991; Shen et al., 2003), described in Chapter 25.

The advantage of fitting depth locations of reflections compared to waveform fitting of the migration image is a more robust convergence to the low-wavenumber velocity model. However, the disadvantage is that the spatial resolution of the image is limited to intermediate wavenumbers. As will be seen in Chapters 25–26, the favored procedure is a hybrid method that initially fits the location of migration events in the image domain, and then fitting the waveforms. This is similar to the multiscale physics strategy of wave-equation traveltime and waveform tomography described in Chapters 20–22.

24.2 Classical ray-based MVA

Prestack migration images can be displayed as the common-image gathers (CIGs) shown in Figure 24.1. Here, the 2D prestack migration images $m(x,z)_s^{\text{mig}}$ are computed by migrating each of the shot gathers indexed by s. If the migration velocity is correct, then all of the migrated primary reflection events should be flat in the CIG given by $m(x_{\text{CIG}}, z)_s^{\text{mig}}$ for all values of s, z, and a specified value of the offset coordinate x_{CIG} (see horizontal dashed line in Figure 24.1b). For a migration velocity that is too slow, the imaged reflector boundary will curve upward as illustrated by the curved dashed line; and if it is too fast, the imaged reflector will curve downward.

The depth misalignments Δz in Figure 24.1b are used to update the model velocity (e.g., Yilmaz and Chambers, 1984; Faye and Jeannot, 1986; Al-Yaha, 1989; Toldi, 1989; Stork, 1991 and 1992; Kosloff et al., 1996; Hardy and Jeannot, 1999; Jones, 2010). For ray-based MVA, the depth residual Δz first is transformed into a time residual, e.g., $\Delta t \approx 2\Delta z/c$ for a vertically incident reflection at a flat interface, and the velocity is updated by smearing the weighted time residual along the raypath for the related

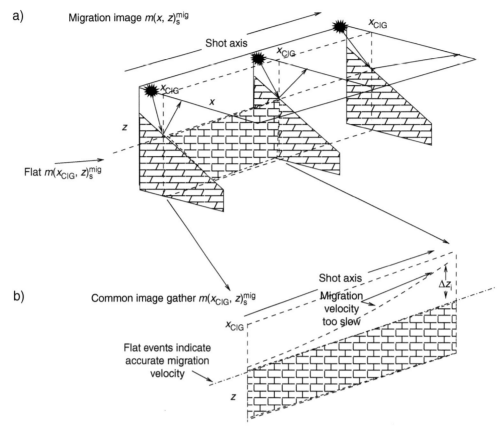

Figure 24.1. (a) Migration image $m(x, z)_s^{\mathrm{mig}}$ cube in the model coordinates of (x, z) and the shot index s; the common-image gather $m(x_{\mathrm{CIG}}, z)_s^{\mathrm{mig}}$ is computed by migrating the shot gathers and displaying the migration image at the fixed value of $x = x_{\mathrm{CIG}}$ for all shot s and depth z values. (b) Common-image gather $m(x_{\mathrm{CIG}}, z)_s^{\mathrm{mig}}$ for the specified coordinate at x_{CIG}.

source-receiver pair. Here, c can be the average velocity along the ray. This leads to a moderate resolution of the velocity model because only the kinematics of events are used to update the velocity model. Migration velocity analysis is largely insensitive to subtle amplitude variations in the traces and is blind to subtle variations in the impedance distribution.

The starting point for ray-based MVA is to define the misfit function

$$\epsilon = \frac{1}{2} \sum_s \sum_i (z_i^s - z_i^{\mathrm{ref}})^2, \qquad (24.1)$$

in which z_i^s is the calculated depth of the ith reflector in the migration image for the sth shot and a specified CIG offset coordinate x, which is silent in this notation. The depth values z_i^s are calculated by picking the depth of the reflector in the CIG migration image for the specified shot index and offset coordinate. The reference depth z_i^{ref} typically is taken to be the calculated depth of the reflector for a ray with zero offset between the source and receiver, and its value is kept fixed for the iterations; this reference depth can be updated if the velocity model is inverted and a new round of

iterations is required. For notational convenience, the summation is over reflectors and only one CIG offset coordinate is considered.[1] The gradient of this misfit function is

$$\frac{\partial \epsilon}{\partial s(\mathbf{x})} = \sum_s \sum_i (z_i^s - z_i^{\mathrm{ref}}) \frac{\partial z_i^s}{\partial s(\mathbf{x})},$$

$$= \sum_s \sum_i (z_i^s - z_i^{\mathrm{ref}}) \frac{\partial z_i^s}{\partial t_i^s} \frac{\partial t_i^s}{\partial s(\mathbf{x})}, \qquad (24.2)$$

where the chain rule is used and t_i^s is the traveltime associated with the ith reflection ray for the sth source, where the reflection point is at $(x_{\mathrm{CIG}}, z_i^s)$. As discussed in Chapter 5, the Fréchet derivative $\partial t_i^s / \partial s(\mathbf{x})$ is approximated by the segment length of the ith ray that visits the slowness cell centered at $\mathbf{x}$. The other Fréchet derivative $\partial z_i^s / \partial t_i^s$ is the variation of the depth of the specified reflector with respect to the traveltime perturbation associated with the ith ray that visits the slowness cell centered at $\mathbf{x}$. It can be found numerically by slightly changing the depth of the reflector by Δz, computing the change in the reflection traveltime Δt by ray tracing, and then taking the ratio $\Delta z / \Delta t$. In practice, the

---

[1] In practice, the sum is over all CIG offset coordinates.

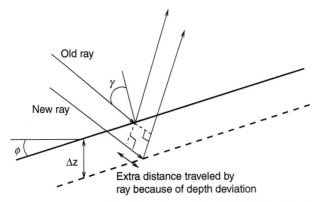

Figure 24.2. Perturbing the reflector depth (solid line) by Δz leads to the traveltime perturbation Δt approximately calculated by equation 24.3. Illustration adapted from Stork (1992).

approximation (Stork, 1992)

$$\Delta t = 2s(\mathbf{x})\Delta z \cos(\phi)\cos(\gamma) \qquad (24.3)$$

can be used in a constant-offset section to calculate the $\Delta z/\Delta t$ ratio, where the terms are defined in Figure 24.2. Here, $s(\mathbf{x})$ is the slowness at the point of reflection.

Equation 24.2 is similar to the misfit gradient in ray-based traveltime tomography, except the traveltime residual is replaced by the depth residual weighted by the $\partial z_i^s/\partial t_i^s$ term. This weighted residual is used to update the velocity model along the reflection raypath. Therefore, classical MVA can be implemented with the following steps:

1. Migrate the data and resort the prestack migration images into CIGs.

2. Automatically pick the depth residual $\Delta z_i^s = z_i^s - z_i^{\text{ref}}$ of a coherent CIG event in Figure 24.1b at the ith shot position; here, z_i^s is the picked depth of the ith reflection at the x_{CIG} offset for the sth migrated shot gather. The depth z_i^{ref} of the reference event for that reflector is estimated from the near-offset trace in that CIG. A computer algorithm can window about the near-offset reflection of interest and use crosscorrelation with neighboring traces in the CIG to estimate the depth lag $z_i - z_i^{\text{ref}}$ associated with the strongest correlation energy. Other possibilities include (1) the use of a local slant-stack method to find the depth lags, or (2) a semblance analysis to find the weighted polynomial in z^2 that best fits the residual moveout (RMO) of the CIG at the fixed depth z_0 (Yilmaz, 2001).

3. The misfit function then is defined as

$$\epsilon = 1/2 \sum_s \sum_i (\Delta z_i^s)^2 + \text{model smoothness constraints}$$

$$(24.4)$$

for each CIG, and the summation is over the shot index in Figure 24.1b.

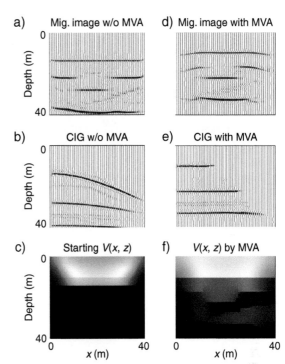

a) Mig. image w/o MVA d) Mig. image with MVA

b) CIG w/o MVA e) CIG with MVA

c) Starting $V(x, z)$ f) $V(x, z)$ by MVA

Figure 24.3. (a) Migration image (Sun, 2001) obtained by prestack migration using the smooth homogeneous velocity model in (c) that is far from the true model approximated in (f). (b) CIG in the shot offset index, where the curved events indicate an incorrect velocity model; (c) incorrect migration velocity model used to compute (a). (d) Migration image obtained after seven iterations of MVA; (e) CIG after seven iterations of MVA; and (f) velocity model inverted by seven iterations of MVA. This result closely resembles the true velocity model. After Sun (2001).

4. The velocity model is updated by a gradient-optimization method such as conjugate gradients, using the gradient in equation 24.2. At each iteration, the velocity is updated by smearing the weighted depth residuals along the reflection raypaths.

5. The data are migrated again using the updated velocity model, and steps 1 to 4 are repeated until ϵ falls below some specified value.

An example of the above procedure is shown in Figure 24.3, where the left column of images depict the migration image obtained with an inaccurate velocity model (Figure 24.3a), the CIG with curved events (Figure 24.3b), and the migration velocity model (Figure 24.3c). After seven iterations of MVA, the right column of figures is obtained. Note that the reflections events in the CIG are flattened and the final-velocity model is almost the same as the actual velocity model.

A field data set recorded from the Gulf of Mexico is migrated to give the image shown in Figure 24.4a. The migration velocity model is shown in Figure 24.4c and is

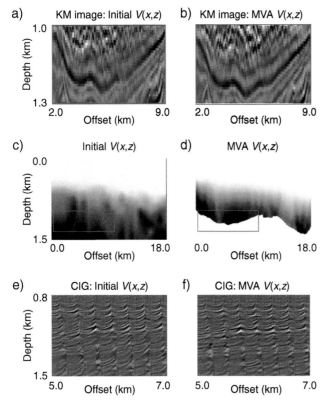

Figure 24.4. Migration images in (a) and (b) obtained by prestack migration of Gulf of Mexico data using the (c) initial and (d) MVA velocity models, respectively. The CIGs in (e and f) are obtained from the initial and MVA velocity models, respectively. After Sun (2001).

obtained by an NMO procedure with interpolation. Then, a ray-based MVA procedure is used to estimate the velocity model shown in Figure 24.4d, and the associated migration image is in Figure 24.4b. It is obvious that the reflectors in the MVA image are more coherent compared to the ones computed from the initial-velocity model. A final comparison is in Figures 24.4e and 24.4f, in which the CIGs obtained from the MVA velocity model are more flattened compared to those obtained from the initial velocity model.

The Gulf of Mexico example is for a velocity model without strong velocity gradients. However, if the velocity model is too complex, then the high-frequency approximation implicit with ray-based MVA is invalid. In this case, a wave-equation MVA method should be used.

One of the problems with MVA applied to CIGs indexed with the shot coordinate is that curved migration artifacts might be caused by uneven source illumination. For example, in a marine survey, the CSG migration image near the end of the recording array might curve upward as illustrated on the right side of Figure 18.1. This curvature is caused by truncation effects in the recording aperture and is not necessarily an indication of velocity errors. To avoid misidentifying this migration curvature as a velocity error in

the shot-domain CIG, common-offset gathers ($|\mathbf{s} - \mathbf{g}| = o$) are formed from the common-shot gathers, and Kirchhoff migration is applied to the COGs. For 2D, the result is a CIG volume $m(\mathbf{x}, o)$ and MVA is applied to the offset-domain CIGs.

24.3 Angle-domain CIGs

Applying Kirchhoff migration to CIGs in the shot coordinate can generate severe artifacts in the migration image for complex models. Xu et al. (1998; 2001), Xu and Huang (2007), and Xu et al. (2011) investigate this issue and conclude that the artifacts are caused by the presence of multiples and the nonuniqueness of imaging solutions when using surface attributes to index the CIGs. These problems are avoided partly by migrating angle-domain common-image gathers (ADCIGs) rather than common-image gathers along the shot axis and then using MVA in the angle domain to update the velocity. Currently, ADCIGs are one of the more widely used domains for MVA (Robein, 2010; Montel and Lambaré, 2011a, 2011b).

An angle-domain CIG is shown in Figure 24.5 and can be computed by ray tracing, in which the velocity can be updated in the following way:

1. An image point $\mathbf{x}$ is selected for a CIG and the source location associated with θ is found by shooting a ray from $\mathbf{x}$ that bisects the normal to the reflector interface at the angle θ. Here, the angle θ is with respect to the normal at the interface with a known dip angle. The intersection of the ray at the surface defines the source $\mathbf{s}$ in the CIG $m(\mathbf{x}, \mathbf{s})$ volume with the incidence and reflection angle θ at $\mathbf{x}$. Thus, the CIG volume $m(\mathbf{x}, \mathbf{s})$ can be transformed into the angle-domain CIG volume $m(\mathbf{x}, \theta)$. The reflector dip at $\mathbf{x}$ might be estimated by applying a local slant-stack semblance analysis to the first-pass migration image at $\mathbf{x}$.

2. The ADCIG should be flat for all angle values at any fixed offset x and depth z if the velocity model is correct. If not, then an angle-domain MVA can be used to update the velocity model. The ADCIGs also can be used for amplitude-versus-offset studies.

If a wave-equation migration method is used, then the back-propagated reflections at $\mathbf{x}$ can be decomposed into local plane waves by either an FK transform or by a local slant-stack procedure. The migration image then is formed for the appropriate source and back-projected reflections that bisect the reflector at the angle θ. This gives the ADCIG $m(\mathbf{x}, \theta)$.

As an alternative, Zhang (2014) proposes an efficient and robust estimation of ADCIGs by an optical flow calculation of a Poynting-like vector (Yoon and Marfurt, 2006).

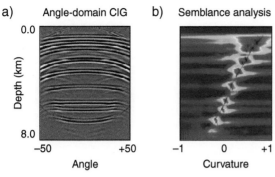

a) Angle-domain CIG

b) Semblance analysis

Figure 24.5. (a) Angle-domain CIG and (b) semblance analysis to determine the optimal curvature parameter that flattens the ADCIG. The fitting equation is $z^2 = z_0^2 + \gamma$ $(z_o \tan \theta)$ (Biondi and Symes, 2004), where γ is the fitting parameter along the horizontal axis in (b). Here, θ is the reflection angle plotted along the horizontal axis in (a), and input shot gathers are generated from a synthetic model. The curved events in the angle-domain CIGs indicate the inaccuracy of the migration velocity model. After Zhang et al. (2012).

This vector, which indicates the direction of propagation, is used in the RTM image condition to create migration sections according to the angles of propagation for the direct-wave $\hat{\mathbf{r}}_{sx}$ and back-propagated reflections $\hat{\mathbf{r}}_{gx}$ at $\mathbf{x}$: i.e., the image $m(\mathbf{x})$ is nonzero only if $\hat{\mathbf{r}}_{sx} + \hat{\mathbf{r}}_{gx}$ is perpendicular to the reflector tangent at $\mathbf{x}$. Zhang (2014) shows promising results for complicated models.

If the velocity model is too far away from the correct one, then there is nothing that stacks in the CIG, so there is nothing to use for velocity updating according to Mulder (2014). In this case, migration in the extended image domain (see Chapter 25) is used, so that even with the incorrect velocity, it is easier to improve focusing to maximize the stack power of prestack migration images (Figure 24.6).

Unexpectedly, numerical simulations revealed that the ADCIG RMO curvatures from RTM and Kirchhoff migrations are different for an incorrect velocity model. Even for RTM, the RMO properties of ADCIGs are different between the offset-stack method and the shot-domain method. It is surprising that nonlinear angle-domain MVA is more complicated than the offset-domain MVA.

24.4 Trim statics MVA

The classical MVA procedure adjusts the velocity model until the reflections in the shot-domain CIGs, offset-domain CIGs, or the ADCIGs align with one another. For CIGs indexed with the shot coordinates, the migration arrivals are shifted only along the z-coordinate. An alternative is to shift the migration arrivals not only in the z-direction but also along the x- and y-directions to align the misaligned prestack images. That is, use the trim-statics

procedure, discussed in Chapter 15 and Huang and Schuster (2014), to find the appropriate statics shifts, and then use MVA to adjust the velocity model until the migration images from each shot gather are aligned with one another. The mathematical formulation for multidimensional MVA is presented next.

Define two prestack migration images as $m(\mathbf{x}')$ and $\tilde{m}(\mathbf{x}')$ obtained by migrating neighboring shot gathers, where the shots are close to one another. The correlation between the square patch of $m(\mathbf{x}')$ and the neighboring patch $\tilde{m}(\mathbf{x}')$ is given by

$$f\left(s(\mathbf{x}), \mathbf{u}_i\right) = \sum_{\mathbf{x}' \in B_i} m(\mathbf{x}')\tilde{m}(\mathbf{x}' + \mathbf{u}_i) \qquad (24.5)$$

in which B_i defines the set of points in the ith square patch and $\mathbf{u}_i = (u_i, w_i)$ is a shift vector. In practice, the width and height of a patch are several wavelengths. The spatial shift vector $\mathbf{u}_i$ is used for trim statics of prestack migration images in Huang and Schuster (2014), and is inverted for the slowness $s(\mathbf{x})$ model by Guo (2015).

Following Guo (2015), the correct spatial shift vector $\Delta\mathbf{u}_i = (\Delta u_i, \Delta w_i)$, calculated from trim statics, aligns $m(\mathbf{x}')$ with $\tilde{m}(\mathbf{x}')$ and maximizes the correlation function:

$$\begin{aligned}
\bar{\boldsymbol{f}}\left(s(\mathbf{x}), \Delta\mathbf{u}_i\right) &= \left(\bar{f}_u(s(\mathbf{x}), \Delta\mathbf{u}_i), \bar{f}_w(s(\mathbf{x}), \Delta\mathbf{u}_i)\right), \\
&\equiv \left(\frac{\partial f\left(s(\mathbf{x}), \mathbf{u}_i\right)}{\partial u_i}, \frac{\partial f\left(s(\mathbf{x}), \mathbf{u}_i\right)}{\partial w_i}\right)\Big|_{\mathbf{u}_i = \Delta\mathbf{u}_i}, \\
&= (0, 0), \qquad (24.6)
\end{aligned}$$

which leads to

$$\begin{aligned}
\bar{f}_u(s(\mathbf{x}), \Delta\mathbf{u}_i) &= \frac{\partial f\left(s(\mathbf{x}), \mathbf{u}_i\right)}{\partial u_i}\Big|_{\mathbf{u}_i = \Delta\mathbf{u}_i}, \\
&= \sum_{\mathbf{x}' \in B_i} m(\mathbf{x}')\frac{\partial \tilde{m}(\mathbf{x}' + \Delta\mathbf{u}_i)}{\partial \Delta u_i}, \qquad (24.7) \\
&= 0,
\end{aligned}$$

and

$$\begin{aligned}
\bar{f}_w(s(\mathbf{x}), \Delta\mathbf{u}_i) &= \frac{\partial f\left(s(\mathbf{x}), \mathbf{u}_i\right)}{\partial w_i}\Big|_{\mathbf{u}_i = \Delta\mathbf{u}_i}, \\
&= \sum_{\mathbf{x}' \in B_i} m(\mathbf{x}')\frac{\partial \tilde{m}(\mathbf{x}' + \Delta\mathbf{u}_i)}{\partial \Delta w_i}, \qquad (24.8) \\
&= 0.
\end{aligned}$$

Next, we will use the shifts $\Delta\mathbf{u}_i$ computed from the trim statics to improve the accuracy of the migration velocity model. Assume the objective function for two migrated shot gathers is given by

$$\epsilon = \frac{1}{2} \sum_{i=1}^{M} \| \Delta \mathbf{u}_i \|^2, \qquad (24.9)$$

in which M is the number of patches in the migration image. The steepest-descent formula for updating the slowness is given by

$$s(\mathbf{x})^{(k+1)} = s(\mathbf{x})^{(k)} - \alpha \frac{\partial \epsilon}{\partial s(\mathbf{x})},$$

$$= s(\mathbf{x})^{(k)} - \alpha \sum_{i=1}^{M} \left\{ \Delta u_i \frac{\partial \Delta u_i}{\partial s(\mathbf{x})} + \Delta w_i \frac{\partial \Delta w_i}{\partial s(\mathbf{x})} \right\}, \qquad (24.10)$$

where $s(\mathbf{x})$ is the slowness model used for migration and α denotes the step length along the gradient direction.

The implicit function theorem can be used to derive formulas for the Fréchet derivatives $\partial \Delta u_i / \partial s(\mathbf{x})$ and $\partial \Delta w_i / \partial s(\mathbf{x})$. The first step is to expand the vectorial connective function in equation 24.6 in a Taylor series, truncate to the linear terms in the variables $s(\mathbf{x})$, Δw_i, and Δu_i, and set to zero to give:

$$\begin{pmatrix} \dfrac{\partial \bar{f}_u}{\partial \Delta u_i} & \dfrac{\partial \bar{f}_u}{\partial \Delta w_i} \\ \dfrac{\partial \bar{f}_w}{\partial \Delta u_i} & \dfrac{\partial \bar{f}_w}{\partial \Delta w_i} \end{pmatrix} \begin{pmatrix} d\Delta u_i \\ d\Delta w_i \end{pmatrix} + \begin{pmatrix} \dfrac{\partial \bar{f}_u}{\partial s(\mathbf{x})} \\ \dfrac{\partial \bar{f}_w}{\partial s(\mathbf{x})} \end{pmatrix} ds(\mathbf{x}) = \begin{pmatrix} 0 \\ 0 \end{pmatrix}. \qquad (24.11)$$

Dividing the above equation by $ds(\mathbf{x})$, setting $\frac{d\Delta u_i}{ds(\mathbf{x})} \rightarrow \frac{\partial \Delta u_i}{\partial s(\mathbf{x})}$ and $\frac{d\Delta w_i}{ds(\mathbf{x})} \rightarrow \frac{\partial \Delta w_i}{\partial s(\mathbf{x})}$, and inverting the 2×2 matrix gives the explicit Fréchet derivatives in equation 24.10:

$$\begin{pmatrix} \dfrac{\partial \Delta u_i}{\partial s(\mathbf{x})} \\ \dfrac{\partial \Delta w_i}{\partial s(\mathbf{x})} \end{pmatrix} = - \begin{pmatrix} \dfrac{\partial \bar{f}_u}{\partial \Delta u_i} & \dfrac{\partial \bar{f}_u}{\partial \Delta w_i} \\ \dfrac{\partial \bar{f}_w}{\partial \Delta u_i} & \dfrac{\partial \bar{f}_w}{\partial \Delta w_i} \end{pmatrix}^{-1} \begin{pmatrix} \dfrac{\partial \bar{f}_u}{\partial s(\mathbf{x})} \\ \dfrac{\partial \bar{f}_w}{\partial s(\mathbf{x})} \end{pmatrix}, \qquad (24.12)$$

where equations 24.7–24.8 say that the terms in equation 24.12 are given by

$$\frac{\partial \bar{f}_u}{\partial \Delta w_i} = \sum_{\mathbf{x}' \in B_i} m(\mathbf{x}') \frac{\partial^2 \tilde{m}(\mathbf{x}' + \Delta \mathbf{u}_i)}{\partial \Delta w_i \partial \Delta u_i},$$

$$\frac{\partial \bar{f}_w}{\partial \Delta u_i} = \sum_{\mathbf{x}' \in B_i} m(\mathbf{x}') \frac{\partial^2 \tilde{m}(\mathbf{x}' + \Delta \mathbf{u}_i)}{\partial \Delta u_i \partial \Delta w_i}, \qquad (24.13)$$

$$\frac{\partial \bar{f}_u}{\partial \Delta u_i} = \sum_{\mathbf{x}' \in B_i} m(\mathbf{x}') \frac{\partial^2 \tilde{m}(\mathbf{x}' + \Delta \mathbf{u}_i)}{\partial \Delta u_i^2},$$

$$\frac{\partial \bar{f}_w}{\partial \Delta w_i} = \sum_{\mathbf{x}' \in B_i} m(\mathbf{x}') \frac{\partial^2 \tilde{m}(\mathbf{x}' + \Delta \mathbf{u}_i)}{\partial \Delta w_i^2}, \qquad (24.14)$$

$$\partial \bar{f}_u / \partial s(\mathbf{x}) = \sum_{\mathbf{x}' \in B_i} \frac{\partial m(\mathbf{x}')}{\partial s(\mathbf{x})} \frac{\partial \tilde{m}(\mathbf{x}' + \Delta \mathbf{u}_i)}{\partial \Delta u_i},$$

$$\partial \bar{f}_w / \partial s(\mathbf{x}) = \sum_{\mathbf{x}' \in B_i} \frac{\partial m(\mathbf{x}')}{\partial s(\mathbf{x})} \frac{\partial \tilde{m}(\mathbf{x}' + \Delta \mathbf{u}_i)}{\partial \Delta w_i}. \qquad (24.15)$$

Here, $m(\mathbf{x}')$ is assumed to be a function of the slowness model, and for simplicity we approximate $\tilde{m}(\mathbf{x})$ as independent of the predicted slowness model. This approximation can be eliminated if we also take the Fréchet derivative of $\tilde{m}(\mathbf{x})$. The explicit expression for $\partial m(\mathbf{x}')/\partial s(\mathbf{x})$ in equation 24.15 is obtained by differentiating the approximation to the single-trace migration equation[2]

$$m(\mathbf{x}') = \int \omega^2 W(\omega) d(\mathbf{g}|\mathbf{s})^* G(\mathbf{x}'|\mathbf{s}) G(\mathbf{x}'|\mathbf{g}) d\omega, \qquad (24.16)$$

with respect to the slowness at $\mathbf{x}$ to get

$$\frac{\partial m(\mathbf{x}')}{\partial s(\mathbf{x})} = \int d\omega \omega^2 W(\omega) d(\mathbf{g}|\mathbf{s})^*$$

$$\times \left\{ \frac{\partial G(\mathbf{x}'|\mathbf{s})}{\partial s(\mathbf{x})} G(\mathbf{x}'|\mathbf{g}) + \frac{\partial G(\mathbf{x}'|\mathbf{g})}{\partial s(\mathbf{x})} G(\mathbf{x}'|\mathbf{s}) \right\}. \qquad (24.17)$$

Substituting the Fréchet derivative $\partial G(\mathbf{x}'|\mathbf{s})/\partial s(\mathbf{x}) = 2s(\mathbf{x})\omega^2 G(\mathbf{x}'|\mathbf{x}) G(\mathbf{x}|\mathbf{s})$ into equation 24.17 leads to

$$\frac{\partial m(\mathbf{x}')}{\partial s(\mathbf{x})} = 2 \int d\omega \omega^4 W(\omega) s(\mathbf{x}) d(\mathbf{g}|\mathbf{s})^* \left\{ G(\mathbf{x}'|\mathbf{g}) G(\mathbf{x}'|\mathbf{x}) \right.$$

$$\left. G(\mathbf{x}|\mathbf{s}) + G(\mathbf{x}'|\mathbf{s}) G(\mathbf{x}'|\mathbf{x}) G(\mathbf{x}|\mathbf{g}) \right\}. \qquad (24.18)$$

Inserting equation 24.18 into equations 24.12–24.15 gives the Fréchet derivatives in the gradient formula 24.10 for updating the slowness model from the trim statistics residuals. Figure 24.6 provides the Fresnel-zone interpretation of the Fréchet derivative for a single trace at $\mathbf{g}$ excited by a source at $\mathbf{s}$.

24.5 Ray-based tomography

According to the summary of ray-based MVA in Lambaré et al. (2014) "Over the last six years, from the industrial situation depicted by Woodward et al. (2008), significant improvements of the ray-based tomography toolbox have emerged. While publications on velocity model building have emphasized FWI, methods based on

---

[2]In practice, the term $2s(\mathbf{x})$ is sometimes excluded in the migration equation.

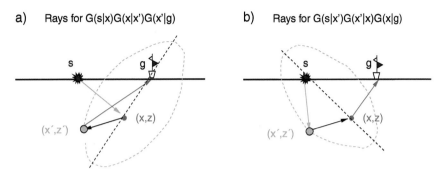

Figure 24.6. Rays associated with Green's functions in a smooth medium where **x** is the position of the migration image and the green dashed quasi-ellipses describe the positions **x′** of the slowness anomaly that provide the same traveltime value (a) $\tau_{xx'} + \tau_{x'g}$ and (b) $\tau_{sx'} + \tau_{x'x}$ for a fixed source-receiver pair and migration image point **x**. The foci of the quasi-ellipses are at (a) **x** and **g** and (b) **x** and **s**; the strongest values of $\partial m(\mathbf{x})/\partial s(\mathbf{x}')$ are at those positions **x′** that cancel the phase in $d(\mathbf{g}|\mathbf{s})$. Thus, the wavepath where the velocity is updated significantly is mostly within the first Fresnel zones of the green ellipses.

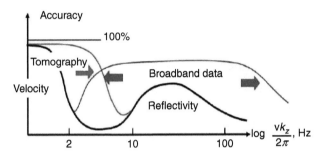

Figure 24.7. Filling of mid-frequency gap. In black, the famous sketch by Claerbout that summarizes the resolution expected from velocity analysis (Velocity) and imaging (Reflectivity). (Claerbout, 1985, Figure 1.13). We see that the mid-frequency range (2–10 Hz) is filled by the improved resolution brought by tomography (red curve) and by the impact of broadband acquisition on imaging (blue curve). Illustration from Lambaré et al. (2014, Figure 3), who suggest that, relative to standard traveltime tomography, slope traveltime tomography can provide a superior starting model for FWI.

picking have improved considerably, reducing important bottlenecks such as resolution and structural conformity, previously presented as strong advantages of FWI. As such, ray-based approaches offer an ideal platform for spurring further development of FWI, possibly including the combination of FWI with ray-based inversions." Their graphical summary of how different velocity inversion methods cover a range of data frequencies is given in Figure 24.7.

24.6 Summary

Migrating unfocused events in recorded traces sometimes can untangle complicated arrivals from one another. This can lead to a simpler objective function so that convergence of migration velocity analysis might be more robust than for full-waveform inversion. To avoid artifacts in the migration image, MVA can be applied to ADCIGs rather than CIGs indexed along the shot axis. However, the penalty for classical MVA methods is an intermediate resolution because the velocity model is updated along the low-wavenumber wavepaths described as rabbit ears.

If the velocity model is too complex, then the high-frequency approximation implicit with ray-based MVA is invalid. In this case, wave-equation MVA methods should be used but the penalty will be a higher computational cost. Even so, if the velocity model is too far away from the correct one, there is nothing that stacks, so there is nothing to use for velocity updating. In this case, the extended image MVA methods sometimes are preferred because it is easier to improve focusing than it is to maximize the stack power in the migration image. As noted earlier, ray-based approaches offer an ideal platform for spurring further development of FWI, possibly including the combination of FWI with ray-based inversions.

Chapter 25: Generalized Differential Semblance Optimization

Wave-equation traveltime and waveform tomography first inverts the smoothly varying traveltimes (see dashed curve in Figure 25.1a) of selected events to obtain the low-wavenumber estimate of the velocity model. Then, the rapidly varying waveforms are inverted during the later iterations to estimate the high-wavenumber portion of the velocity model. This physics-based multiscale procedure can mitigate the tendency for iterative waveform inversion to get stuck in a local minimum. Multiscale physics can be adapted to differential semblance optimization (DSO) in the image domain. That is, the space-lag offset $H(z, h)$ (see dashed curve in Figure 25.1b) can be identified in the subsurface-offset domain as an implicit function of velocity. It describes the smoothly varying moveout $H(z, h)$ of the migration image $m(x, z, h)$ in the subsurface-offset domain, which is analogous to the smoothly varying traveltime residual $\Delta\tau(x)$ of a reflection event in a shot gather. The velocity model is found that minimizes the objective function $\sum_{x,z,h} H(z, h)^2 m(\mathbf{x}, h)^2$, where coherent noise is eliminated everywhere except along the picked moveout curve $H(z, h)$. This method is denoted as generalized differential semblance optimization (GDSO) and mitigates the coherent noise problem with DSO. Numerical examples are presented that empirically demonstrate its effectiveness in providing more accurate velocity models compared to conventional DSO.

25.1 Introduction

Bunks et al. (1995) propose a multiscale inversion strategy where low-frequency data are inverted iteratively to get a smooth estimate of the velocity model. Then, the frequency content of the data is increased gradually with increasing iteration number to build up a more detailed velocity model. In this way, cycle-skipping problems can be avoided as long as the velocity model at each iteration can explain the kinematics of arrivals to within about half of a period.

Another type of multiscale strategy is to invert initially for simplified (or skeletonized) components of the data for the smooth parts of the velocity model. Then, gradually increase the data complexity with an increasing iteration

number to get the finer details of the model. An example of this physics-based multiscale strategy is wave-equation traveltime and waveform inversion (WTW) in the data domain (Luo and Schuster, 1991a, 1991b; Zhou et al., 1995, 1997), in which the simple and smoothly varying traveltime residuals $\Delta\tau(\mathbf{x})$ of selected arrivals in Figure 25.1a are inverted initially to yield a smooth velocity model. At later iterations, the more complex waveforms are inverted to produce the finer details of the velocity model. Numerical results suggest that this strategy sometimes can be robust for inverting crosswell data.

In this chapter, we adapt the skeletonized inversion strategy to the image-domain. In our example, the image domain inversion method under consideration is differential semblance optimization, in which the optimal velocity model is the one that minimizes the sum of the weighted migration intensities $|hm(\mathbf{x}, h)|^2$ in the subsurface-offset domain (Symes and Carrazone, 1991; Shen et al., 2003). Instead of treating the offset parameter h in Figure 25.1b as an independent variable, we now consider it to be a function $H(z, h)$ of velocity so that $H(z, h) = 0$ everywhere except along the Figure 25.1b dashed curve where $H(z, h) = h$.

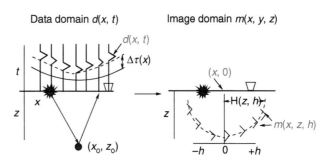

Figure 25.1. (a) Common-shot gather $d(x, t)$ and (b) migration image $m(x, z, h)$ in the subsurface-offset domain. The smoothly varying skeletonized parameters are the (a) traveltime residuals $\Delta\tau(x)$ in the data domain and the (b) subsurface-offset function $H(z, h)$ in the image domain. Here, $H(z, h) = 0$ everywhere except along the dashed curve (peaked migration amplitudes) in (b) where $H(z, h) = h$. The traveltime residual $\Delta\tau(x)$ is the difference between the observed (dashed line) and predicted (solid line) traveltimes in (a).

Similar to the traveltime residual function $\Delta\tau(\mathbf{x})$ in Figure 25.1a, $H(h,z)$ is a simple and smoothly varying function related to the smooth components of the model. Thus, the smoothly varying offset function $H(h,z)$ first is minimized to get a smoothly varying velocity model, then the more complex migration intensity $|m(\mathbf{x},h)|^2$ at $h \neq 0$ is minimized to get the finer details of the model. As will be shown, this strategy denoted as generalized differential optimization (GDSO) is characterized by a more robust convergence rate than DSO.

The next section describes the theory of GDSO, in which the methods of WTW, DSO, and GDSO are described and related to one another. This is followed by the numerical results section where simulations with synthetic data are used to compare the performance of GDSO against that of DSO. Finally, the results are summarized.

25.2 Theory of generalized differential semblance optimization

We first review the multiscale properties of wave-equation traveltime and waveform inversion, then describe the DSO method with its benefits and limitations. These limitations will be the motivation for introducing the multiscale GDSO method.

25.2.1 Wave-equation traveltime and waveform inversion

The starting point for WTW is to define the objective function ϵ in the data domain as

$$\epsilon = 1/2 \sum_i \sum_t [\Delta\tau(x_i)\Delta d(x_i,t)]^2, \qquad (25.1)$$

where the traveltime residual is $\Delta\tau(x_i)$ and x_i is the offset coordinate for the ith trace; the traveltime residual is for specified events such as the reflections in Figure 25.1a. Here, $\Delta d(x_i,t) = d(x_i,t) - d(x_i,t)^{\mathrm{obs}}$ is the ith trace residual at the time t, $d(x_i,t)$ $(d(x_i,t)^{\mathrm{obs}})$ denotes the calculated (observed) trace, and for convenience, a single shot gather is assumed.

A gradient-optimization method typically is used to find the velocity model that minimizes equation 25.1, in which the multiscale gradient is given by

$$\frac{\partial\epsilon}{\partial c(\mathbf{x}')} = \eta \overbrace{\sum_i \tilde{\alpha}_i \frac{\partial\Delta\tau(x_i)}{\partial c(\mathbf{x}')} \Delta\tau(x_i)}^{\gamma^{\mathrm{WT}} = \text{low-wavenumber gradient}}$$

$$+ (1-\eta) \overbrace{\sum_i \sum_t \tilde{\beta}_i \frac{\partial d(x_i,t)}{\partial c(\mathbf{x}')} \Delta d(x_i,t)}^{\gamma^{\mathrm{FWI}} = \text{high-wavenumber gradient}}, \quad (25.2)$$

where $\tilde{\alpha}_i = \sum_t \Delta d(x_i,t)^2$, $\tilde{\beta}_i = \Delta\tau(x_i)^2$, and $\mathbf{x}'$ is an image point in the model-space coordinates. Here, η (for $0 \leq \eta \leq 1$) is the multiscale term that is equal to 1 at the early iterations to invert for the low-wavenumber model with the wave-equation traveltime tomography gradient γ^{WT}. As the iterations proceed, the value of η is reduced gradually to admit the higher wavenumbers of the model (Luo and Schuster, 1991a) with the full-waveform inversion (FWI) gradient γ^{FWI}. Replacing $\tilde{\alpha}_i \to 1$ and $\tilde{\beta}_i \to 1$ reduces equation 25.2 to the WTW formula of Luo and Schuster (1991a) and Zhou et al. (1995).

The early iterations with the $\tilde{\gamma}^{\mathrm{WT}}$ gradient provides the low-wavenumber velocity update along the low-wavenumber tomographic wavepaths (Huang and Schuster, 2014). Moreover, inverting just the traveltimes of picked events is equivalent implicitly to filtering out undesirable noise such as multiples or surface waves that can prevent convergence to the correct model. This filtering aspect and the velocity updating along low-wavenumber wavepaths are important characteristics for successful image-domain inversion presented in the next section.

25.2.2 Differential semblance optimization

A typical image-domain inversion method is the DSO method of Symes and Carrazone (1991), Symes (2008), and Shen et al. (2003). According to Mulder and ten Kroode (2002, 1184), "The DSO functional is expected to have much better global convexity properties than the least-squares functional and, therefore, to suffer less or not at all from local minima (compared to FWI). The method exploits the redundancy in the data and is based on the requirement that the earth be invariant under different seismic experiments." However, the DSO method is limited to intermediate resolution of the velocity model compared to the potential of higher resolution with FWI.

For extended migration images, DSO uses an iterative gradient-optimization method to find the velocity model that minimizes

$$\epsilon = 1/2 \sum_{x,z,h} [h\, m(\mathbf{x},h)]^2. \qquad (25.3)$$

Here, $m(x,z,h)$ is the extended migration image defined in Appendix 25A, in which h is the independent subsurface-offset parameter illustrated in Figure 25.1b. Instead of correlating the downgoing source and back-propagated reflection fields at the same subsurface point $\mathbf{x}$, the neighboring fields at the extended focus points $(x-h,z)$ and $(x+h,z)$ are correlated to give the extended migration $m(\mathbf{x},h)$. The rationale is that, in the presence of a migration velocity error in a layered medium, there will be significant $m(\mathbf{x},h)$ amplitudes for $|h| \gg 0$ at the entangled

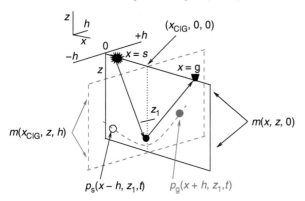

Subsurface offset migration image $m(x, z, h)$

Figure 25.2. Extended migration image $m(x, z_1, h) = \sum_t p_s(x - h, z_1, t)p_g(x + h, z_1, t)$ of a point scatterer (filled circle) is represented by the dashed red smile in the subsurface-offset domain; the panels for a constant offset $x = x_{\mathrm{CIG}}$ and $h = 0$ are depicted in red and black, respectively. A migration velocity that is too fast (slow) will lead to a smile (frown) artifact below (above) the actual scatterer's position.

focusing points $(x \pm h, z)$. Such errantly located amplitudes (see the red dashed smile in Figure 25.2) indicate errors in the migration velocity model, so DSO tries to minimize such amplitudes by iteratively finding a more accurate velocity model that minimizes the objective function in equation 25.3.

As a numerical example, Figure 25.3 depicts the subsurface offset migration responses for a single trace and a shot gather in a point-scatterer model. For an incorrect migration velocity, the reflection energy still is observable in the extended image as curved events compared to incoherent noise in the standard migration image (MacKay and Abma, 1992; Rickett and Sava, 2002; Shen et al., 2003; Sava and Biondi, 2004; Mulder, 2014). This provides an opportunity for DSO to make amends in correcting the velocity model.

However, there are difficulties with DSO related to coherent noise in the subsurface offset domain. Mulder (2014, 17) summarizes these problems:

> In practice, the focusing of extended images produces results of mixed quality. Sometimes, the method works very well, sometimes it has difficulties. The data should be free of multiples, otherwise, the method may converge to the wrong model (Mulder and van Leeuwen, 2008). Point scatterers, diffractions and discontinuities in the background velocity model may cause problems (Vyas et al., 2010). Artifacts in extended images may lead gradient-based optimization methods astray.[1]

Another difficulty is that the sign of the DSO gradient sometimes prevents a reasonable rate of convergence to the global minimum (Luo et al., 2015). To mitigate some of the problems with DSO, a generalized DSO (GDSO) method is developed in the next section.

25.2.3 Generalized differential semblance optimization

To mitigate the coherent noise problem, the physics-based multiscale strategy of Luo and Schuster (1991a and 1991b) is adapted to the image domain. That is, the objective function in equation 25.3 is replaced (Zhang and Schuster, 2013a) with

$$\epsilon = 1/2 \sum_{x,z,h} [H(z,h)m(\mathbf{x},h)]^2, \qquad (25.4)$$

in which $H(z, h) = h$ is a function that is alive only on the dashed curve[2] in Figure 25.1b. This image-domain function $H(z, h)$ is analogous to the smoothly varying traveltime curve in the data domain (see Figure 25.1a), with the additional benefit of eliminating coherent noise in the kernel $H(z, h)m(\mathbf{x}, h)$ except along the picked curve $H(z, h)$. Similar to WTW, focusing attention on a skeletal piece of the data along $H(z, h)$ allows us to avoid problems with the aforementioned noisy parts of the extended migration image.

The velocity model that minimizes equation 25.4 can be found, for example, by the iterative steepest-descent formula

$$c(\mathbf{x}')^{(k+1)} = c(\mathbf{x}')^{(k)} - \alpha\gamma(\mathbf{x}'), \qquad (25.5)$$

in which α is the step length and the velocity gradient $\gamma(\mathbf{x})$ of equation 25.4 is

$$\gamma(\mathbf{x}') = \eta \overbrace{\sum_{x,z,h} m(\mathbf{x},h)^2 H(z,h)\frac{\partial H(z,h)}{\partial c(\mathbf{x}')}}^{\gamma^{H\text{-DSO}} = \text{low-wavenumber gradient}}$$

$$+ (1-\eta) \overbrace{\sum_{x,z,h} H(z,h)^2 m(\mathbf{x},h)\frac{\partial m(\mathbf{x},h)}{\partial c(\mathbf{x}')}}^{\gamma^{\text{DSO}}\ \text{gradient}}. \qquad (25.6)$$

---

[1] As an alternative to the space-lag domain, Yang and Sava (2011) propose a time-lag image condition to construct image perturbations with the assumption that the time lag must be very small and picked at each iteration. For example, the migration image with a general time-lag variable τ in the imaging condition gives the shifted migration image

$m(x, z_1, h, \tau) = \sum_t p_s(x - h, z_1, t - \tau)p_g(x + h, z_1, t + \tau)$. Almomin (2011) presents a velocity inversion method in the image domain by using the crosscorrelation of the observed image with a reference image in the reflection angle domain. The objective function is the sum of the squared depth residuals associated with the observed and calculated migration images, and the velocity model is updated by smearing this depth residual along the associated wavepaths.

[2] The function $H(z, h)$ is an implicit function of the surface offset coordinate x, which is silenced conveniently in our notation.

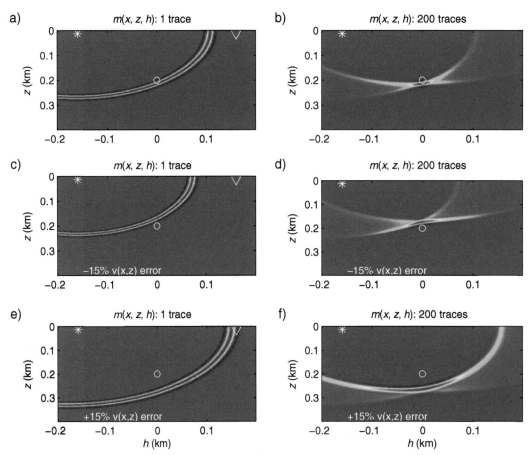

Figure 25.3. Migration images $m(\mathbf{x}, h)$ of a point scatterer (open blue circle) model for a single trace (left column), and a shot gather (right column). The correct migration velocity is used for (a) and (b), and incorrect migration velocity models are used for (c–f); compare the smile in Figure 25.2 to (f). Notice that in (f) the incorrect migration velocity defocuses the migration intensity away from the $h = 0$ axis. Migrating and stacking more shot gathers with the correct velocity model will yield a migration image largely focused along the $h = 0$ axis.

Here, the H-DSO gradient contains the Fréchet derivative $\partial H(z, h)/\partial c(\mathbf{x}')$ associated with the picked curve $H(z, h)$, and η is the multiscale parameter similar to the one discussed for equation 25.2.

The γ^{DSO} gradient in equation 25.6 is associated with the differential semblance optimization of Shen et al. (2003), and it tries to find a velocity model that compresses all of the extended migration energy to $h = 0$. As discussed in Mulder (2014), this ambitious goal can be thwarted by migration noise associated with multiples, point scatterers, and velocity discontinuities.

As an example of the noise problem with point scatterers, Figure 25.4 depicts the extended migration images $m(\mathbf{x}, h)$ for different migration velocity errors in a homogeneous velocity model with four scatterers. Only one of the scatterers (white circle) actually is located at x_{CIG}, i.e., the offset $h = 0$, while the others have offsets $x \neq x_{\text{CIG}}$. Only the migration image of the topmost scatterer in Figure 25.6b should be focused at $h = 0$ for the correct velocity model: while the images for the three off-axis scatterers will be focused away from $h = 0$, as indicated by the three blue

smiles. These blue smiles are coherent noise that will be extant for $|h| \gg 0$ at the correct velocity model. On the other hand, if the peak migration amplitude of the red smile is picked[3] (blue curved line in Figure 25.6b) to give $H(z, h)$, then the distraction of the blue smiles is avoided and convergence can be expedited. Indeed, Figure 25.4a shows that the H-DSO objective function (see equation 25.4) plunges more rapidly than the DSO objective function (see equation 25.3), which suggests the possibility of a more rapid convergence by an iterative optimization method.

H-DSO gradient for low-wavenumber velocity updates

An important property of the H-DSO gradient is that its Fréchet derivative $\partial H/\partial c$ provides the low-wavenumber direction for updating the velocity model. For example, consider the smile artifact in Figure 25.3f, in which the

---

[3]In practice, manual picking of this residual curve sometimes can be avoided as described in the workflow 25.3.

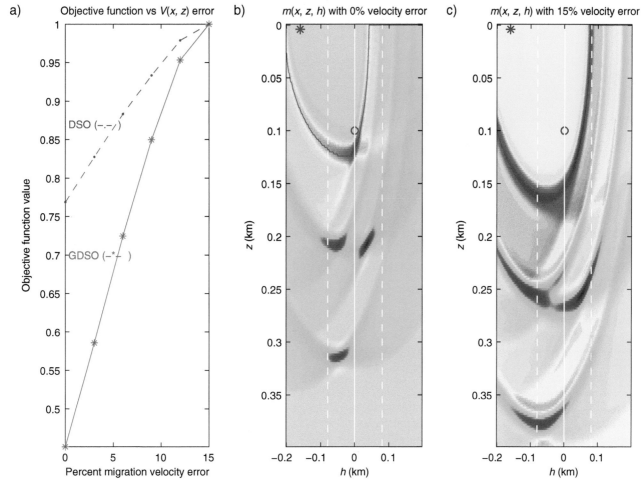

Figure 25.4. (a) Values of the DSO and H-DSO objective functions plotted against percent errors in the migration velocity model. The migration images are computed for the (b) correct and (c) incorrect migration velocity models. The locations of the three off-axis scatterers are at the lowermost portions of the blue smiles in (b). The region between the dashed vertical lines in (b–c) is where the objective functions are calculated, and the only scatterer at $h = 0$ is denoted by the blue circle.

migration velocity is too fast. Therefore, the H-DSO gradient in equation 25.6 should be greater than zero to lower the background velocity model. This is seen to be true by applying the chain rule to the H-DSO gradient:

$$|m(\mathbf{x}, h)|^2 H(z, h) \frac{\partial H(z, h)}{\partial c(\mathbf{x}')}$$

$$= |m(\mathbf{x}, h)|^2 H(z, h) \frac{\partial z}{\partial c(\mathbf{x}')} \frac{\partial H(z, h)}{\partial z}, \qquad (25.7)$$

where

$$H(z, h) \frac{\partial H(z, h)}{\partial z} \geq 0 \qquad (25.8)$$

along the upward curving smile for all values of h and

$$\frac{\partial z}{\partial c(\mathbf{x}')} > 0, \qquad (25.9)$$

is always positive.[4] In contrast, if the migration velocity is too slow, then the migration artifact will be the frown in Figure 25.3d, where $H(z, h) \frac{\partial H(z,h)}{\partial z} \leq 0$. In this case, the velocity update will increase the background velocity, as it should.[5]

As discussed in Appendix 25B, the H-DSO gradient updates the velocity model along low-wavenumber wavepaths. Here, the source (geophone) wavepaths take the shape of ellipses in a homogeneous medium, with the foci at the source (geophone) and migration image points. These low-wavenumber wavepaths have widths proportional to $\sqrt{\lambda z}$ and provide the low-wavenumber estimates of

---

[4]The inequality in equation 25.9 is justified by considering the depth coordinate z in the $H(z, h)$ function to be an implicit function of the velocity model. According to Figures 25.5 and 25.6, if $c(\mathbf{x})$ increases, the curve described by $H(z, h)$ moves downward with increasing depth so $\frac{\partial z}{\partial c(\mathbf{x}')} > 0$.

[5]Bill Symes (personal communication, 2014) first pointed out the importance of the H-DSO direction update to Sanzong Zhang.

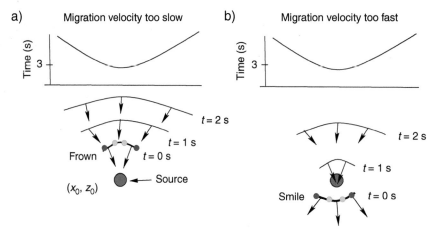

Figure 25.5. Exploding reflector model. At $t = 0$, an impulsive explosion is excited at $\mathbf{x}_0$ in a medium where the resulting wavefields are recorded at the surface. The exploding reflector imaging condition stops the back propagation of the wavefronts at $t = 0$ to give the migration image that appears as a (a) frown or a (b) smile if the migration velocity is too slow or fast, respectively.

the velocity that mitigate cycle-skipping problems in FWI. Here, z is the reflector depth.

DSO gradient velocity updates

The DSO gradient γ^{DSO} in equation 25.6 can, in theory, update the intermediate-wavenumber components of the velocity model. For the example of Figure 25.3f, the Fréchet derivative

$$m(\mathbf{x}, h) H(z, h)^2 \frac{\partial m(\mathbf{x}, h)}{\partial c(\mathbf{x}')} = \frac{m(\mathbf{x}, h) H(z, h)^2 \frac{\partial m(\mathbf{x}, h)}{\partial c(\mathbf{x}')}}{\frac{\partial z}{\partial z}} \frac{\partial m(\mathbf{x}, h)}{\partial z}$$

$$(25.10)$$

has the same polarity as $m(\mathbf{x}, h)$ along either the frown or smile for a zero-phase migration wavelet. In fact, for an oscillatory source wavelet that defines the oscillatory behavior of $m(\mathbf{x}, h)$ across an interface, its gradient $\propto \partial m(\mathbf{x}, h)/\partial z$ is also oscillatory with the same characteristic wavelength.

This inflexible sign of the DSO gradient sometimes can prevent a fast rate of convergence to the global minimum (Luo et al., 2015). If the sign is properly taken into consideration,[6] then the DSO gradient, in theory, also can update low-to-intermediate wavenumbers of the velocity model.

In summary, the multiscale strategy is to use the $\gamma^{\text{H-DSO}}$ gradient to update initially the low-wavenumber components of the velocity model where the kernel $H(z, h) m(\mathbf{x}, h)$ largely ignores noisy artifacts in the extended migration image. After a sufficient number of iterations, the DSO gradient γ^{DSO} with the sign properly accounted for is activated

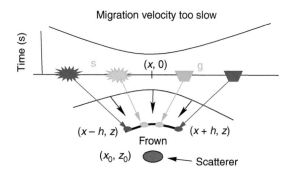

Figure 25.6. Prestack migration with the extended migration imaging condition using too slow of a migration velocity model produces the thick frown-like image. The extended migration imaging condition $T_{\text{sg}}^{\text{refl}} = T_{sx-h} + T_{gx-h}$ will be satisfied along the frown for the source-geophone pairs symmetrically located about the vertical line that intersects $(x, 0)$. Here, $T_{\text{sg}}^{\text{refl}}$ is the reflection time for a source at $\mathbf{s}$, a geophone at $\mathbf{g}$, and the scatterer at $\mathbf{x}_o$. The direct-wave propagation time from $\mathbf{x}$ to $\mathbf{x}'$ is $T_{xx'}$.

to include more details in the velocity model. The workflow for implementing GDSO is given in Box 25.3.1.

25.3 Numerical examples

A finite-difference solution to the 2D acoustic wave equation is used to compute 242 shot gathers for the Marmousi model in Figure 25.7a, in which the shots are evenly distributed along the top of the Marmousi model. The fixed hydrophones are evenly distributed on the top surface with a spacing of 20 m, and a Ricker wavelet peaked at 15 Hz is used for the source wavelet. The starting model is shown in Figure 25.7b, and the DSO and GDSO tomograms after 40 iterations are shown in Figure 25.7c–d, respectively. It

---

[6]If a steepest-descent method is used, the proper sign is discovered by a line search that determines which direction leads to a downhill move.

Box 25.3.1 Workflow for Wave-Equation GDSO

1. Estimate the background velocity model $c(x,z)^{(0)}$, and set $k = 0$.
2. For the migration velocity $c(x,z)^{(k)}$, migrate data to get $m(x,z,h)$.
3. Pick the subsurface-offset function $H(z,h)$ with respect to z for each offset value x. In practice, picking is too tedious so we approximate $H(z,h)$ by the product $h \times m(\mathbf{x},h)$. This implicitly assumes that $|m(\mathbf{x},h)|$ has mostly large amplitudes along $H(z,h)$ and negligible amplitudes elsewhere. It also assumes the migration amplitudes are normalized to the value 1.
4. The total residual $\beta(\mathbf{x},H)$ is computed by multiplying the squared migration image $m(\mathbf{x},H)^2$ by $H/\dot{m}(x,z,H)$, which acts as a virtual reflectivity distribution that is an indicator of errors in the velocity model.
5. Weight the back-propagated reflection field $p_g(x + H,z,t)$ at $(x+H,z)$ with $\beta(\mathbf{x},H)$, and smear it along the source wavepath to get the source-side gradient in equation 25.20 for all values of $\mathbf{x}'$.
6. Weight the forward-propagated source field $p_s(x - H,z,t)$ at $(x - H,z)$ with $\beta(\mathbf{x},H)$, and smear it along the geophone wavepath to get the second term in equation 25.20 for all values of $\mathbf{x}'$.
7. Update the velocity according to equation 25.6 for $\eta = 1$.
8. Increase the index counter k by 1 and repeat steps 2–7 until a satisfactory velocity model is obtained or there is negligible progress in reducing the objective function with increasing iterations. Then, update the higher wavenumbers with the γ^{DSO} gradient in equation 25.6 if the sign is properly taken into consideration, and iterate until convergence. Various strategies can be used, such as iteratively reducing the multiscale parameter η from the value 1.0 to 0.5.

---

is obvious that the GDSO tomogram is more accurate than the DSO tomogram.

The improved accuracy of the GDSO tomogram is validated by the RTM images in Figure 25.8. Here, the GDSO RTM image in Figure 25.8b provides a more accurate reflectivity distribution compared to the DSO migration image in Figure 25.8a. This also is confirmed by the zoom views of the dashed and solid boxes shown in Figure 25.9.

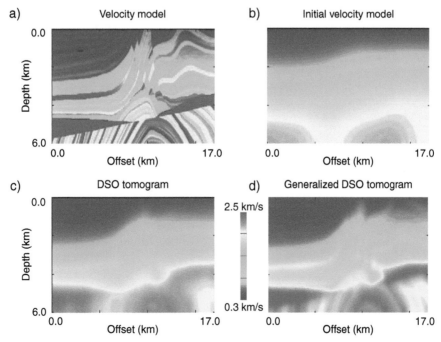

Figure 25.7. The (a) true velocity, (b) initial velocity, (c) DSO, and (d) generalized DSO inverted velocity models. Adapted from Zhang and Schuster (2013b).

Here, the GDSO RTM images provide a significant increase in focusing the reflection energy at the reflectors, especially for the shallow depths in the solid box.

Finally, the angle gathers for different offsets are displayed in Figure 25.10. An angle gather is formed by migrating the data for a specified range of source and reflection angles. The resulting migration trace for a specified offset is displayed for a range of incidence angles and a depth range from 0 to 6 km. In this case, each angle gather is computed for a $\pm 30°$ range of incidence angles. If the migration velocity is accurate, then the migration reflection events at any specified depth should be the same for this range of incidence angles. That is, the angle gathers should be flat. It is obvious that the GDSO angle gathers in Figure

25.10b are noticeably flatter than the DSO angle gathers in Figure 25.10a.

25.4 Summary

Generalized differential semblance optimization finds the velocity model that minimizes the objective function, $\sum_{x,z,h}[H(z,h)m(\mathbf{x},h)]^2$, in which coherent noise is eliminated everywhere except along the picked curve $H(z,h)$. Similar to WTW, the smoothly varying $H(z,h)$ function is used at the early iterations mainly to estimate the low-wavenumber components of the velocity model; later iterations turn on the DSO gradient to refine the higher-wavenumber components of the velocity model. Tests with synthetic data show that, relative to DSO, GDSO can converge to a more accurate solution with intermediate resolution for the Marmousi model. As will be shown in the next chapter, GDSO combined with FWI can reconstruct successfully low-, intermediate-, and high-wavenumber components in the Marmousi velocity model.

Generalized differential semblance optimization has the following characteristics

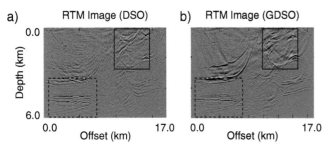

Figure 25.8. Marmousi RTM images computed from the (a) DSO and (b) GDSO velocity models in Figure 25.7. Adapted from Zhang and Schuster (2013b).

1. This method significantly mitigates the coherent noise problem with DSO, which tries to force all of $m(\mathbf{x},h)$ to be focused at $h = 0$.

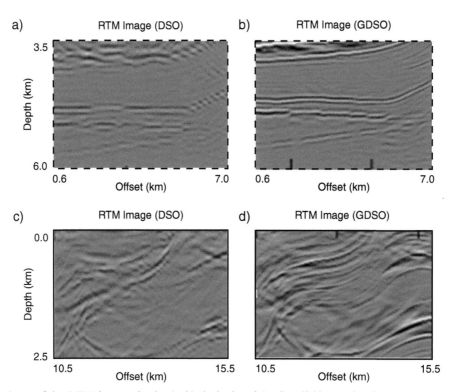

Figure 25.9. Zoom views of the RTM images in the (a–b) dashed and (c–d) solid boxes in Figure 25.8. Adapted from Zhang and Schuster (2013b).

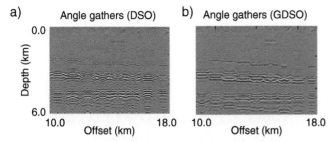

Figure 25.10. Angle gathers obtained by migrating the Marmousi data with the (a) DSO and (b) GDSO velocity models in Figure 25.7. Adapted from Zhang and Schuster (2013b).

2. There is no waveform misfit in the GDSO objective function, which can be an advantage compared to full-waveform inversion if the amplitudes cannot be modeled properly. However, not fitting the observed amplitudes can reduce the resolution of the estimated velocity image. This inability to achieve high resolution in the tomogram also is suggested by the smoothly varying misfit functions for the four-scatterer model.

3. Similar to most inversion methods, if the model is too complex then convergence to the correct velocity model is not guaranteed. If coherent events cannot be seen in the CIGs, then GDSO likely will fail.

4. A significant limitation of GDSO is that, compared to standard migration, the calculation of extended migration images requires an extra spatial dimension for two dimensions and two extra dimensions for three dimensions. Another drawback is that the $H(z, h)$ curves should be picked manually in the extended images if the data are too noisy. Therefore, the GDSO computational costs can be significantly more than standard DSO.

25.5 Exercises

1. Reformulate the GDSO objective function so the intensity of the migration image is replaced by the inner product between the predicted and observed migration images. Call this the correlation GDSO objective function. Derive the formula for the gradient.

2. Derive the formulas for the wavepaths associated with the correlation GDSO objective function. Compare these wavepaths to those for standard GDSO.

3. What are the benefits and limitations of correlation GDSO relative to standard GDSO?

4. Derive a semblance objective function and its gradient in the data domain that is analogous to that for GDSO. Compare its benefits and limitations to that of FWI.

5. Derive the GDSO wavepath formulas in which the product of Green's functions consists of a reflection

Green's function and a direct Green's function. Sketch the associated wavepath.

6. Luo et al. (2015) used the extended-time objective function

$$\epsilon = \frac{1}{2} \sum_{\tau=-T_o}^{T_o} \sum_x \tau^2 I(\mathbf{x}, \tau)^2, \qquad (25.11)$$

in which τ is the time lag between the source wavefield $p_s(x, z, t + \tau)$ and the back-projected receiver field $p_g(x, z, t - \tau)$. Here,

$$I(\mathbf{x}, \tau) = \int p_s(x, z, t + \tau) p_g(x, z, t - \tau) dt, \quad (25.12)$$

is the time-lagged migration image for a single shot gather.[7] The gradient of this objective function is

$$\begin{aligned}
\frac{\partial \epsilon}{\partial s(\mathbf{x})} &= \sum_{\tau=-T_o}^{T_o} \sum_x \tau^2 I(\mathbf{x}, \tau) \frac{\partial I(\mathbf{x}, \tau)}{\partial s(\mathbf{x})}, \\
&= \sum_{\tau=-T_o}^{T_o} \sum_x \tau^2 I(\mathbf{x}, \tau) \frac{\partial I(\mathbf{x}, \tau)}{\partial \tau(\mathbf{x})} \frac{\partial \tau}{\partial s(\mathbf{x})}, \\
&= -\sum_{\tau=-T_o}^{T_o} \sum_x \tau I(\mathbf{x}, \tau)^2 \frac{\partial \tau}{\partial s(\mathbf{x})}, \qquad (25.13)
\end{aligned}$$

where the last step follows by using the product rule $f dg = d(fg) - g df$ and assigning fg to be zero at the endpoints of the summation. The rationale in assigning τ to be a function of $s(\mathbf{x})$ is that Luo et al. (2015) consider τ to maximize the amplitude of the crosscorrelation function $I(\mathbf{x}, \tau)$, so that the Fréchet derivative $\partial \tau / \partial s(\mathbf{x})$ is the same as in equation 20.9 for wave equation traveltime inversion. Luo et al. (2015) denote this methodology as full traveltime inversion (FTI), and it shows promising results when applied to synthetic data when the starting model is very poor. A key assumption in the step $\partial I(\mathbf{x}, \tau) / \partial s(\mathbf{x}) = \partial I(\mathbf{x}, \tau) / \partial \tau(\mathbf{x}) \partial \tau / \partial s(\mathbf{x})$ is the approximation $p(t, s + \Delta s) \approx p(t + \Delta \tau(\Delta s), s)$.

What are the implicit conditions for this approximation to be true? Derive the explicit expression for the FTI gradient with equation 20.9. Write the workflow for implementing FTI.

7. The above equations starts out by assuming τ is an independent variable then suddenly assumes it is a function of slowness. Can you justify this? Reformulate

---

[7] If more than one shot gather is used, then there is an additional summation over shot indexes.

the above misfit function as saying that τ is a picked traveltime in the extended image domain that conforms to the maximum amplitude of $I(\mathbf{x}, \tau)$. Now derive the gradient. Compare and contrast this gradient with the GDSO gradient.

Appendix 25A: Migration images in the subsurface offset domain

The equation for constructing $m(x, z, h)$ (Rickett and Sava, 2002; Sava and Biondi, 2004; Sava and Fomel, 2006) is

$$m(x, z, h) = \sum_t p_s(x - h, z, t) p_g(x + h, z, t) \quad (25.14)$$

in which $p_s(x - h, z, t)$ is the forward-modeled source field

$$p_s(x - h, z, t) = W(t) \star g(x - h, z, t | \mathbf{x}_s, 0) \quad (25.15)$$

at the location $(x - h, z)$, $p_g(x + h, z, t)$ is the back-propagated reflection field

$$p_g(x + h, z, t) = \int p(\mathbf{x}_g, t | \mathbf{x}_s)_{\text{obs}} \star g(x + h, z, -t | \mathbf{x}_g, 0) d\mathbf{x}_g \quad (25.16)$$

at $(x + h, z)$, and the geophones are located at $\mathbf{x}_g$. The source wavelet is denoted by $W(t)$, the acausal Green's function is given by $g(x, z, -t | \mathbf{x}_g, 0)$, and the observed reflection traces are represented by $p(\mathbf{x}_g, t | \mathbf{x}_s)_{\text{obs}}$. Here, we assume a standard migration method that migrates shot gathers recorded on the surface to give the subsurface-offset migration image $m(x, z, h)$ at $(x - h, z)$. For $h = 0$, $m(x, z, h)$ reduces to the conventional migration image at (x, z).

If the velocity model is wrong, then the standard migration image might be so defocused that there are few coherent clues to discover which parts of the velocity model are wrong. In contrast, the extended migration image domain provides an extra spatial dimension that allows for the formation of coherent clues to erroneous velocity models; for example, the smiles or frowns in Figure 25.1. Such information can provide for an accurate update of the model, but it is at the expense of increasing both the dimension of the migration model and the computational cost.

If the migration velocity is too fast (or slow), then the subsurface-offset migration image can form the smile (or frown) artifacts in Figure 25.1b. For a locally layered velocity model, this symmetrical smile appears at pairs of points mirrored across from one another at the same depth. In this case, zero-lag correlation of the source field at $(x - h, z_1)$ with the back-propagated reflections at $(x + h, z_1)$ will produce strong energy at the wrong position $(x - h, z_1)$. If the

medium is not layered, however, then the strong focusing will not take place at the mirror positions $(x \pm h, z)$. This is an inherent limitation of the subsurface-offset migration method if only horizontal offsets are used.

Appendix 25B: H-DSO Fréchet derivative and gradient

The equation for the Fréchet derivative $\partial H(z, h) / \partial c(\mathbf{x}')$ can be found by recognizing that $H(z, h)$ is an implicit function of the velocity model. In general, Luo and Schuster (1991a and 1991b) show that the implicit function theorem can be used with a connective equation to get $\partial H(z, h) / \partial c(\mathbf{x}')$. This connective function is formulated by recognizing that $\partial m(x, z, h) / \partial h = 0$ along the peaks of the dashed smile in Figure 25.1b, where the dashed curve intercepts the peaks of the subsurface-offset migration image. In this case, the h-derivative of the migration image along the smile gives the connective function:

$$\dot{f}(x, z, c, h)|_{h=h^*} = \dot{m}(x, z, h^*) = 0, \quad (25.17)$$

in which $\dot{m}(x, z, h) = \partial m(x, z, h) / \partial h$, and h^* is the stationary space lag that defines the h-offset along the smile in Figure 25.2. The total derivative $d\dot{f} = \partial \dot{f} / \partial c dc + \partial \dot{f} / \partial h dh$ of the connective function in equation 25.17 then can be set to zero and rearranged to give the Fréchet derivative

$$\frac{\partial h}{\partial c(x', z')} = -\frac{\partial \dot{f}}{\partial c(x', z')} \bigg/ \frac{\partial \dot{f}}{\partial h} \bigg|_{h=h^*}$$
$$= -\frac{1}{\ddot{m}(x, z, h)} \frac{\partial \dot{m}(x, z, h)}{\partial c(x', z')} \bigg|_{h=h^*}. \quad (25.18)$$

The stationary offset h^* is a function of z and h (for a fixed x) and so is the same as the surface-offset function $H(z, h)$.

Therefore, the Fréchet derivative $\partial \dot{m}(x, z, H) / \partial c(x', z')$ associated with the migration image is obtained by differentiating equation 25.14 to get

$$\frac{\partial \dot{m}(x, z, H)}{\partial c(x', z')} = \frac{\partial}{\partial H} \left[\frac{\partial p_s(x - H, z, t)}{\partial c(x', z')} \tilde{\otimes} p_g(x + H, z, t) \right.$$
$$\left. + p_s(x - H, z, t) \tilde{\otimes} \frac{\partial p_g(x + H, z, t)}{\partial c(x', z')} \right], \quad (25.19)$$

and $\tilde{\otimes}$ indicates zero-lag correlation in the time domain. Inserting equation 25.19 into 25.18 and plugging the result into the H-DSO gradient $\gamma^{\text{H-DSO}}$ (see equation 25.6) gives

$$\gamma(\mathbf{x'})^{\text{H-DSO}} = -\sum_{x,z,h} \beta(\mathbf{x},H) \frac{\partial}{\partial H}$$

$$\times \left[\overbrace{\frac{\partial p_s(x-H,z,t)}{\partial c(x',z')}}^{\text{update along source wavepath}} \tilde{\otimes} p_g(x+H,z,t) \right.$$

$$\left. + \overbrace{p_s(x-H,z,t) \tilde{\otimes} \frac{\partial p_g(x+H,z,t)}{\partial c(x',z')}}^{\text{update along geophone wavepath}} \right],$$

$$(25.20)$$

in which the subsurface-offset function is

$$\beta(\mathbf{x},H) = \frac{m(x,z,H)^2 H}{\ddot{m}(x,z,H)}. \qquad (25.21)$$

The first term on the right side of equation 25.20 updates the velocity by weighting the backward-propagated data $p_g(x+H,z,t)$ with the $\beta(x,z,H)$, and smearing it along the source-side wavepath from $\mathbf{s}$ to $(x-H,z)$. The second term is similar, except the velocity is updated by weighting the forward-propagated source field $p_s(x-H,z,t)$ with $\beta(x,z,H)$, and smearing it along the geophone wavepath from $\mathbf{g}$ to $(x+H,z)$.

The Fréchet derivative $\partial p_g(x+H,z,t)/\partial c(x',z')$ in equation 25.20 is similar to the Fréchet derivative in equation 24.19, so its interpretation is that the residuals are smeared along the cigar-like wavepaths bounded by ellipses similar to those depicted in Figure 24.6. Updating the velocity along these ellipses makes intuitive sense because it describes the extrapolation path of the source wavefield, which likely contains the migration velocity errors that lead to the mispositioned migration image. Therefore, the velocity should be corrected along the cigar-like ellipses that update low-wavenumber components of the velocity model.

Chapter 26: Generalized Image-Domain Inversion

The gradient formula $\gamma(\mathbf{y}) = \partial\epsilon/\partial s(\mathbf{y})$ is derived for the generalized image objective function $\epsilon = 0.5 \sum_i H_i^2 \Delta m_i^2$, in which Δm_i is the migration image residual and H_i is the h-offset moveout curve in the extended image domain; in practice the objective function has an extra summation over all model points in the subsurface. The summation is over the subsurface offset indices. The result shows that $\gamma(\mathbf{y})$ is a summation of three gradients: a low-wavenumber generalized semblance optimization (H-DSO) gradient, the intermediate-wavenumber gradient associated with differential semblance optimization (DSO), and a high-wavenumber gradient associated with full-waveform inversion (FWI). This image-domain gradient has multi-scale features similar to those of wave-equation-traveltime waveform inversion in the data domain, and it can be used to partly overcome the cycle-skipping problem with FWI.

26.1 Introduction

Wave-equation migration velocity analysis (WEMVA) is an image-domain inversion method that uses numerical solutions to the one-way or two-way wave equations. Several WEMVA methods have been proposed to extract velocity information from the migration image. Differential semblence optimization (Symes and Kern, 1994) uses either the zeroth- or first-order derivative of the migration image along the angle axis to produce the image perturbation. It also uses the subsurface-offset-domain data to construct a penalty operator, which annihilates the energy at nonzero lags, and enhances the migration energy at zero lag. This objective function can partly avoid cycle-skipping problems, but will falsely overpenalize focused common-image gathers (CIGs) with variable amplitudes (Zhang and Biondi, 2013). It can experience some difficulties with unfocused images in complex subsurface regions because of poor illumination even if the velocity is correct.

As an alternative, Zhang and Schuster (2013a) present a generalized differential optimization (GDSO) method

which finds the 2D slowness distribution $s(\mathbf{x})$ that minimizes the objective function

$$\epsilon = \frac{1}{2}\sum_{h,i} \left[\overbrace{H(\mathbf{x_i},h)}^{\text{offset moveout curve}} \overbrace{\Delta m(\mathbf{x_i},h)}^{\text{migration residual}} \right]^2,$$

$$= \frac{1}{2}\Delta\mathbf{m}^T\mathbf{H}^T\mathbf{H}\Delta\mathbf{m}. \quad (26.1)$$

Here, $H(\mathbf{x_i},h)$, the element of the diagonal matrix $\mathbf{H}$, describes the moveout trajectory of a migration image in the subsurface offset domain (x,z,h), in which h is the subsurface offset coordinate.[1] Here, $\Delta m(\mathbf{x},h)$, the element of the migration residual vector $\Delta\mathbf{m}$, is the difference between the predicted and observed migration images. In matrix-vector notation, we have the residual vector

$$\Delta\mathbf{m} = \mathbf{L}^T\Delta\mathbf{d}, \quad (26.2)$$

where $\mathbf{L}^T$ is the migration operator and $\Delta\mathbf{d}$ is the data residual, both of which are a function of the slowness model. Inserting equation 26.2 into equation 26.1 gives

$$\epsilon = \frac{1}{2}\Delta\mathbf{d}^T\mathbf{L}\mathbf{H}^T\mathbf{H}\mathbf{L}^T\Delta\mathbf{d}. \quad (26.3)$$

The GDSO approach only considers $\mathbf{H}$ and $\mathbf{L}$ to be functions of the perturbed slowness model, so the gradient of equation 26.3 takes the form

$$\frac{\partial\epsilon}{\partial s(\mathbf{y})} = \Delta\mathbf{d}^T\mathbf{L}\mathbf{H}^T\left[\overbrace{\frac{\partial\mathbf{H}}{\partial s(\mathbf{y})}\mathbf{L}^T\Delta\mathbf{d}}^{\text{H-DSO}} + \overbrace{\mathbf{H}\frac{\partial\mathbf{L}^T}{\partial s(\mathbf{y})}\Delta\mathbf{d}}^{\text{DSO}} \right]. \quad (26.4)$$

Here, the H-DSO and DSO terms can update the low- and intermediate-wavenumber portions of the slowness model.

---

[1] For example, if the image is that of a reflection migrated with too slow of a velocity, $H(\mathbf{x_i},h)$ will describe a smile in the subsurface-offset section. This moveout curve is similar to that for the traveltime of a reflection event in the data domain, and it provides low-wavenumber updates to the velocity model.

The optimization strategy is to update initially the low-wavenumber portion of the velocity model using only the H-DSO gradient, and then activate the DSO gradient to update the intermediate wavenumbers of the model. Numerically, this multiscale strategy is shown to be superior to a pure DSO optimization, but it cannot reconstruct the high wavenumbers of the model that sometimes are obtained by full-waveform inversion (FWI).

Next, a generalized misfit function is derived in the image domain that incorporates an FWI-like term that can achieve a high-wavenumber reconstruction of the velocity model (Zhang and Schuster, 2013b). This generalized gradient now considers $\Delta\mathbf{d}$ in equation 26.1 to be a function of the slowness model. Hence, the gradient will now consist of three terms:

$$
\frac{\partial\epsilon}{\partial s(\mathbf{y})} = \Delta\mathbf{d}^T\mathbf{L}\mathbf{H}^T \left[\alpha \overbrace{\frac{\partial\mathbf{H}}{\partial s(\mathbf{y})}}^{\text{H-DSO}}\mathbf{L}^T\Delta\mathbf{d} + \beta\,\mathbf{H}\overbrace{\frac{\partial\mathbf{L}^T}{\partial s(\mathbf{y})}}^{\text{DSO}}\Delta\mathbf{d} \right.
$$

$$
\left. + \eta\,\mathbf{H}\mathbf{L}^T\overbrace{\frac{\partial\Delta\mathbf{d}}{\partial s(\mathbf{y})}}^{\text{FWI}} \right], \tag{26.5}
$$

in which α, β, and η are scalars that take on values between 0 and 1. Similar to the WTW method (Luo and Schuster, 1991a and 1991b), they gradually are changed as the iterations proceed to admit higher wavenumbers gradually into the solution. For equation 26.5, the H-DSO, DSO, and FWI gradient terms give the low-wavenumber, intermediate-wavenumber, and high-wavenumber parts of the model, respectively. This multiscale strategy sometimes can overcome the local minima problem in waveform inversion.

The next section presents the mathematical derivation of the generalized image-domain inversion (GIDI) formulas. Then, numerical examples are presented to demonstrate the effectiveness of GIDI for velocity inversion. The final section presents a discussion and conclusions.

26.2 Theory of generalized image-domain inversion

The velocity update formula by a method of steepest descent is given by

$$
c(\mathbf{x}')^{k+1} = c(\mathbf{x}')^k - \alpha\gamma(\mathbf{x}'), \tag{26.6}
$$

in which the gradient $\gamma(\mathbf{x}')$ of the misfit function in equation 26.1 is

$$
\gamma(\mathbf{x}') = \sum_{\mathbf{x},\mathbf{h}} Re\left[\overbrace{|\Delta m(\mathbf{x},\mathbf{h})|^2\frac{\partial H(\mathbf{x},\mathbf{h})}{\partial c(\mathbf{x}')}}^{\text{H-DSO gradient}} \right.
$$

$$
\left. \overbrace{+\, H(\mathbf{x},h)^2\Delta m(\mathbf{x},\mathbf{h})^*\frac{\partial\Delta m(\mathbf{x},\mathbf{h})}{\partial c(\mathbf{x}')}}^{\text{DSO+FWI gradients}} \right]. \tag{26.7}
$$

Here, the extended image residual $\Delta m(\mathbf{x},\mathbf{h})$ (see Chapter 25) is

$$
\Delta m(\mathbf{x},\mathbf{h}) = \sum_{\mathbf{x}_s,\mathbf{x}_g,\omega} W(\omega)G(\mathbf{x}-\mathbf{h},\omega|\mathbf{x}_s)
$$

$$
\times\, G(\mathbf{x}+\mathbf{h},\omega|\mathbf{x}_g)\Delta d(\mathbf{x}_g,\omega|\mathbf{x}_s)^*, \tag{26.8}
$$

and the data residual $\Delta d(\mathbf{x}_g,\omega|\mathbf{x}_s)$ is

$$
\Delta d(\mathbf{x}_g,\omega|\mathbf{x}_s) = d(\mathbf{x}_g,\omega|\mathbf{x}_s) - d(\mathbf{x}_g,\omega|\mathbf{x}_s)_{\text{obs}}, \tag{26.9}
$$

in which $d(\mathbf{x}_g,\omega|\mathbf{x}_s)$ is the predicted data obtained by forward modeling the data with the kth velocity model.

Substituting equations 26.8 and 26.9 into equation 26.7 decomposes $\gamma(\mathbf{x}')$ into four components:

$$
\gamma(\mathbf{x}') = \gamma(\mathbf{x}')^{\text{H-DSO}} + \gamma(\mathbf{x}')^{\text{DSO}_1} + \gamma(\mathbf{x}')^{\text{DSO}_2} + \gamma(\mathbf{x}')^{\text{FWI}}. \tag{26.10}
$$

Here,

$$
\gamma(\mathbf{x}')^{\text{H-DSO}} = \sum_{\mathbf{x},\mathbf{h}} Re\left[|\Delta m(\mathbf{x},\mathbf{h})|^2\frac{\partial H(\mathbf{x},\mathbf{h})}{\partial c(\mathbf{x}')} \right], \tag{26.11}
$$

$$
\gamma(\mathbf{x}')^{\text{DSO}_1} = Re\left[\sum_{\mathbf{x},\mathbf{h},\mathbf{x}_s,\mathbf{x}_g,\omega} W(\omega)H(\mathbf{x},h)^2\frac{\partial G(\mathbf{x}-\mathbf{h},\omega|\mathbf{x}_s)}{\partial c(\mathbf{x}')} \right.
$$

$$
\left. \times\, \Delta m(\mathbf{x},\mathbf{h})^*G(\mathbf{x}+\mathbf{h},\omega|\mathbf{x}_g)\Delta d(\mathbf{x}_g,\omega|\mathbf{x}_s)^* \right], \tag{26.12}
$$

$$
\gamma(\mathbf{x}')^{\text{DSO}_2} = Re\left[\sum_{\mathbf{x},\mathbf{h},\mathbf{x}_s,\mathbf{x}_g,\omega} W(\omega)H(\mathbf{x},h)^2G(\mathbf{x}-\mathbf{h},\omega|\mathbf{x}_s) \right.
$$

$$
\left. \times\, \Delta m(\mathbf{x},\mathbf{h})^*\frac{\partial G(\mathbf{x}+\mathbf{h},\omega|\mathbf{x}_g)}{\partial c(\mathbf{x}')}\Delta d(\mathbf{x}_g,\omega|\mathbf{x}_s)^* \right], \tag{26.13}
$$

and

$$
\gamma(\mathbf{x}')^{\text{FWI}} = Re\left[\sum_{\mathbf{x},\mathbf{h},\mathbf{x}_s,\mathbf{x}_g,\omega} W(\omega)H(\mathbf{x},h)^2G(\mathbf{x}-\mathbf{h},\omega|\mathbf{x}_s) \right.
$$

$$
\left. \times\, \Delta m(\mathbf{x},\mathbf{h})^*G(\mathbf{x}+\mathbf{h},\omega|\mathbf{x}_g)\frac{\partial\Delta d(\mathbf{x}_g,\omega|\mathbf{x}_s)^*}{\partial c(\mathbf{x}')} \right], \tag{26.14}
$$

Box 26.2.1 Workflow for Generalized Image-Domain Inversion

1. Estimate the background velocity model $c(x,z)^{(0)}$, and set $k = 0$.

2. For the migration velocity $c(x,z)^{(k)}$, compute the predicted data, and subtract it from the observed data to get the data residual $\Delta\mathbf{d}^{(k)}$. Migrate this data residual $\Delta\mathbf{d}^{(k)}$ to get the migration residual $\Delta m(x,z,h)^{(k)}$ for $k = 0$. Also migrate the recorded data to get the migration image $m(x,z,h)^{(k)}$, which is to be used for estimating the DSO and H-DSO gradients.

3. Use the migration image $m(x,z,h)^{(k)}$ and the migration residual $\Delta m(x,z,h)^{(k)}$ to compute the gradients in equations 26.11–26.14.

4. Update[2] the velocity model according to equations 26.6 and 26.7. A multiscale approach can be used in which the H-DSO gradient first is used to estimate the low-wavenumber components of the velocity, and then the DSO gradient is used to recover the intermediate components. Finally, the FWI gradient is activated to recover the high-wavenumber details of the model.

5. Increase the index counter k by 1 and repeat the previous steps until a satisfactory velocity model is obtained or there is negligible progress in reducing the objective function. Other multiscale strategies also can be used, such as low-pass filtering the data and/or limiting the data to short time windows and short offsets, and inverting for a model with limited depth penetration and wavenumber content. Higher frequencies and wider windows in time and offset can be incorporated gradually as the iterations proceed.

---

where, under the Born approximation, we have

$$\frac{\partial \Delta d(\mathbf{x}_g, \omega | \mathbf{x}_s)^*}{\partial c(\mathbf{x}')} = -\frac{2\omega^2}{c(\mathbf{x}')^3} W(\omega)^* G(\mathbf{x}', \omega | \mathbf{x}_s)^* G(\mathbf{x}_g, \omega | \mathbf{x}')^*.$$

$$(26.15)$$

Substituting equation 26.15 into equation 26.14 yields the formula for the FWI-like gradient:

$$\gamma(\mathbf{x}')^{\text{FWI}} = -\frac{2}{c(\mathbf{x}')^3} Re\left[\sum_{\mathbf{x},\mathbf{h},\mathbf{x}_s,\mathbf{x}_g,\omega} \omega^2 |W(\omega)|^2 H(\mathbf{x},h)^2 \right.$$
$$\times G(\mathbf{x} - \mathbf{h}, \omega | \mathbf{x}_s) \Delta m(\mathbf{x},h)^* G(\mathbf{x} + \mathbf{h}, \omega | \mathbf{x}_g)$$
$$\left. \times G(\mathbf{x}', \omega | \mathbf{x}_s)^* G(\mathbf{x}_g, \omega | \mathbf{x}')^* \right].$$

$$(26.16)$$

26.2.1 Interpretation of the gradient functions

The H-DSO and DSO gradients in equations 26.11–26.13 are similar to the ones discussed in Chapter 25, except they are weighted with the extended migration residual rather than the extended migration image. The H-DSO gradient $\gamma(\mathbf{x})^{\text{H-DSO}}$ updates the low-wavenumber part of the velocity model by smearing $|\Delta m(\mathbf{x},h)|^2$ along the wavepaths in the extended image domain. For the intermediate-wavenumber update, the DSO terms smear

the weighted data residuals $\delta d(\mathbf{x}_g, \omega | \mathbf{x}_s)$ along similar wavepaths. For example, the term $\gamma(\mathbf{x}')^{\text{DSO}_1}$ says that the velocity is updated by weighting the backward-propagated data $G^*(\mathbf{x} + \mathbf{h}, \omega | \mathbf{x}_g) \Delta d$ with the weighted image residual $\Delta m(\mathbf{x}, \mathbf{h})^*$, and smearing it along the source wavepath from $\mathbf{x}_s$ to $\mathbf{x} - \mathbf{h}$. The $\gamma(\mathbf{x}')^{\text{DSO}_2}$ term is similar, except the velocity is updated by weighting the forward-propagated source field $W(\omega)G(\mathbf{x} - \mathbf{h}, \omega | \mathbf{x}_s)$ with the image residual $\Delta m(\mathbf{x}, \mathbf{h})^*$, and smearing it along the geophone wavepath from $\mathbf{x}_g$ to $\mathbf{x} - \mathbf{h}$.

The FWI-like term $\gamma(\mathbf{x}')^{\text{FWI}}$ is interpreted as calculating the data residual by demigrating the subsurface-offset-domain image residual $W(\omega)G(\mathbf{x} - \mathbf{h}, \omega | \mathbf{x}_s)\Delta m(\mathbf{x}, \mathbf{h})^* G(\mathbf{x}_g, \omega | \mathbf{x}_g + \mathbf{h})$ to get the predicted data. The predicted data is used to calculate the data residual, which is then reverse time migrated to update the velocity. This is similar to the scaled gradient for the data-domain FWI that can achieve high-resolution updates to the velocity model.

In summary, $\gamma^{\text{H-DSO}}$ and $\gamma^{\text{DSO}_1} + \gamma^{\text{DSO}_2}$ update the low- and intermediate-wavenumber components of the velocity model, and γ^{FWI} is the gradient seen in data-domain FWI that updates the high-wavenumber components of velocity. These lower- and higher-wavenumber characteristics of the gradients next will be illustrated with numerical examples. In practice, a multiscale strategy is used in which only the low-wavenumber H-DSO gradient is used in the early iterations. Then, the DSO and FWI gradually are activated to update both the intermediate- and high-wavenumber components. The workflow for implementing GIDI is given in Box 26.2.1.

---

[2]Zhang, S., 2016, Multiscale Seismic Inversion in the Data and Image Domains: PhD Dissertation, King Abdullah University of Science and Technology.

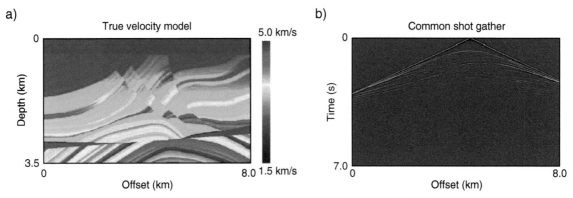

Figure 26.1. (a) Marmousi velocity model and (b) common-shot gather. The bandwidth of the synthetic traces is from 5 Hz to 50 Hz (Zhang and Schuster, 2013b).

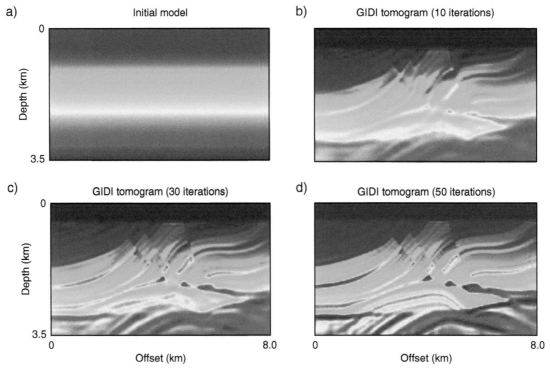

Figure 26.2. (a) Initial velocity model and (b–d) GIDI tomograms after 10, 30, and 50 iterations, respectively (Zhang and Schuster, 2013b).

26.3 Numerical results

To test the effectiveness of GIDI, synthetic data are generated from the Marmousi model shown in Figure 26.1. The data were modeled for 128 shots with a 70-m source spacing and a source bandwidth of 5 to 50 Hz. The reflected wavefields are recorded by 801 receivers with a fixed-spread shooting geometry and a 10-m geophone spacing; a typical shot gather is shown in Figure 26.1b. The initial velocity shown in Figure 26.2 increases with depth and Figure 26.2b and 26.2c depict the GIDI tomograms after 10, 30, and 50 iterations. We can see that, for this example, GIDI correctly reconstructs the velocity model even with the absence of the 0–5 Hz frequencies and a poor initial velocity.

The GIDI image residuals after 1, 10, 30, and 50 iterations are shown in Figure 26.3. Unlike the residuals with the initial velocity model, the GIDI image residuals tend to focus at $h = 0$ with an increasing number of iterations. This successful convergence is due partly to the lower wavenumber character of the gradients shown in Figure 26.4. Conventional FWI gives the high-wavenumber gradient shown in Figure 26.5. Low-wavenumber gradients are important if low frequencies are missing in the original data.

The second example is for marine data recorded in the Gulf of Mexico. This streamer data set was acquired

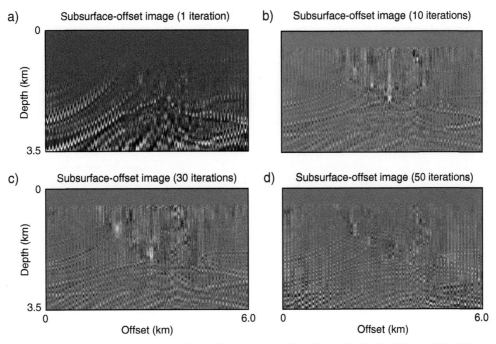

Figure 26.3. CIG migration residuals in the subsurface-offset domain after (a) 1, (b) 10, (c) 30, and (d) 50 iterations. The thin slabs are CIG migration images in (h, z) for different offsets (Zhang and Schuster, 2013b).

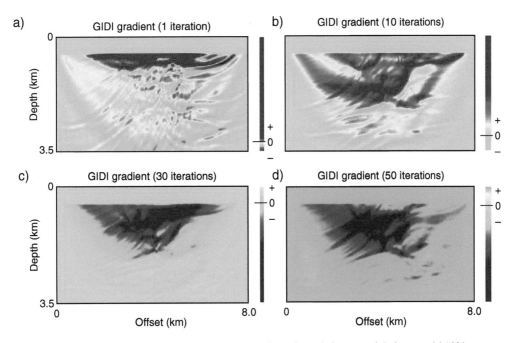

Figure 26.4. GIDI gradients after (a) 1, (b) 10, (c) 30, and (d) 50 iterations (Zhang and Schuster, 2013b).

using 496 shots with a shot interval of 37.5 m, a time-sampling interval of 1 ms, a trace length of 5 s, and 480 active hydrophones per shot. The hydrophone interval was 6.25 m, with a near-offset of 198 m and a far-offset of 6 km. The source wavelet was estimated by stacking along the first arrival at the nearest offset of each shot. The data are low-pass filtered to the frequency range from 4 to 45 Hz. Figure 26.6 shows a common-shot gather after low-pass

filtering the data set. The initial velocity model shown in Figure 26.6b is obtained by inverting the first-arrival traveltimes. This tomogram serves as the initial velocity model for GIDI.

The subsurface-offset-domain image residuals calculated from the initial velocity model are displayed in Figure 26.7. From these figures, we can see that first-arrival traveltime tomography provides an accurate velocity model that

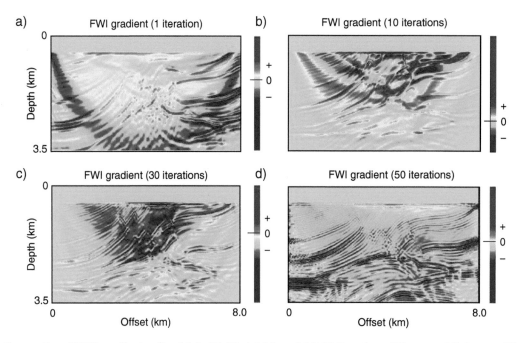

Figure 26.5. Conventional FWI gradients after (a) 1, (b) 10, (c) 30, and (d) 50 iterations (Zhang and Schuster, 2013b).

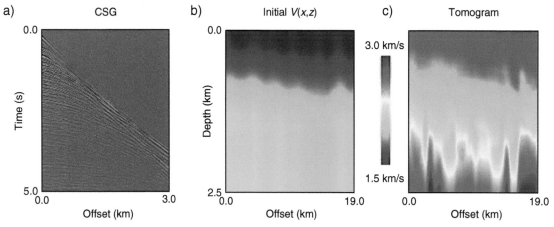

Figure 26.6. (a) Common-shot gather with a 4 to 45 Hz bandwidth for data from the Gulf of Mexico, (b) initial velocity model, and (c) GIDI tomogram after 70 iterations (Zhang and Schuster, 2013b).

flattens the CIGs above 2 km, but not for the reflectors deeper than 2 km. This is because the limited recording aperture prevents the turning wave from penetrating deeper than 2 km. To image the deeper velocities, GIDI inverts the reflections from the deeper layers.

The GIDI tomogram is displayed in Figure 26.6c, and Figure 26.7b shows the subsurface-offset-domain image residual calculated from the inverted velocity model. The GIDI residuals deeper than 2 km are much more focused at $h = 0$ compared to the residuals in Figure 26.7a. Most of the maximum energy in the GIDI residual focuses at $h = 0$.

To verify that the reconstructed velocity model is more accurate than the initial velocity model, the reverse time

migration (RTM) images computed with different velocity models are compared to each other in Figure 26.8. As seen in the zoom views in Figure 26.9, the GIDI RTM images appear to be better focused than those obtained from the traveltime tomogram.

To illustrate the multiscale nature of GIDI, Figure 26.10 compares the gradients of GIDI and conventional FWI. Figure 26.10a and 26.10b depict the lower-wavenumber DSO gradient and the higher-wavenumber FWI gradient from GIDI, respectively. The sum of these two gradients is shown in Figure 26.10c, and the gradient from conventional FWI is plotted next to it in Figure 26.10d. These figures illustrates that the image-domain gradient contains more lower-wavenumber components

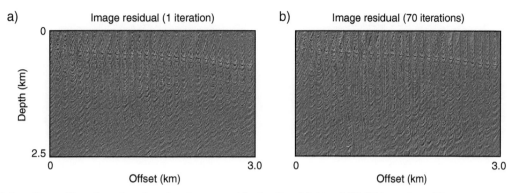

Figure 26.7. Subsurface-offset-domain migration image residuals after (a) 1 and (b) 70 iterations. Figures courtesy of Sanzong Zhang (2016).

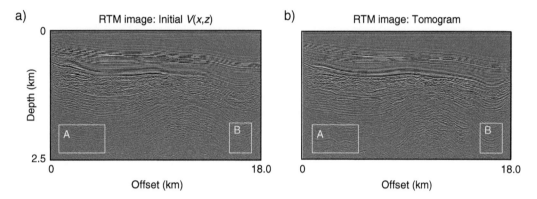

Figure 26.8. RTM images using the (a) initial and (b) inverted velocity models. Figures courtesy of Sanzong Zhang (2016).

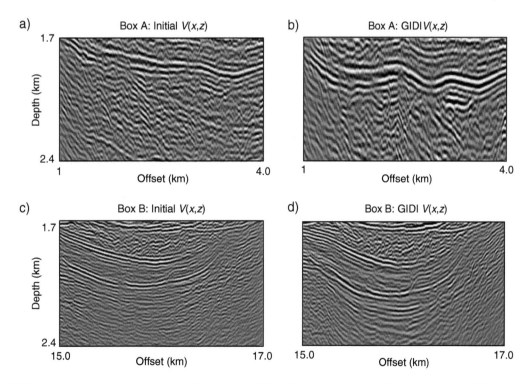

Figure 26.9. RTM images for inset boxes A and B in Figure 26.8. Figures courtesy of Sanzong Zhang (2016).

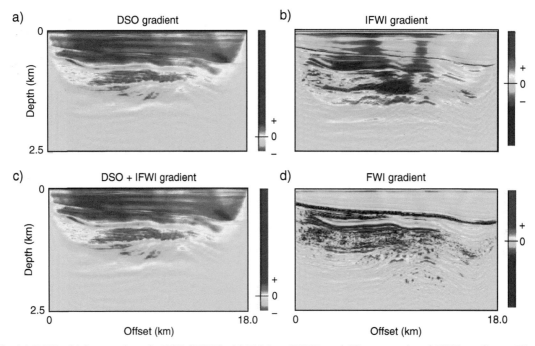

Figure 26.10. (a) DSO, (b) image-domain FWI (IFWI), (c) DSO + IFWI, and (d) conventional FWI gradients. The DSO + IFWI gradient is richer in lower-wavenumber components than the conventional FWI gradient. Figures courtesy of Sanzong Zhang (2016).

than the gradient of conventional FWI. Hence, it is less prone to cycle skipping in the absence of low frequencies in the data.

26.4 Summary

A generalized image-domain domain inversion method is presented that defines the misfit function as the weighted migration residual in the subsurface-offset-domain. The GIDI gradient is a combination of the gradients related to H-DSO, DSO, and FWI. Compared to the conventional FWI, empirical results suggest that GIDI is less sensitive to errors in the initial-velocity model and cycle skipping, and is more effective in updating the lower-wavenumber components of velocity. For the Marmousi data and the selected Gulf of Mexico data, image-domain FWI estimated a more accurate velocity model than conventional FWI. The main limitation of GIDI is that it requires significantly more computation (by at least one order of magnitude for 2D data), and memory than conventional FWI.

References

Aarts, E., and J. Korst, 1991, Simulated annealing and Boltzmann machines: John Wiley and Sons.

Akcelik, V., G. Biros, and O. Ghattas, 2002, Parallel multiscale Gauss-Newton-Krylov methods for inverse wave propagation: Proceedings of the ACM/IEEE 2002 Conference on Supercomputing, 41.

Aki, K., A. Christoffersson, and E. S. Husebye, 1977, Determination of the three-dimensional seismic structure of the lithosphere: Journal of Geophysical Research, **82**, 277–296, http://dx.doi.org/10.1029/JB082i002p00277.

Aki, K., and P. Richards, 1980, Quantitative seismology: W. H. Freeman and Company.

Almomin, A., 2011, Correlation-based wave-equation migration velocity analysis: 81st Annual International Meeting, SEG, Expanded Abstracts, 3887–3891, http://dx.doi.org/10.1190/1.3628017.

Almomin, A., and B. Biondi, 2012, Tomographic full waveform inversion: Practical and computationally feasible approach: 82nd Annual International Meeting, SEG, Expanded Abstracts, 1–5, http://dx.doi.org/10.1190/segam2012-0976.1.

Almomin, A., and B. Biondi, 2013, Tomographic full waveform inversion (TFWI) by successive linearizations and scale separations: 83rd Annual International Meeting, SEG, Expanded Abstracts, 1048–1052, http://dx.doi.org/10.1190/segam2013-1378.1.

AlTheyab, A., 2011, Multisource least-squares reverse time migration filtering for wave separation: Annual CSIM report, 65–69.

AlTheyab, A., 2013, Short note: On automatic internal multiples attenuation using LSRTM after FWI: CSIM Midyear Report, 75–77.

AlTheyab, A., 2014, 3D time-domain FWI applied to OBS data: CSIM Annual Report.

AlTheyab, A., 2015, Full waveform inversion: Ph.D. dissertation, King Abdullah University of Science and Technology.

AlTheyab, A., 2016, Imaging of scattered wavefields in passive and controlled-source seismology: Ph.D, dissertation, King Abdullah University of Science and Technology, http://repository.kaust.edu.sa/kaust/handle/10754/595157.

AlTheyab, A., and G. Dutta, 2014, Multiscale velocity model building by solving a sequence of full-waveform inversion problems with nearly consistent subsets of data residuals: CSIM Annual Report.

AlTheyab, A., and G. Schuster, 2015, Reflection full-waveform inversion for inaccurate starting models: 2015 Workshop: Depth Model Building: Full-waveform Inversion: SEG, Expanded Abstracts, 18–22, http://dx.doi.org/10.1190/FWI2015-005.

AlTheyab, A., and X. Wang, 2013, Hybrid linear and non-linear full-waveform inversion of Gulf of Mexico data: 83rd Annual International Meeting, SEG, Expanded Abstracts, 1003–1007, http://dx.doi.org/10.1190/segam2013-0538.1.

AlTheyab, A., X. Wang, and G. T. Schuster, 2013, Time-domain incomplete Gauss-Newton full-waveform inversion of Gulf of Mexico data: 83rd Annual International Meeting, SEG, Expanded Abstracts, 5175–5179, http://dx.doi.org/10.1190/segam2013-1478.1.

Al-Yahya, K., 1989, Velocity analysis by iterative profile migration: Geophysics, **54**, 718–729, http://dx.doi.org/10.1190/1.1442699.

Al-Yaqoobi, A., and M. Warner, 2013, Full waveform inversion — Dealing with limitations of 3D onshore seismic data: 83rd Annual International Meeting, SEG, Expanded Abstracts, 934–938, http://dx.doi.org/10.1190/segam2013-0799.1.

Aoki, N., 2008, Fast least-squares migration with a deblurring filter: M.S. thesis, University of Utah.

Aoki, N., and G. T. Schuster, 2009, Fast least-squares migration with a deblurring filter: Geophysics, **74**, no. 6, WCA83–WCA93, http://dx.doi.org/10.1190/1.3155162.

Asnaashari, A., R. Brossier, C. Castellanos, B. Dupuy, V. Etienne, Y. Gholami, G. Hu, L. Metivier, S. Operto, D. Pageot, V. Prieux, A. Ribodetti, A. Roques, and J. Virieux, 2012, Hierarchical approach of seismic full waveform inversion: Numerical Analysis and Applications, **5**, 99–108, http://dx.doi.org/10.1134/S1995423912020012.

Aster, R. C., B. Borchers, and C. H. Thurber, 2005, Parameter estimation and inverse problems: Elsevier Academic Press.

Bank, R., and H. Mittelmann, 1989, Stepsize selection in continuation procedures and damped Newton's method: Journal of Computational and Applied Mathematics, **26**, 67–77, http://dx.doi.org/10.1016/0377-0427(89)90148-9.

Barton, G., 1989, Elements of Green's functions and propagation: Oxford Press.

Baumstein, A., W. Ross, and S. Lee, 2011, Simultaneous source elastic inversion of surface waves: 73rd Conference and Exhibition, EAGE, Extended Abstracts, C040, http://dx.doi.org/10.3997/2214-4609.20149055.

Baysal, E., D. D. Kosloff, and J. W. C. Sherwood, 1983, Reverse time migration: Geophysics, **48**, 1514–1524, http://dx.doi.org/10.1190/1.1441434.

Berenger, J. P., 1994, A perfectly matched layer for the absorption of electromagnetic waves: Journal of Computational Physics, **114**, 185–200, http://dx.doi.org/10.1006/jcph.1994.1159.

Berkhout, A. J., 1984, Seismic resolution: A quantitative analysis of resolving power of acoustical echo techniques: Geophysical Press.

Berkhout, A. J., 2012, Joint migration inversion: Combining full wavefield migration with anisotropic velocity estimation: 82nd Annual International Meeting, SEG, Expanded Abstracts, 1–5, http://dx.doi.org/10.1190/segam2012-1077.1.

Berkhout, A. J., and D. W. Van Wulfften Palthe, 1979, Migration in terms of spatial deconvolution: Geophysical Prospecting, **27**, 261–291, http://dx.doi.org/10.1111/j.1365-2478.1979.tb00970.x.

Berryman, J., 1991, Lecture notes on nonlinear inversion and tomography: Lawrence Livermore National Laboratory Technical Report: UCRL-LR-105358-rev.1.

Beydoun, W. B., and M. Mendes, 1989, Elastic ray-Born l2-migration/inversion: Geophysical Journal International, **97**, 151–160, http://dx.doi.org/10.1111/j.1365-246X.1989.tb00490.x.

Beydoun, W. B., and A. Tarantola, 1988, First Born and Rytov approximations: Modeling and inversion conditions in a canonical example: The Journal of the Acoustical Society of America, **83**, 1045–1054, http://dx.doi.org/10.1121/1.396537.

Beylkin, G., 1984, Imaging of discontinuities in the inverse scattering problem by inversion of a causal generalized Radon transform: Journal of Mathematical Physics, **26**, 99–108, http://dx.doi.org/10.1063/1.526755.

Beylkin, G., M. Oristaglio, and D. Miller, 1985, Spatial resolution of migration algorithms, in A. J. Berkhout, J. Ridder, and L. E. van der Waals, eds., 14th International Symposium on Acoustical Imaging, Proceedings, 155–167.

Bijwaard, H., W. Spakman, and E. R. Engdahl, 1998, Closing the gap between regional and global travel time tomography: Journal of Geophysical Research, **103**, B12, 30055–30078, http://dx.doi.org/10.1029/98JB02467.

Bilbro, G. L., W. E. Snyder, S. J. Garnier, and J. W. Gault, 1992, Mean field annealing: A formalism for constructing GNC-like algorithms: IEEE Transactions on Neural Networks, **3**, 131–138, http://dx.doi.org/10.1109/72.105426.

Billette, F., P. Podvin, and G. Lambaré, 1998, Stereotomography with automatic picking: Application to the Marmousi dataset: 68th Annual International Meeting, SEG, Expanded Abstracts, 1317–1320, http://dx.doi.org/10.1190/1.1820143.

Biondi, B., and W. Symes, 2004, Angle-domain common-image gathers for migration velocity analysis by wavefield-continuation imaging: Geophysics, **69**, 1283–1298, http://dx.doi.org/10.1190/1.1801945.

Bishop, T. N., K. P. Bube, R. T. Cutler, R. T. Langan, P. L. Love, J. R. Resnick, R. T. Shuey, D. A. Spindler, and H. W. Wyld, 1985, Tomographic determination of velocity and depth in laterally varying media: Geophysics, **50**, 903–923, http://dx.doi.org/10.1190/1.1441970.

Blanch, J., and W. Symes, 1995, Efficient iterative viscoacoustic linearized inversion: 65th Annual International Meeting, SEG, Expanded Abstracts, 627–630, http://dx.doi.org/10.1190/1.1887406.

Bleistein, N., 1984, Mathematical methods for wave phenomena: Academic Press, Inc.

Bleistein, N., J. W. Stockwell, Jr., and J. K. Cohen, 2001, Mathematics of multidimensional seismic imaging, migration, and inversion: Springer-Verlag.

Boonyasiriwat, C., 2007, Acoustic waveform inversion of 2D Gulf of Mexico data: M.S. Thesis, University of Utah.

Boonyasiriwat, C., and G. T. Schuster, 2010, 3D multisource full-waveform inversion using dynamic random phase encoding: 80th Annual International Meeting, SEG, Expanded Abstracts, 1044–1049, http://dx.doi.org/10.1190/1.3513025.

Boonyasiriwat, C., G. T. Schuster, P. Valasek, and W. Cao, 2010, Applications of multiscale waveform inversion to marine data using a flooding technique and dynamic early-arrival windows: Geophysics, **75**, no. 6, R129–R136, http://dx.doi.org/10.1190/1.3507237.

Boonyasiriwat, C., P. Valasek, P. Routh, W. Cao, G. T. Schuster, and B. Macy, 2009, A multiscale method for time-domain waveform tomography: Geophysics, **74**, no. 6, WCC59–WCC68, http://dx.doi.org/10.1190/1.3151869.

Bozdağ, E., J. Trampert, and J. Tromp, 2011, Misfit functions for full waveform inversion based on instantaneous phase and envelope measurements: Geophysical Journal International, **185**, 845–870, http://dx.doi.org/10.1111/j.1365-246X.2011.04970.x.

Bracewell, R. N., 1990, Numerical transforms: Science, **248**, 697–704, http://dx.doi.org/10.1126/science.248.4956.697.

Brebbia, C. A., 1978, The boundary element method for engineers: John Wiley & Sons.

Briggs, W. L., 1987, A multigrid tutorial: SIAM.

Brown, M., 2002, Least-squares joint imaging of primaries and multiples: 72nd Annual International Meeting, SEG, Expanded Abstracts, 890–893, http://dx.doi.org/10.1190/1.1817405.

Bube, K., D. Jovanovich, R. Langan, J. Resnick, R. Shuey, and D. Spindler, 1985, Well-determined and poorly determined features in seismic reflection tomography, Part II: 55th Annual International Meeting, SEG, Expanded Abstracts, 608–610, http://dx.doi.org/10.1190/1.1892795.

Bube, K., and R. Langan, 1997, A hybrid $\ell1/\ell2$ minimization with applications to tomography: Geophysics, **62**, 1183–1195, http://dx.doi.org/10.1190/1.1444219.

Bube, K., and M. Meadows, 1998, Characterization of the null space of a generally anisotropic medium in linearized crosswell tomography: Geophysical Journal International, **133**, 65–84, http://dx.doi.org/10.1046/j.1365-246X.1998.1331467.x.

Buck, B., and V. Macauly, 1994, Maximum entropy in action: Clarendon Press.

Buddensiek, M., 2004, Colluvial wedge imaging using traveltime tomography along the Wasatch Fault near Mapleton, Utah: M.S. thesis, University of Utah.

Buddensiek, M., J. Sheng, T. Crosby, G. T. Schuster, R. L. Bruhn, and R. He, 2008, Colluvial wedge imaging using traveltime and waveform tomography along the Wasatch Fault near Mapleton, Utah: Geophysical Journal International, **172**, 686–697, http://dx.doi.org/10.1111/j.1365-246X.2007.03667.x.

Bulcao, A., D. M. Soares Filho, F. Loureiro, G. Alves, F. Farias, and L. Santos, 2013, FWI Comparison between different objective functions: Proceedings of the 13th International Congress of the Brazilian Geophysical Society and EXPOGEF, Sociedade Brasileira de Geofísica, http://sys2.sbgf.org.br/congresso/abstracts/trabalhos/sbgf_4181.pdf, accessed 10 October 2014.

Bunks, C., F. Saleck, S. Zaleski, and G. Chavent, 1995, Multiscale seismic waveform inversion: Geophysics, **60**, 1457–1473, http://dx.doi.org/10.1190/1.1443880.

Cabrales-Vargas, A., and K. Marfurt, 2013, Amplitude-preserving imaging of aliased data using preconditioned Kirchhoff least-squares depth migration: 83rd Annual International Meeting, SEG, Expanded Abstracts, 3726–3729, http://dx.doi.org/10.1190/segam2013-1442.1.

Cadzow, J., 1987, Foundations of digital signal processing and data analysis: McMillian.

Cai, W., and G. T. Schuster, 1993, Processing friendswood cross-well seismic data for reflection imaging: 63rd Annual International Meeting, SEG, Expanded Abstracts, 92–94, http://dx.doi.org/10.1190/1.1822658.

Calnan, C., 1989, Crosswell tomography with reflection and transmission data: M.S. thesis, University of Utah.

Calvetti, D., L. Reichel, and Q. Zhang, 1999, Iterative solution methods for large linear discrete ill-posed problems: Applied and Computational Control: Signals and Circuits, 1, 313–367, http://dx.doi.org/10.1007/978-1-4612-0571-5_7.

Carcione, J. M., 2001, Wave fields in real media: Wave propagation in anisotropic, anelastic and porous media: Handbook of Geophysical Exploration, 31, Pergamon Press.

Carcione, J., D. Kosloff, and R. Kosloff, 1988, Wave propagation simulation in a linear viscoelastic medium: Geophysical Journal, 95, 597–611, http://dx.doi.org/10.1111/j.1365-246X.1988.tb06706.x.

Cerjan, C., D. Kosloff, R. Kosloff, and M. Reshef, 1985, A nonreflecting boundary condition for discrete acoustic and elastic wave equations: Geophysics, 50, 705–708, http://dx.doi.org/10.1190/1.1441945.

Červený, V., and E. Soares, 1992, Fresnel volume ray tracing: Geophysics, 57, 902–915, http://dx.doi.org/10.1190/1.1443303.

Chan, H., E. Chung, and G. Cohen, 2013, Stability and dispersion analysis of staggered discontinuous Galerkin method for wave propagation: International Journal on Numerical Analysis and Modeling, 10, 233–256, http://www.math.ualberta.ca/ijnam/Volume-10-2013/No-1-13/2013-01-12.pdf, accessed 9 September 2014.

Chattopadhyay, S., and G. McMechan, 2008, Imaging conditions for prestack reverse-time migration: Geophysics, 73, S81–S89, http://dx.doi.org/10.1190/1.2903822.

Chauris, H., and M. Noble, , 1998, Testing the behavior of differential semblance for velocity estimation: 68th Annual International Meeting, SEG, Expanded Abstracts, 1305–1308, http://dx.doi.org/10.1190/1.1820140.

Chen, J., and G. T. Schuster, 1999, Resolution limits of migrated images: Geophysics, 64, 1046–1053, http://dx.doi.org/10.1190/1.1444612.

Chen, S. T., L. J. Zimmerman, and J. K. Tugnait, 1990, Subsurface imaging using reversed vertical seismic profiling and crosshole tomographic methods: Geophysics, 55, 1478–1487, http://dx.doi.org/10.1190/1.1442795.

Cheng, X., K. Jiao, D. Sun, and D. Vigh, 2014, Anisotropic parameter estimation with full-waveform inversion of surface seismic data: 84th Annual International Meeting, SEG, Expanded Abstracts, 1072–1077, http://dx.doi.org/10.1190/segam2014-0821.1.

Chen, Z., S. Fomel, and W. Lu, 2013, Omnidirectional plane-wave destruction: Geophysics, 78, V171–V179, http://dx.doi.org/10.1190/geo2012-0467.1.

Chi, B., L. Dong, and Y. Liu, 2013, Full waveform inversion based on envelope objective function: 74th Annual Conference and Exhibition, EAGE, Extended Abstracts, P04–P09.

Chi, B., L. Dong, and Y. Liu, 2014, Full waveform inversion method using envelope objective function without low-frequency data: Journal of Applied Geophysics, 109, 36–46, http://dx.doi.org/10.1016/j.jappgeo.2014.07.010.

Christensen, R. M., 1982, Theory of viscoelasticity: An introduction: Academic Press.

Chung, E., P. Ciarlet, Jr., and T. Yu, 2013, Convergence and superconvergence of staggered discontinuous Galerkin methods for the three-dimensional Maxwell's equations on Cartesian grids: Journal of Computational Physics, 235, 14–31, http://dx.doi.org/10.1016/j.jcp.2012.10.019.

Chung, E., and B. Engquist, 2009, Optimal discontinuous Galerkin methods for acoustic wave propagation in higher dimensions: SIAM Journal on Numerical Analysis, 47, 3820–3848, http://dx.doi.org/10.1137/080729062.

Chung, E., and B. Engquist, 2006, Optimal discontinuous Galerkin methods for wave propagation: SIAM Journal on Numerical Analysis, 44, 2131–2158, http://dx.doi.org/10.1137/050641193.

Claerbout, J. F., 1992, Earth soundings analysis: Processing vs. inversion: Blackwell Scientific.

Claerbout, J. F., 1985, Fundamentals of geophysical data processing with applications to petroleum prospecting: Blackwell Scientific.

Claerbout, J. F., 1985, Imaging the earth's interior: Blackwell Scientific.

Claerbout, J. F., 1971, Toward a unified theory of reflector mapping: Geophysics, 36, 467–481, http://dx.doi.org/10.1190/1.1440185.

Claerbout, J. F., and S. Fomel, 2009, Image estimation by example: Geophysical soundings image construction: http://sepwww.stanford.edu/sep/prof/gee8.08.pdf, accessed 14 September 2014.

Clayton, R. W., and B. Engquist, 1977, Absorbing boundary conditions for acoustic and elastic wave equations: Bulletin of the Seismological Society of America, 6, 1529–1540.

Clinthorne, N. H., T. S. Pan, P. C. Chiao, W. L. Rogers, and J. A. Stamos, 1993, Preconditioning methods for improved convergence rates in iterative reconstructions: IEEE Transactions on Medical Imaging, 12, 78–83, http://dx.doi.org/10.1109/42.222670.

Cole, S., and M. Karrenbach, 1992, Least-squares Kirchhoff migration: SEP–75, 101–110.

Colton, D., and R. Kress, 1998, Integral equation methods in scattering theory: John Wiley and Sons, 121.

Constable, S., R. Parker, and C. Constable, 1987, Occam's inversion: A practical algorithm for generating smooth models from electromagnetic sounding data: Geophysics, 52, 289–300, http://dx.doi.org/10.1190/1.1442303.

Crase, E., C. Wideman, M. Noble, and A. Tarantola, 1992, Nonlinear elastic waveform inversion of land seismic reflection data: Journal of Geophysical Research, 97, B4, 4685–4704, http://dx.doi.org/10.1029/90JB00832.

Dablain, M. A., 1986, The application of high-order differencing to the scalar wave equation: Geophysics, 51, 54–66, http://dx.doi.org/10.1190/1.1442040.

Dahlen, F., 2004, Resolution limit of traveltime tomography: Geophysical Journal International, 157, 315–331, http://dx.doi.org/10.1111/j.1365-246X.2004.02214.x.

Dahlen, F., S. Hung, and G. Nolet, 2002, Fréchet kernels for finite-frequency traveltimes I: Theory: Geophysical Journal International, 141, 157–174.

Dahlen, F., and J. Tromp, 1998, Theoretical global seismology: Princeton University Press.

Dai, W., 2012a, Multisource least-squares migration and prism wave migration: Ph.D. dissertation, University of Utah.

Dai, W., 2012b, Multisource least-squares reverse time migration: Ph.D. dissertation, King Abdullah University of Science and Technology.

Dai, W., P. Fowler, and G. T. Schuster, 2012, Multi-source least-squares reverse time migration: Geophysical Prospecting, 60, 681–695, http://dx.doi.org/10.1111/j.1365-2478.2012.01092.x.

Dai, W., Y. Huang, and G. Schuster, 2013, Least-squares reverse time migration of marine data with frequency-selection encoding: Geophysics, **78**, S233–S242, http://dx.doi.org/10.1190/geo2013-0003.1.

Dai, W., and G. T. Schuster, 2009, Least-squares migration of simultaneous sources data with a deblurring filter: 79th Annual International Meeting, SEG, Expanded Abstracts, 2990–2994, http://dx.doi.org/10.1190/1.3255474.

Dai, W., and G. T. Schuster, 2013, Plane-wave least-squares reverse time migration: Geophysics, **78**, S165–S177, http://dx.doi.org/10.1190/geo2012-0377.1.

Davydenko, M., X. M. Staal, and D. J. Verschuur, 2012, Full wavefield migration in multidimensional media: 82nd Annual International Meeting, SEG, Expanded Abstracts, http://dx.doi.org/10.1190/segam2012-1583.1.

de Fornel, F., 2001, Evanescent waves from Newtonian optics to atomic physics: Springer-Verlag.

de Hoop, M. V., and R. D. Van der Hilst, 2005, On sensitivity kernels for wave equation transmission tomography: Geophysical Journal International, **160**, http://dx.doi.org/10.1111/j.1365-246X.2004.02509.x.

Devaney, A. J., 1984, Geophysical diffraction tomography: IEEE Transactions on Geoscience and Remote Sensing, GE-22, 3–13, http://dx.doi.org/10.1109/TGRS.1984.350573.

Diet, J. P., and P. Lailly, 1984, Choice of scheme and parameters for optimal finite-difference migration in 2-D: 54th Annual International Meeting, SEG, Expanded Abstracts, 454–456, http://dx.doi.org/10.1190/1.1894065.

Dines, K., and R. Lytle, 1979, Computerized geophysical tomography: Proceedings of the IEEE, **67**, 1065–1073, http://dx.doi.org/10.1109/PROC.1979.11390.

Dong, S., Y. Luo, X. Xiao, S. Chavez-Perez, and G. T. Schuster, 2009, Fast 3D target-oriented reverse time datuming: Geophysics, **74**, WCA141–WCA151, http://dx.doi.org/10.1190/1.3261746.

Dong, W., M. Bouchon, and M. N. Toksöz, 1995, Borehole seismic-source radiation in layered isotropic and anisotropic media: Boundary element modeling: Geophysics, **60**, 735–747, http://dx.doi.org/10.1190/1.1443812.

Dong, W., and M. N. Toksöz, 1995, Borehole seismic-source radiation in layered isotropic and anisotropic media: Real data analysis: Geophysics, **60**, 748–757, http://dx.doi.org/10.1190/1.1443813.

Duquet, B., K. Marfurt, and J. Dellinger, 1998, Efficient estimates of subsurface illumination for Kirchhoff prestack depth migration: 68th Annual International Meeting, SEG, Expanded Abstracts, 1116–1119, http://dx.doi.org/10.1190/1.1820083.

Duquet, B., K. Marfurt, and J. Dellinger, 2000, Kirchhoff modeling, inversion for reflectivity, and subsurface illumination: Geophysics, **65**, 1195–1209, http://dx.doi.org/10.1190/1.1444812.

Duric, N., P. Littrup, L. Poulo, A. Babkin, R. Pevzner, E. Holsapple, O. Rama, and C. Glide, 2007, Detection of breast cancer with ultrasound tomography: First results with the computed ultrasound risk evaluation (CURE) prototype: Medical Physics, **34**, 773–785, http://dx.doi.org/10.1118/1.2432161.

Dutta, G., M. Giboli, P. Williamson, and G. T. Schuster, 2015, Least-squares reverse time migration with factorization-free prior conditioning: 85th Annual International Meeting, SEG, Expanded Abstracts, 4270–4275, http://dx.doi.org/10.1190/segam2015-5912138.1.

Dutta, G., Y. Huang, W. Dai, X. Wang, and G. T. Schuster, 2014, Making the most out of the least (squares migration): 84th Annual International Meeting, SEG, Expanded Abstracts, 4405–4410, http://dx.doi.org/10.1190/segam2014-1242.1.

Dutta, G., K. Lu, X. Wang, and G. T. Schuster, 2013, Attenuation compensation in least-squares reverse time migration using the visco-acoustic wave equation: 83rd Annual International Meeting, SEG, Expanded Abstracts, 3721–3725, http://dx.doi.org/10.1190/segam2013-1131.1.

Dutta, G., and G. T. Schuster, 2014, Attenuation compensation for least-squares reverse time migration using the viscoacoustic-wave equation: Geophysics, **79**, S251–S262, http://dx.doi.org/10.1190/geo2013-0414.1.

Duveneck, E. P., and P. Milcik, P. M. Bakker, and C. Perkins, 2008, Acoustic VTI wave equations and their application for anisotropic reverse-time migration: 78th Annual International Meeting, SEG, Expanded Abstracts, 2186–2189, http://dx.doi.org/10.1190/1.3059320.

Dziewonski, A., and D. Anderson, 1984, Seismic tomography of the earth's interior: American Scientist, **72**, 483–494.

Erlangga, Y. A., and F. J. Herrmann, 2009, Seismic waveform inversion with Gauss-Newton-Krylov method: 79th Annual International Meeting, SEG, Expanded Abstracts, 2357–2361, http://dx.doi.org/10.1190/1.3255332.

Etgen, J. T., 2005, How many angles do we really need for delayed-shot migration?: 75th Annual International Meeting, SEG, Expanded Abstracts, 1985–1988, http://dx.doi.org/10.1190/1.2148097.

Fawcett, J., and R. Clayton, 1984, Tomographic reconstruction of velocity anomalies: BSSA, **74**, 2201–2219.

Faye, J.-P., and J.-P. Jeannot, 1986, Prestack migration velocities from focusing depth analysis: 56th Annual International Meeting, SEG, Expanded Abstracts, 438–440, http://dx.doi.org/10.1190/1.1893053.

Fei, T., Y. Luo, and G. T. Schuster, 2010, De-blending reverse time migration: 80th Annual International Meeting, SEG, Expanded Abstracts, 3130–3134, http://dx.doi.org/10.1190/1.3513496

Fichtner, A., 2011, Full seismic waveform modeling and inversion: Springer-Verlag.

Fichtner, A., B. L. N. Kennett, H. Igel, and H. P. Bunge, 2009, Full seismic waveform tomography for upper-mantle structure in the Australasian region using adjoint methods: Geophysical Journal International, **179**, 1703–1725, http://dx.doi.org/10.1111/j.1365-246X.2009.04368.x.

Fichtner, A., and J. Trampert, 2011a, Hessian kernels of seismic data functionals based upon adjoint techniques: Geophysical Journal International, **185**, 775–798, http://dx.doi.org/10.1111/j.1365-246X.2011.04966.x.

Fichtner, A., and J. Trampert, 2011b, Resolution analysis in full waveform inversion: Geophysical Journal International, **187**, 1604–1624, http://dx.doi.org/10.1111/j.1365-246X.2011.05218.x.

Fink, M., 2008, Time-reversal waves and super resolution: Journal of Physics: Conference Series, **124**, 1–29, http://dx.doi.org/10.1088/1742-6596/124/1/012004.

Fleming, M. J., 2008, Far-field super resolution: Ph.D. dissertation, Imperial College London.

Fletcher, R., 1980, Practical methods of optimization. Volume 1: Unconstrained optimization: John Wiley and Sons.

Fletcher, R. F., P. Fowler, P. Kitchenside, and U. Albertin, 2005, Suppressing artifacts in prestack reverse time migration: 75th Annual International Meeting, SEG, Expanded Abstracts, 2049–2051, http://dx.doi.org/10.1190/1.2148113.

Fleury, C., and R. Snieder, 2012, Increasing illumination and sensitivity of RTM with internal multiples: 74th Conference and Exhibition, EAGE, Extended Abstracts, X042.

Fomel, S., 2000, 3-D data regularization: Ph.D. dissertation, Stanford University.

Fomel, S., J. Berryman, R. Clapp, and M. Prucha, 2002, Iterative resolution estimation in least-squares Kirchhoff migration: Geophysical Prospecting, **50**, 577–588, http://dx.doi.org/10.1046/j.1365-2478.2002.00341.x.

Fornberg, B., 1988, Generation of finite difference formulas on arbitrarily spaced grids: Mathematics of Computation, **51**, 699–706, http://dx.doi.org/10.1090/S0025-5718-1988-0935077-0.

Forst, W. and Hoffmann, D., 2010, Global optimization: Theory and practice: Springer Undergraduate Texts in Mathematics and Technology.

French, W., 1974, Two-dimensional and three-dimensional migration of model-experiment reflection profiles: Geophysics, **39**, 265–277, http://dx.doi.org/10.1190/1.1440426.

Fu, M., and J. Hu, 1997, Conditional Monte Carlo: Gradient estimation and optimization applications: Kluwer Academic Publishers.

Gardner, G. H. F., L. W. Gardner, and A. R. Gregory, 1974, Formation velocity and density – The diagnostic basics for stratigraphic traps: Geophysics, **39**, 770–780, http://dx.doi.org/10.1190/1.1440465.

Gauthier, O., J. Virieux, and A. Tarantola, 1986, Two-dimensional nonlinear inversion of seismic waveforms: Numerical results: Geophysics, **51**, 1387–1403, http://dx.doi.org/10.1190/1.1442188.

Gazdag, J., 1978, Wave equation migration with the phase-shift method: Geophysics, **43**, 1342–1351, http://dx.doi.org/10.1190/1.1440899.

Gersztenkorn, A., J. B. Bednar, and L. Lines, 1986, Robust iterative inversion for the one-dimensional acoustic wave equation: Geophysics, **51**, 357–368, http://dx.doi.org/10.1190/1.1442095.

Gholami, Y., R. Brossier, S. Operto, A. Ribodetti, and J. Virieux, 2013, Which parameterization is suitable for acoustic vertical transverse isotropic full waveform inversion? Part 1: Sensitivity and trade-off analysis: Geophysics, **78**, R81–R105, http://dx.doi.org/10.1190/geo2012-0204.1.

Gill, P., W. Murray, and M. Wright, 1981, Practical optimization: Academic Press.

Golub, G., M. Heath, and G. Wahba, 1979, Generalized cross-validation as a method for choosing a good ridge parameter: Technometrics, **21**, 215–223.

Golub, G., and U. von Matt, 1997, Generalized cross-validation for large-scale problems: Journal of Computational and Graphical Statistics, **6**, 1–34.

Gottschammer, E., and K. Olson, 2001, Accuracy of the explicit planar free-surface boundary condition implemented in a fourth-order staggered-grid velocity-stress finite-difference scheme: Bulletin of the Seismological Society of America, **91**, 617–623, http://dx.doi.org/10.1785/0120000244.

Grant, F. S., and G. F. West, 1965, Interpretation theory in applied geophysics: McGraw-Hill Book Company.

Groetsch, C., 1993, Inverse problems in mathematical science: Vieweg Publishing.

Gu, M., 2000, Advanced optical imaging theory: Springer-Verlag.

Guitton, A., 2004, Amplitude and kinematic corrections of migrated images for nonunitary imaging operators: Geophysics, **69**, 1017–1024, http://dx.doi.org/10.1190/1.1778244.

Guitton, A., B. Kaelin, and B. Biondi, 2006, Least-square attenuation of reverse time migration artifacts: 76th Annual International Meeting, SEG, Expanded Abstracts, 2348–2352, http://dx.doi.org/10.1190/1.2370005.

Guo, B., 2015, Migration velocity analysis with trim statics: 2015 CSIM Annual Report, KAUST.

Hadamard, J., 1902, Sur les problèmes aux dérivées partielles et leur signification physique: Princeton University Bulletin, 49–52.

Hagedoorn, J. G., 1954, A process of reflection interpretation: Geophysical Prospecting, **2**, 85–127, http://dx.doi.org/10.1111/j.1365-2478.1954.tb01281.x.

Hanafy, S., and H. Yu, 2013, Early arrival waveform inversion of shallow seismic land data: 83rd Annual International Meeting, SEG, Expanded Abstracts, 1738–1742, http://dx.doi.org/10.1190/segam2013-0351.1.

Hanke, M., 1996, Limitations of the L-curve method in ill-posed problems: BIT Numerical Mathematics, **36**, 287–301, http://dx.doi.org/10.1007/BF01731984.

Hansen, P., 1992, Analysis of discrete ill-posed problems with the L-curve: SIAM Review, **34**, 561–580, http://dx.doi.org/10.1137/1034115.

Hansen, P., and D. P. O'Leary, 1993, The use of the L-curve: SIAM Journal on Scientific and Statistical Computing, **14**, 1487–1503, http://dx.doi.org/10.1137/0914086.

Hardy, P., and J. P. Jeannot, 1999, 3D reflection tomography in time-migrated space: 69th Annual International Meeting, SEG, Expanded Abstracts, 1287–1290, http://dx.doi.org/10.1190/1.1820744.

Harlan, W. S., 1986, Signal-noise separation and seismic inversion: Ph.D. thesis, Stanford University.

Harlan, W., 1990, Tomographic estimation of shear velocities from shallow crosswell data; 60th Annual International Meeting, SEG, Expanded Abstracts, 86–89, http://dx.doi.org/10.1190/1.1890369.

Harris, J. M., R. Nolen-Hoeksema, J. W. Rector, M. V. Schack, and S. K. Lazaratos, 1992, High resolution crosswell imaging of a west Texas carbonate reservoir: Part 1. Data acquisition and project overview: 62nd SEG Annual International Meeting, SEG, Expanded Abstracts, 35–39, http://dx.doi.org/10.1190/1.1822089.

He, R., and G. Schuster, 2003, Least-squares migration of both primaries and multiples: 73rd SEG Annual International Meeting, SEG, Expanded Abstracts, 1035–1038, http://dx.doi.org/10.1190/1.1817448.

Herman, G., 1992, Generalization of traveltime inversion: Geophysics, **57**, 9–14, http://dx.doi.org/10.1190/1.1443193.

Hestenes, M. R., and E. Stiefel, 1952, Methods of conjugate gradients for solving linear systems: Journal of Research of the National Bureau of Standards, **49**, 409–436.

Higdon, R. L., 1991, Absorbing boundary conditions for elastic waves: Geophysics, **56**, 231–241, http://dx.doi.org/10.1190/1.1443035.

Hill, N. R., 1990, Gaussian beam migration: Geophysics, **55**, 1416–1428, http://dx.doi.org/10.1190/1.1442788.

Hill, N. R., 2001, Prestack Gaussian-beam depth migration: Geophysics, **66**, 1240–1250, http://dx.doi.org/10.1190/1.1487071.

Hill, N. R., and P. C. Wuenschel, 1985, Numerical modeling of refraction arrivals in complex areas: Geophysics, **50**, 90–98, http://dx.doi.org/10.1190/1.1441840.

Holister, Scott, 2014, Constitutive equations: Viscoelasticity: BME 332: Introduction to Biomaterials: Section 7: http://

www.umich.edu/~bme332/ch7consteqviscoelasticity/bme332co nsteqviscoelasticity.htm, accessed 15 September 2014.

Horst, R., and P. Pardalos, 1995, Handbook of global optimization: Kluwer Academic Publications.

Horst, R., P. Pardalos, and N. Thoai, 2000, Introduction to global optimization: Kluwer Academic Publications.

Hu, J., G. T. Schuster, and P. Valasek, 2001, Poststack migration deconvolution: Geophysics, **66**, 939–952, http://dx.doi.org/10.1190/1.1444984.

Huang, Y., G. Dutta, W. Dai, X. Wang, G. T. Schuster, and J. Yu, 2014a, Making the most out of least-squares migration: The Leading Edge, **33**, 954–956, http://dx.doi.org/10.1190/tle3309 0954.1.

Huang, Y., and G. T. Schuster, 2014, Resolution limits for wave equation imaging: Journal of Applied Geophysics, **107**, 137–148, http://dx.doi.org/10.1016/j.jappgeo.2014.05.018.

Huang, Y., and G. T. Schuster, 2012, Multisource least-squares migration of marine streamer and land data with frequency-division encoding: Geophysical Prospecting, **60**, 663–680, http://dx.doi.org/10.1111/j.1365-2478.2012.01086.x.

Huang, Y., X. Wang, and G. T. Schuster, 2014b, Non-local means filter for trim statics: 84th SEG Annual International Meeting, SEG, Expanded Abstracts, 3925–3929, http://dx.doi.org/10.1190/segam2014-0352.1.

Humphreys, E., R. W. Clayton, and B. Hager, 1984, A tomographic image of mantle structure beneath southern California: Geophysical Research Letters, **11**, 625–627, http://dx.doi.org/10.1029/GL011i007p00625.

Ivansson, S., 1985, A study of methods for tomographic velocity estimation in the presence of low-velocity zones: Geophysics, **50**, 969–988, http://dx.doi.org/10.1190/1.1441975.

Iyer, H., 1989, Seismic tomography, *in* D. James, ed., The encyclopedia of solid earth geophysics, Van Nostrand-Reinhold, 1133–1151.

Iyer, H., and K. Hirahara, 1993, Seismic tomography: Theory and practice: Chapman and Hall.

Jackson, D. D., 1972, Interpretation of inaccurate, insufficient, and inconsistent data: Geophysical Journal of the Royal Astronomical Society, **28**, 97–109, http://dx.doi.org/10.1111/j.1365-246X.1972.tb06115.x.

Jannane, M., W. Beydoun, E. Crase, D. Cao, Z. Koren, E. Landa, M. Mendes, A. Pica, M. Noble, S. Roeth, S. Singh, R. Snieder, A. Tarantola, D. Trezeguet, and M. Xie, 1989, Wavelength of earth structure that can be resolved from seismic reflection data: Geophysics, **54**, 906–910, http://dx.doi.org/10.1190/1.1442719.

Jansson, P., 1997, Deconvolution of images and spectra: Academic Press.

Jones, I., 2010, Tutorial: Velocity estimation via ray-based tomography: First Break, **28**, 45–52, http://dx.doi.org/10.3997/1365-2397.2010006.

Jousselin, P., B. Duquet, F. Audebert, and J. Sirgue, 2009, Bridging the gap between ray-based tomography and wave-equation migration image gathers: 79th SEG Annual International Meeting, SEG, Expanded Abstracts, 3979–3983, http://dx.doi.org/10.1190/1.3255700.

Kaelin, B., and A. Guitton, 2006, Imaging condition for reverse time migration: 76th Annual International Meeting, SEG, Expanded Abstracts, 2594–2598, http://dx.doi.org/10.1190/1.2370059.

Kelley, C. T., 1999, Iterative methods for optimization: Frontiers in applied mathematics, SIAM Press.

Kelly, K., S. Ward, S. Treitel, and M. Alford, 1976, Synthetic seismograms: A finite difference approach: Geophysics, **41**, 2–27, http://dx.doi.org/10.1190/1.1440605.

Kennett, B. L., M. S. Sambridge, and P. R. Williamson, 1988, Subspace methods for large inverse problems with multiple parameter classes: Geophysical Journal, **94**, 237–247, http://dx.doi.org/10.1111/j.1365-246X.1988.tb05898.x.

Keys, R. G., 1985, Absorbing boundary conditions for acoustic media: Geophysics, **50**, 892–902, http://dx.doi.org/10.1190/1.1441969.

Kissling, E., 1988, Geotomography with local earthquake data: Reviews of Geophysics, **26**, 659–698, http://dx.doi.org/10.1029/RG026i004p00659.

Kissling, E., S. Husen, and F. Haslinger, 2001, Model parametrization in seismic tomography: A choice of consequence for the solution quality: Physics of the Earth and Planetary Interiors, **123**, 89–101, http://dx.doi.org/ 10.1016/S0031-9201(00) 00203-X.

Komatitsch, D., S. Tsuboi, and J. Tromp, 2005, The spectral-element method in seismology: Geophysical Monograph Series, **157**, 205–227, http://dx.doi.org/10.1029/157GM13.

Kornhuber, R., 1998, On robust multigrid methods for non-smooth variational problems: *in* W. Hackbusch, ed., Multigrid methods V: Lecture notes in computational science and engineering (Vol. 3): Springer, 173–188.

Kosloff, D., and E. Baysal, 1982, Forward modeling by a Fourier method: Geophysics, **47**, 1402–1412, http://dx.doi.org/10.1190/1.1441288.

Kosloff, D., M. Reshef, and D. Loewenthal, 1984, Elastic wave calculations by the Fourier method: Bulletin of the Seismological Society of America, **74**, 875–891.

Kosloff, D., J. Sherwood, Z. Koren, E. Machet, and Y. Falkovitz, 1996, Velocity and interface depth determination by tomography of depth migrated gathers: Geophysics, **61**, 1511–1523, http://dx.doi.org/10.1190/1.1444076.

Kravtsov, Y. A., and Y. I. Orlov, 1980, Geometrical optics of inhomogeneous media: Springer-Verlag.

Krebs, J. R., J. Anderson, D. Hinkley, R. Neelamani, S. Lee, A. Baumstein, and M. D. Lacasse, 2009, Fast full-wavefield seismic inversion using encoded sources: Geophysics, **74**, WCC177–WCC188, http://dx.doi.org/10.1190/1.3230502.

Kreiss, H.-O., and J. Oliger, 1972, Comparison of accurate methods for the integration of hyperbolic equations: Tellus, **24**, 199–215, http://dx.doi.org/10.1111/j.2153-3490.1972.tb01547.x.

Kudela, P., M. Krawczuk, and W. Ostachowicz, 2007, Wave propagation modelling in 1D structures using spectral finite elements: Journal of Sound and Vibration, **300**, 88–100, http://dx.doi.org/10.1016/j.jsv.2006.07.031.

Kühl, H., and M. Sacchi, 2003, Least-squares wave-equation migration for AVP/AVA inversion: Geophysics, **68**, 262–273, http://dx.doi.org/10.1190/1.1543212.

Kurkjian, A. L., H. Achmidt, J. E. White, T. L. Marzetta, and C. Chouzenoux, 1992, Numerical modeling of cross-well seismic monopole data: 62nd Annual International Meeting, SEG, Expanded Abstracts, 141–144, http://dx.doi.org/10.1190/1.1822022.

Lafond, C., and A. Levander, 1993, Migration moveout analysis and depth focusing: Geophysics, **58**, 91–100, http://dx.doi.org/10.1190/1.1443354.

Lailly, P., 1983, Migration methods: Partial but efficient solutions to the seismic inverse problem: *in* Y. Pao, F. Santosa, and W.

Symes, eds., Inverse problems of acoustic and elastic waves, SIAM, 182–214.

Lambaré, G., 2008, Stereotomography: Geophysics, **73**, VE25–VE34, http://dx.doi.org/10.1190/1.2952039.

Lambaré, G., P. Guillaume, and J. P. Montel, 2014, Recent advances in ray-based tomography: 76th Conference and Exhibition, EAGE, Extended Abstracts, G103.

Landa, E., W. Beydoun, and A. Tarantola, 1989, Reference velocity model estimation from prestacked waveforms: Coherency optimization by simulated annealing: Geophysics, **54**, 984–990, http://dx.doi.org/10.1190/1.1442741.

Lawson, L., and R. Hanson, 1974, Solving least squares problems: Prentice-Hall.

Lazaratos, S., I. Chikichev, and K. Wang, 2013, Improving the convergence rate of full wavefield inversion using spectral shaping: 81st Annual International Meeting, SEG, Expanded Abstracts, 2428–2431.

Le Bégat, S., H. Chauris, V. Devaux, S. Nguyen, and M. Noble, 2004, Velocity model estimation for depth imaging: Comparison of three tomography methods on a 2D real data set: Geophysical Prospecting, **52**, 427–438, http://dx.doi.org/10.1111/j.1365-2478.2004.00427.x.

Lecomte, I., H. Gjøystdal, and A. Drottning, 2003, Simulated prestack local imaging: A robust and efficient interpretation tool to control illumination, resolution, and time-lapse properties of reservoirs: 73rd Annual International Meeting, SEG, Expanded Abstracts, 1525–1528, http://dx.doi.org/10.1190/1.1817585.

Lee, K. H., and H. J. Kim, 2003, Source-independent full waveform inversion of seismic data: Geophysics, **68**, 2010–2015, http://dx.doi.org/10.1190/1.1635054.

Leonard, K., E. V. Malyarenko and M. Hinders, 2002, Ultrasonic Lamb wave tomography: Inverse Problems, **18**, 1795–1808.

Levander, A., 1988, Fourth-order finite-difference P-SV seismograms: Geophysics, **53**, 1425–1436, http://dx.doi.org/10.1190/1.1442422.

Lévêque, J. J., L. Rivera, and G. Wittlinger, 1993, On the use of checkerboard test to assess the resolution of tomographic inversions: Geophysical Journal International, **115**, 313–318, http://dx.doi.org/10.1111/j.1365-246X.1993.tb05605.x.

Li, K., and H. Chen, 2012, Illumination and resolution analyses on marine seismic data acquisitions by the adjoint wavefield method: Geophysical Prospecting, **23**, http://dx.doi.org/10.3319/TAO.2012.06.15.01(T).

Li, J., Z. Feng, and G.T. Schuster, 2017, Skeletonized wave-equation dispersion inversion: Geophys. J. Inter., (in press).

Liao, Q., and G. A. McMechan, 1997, Tomographic imaging of velocity and Q, with application to crosswell seismic data from the Gypsy pilot site, Oklahoma: Geophysics, **62**, 1804–1811, http://dx.doi.org/10.1190/1.1444281.

Lines, L., 1988, Inversion of geophysical data: SEG Geophysics Reprints No. 9.

Lines, L. R., and S. Treitel, 1984, Tutorial, review of least-squares inversion and its application to geophysical problems: Geophysical Prospecting, **32**, 159–186, http://dx.doi.org/10.1111/j.1365-2478.1984.tb00726.x.

Liu, F., G. Zhang, S. Morton, and J. Leveille, 2011, An effective imaging condition for 711 reverse time migration using wavefield decomposition: Geophysics, **76**, S29–S39, http://dx.doi.org/10.1190/1.3533914.

Liu, F., G. Zhang, S. A. Morton, and J. P. Leveille, 2007, Reverse-time migration using one-way wavefield imaging condition: 77th Annual International Meeting, SEG, Expanded Abstracts, 2170–2174.

Liu, W., and Y. Wang, 2008, Target-oriented reverse time migration for two-way prestack depth imaging: 78th Annual International Meeting, SEG, Expanded Abstracts, 2326–2330.

Liu, Y., L. Dong, Y. Wang, J. Zhu, and Z. Ma, 2009, Sensitivity kernels for seismic Fresnel volume tomography: Geophysics, **74**, U35–U46, http://dx.doi.org/10.1190/1.3169600.

Liu, Y., and M. K. Sen, 2010, A hybrid scheme for absorbing edge reflections in numerical modeling of wave propagation: Geophysics, **75**, A1–A6, http://dx.doi.org/10.1190/1.3295447.

Liu, Y., and M. K. Sen, 2012, A hybrid absorbing boundary condition for elastic staggered-grid modelling: Geophysical Prospecting, **60**, 1114–1132, http://dx.doi.org/10.1111/j.1365-2478.2011.01051.x.

Lizarralde, D., and S. Swift, 1999, Smooth inversion of VSP traveltime data: Geophysics, **64**, 659–661, http://dx.doi.org/ 10.1190/1.1444574.

Loewenthal, D., P. Stoffa, and E. Faria, 1987, Suppressing the unwanted reflections of the full wave equations: Geophysics, **52**, 1007–1012, http://dx.doi.org/10.1190/1.1442352.

Lu, K., and G. T. Schuster, 2013, Anti-aliasing test of least-squares migration: CSIM annual report, 2012, 213–220.

Luo, S., and P. Sava, 2011, A deconvolution-based objective function for wave-equation inversion: 81st Annual International Meeting, SEG, Expanded Abstracts, 2788–2792, http://dx.doi.org/10.1190/1.3627773.

Luo, Y., 1991, Calculation of wavepaths for band-limited seismic waves: 61st Annual International Meeting, SEG, Expanded Abstracts, 1509–1512, http://dx.doi.org/10.1190/1.1889004.

Luo, Y., and G. T. Schuster, 1990, Parsimonious staggered grid finite differencing of the wave equation: Geophysical Research Letters, **17**, 155–158, http://dx.doi.org/10.1029/GL017i002p00155.

Luo, Y., and G. T. Schuster, 1991a, Wave equation inversion of skeletalized geophysical data: Geophysical Journal International, **105**, 289–294, http://dx.doi.org/10.1111/j.1365-246X.1991.tb06713.x.

Luo, Y., and G. T. Schuster, 1991b, Wave equation traveltime inversion: Geophysics, **56**, 645–653, http://dx.doi.org/10.1190/1.1443081.

Luo, Y., and G. T. Schuster, 1992, Wave packet transform and data compression: 62nd Annual International Meeting, SEG, Expanded Abstracts, 1187–1190, http://dx.doi.org/10.1190/1.1821944.

Luo, Y., Y. Ma, and Y. Wu, 2016, Full traveltime inversion: Geophysics, **81**, R261–R274, http://dx.doi.org/10.1190/geo2015-0353.1.

Ma, X., 2001, A constrained global inversion method using an overparameterized scheme: Application to poststack data: Geophysics, **66**, 613–626, http://dx.doi.org/10.1190/1.1444952.

MacKay, S., and R. Abma, 1992, Imaging and velocity analysis with depth-focusing analysis: Geophysics, **57**, 1608–1622, http://dx.doi.org/10.1190/1.1443228.

Mackie, R., and T. Madden, 1993, Three-dimensional magnetotelluric inversion using conjugate gradients: Geophysical Journal International, **115**, 215–229, http://dx.doi.org/10.1111/j.1365-246X.1993.tb05600.x.

Malcolm, A. E., M. V. De Hoop, and B. Ursin, 2011, Recursive imaging with multiply scattered waves using partial image regularization: A North Sea case study: Geophysics, **76**, B33–B42, http://dx.doi.org/10.1190/1.3537822.

Marfurt, K. J., 1984, Accuracy of finite-difference and finite-element modeling of the scalar and elastic wave equations: Geophysics, **49**, 533–549, http://dx.doi.org/10.1190/1.1441689.

Marquering, H., F. A. Dahlen, and G. Nolet, 1999, Three-dimensional sensitivity kernels for finite-frequency traveltimes: The banana-doughnut paradox: Geophysical Journal International, **137**, 805–815, http://dx.doi.org/10.1046/j.1365-246x.1999.00837.x.

Masoni, J., R. Brossier, J. Virieux, and J. L. Boelle, 2013, Alternative misfit functions for FWI applied to surface waves: 74th Annual Conference and Exhibition, EAGE, Extended Abstracts, P10-P13.

McMechan, G. A., 1983, Migration by extrapolation of time-dependent boundary values: Geophysical Prospecting, **31**, 413–420, http://dx.doi.org/10.1111/j.1365-2478.1983.tb01060.x.

Menke, W., 1984, Geophysical data analysis: Discrete inverse theory: Academic Press.

Métivier, L., R. Brossier, J. Virieux, and S. Operto, 2012, Toward Gauss-Newton and exact Newton optimization for full waveform inversion: 74th Annual Conference and Exhibition, EAGE, Extended Abstracts.

Meyer, M., J. P. Hermand, J. C. Le Gac, and M. Asch, 2004, Penalization method for wave adjoint-based inversion of an acoustic field: Presented at the 7th European Conference on Underwater Acoustics.

Meyers, M., and K. Chawla, 1999, Mechanical behavior of materials: Prentice-Hall.

Mitchell, A. R., and D. F. Griffiths, 1980, The finite-difference method in partial differential equations: John Wiley and Sons.

Mo, L., and J. Harris, 2002, Finite-difference calculation of direct-arrival traveltimes using the eikonal equation: Geophysics, **67**, 1270–1274, http://dx.doi.org/10.1190/1.1500389.

Montel, J., and G. Lambaré, 2011a, Asymptotic analysis of ADCIG from slant stacked subsurface offset gather: 73rd Conference and Exhibition, EAGE, Extended Abstracts, P06–P12.

Montel, J., and G. Lambaré, 2011b, RTM and Kirchhoff angle domain common-image gathers for migration velocity analysis: 84th Annual International Meeting, SEG, Expanded Abstracts, 3120–3124, http://dx.doi.org/10.1190/1.3627844.

Montelli, R., G. Nolet, G. Masters, F. Dahlen, and S. Hung, 2004, Global P and PP traveltime tomography: Rays versus waves: Geophysical Journal International, **158**, 637–654, http://dx.doi.org/10.1111/j.1365-246X.2004.02346.x.

Mora, P., 1987, Nonlinear two-dimensional elastic inversion of multioffset seismic data: Geophysics, **52**, 1211–1228, http://dx.doi.org/10.1190/1.1442384.

Mora, P., 1989, Inversion = migration + tomography: Geophysics, **54**, 1575–1586, http://dx.doi.org/10.1190/1.1442625.

Morey, D., and G. T. Schuster, 1999, Paleoseismicity of the Oquirrh fault, Utah from shallow seismic tomography: Geophysical Journal International, **138**, 25–35, http://dx.doi.org/10.1046/j.1365-246x.1999.00814.x.

Morozov, I., 2014, First principles of viscoelasticity: seisweb. usask.ca/ibm/papers/Q/Morozov_viscoelasticity.pdf, accessed 15 September 2014.

Morse, P. and H. Feshbach, 1953, Methods of theoretical physics: McGraw-Hill.

Mulder, W., 2014, Subsurface offset behaviour in velocity analysis with extended reflectivity images: Geophysical Prospecting, **62**, 17–33, http://dx.doi.org/10.1111/1365-2478.12073.

Mulder, W. A., and R.-E. Plessix, 2003, One-way and two-way wave-equation migration: 73rd Annual International Meeting, SEG, Expanded Abstracts, **22**, 881–884, http://dx.doi.org/10.1190/1.1818081.

Mulder, W. and A. ten Kroode, 2002, Automatic velocity analysis by differential semblance optimization: Geophysics, **67**, 1184–1191, http://dx.doi.org/10.1190/1.1500380

Mulder, W., and T. van Leeuwen, 2008, Automatic migration velocity analysis and multiples: 78th Annual International Meeting, SEG, Expanded Abstracts, 3128–3132, http://dx.doi.org/10.1190/1.3063996.

Natterer, F., 1986, The mathematics of computerized tomography: John Wiley and Sons.

Nemeth, T., 1996, Imaging and filtering by least-squares migration: Ph.D. dissertation, University of Utah.

Nemeth, T., E. Normark, and F. Qin, 1997, Dynamic smoothing in cross-well traveltime tomography: Geophysics, **62**, 168–176, http://dx.doi.org/10.1190/1.1444115.

Nemeth, T., H. Sun, and G. T. Schuster, 2000, Separation of signal and coherent noise by migration filtering: Geophysics, **65**, 574–583, http://dx.doi.org/10.1190/1.1444753.

Nemeth, T., C. Wu, and G. T. Schuster, 1999, Least-squares migration of incomplete reflection data: Geophysics, **64**, 208–221, http://dx.doi.org/10.1190/1.1444517.

Nocedal, J., 1980, Updating quasi-Newton matrices with limited storage: Mathematics of Computation, **35**, 773–782, http://dx.doi.org/10.1090/S0025-5718-1980-0572855-7.

Nocedal, J., and S. Wright, 1999, Numerical optimization: Springer-Verlag.

Nolet, G., 1987, Seismic tomography: D. Reidel Publishing.

Nowack, R., M. Sen, and P. Stoffa, 2003, Gaussian beam migration for sparse common-shot and common-receiver data: 73rd Annual International Meeting, SEG, Expanded Abstracts, 1114–1117.

Nur, A., and Z. Wang, 1988, Seismic and acoustic velocities in reservoir rocks: Volume 1: SEG Geophysics Reprint Series No. 19.

Oldenburg, D., P. McGillivray, and R. Ellis, 1993, Generalized subspace methods for large-scale inverse problems: Geophysical Journal International, **114**, 12–20, http://dx.doi.org/10.1111/j.1365-246X.1993.tb01462.x.

Olig, S. S., W. R. Lund, B. D. Black, and B. H. Mayes, 1996, Paleoseismic investigation of the Oquirrh fault zone, Tooele County, Utah: Utah Geological Survey Special Study, **88**, 22–54.

Ostashev, V., S. Vecherin, D. Wilson, A. Ziemann, and G. Goedecke, 2009, Recent progress in acoustic traveltime tomography of the atmospheric surface layer: Meteorologische Zeitschrift, **18**, 125–133, http://dx.doi.org/10.1127/0941-2948/2009/0364.

Paige, C. C., and M. A. Saunders, 1982, LSQR: an algorithm for sparse linear equations and sparse least squares: ACM Transactions on Mathematical Software, **8**, 43–71, http://dx.doi.org/10.1145/355984.355989.

Pan, G., 1993, Measure for the resolving power and bias effect in the nonlinear inverse analysis of geophysical potential fields: Geophysics, **58**, 626–636, http://dx.doi.org/10.1190/1.1443446.

Pardalos, P., and H. E. Romeijn, 2002, Handbook of global optimization: Volume 2, Kluwer Academic Publishers.

Paulsson, B., N. Cook, and T. McEvilly, 1985, Elastic-wave velocities and attenuation in an underground granitic repository for nuclear waste: Geophysics, **50**, 551–570, http://dx.doi.org/10.1190/1.1441932.

Pelissier, M. A., H. Hoeber, N. van de Coevering, and I. F. Jones, 2007, Classics of elastic wave theory: SEG Geophysical Reprint Series No. 24.

Peng, C., M. N. Toksöz, and J. M. Lee, 1993, Pressure in a fluid-filled borehole due to a source in a stratified formation: 63rd Annual International Meeting, SEG, Expanded Abstracts, 321–324, http://dx.doi.org/10.1190/1.1822470.

Perez Solano, C., D. Donno, and H. Chauris, 2012, Alternative objective function for inversion of surface waves in 2D media: Expanded Abstracts, 18th European Meeting of Environmental and Engineering Geophysics, Near Surface Geoscience, A21.

Pica, A., J. P. Diet, and A. Tarantola, 1990, Nonlinear inversion of seismic reflection data in a laterally invariant medium: Geophysics, **55**, 284–292, http://dx.doi.org/10.1190/1.1442836.

Plessix, R. E., 2006, A review of the adjoint-state method for computing the gradient of a functional with geophysical applications: Geophysical Journal International, **167**, 495–503, http://dx.doi.org/10.1111/j.1365-246X.2006.02978.x.

Plessix, R. E., G. Baeten, J. W. de Maag, M. Klaassen, Z. Rujie, and T. Zhifei, 2010, Application of acoustic full waveform inversion to a low-frequency large-offset land data set: 80th Annual International Meeting, SEG, Expanded Abstracts, 930–934, http://dx.doi.org/10.1190/1.3513930.

Plessix, R. E. and W. A. Mulder, 2004, Frequency-domain finite-difference amplitude-preserving migration: Geophysical Journal International, **157**, 975–987, http://dx.doi.org/10.1111/j.1365-246X.2004.02282.x.

Plessix, R., A. Stopin, P. Milcik, and K. Matson, 2014, Acoustic and anisotropic multiparameter seismic full waveform inversion case studies: 84th Annual International Meeting, SEG, Expanded Abstracts, 1056–1060, http://dx.doi.org/10.1190/segam2014-0646.1.

Podvin, P., and I. Lecomte, 1991, Finite difference computation of traveltimes in very contrasted velocity models: A massively parallel approach and its associated tools: Geophysical Journal International, **105**, 271–284, http://dx.doi.org/10.1111/j.1365-246X.1991.tb03461.x.

Pratt, R. G., and N. R. Goulty, 1991, Combining wave-equation imaging with traveltime tomography to form high-resolution images from crosshole data: Geophysics, **56**, 208–224, http://dx.doi.org/10.1190/1.1443033.

Pratt, R. G., C. Shin, and G. J. Hicks, 1998, Gauss-Newton and full Newton methods in frequency-space seismic waveform inversion: Geophysical Journal International, **133**, 341–362, http://dx.doi.org/10.1046/j.1365-246X.1998.00498.x.

Press, W., S. Teukolsky, W. Vetterling, and B. Flannery, 2007, Numerical recipes: The art of scientific computing: Cambridge University Press.

Prieux, V., G. Lambaré, S. Operto, and J. Virieux, 2013, Building starting models for full waveform inversion from wide-aperture data by stereotomography: Geophysical Prospecting, **61**, 109–137, http://dx.doi.org/10.1111/j.1365-2478.2012.01099.x.

Qin, F., Y. Luo, K. B. Olsen, W. Cai, and G. T. Schuster, 1992, Finite-difference solution of the eikonal equation along expanding wavefronts: Geophysics, **57**, 478–487, http://dx.doi.org/10.1190/1.1443263.

Qin, F., and G. T. Schuster, 1993, Constrained Kirchhoff migration of crosswell seismic data: 63rd Annual International Meeting, SEG, Expanded Abstracts, 99–102, http://dx.doi.org/10.1190/1.1822678.

Ramírez, A., and A. Weglein, 2009, Green's theorem as a comprehensive framework for data reconstruction, regularization, wavefield separation, seismic interferometry, and wavelet estimation: A tutorial: Geophysics, **74**, W35–W62, http://dx.doi.org/10.1190/1.3237118.

Ravaut, C., S. Operto, L. Improta, J. Virieux, A. Herrero, and P. Dell'Aversana, 2004, Multiscale imaging of complex structures from multifold wide-aperture seismic data by frequency-domain full-waveform tomography: Application to a thrust belt: Geophysical Journal International, **159**, 1032–1056, http://dx.doi.org/10.1111/j.1365-246X.2004.02442.x.

Renaut, R., and J. Petersen, 1989, Stability of wide-angle absorbing boundary conditions for the wave equation: Geophysics, **54**, 1153–1163, http://dx.doi.org/10.1190/1.1442750.

Rickett, J., 2003, Illumination-based normalization for wave-equation depth migration: Geophysics, **68**, 1371–1379, http://dx.doi.org/10.1190/1.1598130.

Rickett, J., and P. Sava, 2002, Offset and angle-domain common image-point gathers for shot-profile migration: Geophysics, **67**, 883–889, http://dx.doi.org/10.1190/1.1484531.

Robein, E., 2010, Seismic imaging: EAGE Publications.

Robertsson, J., J. Blanch, and W. Symes, 1994, Viscoelastic finite-difference modelling: Geophysics, **59**, 1444–1456, http://dx.doi.org/10.1190/1.1443701.

Rodi, W., and R. Mackie, 2001, Nonlinear conjugate gradients algorithm for 2-D magnetotelluric inversion: Geophysics, **66**, 174–187, http://dx.doi.org/10.1190/1.1444893.

Routh, P., J. Krebs, S. Lazaratos, A. Baumstein, S. Lee, Y. Cha, I. Chikichev, N. Downey, D. Hinkley, and J. Anderson, 2011, Encoded simultaneous source full-wavefield inversion for spectrally shaped marine streamer data: 81st Annual International Meeting, SEG, Expanded Abstracts, 2433–2438, http://dx.doi.org/10.1190/1.3627697.

Romero, L. A., D. C. Ghiglia, C. C. Ober, and S. A. Morton, 2000, Phase encoding of shot records in prestack migration: Geophysics, **65**, 426–436, http://dx.doi.org/10.1190/1.1444737.

Sacchi, M. D., J. Wang, and H. Kuehl, 2006, Regularized migration/inversion: new generation of imaging algorithms: CSEG Recorder (Special Edition), **31**, 54–59.

Sacchi, M. D., J. Wang, and H. Kuehl, 2007, Estimation of the diagonal of the migration blurring kernel through a stochastic approximation: 77th Annual International Meeting, SEG, Expanded Abstracts, 2437–2441, http://dx.doi.org/10.1190/1.2792973.

Safar, M. H., 1985, On the lateral resolution achieved by Kirchhoff migration: Geophysics, **50**, 1091–1099, http://dx.doi.org/10.1190/1.1441981.

Saha, R. K., and S. K. Sharma, 2005, Validity of a modified Born approximation for a pulsed plane wave in acoustic scattering problems: Physics in Medicine and Biology, **50**, 2823–2836, http://dx.doi.org/10.1088/0031-9155/50/12/007.

Saito, H., 1990, Ray tracing based on Huygens' principle: 60th Annual International Meeting, SEG, Expanded Abstracts, 1024–1027, http://dx.doi.org/10.1190/1.1889897.

Salo, E., and G. Schuster, 1989, Traveltime inversion of both direct and reflected arrivals in vertical seismic profile data: Geophysics, **54**, 49–56, http://dx.doi.org/10.1190/1.1442576.

Sava, P., and B. Biondi, 2004, Wave-equation migration velocity analysis. I. Theory: Geophysical Prospecting, **52**, 593–606, http://dx.doi.org/10.1111/j.1365-2478.2004.00447.x.

Sava, P., and S. Fomel, 2006, Time-shift imaging condition in seismic migration: Geophysics, **71**, S209–S217, http://dx.doi.org/10.1190/1.2338824.

Scales, J., 1985, Introduction to non-linear optimization: Springer-Verlag.

Scales, J., 1987, Tomographic inversion via the conjugate gradient method: Geophysics, **52**, 179–185, http://dx.doi.org/10.1190/1.1442293.

Scales, J., and A. Gersztenkorn, 1988, Robust methods in inverse theory: Inverse Problems, **4**, 1071–1091, http://dx.doi.org/10.1088/0266-5611/4/4/010.

Scales, J., A. Gersztenkorn, and S. Treitel, 1988, Fast lp solution of large, sparse linear systems: Application to seismic travel time tomography: Journal of Computational Physics, **75**, 314–333, http://dx.doi.org/10.1016/0021-9991(88)90115-5.

Schleicher, J., M. Tygel, and P. Hubral, 2007, Seismic true-amplitude imaging: SEG Geophysical Development Series No. 12, 1–351.

Schuster, G. T., 1985, A hybrid BIE + Born series modeling scheme: Generalized Born series: Journal of the Acoustical Society of America, **77**, 865–879.

Schuster, G. T., 1988, An analytic generalized inverse for common-depth-point and vertical seismic profile traveltime equations: Geophysics, **53**, 314–325, http://dx.doi.org/10.1190/1.1442465.

Schuster, G. T., 1993, Decomposition of the waveform gradient into short- and long-wavelength components: 1993 Annual Report, Utah Tomography and Modeling/Migration Consortium, 79–88.

Schuster, G. T., 1996, Resolution limits for crosswell migration and traveltime tomography: Geophysical Journal International, **127**, 427–440, http://dx.doi.org/10.1111/j.1365-246X.1996.tb04731.x.

Schuster, G. T., 1997, Green's functions for migration: 67th Annual International Meeting, SEG, Expanded Abstracts, 1754–1758, http://dx.doi.org/10.1190/1.1885771.

Schuster, G. T., 2002, Reverse-time migration = generalized diffraction-stack migration: 72nd Annual International Meeting, SEG, Expanded Abstracts, 1280–1283, http://dx.doi.org/10.1190/1.1816888.

Schuster, G. T., S. Hanafy, and Y. Huang, 2012, Theory and feasibility tests for a seismic scanning tunnelling macroscope: Geophysical Journal International, **190**, 1593–1606, http://dx.doi.org/10.1111/j.1365-246X.2012.05564.x.

Schuster, G. T., and J. Hu, 2000, Green's functions for migration: Continuous recording geometry: Geophysics, **65**, 167–175, http://dx.doi.org/10.1190/1.1444707.

Schuster, G. T., and Y. Huang, 2014, Far-field superresolution by imaging of resonant scattering: Geophysical Journal International, **199**, 1943–1949, http://dx.doi.org/10.1093/gji/ggu350.

Schuster, G. T., D. P. Johnson, and D. J. Trentman, 1988, Numerical verification and extension of an analytic generalized inverse for common-depth-point and vertical-seismic-profile traveltime equations: Geophysics, **53**, 326–333, http://dx.doi.org/10.1190/1.1442466.

Schuster, G., and A. Quintus-Bosz, 1993, Wavepath eikonal traveltime inversion: Theory: Geophysics, **58**, 1314–1323, http://dx.doi.org/10.1190/1.1443514.

Sen, M., and P. Stoffa, 1991, Nonlinear one-dimensional seismic waveform inversion using simulated annealing: Geophysics, **56**, 1624–1638, http://dx.doi.org/10.1190/1.1442973.

Sen, M., and P. Stoffa, 1992, Rapid sampling of model space using genetic algorithms: Examples from seismic waveform inversion: Geophysical Journal International, **108**, 281–292, http://dx.doi.org/10.1111/j.1365-246X.1992.tb00857.x.

Sen, M., and P. Stoffa, 1995, Global optimization methods in geophysical inversion: Elsevier.

Sethian, J., and A. M. Popovici, 1999, 3-D traveltime computation using the fast marching method: Geophysics, **64**, 516–523, http://dx.doi.org/10.1190/1.1444558.

Sevink, A., and G. Herman, 1994, Fast iterative solution of sparsely sampled seismic inverse problems: Inverse Problems, **10**, 937–948, http://dx.doi.org/10.1088/0266-5611/10/4/012.

Shah, N., M. Warner, T. Nangoo, A. Umpleby, I. Stekl, J. Morgan, and L. Guaschi, 2012, Quality assured full-waveform inversion: Ensuring starting model adequacy: 82nd Annual International Meeting, SEG, Expanded Abstracts, 1–5, http://dx.doi.org/10.1190/segam2012-1228.1.

Sheley, D., and G. T. Schuster, 2003, Reduced-time migration of transmitted PS waves: Geophysics, **68**, 1695–1707, http://dx.doi.org/10.1190/1.1620643.

Shen, P., W. Symes, and C. Stolk, 2003, Differential semblance velocity analysis by wave-equation migration: 73rd Annual International Meeting, SEG, Expanded Abstracts, 2132–2135, http://dx.doi.org/10.1190/1.1817759.

Shen, X., 2010, Near-surface velocity estimation by weighted early-arrival waveform inversion: 80th Annual International Meeting, SEG, Expanded Abstracts, 1975–1979, http://dx.doi.org/10.1190/1.3513230.

Shen, X., T. Tonellot, Y. Luo, T. Keho, and R. Ley, 2012, A new waveform inversion workflow: Application to near-surface velocity estimation in Saudi Arabia: 83rd Annual International Meeting, SEG, Expanded Abstracts, 1–5, http://dx.doi.org/10.1190/segam2012-0024.1.

Sheng, J., 2004, High resolution seismic tomography with the generalized radon transform and early arrival waveform inversion: Ph.D. dissertation, University of Utah.

Sheng, J., A. Leeds, M. Buddensiek, and G. T. Schuster, 2006, Early arrival waveform tomography on near-surface refraction data: Geophysics, **71**, U47–U57, http://dx.doi.org/10.1190/1.2210969.

Sheng, J., and G. T. Schuster, 2003, Finite-frequency resolution limits of wave path traveltime tomography for smoothly varying velocity models: Geophysical Journal International, **152**, 669–676, http://dx.doi.org/10.1046/j.1365-246X.2003.01878.x.

Shewchuk, J., 1994, An introduction to the conjugate gradient method without the agonizing pain: Technical Report: Carnegie Mellon University, http://www.cs.cmu.edu/~quake-papers/painless-conjugate-gradient.pdf, accessed 1 September 1994.

Shin, C., and Y. H. Cha, 2008, Waveform inversion in the Laplace domain: Geophysical Journal International, **173**, 922–931, http://dx.doi.org/10.1111/j.1365-246X.2008.03768.x.

Shin, C., and D. Min, 2006, Waveform inversion using a logarithmic wavefield: Geophysics, **71**, R31–R42, http://dx.doi.org/10.1190/1.2194523.

Sirgue, L., J. T. Etgen, and U. Albertin, 2008, 3D frequency-domain waveform inversion using time-domain finite-difference methods: 70th Annual International Meeting, EAGE, Extended Abstracts.

Sirgue, L., J. T. Etgen, U. Albertin, and S. Brandsberg-Dahl, 2007, 3D frequency-domain waveform inversion based on 3D time-domain forward modeling: U. S. Patent No. 20 070 282 535A1.

Sirgue, L., and R. G. Pratt, 2004, Efficient waveform inversion and imaging: A strategy for selecting temporal frequencies: Geophysics, **69**, 231–248, http://dx.doi.org/10.1190/1.1649391.

Sjoeberg, T. A., L. Gelius, and I. Lecomte, 2003, 2-D deconvolution of seismic image blur: 73rd Annual International Meeting, SEG, Expanded Abstracts, 1055–1059, http://dx.doi.org/10.1190/1.1817453.

Snieder, R., M. Xie, A. Pica, and A. Tarantola, 1989, Retrieving both the impedance contrast and background velocity: A global strategy for the seismic reflection problem: Geophysics, **54**, 991–1000, http://dx.doi.org/10.1190/1.1442742.

Soldati, G., and L. Boschi, 2005, The resolution of whole Earth seismic tomographic models: Geophysical Journal International, **161**, 143–153, http://dx.doi.org/10.1111/j.1365-246X.2005.02551.x.

Soni, A., and D. J. Verschuur, 2013, Imaging blended VSP data using full wavefield migration: 83rd Annual International Meeting, SEG, Expanded Abstracts, 5046–5051, http://dx.doi.org/10.1190/segam2013-0583.1.

Squires, L., and G. Cambois, 1992, A linear filter approach to designing off-diagonal damping matrices for least-squares inverse problems: Geophysics, **57**, 948–951, http://dx.doi.org/10.1190/1.1443308.

Stenger, F., 2011, Handbook of SINC numerical methods: CRC Press.

Stein, S., and M. Wysession, 2003, An introduction to seismology: Earthquakes and earth structure: Blackwell Publishing.

Stoffa, P. L., J. T. Fokkema, R. M. de Luna Freire, and W. P. Kessinger, 1990, Split-step Fourier migration: Geophysics, **55**, 410–421, http://dx.doi.org/10.1190/1.1442850.

Stolt, R., and A. Benson, 1986, Seismic migration: Theory and practice: Handbook of geophysical exploration, volume 5: Pergamon Press.

Stork, C., 1991, High resolution SVD analysis of the coupled velocity determination and reflector imaging problem: 74th Annual International Meeting, SEG, Expanded Abstracts, 981–985, http://dx.doi.org/10.1190/1.1888773.

Stork, C., 1992, Reflection tomography in the postmigrated domain: Geophysics, **57**, 680–692, http://dx.doi.org/10.1190/1.1443282.

Stork, C., 2013, Eliminating nearly all dispersion error from FD modeling and RTM with minimal cost increase: 75th Conference and Exhibition, EAGE, Extended Abstracts, http://dx.doi.org/10.3997/2214-4609.20130478.

Stork, C., and J. Kapoor, 2004, How many P values do you want to migrate for delayed shot wave equation migration?: 74th Annual International Meeting, SEG, Expanded Abstracts, 1041–1044, http://dx.doi.org/10.1190/1.1843291.

Souza, A., A. Bulcao, B. Pereira Dias, B. Soares Filho, F. Loureiro, F. Farias, G. Alves, L. Santos, and R. da Cruz, 2013, Application of regularization to FWI in noisy data: Presented at the 13th International Congress of the Brazilian Geophysical Society and EXPOGEF.

Sun, H., 2001, Wavepath migration for depth imaging and velocity analysis: Ph.D. dissertation, University of Utah.

Sun, Y., 1991, Source focusing inversion for crosswell seismic data: 1991 UTAM Annual Report, University of Utah, 114–127, http://utam.gg.utah.edu/tomo91/91_ann/91_ann.pdf, accessed 9 September 2014.

Sun, Y., 1992, Tomographic smoothing, cooperative inversion, and constraints by a Lagrange multiplier method: 1992 UTAM Annual Report, University of Utah, 78–90.

Sun, Y., and G. Schuster, 1993, Time domain phase inversion: 63rd Annual International Meeting, SEG, Expanded Abstracts, 684–687, http://dx.doi.org/10.1190/1.1822588.

Sword, C., 1987, Tomographic determination of interval velocities from reflection seismic data: The method of controlled directional reception: Ph.D. dissertation, Stanford University.

Symes, W., 2008, Migration velocity analysis and waveform inversion: Geophysical Prospecting, **56**, 765–790, http://dx.doi.org/10.1111/j.1365-2478.2008.00698.x.

Symes, W., and J. Carazzone, 1991, Velocity inversion by differential semblance optimization: Geophysics, **56**, 654–663, http://dx.doi.org/10.1190/1.1443082.

Symes, W., and M. Kern, 1994, Inversion of reflection seismograms by differential semblance analysis: Algorithm structure and synthetic examples: Geophysical Prospecting, **42**, 565–614, http://dx.doi.org/10.1111/j.1365-2478.1994.tb00231.x.

Tang, Y., 2009, Target-oriented wave-equation least-squares migration/inversion with phase-encoded Hessian: Geophysics, **74**, WCA95–WCA107, http://dx.doi.org/10.1190/1.3204768.

Tang, Y., and B. Biondi, 2009, Least-squares migration/inversion of blended data: 79th Annual International Meeting, SEG, Expanded Abstracts, 2859–2863, http://dx.doi.org/10.1190/1.3255444.

Tang, Y., S. Lee, A. Baumstein, and D. Hinkley, 2013, Tomographically enhanced full wavefield inversion: 83rd Annual International Meeting, SEG, Expanded Abstracts, 1037–1040, http://dx.doi.org/10.1190/segam2013-1145.1.

Tape, C., Q. Liu, A. Maggi, and J. Tromp, 2009, Adjoint tomography of the southern California crust: Science, **325**, 988–992, http://dx.doi.org/10.1126/science.1175298.

Tarantola, A., 1984a, Inversion of seismic reflection data in the acoustic approximation: Geophysics, **49**, 1259–1266, http://dx.doi.org/10.1190/1.1441754.

Tarantola, A., 1984b, Linearized inversion of seismic reflection data: Geophysical Prospecting, **32**, 998–1015, http://dx.doi.org/10.1111/j.1365-2478.1984.tb00751.x.

Tarantola, A., 1987, Inverse problem theory methods for data fitting and model parameter estimation: Elsevier.

Tarantola, A., I. Fosse, M. Mendes, and A. Nercessian, 1985, The choice of model parameters for linearized elastic inversion of seismic reflection data: Technical Report, Équipe de Tomographie du Géophysique, rep. 2, Institut de Paris du Globe.

Tarantola, A., and B. Valette, 1982, Inversion problems = Quest for information: Journal of Geophysics, **50**, 159–170.

Thomsen, L., 1986, Weak elastic anisotropy: Geophysics, **51**, 1954–1966, http://dx.doi.org/10.1190/1.1442051.

Thomsen, L., 2013, On the use of isotropic parameters λ, E, ν, and K to understand anisotropic shale behavior: 83rd Annual International Meeting, SEG, Expanded Abstracts, 320–324, http://dx.doi.org/10.1190/segam2013-1080.1.

Thorson, J., and J. F. Claerbout, 1985, Velocity-stack and slant-stack stochastic inversion: Geophysics, **50**, 2727–2741, http://dx.doi.org/10.1190/1.1441893.

Toldi, J., 1989, Velocity analysis without picking: Geophysics, **54**, 191–199, http://dx.doi.org/10.1190/1.1442643.

Torn, A., and A. Zilinskas, 1989, Global optimization: Springer-Verlag.

Toxopeus, G., J. Thorbecke, K. Wapenaar, S. Petersen, E. Slob, and J. Fokkema, 2008, Simulating migrated and inverted seismic data by filtering a geologic model: Geophysics, **73**, T1–T10, http://dx.doi.org/10.1190/1.2827875.

Trad, D., T. Ulrych, and M. Sacchi, 2002, A hybrid linear-hyperbolic Radon transform: Journal of Seismic Exploration, **9**, 303–318.

Trad, D., T. Ulrych, and M. Sacchi, 2003, Latest views of the sparse Radon transform: Geophysics, **68**, 386–399, http://dx.doi.org/10.1190/1.1543224.

Trefethen, L., 2000, Spectral methods in MATLAB: SIAM Press.

Treitel, S., and L. R. Lines, 1982, Linear inverse theory and deconvolution: Geophysics, **47**, 1153–1159, http://dx.doi.org/10.1190/1.1441378.

Tryggvason, A., S. Rognvaldsson, and O. G. Flovenz, 2002, Three-dimensional imaging of the P- and S-wave velocity structure and earthquake locations beneath Southwest Iceland: Geophysical Journal International, **151**, 848–866, http://dx.doi.org/10.1046/j.1365-246X.2002.01812.x.

van der Hilst, R., and M. de Hoop, 2006, Reply to comment by R. Montelli, G. Nolet, and F.A. Dahlen on "Banana-doughnut kernels and mantle tomography": Geophysical Journal International, **167**, 1211–1214, http://dx.doi.org/10.1111/j.1365-246X.2006.03211.x.

Van Leeuwen, T., and W. A. Mulder, 2010, A correlation-based misfit criterion for wave-equation traveltime tomography: Geophysical Journal International, **182**, 1383–1394, http://dx.doi.org/10.1111/j.1365-246X.2010.04681.x.

Vasco, D. W., L. R. Johnson, and O. Marques, 1998, Global earth structure: Inference and assessment: Geophysical Journal International, **137**, 381–407, http://dx.doi.org/10.1046/j.1365-246X.1999.00823.x.

Vasco, D. W., and E. L. Majer, 1993, Wavepath traveltime tomography: Geophysical Journal International, **115**, 1055–1069, http://dx.doi.org/10.1111/j.1365-246X.1993.tb01509.x.

Vasco, D. W., J. E. Peterson Jr., and E. L. Majer, 1995, Beyond ray tomography: Wavepaths and Fresnel volumes: Geophysics, **60**, 1790–1804, http://dx.doi.org/10.1190/1.1443912.

Vermeer, G., 1999, Factors affecting spatial resolution: Geophysics, **64**, 942–953, http://dx.doi.org/10.1190/1.1444602.

Versteeg, R. J., 1993, Sensitivity of prestack depth migration to the velocity model: Geophysics, **58**, 873–882, http://dx.doi.org/10.1190/1.1443471.

Vidale, J., 1988, Finite-difference calculation of traveltimes: Bulletin of the Seismological Society of America, **78**, 2062–2076.

Vigh, D., X. Cheng, K. Jiao, D. Sun, and J. Kapoor, 2014b, Multiparameter TTI full waveform inversion on long-offset broadband acquisition: A case study: 84th Annual International Meeting, SEG, Expanded Abstracts, 1061–1065, http://dx.doi.org/10.1190/segam2014-0530.1.

Vigh, D., K. Jiao, D. Watts, and D. Sun, 2014a, Elastic full-waveform inversion application using multicomponent measurements of seismic data collection: Geophysics, **79**, no. 2, R63–R77, http://dx.doi.org/10.1190/geo2013-0055.1.

Vigh, D., and E. Starr, 2008, 3D prestack plane-wave, full-waveform inversion: Geophysics, **73**, no. 5, VE135–VE144, http://dx.doi.org/10.1190/1.2952623.

Vigh, D., E. Starr, and J. Kapoor, 2009, Developing earth models with full waveform inversion: The Leading Edge, **28**, 432–435, http://dx.doi.org/10.1190/1.3112760.

Virieux, J., 1984, SH-wave propagation in heterogeneous media: Velocity-stress finite-difference method: Geophysics, **49**, 1933–1942, http://dx.doi.org/10.1190/1.1441605.

Virieux, J., 1986, P-SV wave propagation in heterogeneous media: Velocity-stress finite-difference method: Geophysics, **51**, 889–901, http://dx.doi.org/10.1190/1.1442147.

Virieux, J., V. Etienne, V. Cruz-Atienza, R. Brossier, E. Chaljub, O. Coutant, S. Garambois, D. Mercerat, V. Prieux, S. Operto, A. Ribodetti, and J. Tago, 2012, Modelling seismic wave propagation for geophysical imaging, *in* M. Kanao, ed., Seismic waves – Research and analysis: InTech.

Virieux, J., and S. Operto, 2009, An overview of full-waveform inversion in exploration: Geophysics, **74**, WCC1–WCC26, http://dx.doi.org/10.1190/1.3238367.

Wikipedia.org, 2014, Viscoelasticity: https://en.wikipedia.org/wiki/Viscoelasticity, accessed 9/14/2014.

von Seggern, D., 1991, Spatial resolution of acoustic imaging with the Born approximation: Geophysics, **56**, 1185–1202, http://dx.doi.org/10.1190/1.1443139.

von Seggern, D., 1994, Depth-imaging resolution of 3-D seismic recording patterns: Geophysics, **59**, 564–576, http://dx.doi.org/10.1190/1.1443617.

Vyas, M., W. Geco, and Y. Tang, 2010, Gradients for wave-equation migration velocity analysis: 80th Annual International Meeting, SEG, Expanded Abstracts, 4077–4081, http://dx.doi.org/10.1190/1.3513711.

Wang, C., D. Yingst, J. Brittan, P. Farmer, and J. Leveille, 2014, Fast multi-parameter anisotropic full waveform inversion with irregular shot sampling: 84th Annual International Meeting, SEG, Expanded Abstracts, 1147–1151, http://dx.doi.org/10.1190/segam2014-0234.1.

Wang, J., and M. D. Sacchi, 2007, High-resolution wave-equation amplitude-variation-with-ray-parameter (AVP) imaging with sparseness constraints: Geophysics, **72**, no. 1, S11–S18, http://dx.doi.org/10.1190/1.2387139.

Wang, X., W. Dai, and G. Schuster, 2013, Regularized plane-wave least-squares Kirchhoff migration: 83rd Annual International Meeting, SEG, Expanded Abstracts, 3242–3246, http://dx.doi.org/10.1190/segam2013-0278.1.

Wang, Y., 1995, Preliminary results for viscoelastic WTW inversion of crosswell data: 1995 UTAM Annual Report, University of Utah, 217–231.

Wang, Y., 1997a, Multi-component separation of P-P and P-SV waves by a least-squares migration method: Synthetic tests on CDP data: 1997 UTAM Annual Report, University of Utah, 303–319.

Wang, Y., 1997b, Viscoelastic waveform inversion as a tool for AVO studies: 1997 UTAM Annual Report, University of Utah, 173–196.

Wang, Y., 1998, Comparison of multiple attenuation methods with least-squares migration filtering: 1998 UTAM Annual Report, University of Utah, 311–342.

Wang, Y. and F. Qin, 1997, New damping absorbing boundary condition: 1997 UTAM Annual Report, University of Utah, 1–9.

Warner, M., and L. Guasch, 2014, Adaptive waveform inversion: Theory: 84th Annual International Meeting, SEG, Expanded Abstracts, 1089–1093, http://dx.doi.org/10.1190/segam2014-0371.1.

Warner, M., T. Nangoo, N. Shah, A. Umpleby, and J. Morgan, 2013a, Full-waveform inversion of cycle-skipped seismic data by frequency down-shifting: 83rd Annual International Meeting, SEG, Expanded Abstracts, 903–907, http://dx.doi.org/10.1190/segam2013-1067.1.

Warner, M., A. Ratcliffe, T. Nangoo, J. Morgan, A. Umpleby, N. Shah, V. Vinje, I. Stekl, L. Guasch, C. Win, G. Conroy, and A. Bertrand, 2013b, Anisotropic 3D full-waveform inversion: Geophysics, **78**, R59–R80, http://dx.doi.org/10.1190/geo2012-0338.1.

White, J., and M. Lessenger, 1988, Caliper effects on borehole coupling: Exploration Geophysics, **19**, 201–205, http://dx.doi.org/10.1071/EG988201.

Whiting, P., 1998, Reflection tomography without picking: 68th Annual International Meeting, SEG, Expanded Abstracts, 1226–1230, http://dx.doi.org/10.1190/1.1820116.

Whitmore, N. D., 1983, Iterative depth migration by backward time propagation: 53rd Annual International Meeting, SEG, Expanded Abstracts, 382–385, http://dx.doi.org/10.1190/1.1893867.

Williamson, P. R., 1991, A guide to the limits of resolution imposed by scattering in ray tomography: Geophysics, **56**, 202–207, http://dx.doi.org/10.1190/1.1443032.

Williamson, P. R., and M. H. Worthington, 1993, Resolution limits in ray tomography due to wave behavior: Numerical experiments: Geophysics, **58**, 727–735, http://dx.doi.org/10.1190/1.1443457.

Witten, A., and J. E. Molyneux, 1988, Geophysical imaging with arbitrary source illumination: IEEE Transactions on Geoscience and Remote Sensing, **26**, 409–419, http://dx.doi.org/10.1109/36.3044.

Wirgin, A., 2008, The inverse crime: http://arxiv.org/pdf/math-ph/0401050.pdf, accessed 28 January 2015.

Woodward, M., 1989, Wave-equation tomography: Ph.D. dissertation, Stanford University.

Woodward, M., 1992, Wave equation tomography: Geophysics, **57**, 15–26, http://dx.doi.org/10.1190/1.1443179.

Woodward, M. J., D. Nichols, O. Zdraveva, P. Whitfield, and T. Johns, 2008, A decade of tomography: Geophysics, **73**, VE5–VE11, http://dx.doi.org/10.1190/1.2969907.

Wu, R. S., J. Luo, and B. Wu, 2014, Seismic envelope inversion and modulation signal model: Geophysics, **79**, WA13–WA24, http://dx.doi.org/10.1190/geo2013-0294.1.

Wu, R. S., and M. N. Toksöz, 1987, Diffraction tomography and multisource holography applied to seismic imaging: Geophysics, **52**, 11–25, http://dx.doi.org/10.1190/1.1442237.

Xu, K., S. A. Greenhalgh, and M. Y. Wang, 2006, Comparison of source-independent methods of elastic waveform inversion: Geophysics, **71**, R91–R100, http://dx.doi.org/10.1190/1.2356256.

Xu, S., H. Chauris, G. Lambaré, and M. Noble, 1998, Common-angle image gather: A strategy for imaging complex media: 68th Annual International Meeting, SEG, Expanded Abstracts, 1538–1541, http://dx.doi.org/10.1190/1.1820207.

Xu, S. H., H. Chauris, G. Lambaré, and M. Noble, 2001, Common-angle migration: A strategy for imaging complex media: Geophysics, **66**, 1877–1894, http://dx.doi.org/10.1190/1.1487131.

Xu, S., and T. Huang, 2007, Migration artifacts and velocity analysis: 77th Annual International Meeting, SEG, Expanded Abstracts, 3019–3023, http://dx.doi.org/10.1190/1.2793098.

Xu, S., Y. Zhang, and B. Tang, 2011, 3D angle gathers from reverse time migration: Geophysics, **76**, S77–S92, http://dx.doi.org/10.1190/1.3536527.

Xu, W., and X. Xie, 2009, How serious is the nonlinear effect on traveltime delays predicted by sensitivity kernels: 79th Annual International Meeting, SEG, Expanded Abstracts, 4049–4053, http://dx.doi.org/10.1190/1.3255715.

Yao, Z., G. Roberts, and A. Tryggvason, 1999, Calculating resolution and covariance matrices for seismic tomography with the LSQR method: Geophysical Journal International, **138**, 886–894, http://dx.doi.org/10.1046/j.1365-246x.1999.00925.x.

Yaqoobi, A., and M. Warner, 2013, Full waveform inversion — A strategy to invert cycle-skipped 3D onshore seismic data: 75th Conference and Exhibition, EAGE, Extended Abstracts.

Yi, M., J. Kim, and S. Chung, 2003, Enhancing the resolving power of least-squares inversion with active constraint balancing: Geophysics, **68**, 931–941, http://dx.doi.org/10.1190/1.1581045.

Yilmaz, Ö., 2001, Seismic data analysis: Processing, inversion, and interpretation of seismic data: SEG Investigations in Geophysics No. 10.

Yilmaz, Ö., and R. Chambers, 1984, Migration velocity analysis by wavefield extrapolation: Geophysics, **49**, 1664–1674, http://dx.doi.org/10.1190/1.1441574.

Yoon, K., and K. J. Marfurt, 2006, Reverse time migration using the Poynting vector: Exploration Geophysics, **37**, 102–107, http://dx.doi.org/10.1071/EG06102.

Yoon, K., K. J. Marfurt, and W. Starr, 2004, Challenges in reverse time migration: 74th Annual International Meeting, SEG, Expanded Abstracts, 1057–1060, http://dx.doi.org/10.1190/1.1851068.

Yu, H., and S. Hanafy, 2014, An application of multiscale early arrival waveform inversion to shallow seismic data: Near Surface Geophysics, http://dx.doi.org/10.3997/1873-0604.2014002.

Yu, J., J. Hu, G. T. Schuster, and R. Estill, 2006, Prestack migration deconvolution: Geophysics, **71**, S53–S62, http://dx.doi.org/10.1190/1.2187783.

Yu, J. and Y. Wang, 1999, Separating P-P and P-SV of multicomponent data with least squares migration filtering: UTAM Midyear Report, University of Utah, 147–156, http://utam.gg.utah.edu/tomo99/99mid/html/node107.html#val1, accessed 1 September 2014.

Yu, H., D. Zhang, and X. Wang, 2014, Application of weighted early-arrival waveform inversion to shallow land data: Journal of Applied Geophysics, **102**, 68–76, http://dx.doi.org/10.1016/j.jappgeo.2014.01.003.

Zelt, C. A., and R. B. Smith, 1992, Seismic traveltime inversion for 2-D crustal velocity structure: Geophysical Journal International, **108**, 16–34, http://dx.doi.org/10.1111/j.1365-246X.1992.tb00836.x.

Zemanian, A., 1965, Distribution theory and transform analysis: Dover Publications.

Zhan, G., W. Dai, and G. T. Schuster, 2009, Acoustic multisource waveform inversion with deblurring: 2009 UTAM Annual Report, University of Utah.

Zhan, G., Y. Luo, and G. T. Schuster, 2010, Modified form of reverse time migration tuned to multiples: 72nd Conference and Exhibition, EAGE, Extended Abstracts, 594–597.

Zhan, G., W. Dai, M. Zhou, Y. Luo, and G. T. Schuster, 2014, Generalized diffraction-stack migration and filtering of coherent noise: Geophysical Prospecting, **62**, 427–442, http://dx.doi.org/10.1111/1365-2478.12086.

Zhan, G., R. Pestana, and P. Stoffa, 2012, Decoupled equations for reverse time migration in tilted transversely isotropic media: Geophysics, **77**, T37–T45, http://dx.doi.org/10.1190/geo2011-0175.1.

Zhan, G., and G. T. Schuster, 2012a, Anti-aliasing filter for reverse-time migration: 74th Conference and Exhibition, EAGE, Extended Abstracts.

Zhan, G., and G. T. Schuster, 2012b, Mitigation of artifacts in RTM with migration kernel decomposition: 74th Conference and Exhibition, EAGE, Extended Abstracts.

Zhan, G., and G. T. Schuster, 2011, Skeletonized least-squares wave-equation migration: 81st Annual International Meeting, SEG, Expanded Abstracts, 3380–3384, http://dx.doi.org/10.1190/1.3513550.

Zhang, H., and C. H. Thurber, 2007, Estimating the model resolution matrix for large seismic tomography problems based on Lanczos bidiagonalization with partial reorthogonalization: Geophysical Journal International, **170**, 337–345, http://dx.doi.org/10.1111/j.1365-246X.2007.03418.x.

Zhang, J., and G. A. McMechan, 1995, Estimation of resolution and covariance for large matrix inversions: Geophysical Journal International, **121**, 409–426, http://dx.doi.org/10.1111/j.1365-246X.1995.tb05722.x.

Zhang, J., and G. A. McMechan, 1996, Reply to comment by M. M. Deal and G. Nolet on "Estimation of resolution and covariance for large matrix inversions": Geophysical Journal International, **127**, 251–252, http://dx.doi.org/10.1111/j.1365-246X.1996.tb01549.x.

Zhang, J., and N. Toksöz, 1998, Nonlinear refraction traveltime tomography: Geophysics, **63**, 1726–1737, http://dx.doi.org/10.1190/1.1444468.

Zhang, J., and Z. Yao, 2013, Optimized finite-difference operator for broadband seismic wave modeling: Geophysics, **78**, SM1–SM6, http://dx.doi.org/10.1190/geo2012-0277.1.

Zhang, Q., 2014, RTM angle gathers and specular filter (SF) RTM using optical flow: 84th Annual International Meeting, SEG, Expanded Abstracts, 3815–3819, http://dx.doi.org/10.1190/segam2014-0792.1.

Zhang, S., and G. Schuster, 2013a, Generalized differential semblance optimization: 75th Conference and Exhibition, EAGE, Extended Abstracts.

Zhang, S., and G. Schuster, 2013b, Image-domain full waveform inversion: 84th Annual International Meeting, SEG, Expanded Abstracts: 861–865, http://dx.doi.org/10.1190/segam2013-1238.1.

Zhang, S., G. Schuster, and Y. Luo, 2012, Angle-domain migration velocity analysis using wave equation reflection traveltime inversion: 82nd Annual International Meeting, SEG, Expanded Abstracts, 1–6, http://dx.doi.org/10.1190/segam2012-1123.1.

Zhang, Y., and B. Biondi, 2013, Moveout-based wave-equation migration velocity analysis: Geophysics, **78**, U31–U39, http://dx.doi.org/10.1190/geo2012-0082.1.

Zhang, Y., L. Duan, and Y. Xie, 2013, A stable and practical implementation of least-squares reverse time migration: 83rd Annual International Meeting, SEG, Expanded Abstracts, 3716–3720, http://dx.doi.org/10.1190/segam2013-0577.1.

Zhang, Y., J. Sun, C. Notfors, S. Gray, L. Chernis, and J. Young, 2005, Delayed-shot 3D depth migration: Geophysics, **70**, E21–E28, http://dx.doi.org/10.1190/1.2057980.

Zhang, Y., and D. Wang, 2009, Traveltime information-based wave-equation inversion: Geophysics, **74**, WCC27–WCC36, http://dx.doi.org/10.1190/1.3243073.

Zhou, C., W. Cai, Y. Luo, G. T. Schuster, and S. Hassanzadeh, 1995, Acoustic wave-equation traveltime and waveform inversion of crosshole seismic data: Geophysics, **60**, 765–773, http://dx.doi.org/10.1190/1.1443815.

Zhou, C., and G. T. Schuster, 1993, Waveform inversion of subwell velocity structure: 63rd Annual International Meeting, SEG, Expanded Abstracts, 106–109, http://dx.doi.org/10.1190/1.1822298.

Zhou, C., G. T. Schuster, S. Hassanzadeh, and J. M. Harris, 1997, Elastic wave-equation traveltime and waveform inversion of crosswell data: Geophysics, **62**, 853–868, http://dx.doi.org/10.1190/1.1444194.

Zhou, M., 2001, Wave equation waveform inversion of crosswell data: 2001 UTAM Annual Report, University of Utah, 1–11, http://utam.gg.utah.edu/tomo01/01_annual/tomobk_html/node124.html.

Zhou, M., 2004, POIC-radon filtering of near-offset multiples: 74th Annual International Meeting, SEG, Expanded Abstracts, 1317–1320, http://dx.doi.org/10.1190/1.1851108.

Zhou, M., and G. T. Schuster, 2000, Interferometric travel time tomography: 70th Annual International Meeting, SEG, Expanded Abstracts, 2138–2141, http://dx.doi.org/10.1190/1.1815871.

Zhou, M., and G. T. Schuster, 2002, Wave-equation wavefront migration: 72nd Annual International Meeting, SEG, Expanded Abstracts, 1292–1295, http://dx.doi.org/10.1190/1.1816891.

Zhou, M., H. Sun, and G. T. Schuster, 2003, The application of primary-only imaging condition to SMAART data: 73rd Annual International Meeting, SEG, Expanded Abstracts, 1012–1015, http://dx.doi.org/10.1190/1.1817441.

Zhu, C., R. Byrd, P. Lu, and J. Nocedal, 1997, Algorithm 778: L-BFGS-B: FORTRAN subroutines for large-scale bound-constrained optimization: ACM Transactions on Mathematical Software, **23**, 550–560, http://dx.doi.org/10.1145/279232.279236.

Index

Note: Page numbers followed by "*fn*" indicate footnotes.